American Inventors

Seated, left to right: *Charles Goodyear, rubber vulcanization; Jordan L. Mott, self-feeding stove; Eliphalet Nott, anthracite burning stove; Frederick E. Sickels, cut-off valve in steam engine; Samuel F. B. Morse, telegraph; Henry Burden, horseshoe-making machine; Richard M. Hoe, revolving cylinder printing press; Isaiah Jennings, Promethean matches; Thomas Blanchard, gun-barrel lathe; Elias Howe, sewing machine.*

MEN OF SCIENCE
IN AMERICA

The Story of American Science

Told through the Lives and Achievements

of Twenty Outstanding Men

from Earliest Colonial Times

to the Present Day

———— ◦—◦ ————

by

BERNARD JAFFE

REVISED EDITION

SIMON AND SCHUSTER · NEW YORK · 1958

Q
127
U6
J27

1349

SECOND PRINTING

MANUFACTURED IN THE UNITED STATES OF AMERICA
BY H. WOLFF BOOK MFG. CO., INC., NEW YORK

AGAIN TO CELE,
THE CATALYTIC COLLABORATOR

Each new discovered truth in science works its way with prodigious power into the very framework of society and produces rapid and permanent changes in the habits, the opinions, and the laws of a people.

ALBERT BARNES

The great object in trying to understand history, political, religious, literary or scientific, is to get behind men, and to grasp ideas.

LORD ACTON

TABLE OF CONTENTS

ILLUSTRATIONS

PLATES

[SECTION FOLLOWS PAGE XXVIII.]

ix

ILLUSTRATIONS IN TEXT

PAGE

FOREWORD

IF HALF OF THE MEMBERS of an orchestra were absent at the beginning of a concert and the others persisted in playing alone, the result would be very strange. It might be difficult to recognize the composer's intentions, for one cannot omit some of the parts without spoiling the whole pattern. For similar reasons one might say that it is impossible to tell the history of American science. If one tried to explain the simultaneous development of European science, the account would be enormously lengthened; if one spoke only of American achievements, the story would be like a symphony with the brasses and woods left out.

Science is essentially international or supranational. There are no scientific problems which are exclusively American. There is no American science, but there are American scientists, a good many of them, and some of them as great as may be met anywhere else in the world. The best way to explain American achievements is to focus the reader's attention upon a few of the leading scientists. Bernard Jaffe has done that remarkably well, restricting his account to some twenty leaders, but taking care to introduce into his narrative a host of other men, some of them as distinguished as the leaders themselves. By the way, in spite of the author's skill in selecting chapters which were richer in American deeds, he has been frequently obliged to speak of European ones, otherwise his story would have ceased to be intelligible. This bears out what we said at the beginning: even the most American sections of the history of science are international to a degree.

The first chapter, devoted to Thomas Harriot, who published his description of Virginia as early as 1588, is a sort of colo

troduction. The three following chapters introducing the two
Benjamins, Franklin and Thompson, and Thomas Cooper, Jefferson's friend, illustrate the gradual transition to independence. The
rest—that is, the bulk of the book—tells the story of the nineteenth
and twentieth centuries. Thus many successive chapters deal with
contemporaries, we are given many interlocking views of the same
periods and the same environments, and the total is a very striking
picture of what might be called after all "American science,"
meaning science in America.

The selection of the twenty leaders is somewhat arbitrary, and
no two scholars would agree on it completely; yet it is satisfactory,
because its disputable exclusiveness is compensated by an abundance of well-chosen digressions. For the sake of curiosity, rather
than criticism, I asked myself how these twenty men were distributed as to their geographical origin. Five were born in Europe,
two of them (Harriot and Cooper) in England, one in Germany
(Michelson), one in Switzerland (Agassiz), and one in Constantinople (Rafinesque); the two last named might be said to represent French culture. As to the fifteen American-born, almost one
third (Franklin, Thompson, Morton, Langley) hailed from Massachusetts; three came from New York State (Henry, Dana,
Marsh), and the remaining eight are the sons of eight different
states, Connecticut (Gibbs), Pennsylvania (Say), Virginia
(Maury), Kentucky (Morgan), Georgia (Long), Missouri
(Hubble), South Dakota (Lawrence), and California (Evans).
The geographical distribution would not be sufficiently broad, if
Jaffe's selection had to be ratified by the United States Senate, but
it is pretty good. I imagine that the author did not bother about it.
It is accidental, and it is for that reason that it is so interesting.

The book will give every American much pleasure and much
pride. The scientific progress achieved in less than two centuries
is almost incredible. It is true we began nobly with such men as

Franklin and Jefferson, and there never was a time since when
Americans could not refer with pardonable vanity to a few contemporary scientists, yet collective triumphs began only in this
our century. Consider, e.g., this statement: "The year 1932 was
a real *annus mirabilis* in the history of science. Four great discoveries and inventions were made in that single year. The
neutron, heavy hydrogen, and the positron were all brought
to light for the first time, while the first practical cyclotron
was added to the key instruments of physical science. It is interesting to note in this connection that three of these four
milestones were first reached by young American scientists,
while the fourth, predicted by an American, was discovered by
an Englishman. The tempo of first-rate American contributions
in science had definitely reached a new high." Jaffe's book is
so stimulating, so many of the stories he has to tell are so wonderful, that instead of inviting the reader to appreciate it—as a
good prefacer should—I feel it rather my duty to warn him
against the danger of being too enthusiastic. Our scientists have
done wonders, that is agreed, yet we should not take too optimistic a view of the future.

To begin with, we might remark, in a general way, that complacency is always a symptom of mediocrity and immaturity. It
is always better to distrust one's powers and one's wisdom. Boasting cannot be forgiven except to the very young or the very old.
American science is in the full bloom of its maturity. The time of
boasting is definitely past. If some of our scientists are still tactless
enough to indulge in it they should be sent to Coventry.

Even in California, which, if we may judge from the author's
selection of living heroes, is the most promising state for the future
of science, even in California, the number of scientists per thousand people or per square mile (count it as you please) is still pitifully small. Our scientific potential is very high in a few places,

but very low all around. The scientific education (as distinguished from the purely technical training) of our people has been neglected, and the result for all to see is the almost unbelievable success obtained by quacks, faddists, and cultists of every kind.* That success is possible only because of the poverty of the scientific spirit, the lack of resistance to irrationality. It is urgent to build up that resistance. The danger is great and the more so, because it is not generally suspected. In fact, there are a good many people who believe themselves to be scientifically minded, because they can make a show of scientific knowledge (often the latest and most controversial), yet have no definite idea of scientific method; their science is pseudo-science, which is worse than ignorance. It is not at all necessary that the average man should be acquainted with the latest theory of the universe or the newest hormone, but it is very necessary that he should understand as clearly as possible the purpose and methods of science. This is the business of our schools, not simply of the colleges but of all the schools from the kindergarten up.

To nourish superstitions is somewhat comparable to harboring lice and equally disgusting, and if I may push this comparison to its bitter end, I would say that too many of our people—not only of the poor and uneducated, but of the rich, prominent, and fashionable—are lousy. There is nothing in that to brag about. The shops of astrologers, chiromancers, and clairvoyants are as discreditable to a community, and as dangerous to its members, as opium dens. Yet how many people, albeit good, realize that? How many realize that public sanity is as important a matter as public health?

---

* Readers doubting this statement will find abundant proofs of it in Gilbert Seldes: *The Stammering Century* (New York, 1928), Charles Wright Ferguson: *The Confusion of Tongues* (New York, 1928), Bart J. Bok and Margaret W. Mayall: *Scientists Look at Astrology* (*Scientific Monthly*, March, 1941).

Finally, one should bear in mind that even if science and the scientific spirit were better understood and more widely spread, still we should not be too pleased with ourselves. Science, however necessary it may be, is not sufficient, and it will become more and more insufficient as it increases. There was a time when science sprang up as it were in the shadow of wisdom, but it has grown so exuberantly that wisdom is choked—and that is really frightening. If the same development continued much longer without compensation, science would end in turning itself against humanity. The political events of the last forty years have made this clear to all but the blind.

Half a millennium ago the Dutch author of the *Imitation of Christ* wrote, "What availeth it to cavil and dispute much about dark and hidden things. . . ." Modernizing the expression of that sentiment one might say, "What is the good of counting galaxies, analyzing stars, and splitting atoms if we have so little wisdom that we make a hell of life?"

The more science there is, the greater the need of toleration and kindliness, not to speak of justice, the greater the need of humanities without which science is not worth knowing and life is not worth living.

To return to Jaffe, the book he has written is the very kind to awaken scientific vocations and to give intelligent and ambitious young men—the potential leaders of tomorrow—the enthusiasm and tenacity which are the conditions of victory. I hope it will strengthen in every reader the love of science, that is, the love of controllable truth and the dislike of error and superstition, without weakening his feelings of reverence, of humility and charity, without which all the rest is as nothing.

GEORGE SARTON

Harvard Library,
Cambridge, Massachusetts.

ACKNOWLEDGMENTS

THE WRITING of this book was made much easier and its scope more complete by the help of a number of public and private institutions. The rare-book divisions of the New York Public Library and of the Library of Congress in Washington enabled me to consult the original writings of some of America's pioneer naturalists. The Henry E. Huntington Library at San Marino, California, permitted me to register as a "reader" during the Fall of 1941, thus giving me access to its excellent collection of rare books and prints dealing with the earliest days of American science. The Academy of Natural Sciences of Philadelphia, the American Philosophical Society, the American Association for the Advancement of Science, the American Association of University Women, the Bell Telephone Laboratories, Chromatic Television Laboratories, the Carnegie Institution of Washington, the Department of Mines and Resources of Canada, the Mount Wilson Observatory, the National Association for the Advancement of Colored People, the Smithsonian Institution of Washington, the United States Hydrographic Office, the United States Naval Academy, the United States Public Health Service, Princeton's Palmer Physical Laboratory, and Yale's Peabody Museum of Natural History all helpfully furnished me with essential information, maps and photographs.

I owe thanks, too, to many individuals who gave me generously of their time and knowledge in the planning and completion of the manuscript. Among these are Professor Eric T. Bell of the California Institute of Technology; Dr. Ralph G. Van Name of Yale University; Professor Raymond W. Barratt of Dartmouth College; Dr. M. M. Rhoades of the University of Illinois; Dr. H. L. Everett of Cornell University; Mrs. Edwin Hubble of San Marino, California; Roger Stanton, Director of Libraries, California Institute of Technology; Dr. Edwin B. Wilson of the School of Public Health of Harvard University; Dr. Norris Rakestraw of the *Journal of Chemical Education;* Willard E. Shanteau, Death Valley ranger; Katherine S. Brehme of Wellesley College; Dr. J. Rion McKissock, president of the University of South Carolina; Mrs. Charles F. Norton, librarian of Transylvania College; Mr. J. A. Baker, postmaster of Danielsville, Georgia; Mr. C. E. Hardy, mayor of Jefferson, Georgia; Louise M. Husband, librarian of the library of the Workingmen's Institute of New Harmony, Indiana; Dr. Charles H. Wesley of Howard University; Senator Joseph C. O'Mahoney of Wyoming; Doris Cattell of the American Association of Scientific Workers; members of the Michelson family; Harold Ward, and many of the contemporary scientists mentioned in the book. The excellent private library dealing with the history of science which Dr. Herbert M. Evans of the University of California placed at my disposal was also of great help.

Especially, I want to express my gratitude to Miss Galina Terr who, for the third time, took up one of my manuscripts in the raw, and accomplished a painstaking and skillful piece of editing.

BERNARD JAFFE

INTRODUCTION

THE INCENTIVE which led to this project was twofold. First, there is the general lack of knowledge and appreciation by the American public of the lives and achievements of our own men of science. This ignorance pervades even the ranks of professional scientists, teachers of science, and students of American history. Historians of the United States have, with glaring uniformity, underestimated the importance of these men to the development of our country. The teaching of key events in the political and economic history of America has been the standard mental diet in our schools for generations. Crucial events in the history of our scientific progress have been almost completely ignored. Little has been taught of the stirring revolutions in human thought which have resulted from scientific advance. We have failed to integrate science into our culture.

Secondly, no full-bodied attempt has been made by historians of science or biographers of American scientists to paint a complete picture of the growth of science in the United States, especially as it modified the development of our social structure or as the rise of America influenced the kind of science which flourished here. This, too, is a serious omission, for science is an activity and not simply a body of facts. Just as the literature and art of a country are an inseparable part of its history, so a scientific advance may change the course of its destiny. A nation faces a problem which science attacks and solves, and the way of life of millions of people is thereby significantly altered.

Several reasons present themselves for this neglect of so important a phase of the American story. Most writers of the history of the United States have had little training in the sciences and have not, therefore, been equipped for such a task. Other historians have dismissed the problem as one of no great consequence and hence not worth the research which such a treatment would require. Finally, there were others who feared to explore a field so burdened with pitfalls and obstacles. They were repelled by the obvious difficulties to be encountered in attempting to trace relationships between the march of science and our changing social structure. It is easy enough, of course, to see the cause-and-effect relationships between the invention of the cotton gin and the growth of slavocracy, or between the invention of the telegraph and the development of our railroads and the problems which arose from the peopling of the West. On the other hand, it is not so simple a matter to find interconnections between, let us say, the first synthesis of an organic compound, in 1828, and the intellectual and physical revolutions which this unheralded beginning of synthetic chemistry brought in its train. Similarly, it is not so easy to show the impact of the theory of evolution, which reached our shores in 1859, on the thinking of our people regarding such social questions as the rights of the Negro or the principle that all men are created equal.

Professor Charles Beard expressed the challenge of such an undertaking in his introduction to *The Rise of American Civilization:* "The risks of error are staggering; the danger of folly is greater. But what is the alternative for those who are not content to treat life as an inorganic one-thing-after-another, and history as a string of anecdotes? Perhaps those who try to find paths, even where there are none, stimulate path-finding if only by their mistakes."

It was in this spirit, and with the encouragement of Professor George Sarton of Harvard University, editor of *Isis,* organ of the History of Science Society, that I approached this project. Sarton believed that "the history of science should be the leading thread in the history of civilization," and few today will disagree with him. I set up as my goal the examination of the record, with a view to finding possible relationships between the kind of science which developed in America and the type of civilization which has flourished here. I did not plan to prove any thesis as sweeping as that which insists that "the history of the United States is fundamentally a history of invention and science."

As my jumping-off time and place, I took the visit in 1585 of Thomas Harriot to the New World, which resulted in the publication of his *A Briefe and True Report of the New Found land of Virginia,* the first book in English devoted to the flora and fauna of what is now the United States. Surveying in this flight a time period of more than three and a half centuries, I was confronted with the task of gleaning from a host of workers in science just a handful of outstanding men around whom the story could be most accurately and fully told.

The problem of choosing a score of men among several hundred was not a simple one. I therefore set up a basis of selection. The first and most important criterion was the significance of the man's scientific contributions when judged as *pioneer* research. These pioneers were given first placement regardless of all other considerations because first steps in a new field are usually the most difficult. On this basis, for example, the researches of Benjamin Thompson on the nature of heat, which ultimately destroyed the mischievous theory of caloric, could not be omitted.

Other, less important considerations were: (1) The awareness of the scientist of the social scene in which he worked, at least insofar as he participated in the political, economic, or social movements of his day. By this standard Thomas Cooper, friend of Jefferson, Priestley, and Paine, an active participant in the political and educational turmoil of the early years of the struggling republic, was chosen over Robert Hare, inventor of the oxyhydrogen blowpipe used in chemical analysis. (2) The field in which the scientist labored, so that as many different segments of scientific exploration as possible could be included in the final picture. On this basis, Thomas Say, pioneer entomologist, was chosen rather than William Beaumont, whose researches in physiological chemistry could nevertheless be mentioned in the chapter dealing with medical advance. (3) Emphasis on fundamental research and pure science rather than on invention and applied science. Hence Samuel Langley's work in aerodynamics was given preference over the pioneer experiments of the Wright brothers with heavier-than-air flying machines. The five final chapters were reserved for the researches of contemporary scientists in those fields where American men of science have pioneered with outstanding success.

For a consensus on whom to include in this select galaxy of twenty men, I consulted several published lists of eminent American scientists, such as David S. Jordan's *Leading American Men of Science* and William J. Youmans' *Pioneers of Science in America*. I also examined the list of ten men selected by the American Museum of

Natural History in 1906 as those who had done most to advance
science in America. (This list consisted of Agassiz, Audubon, Baird,
Cope, Dana, Franklin, Henry, Humboldt, Leidy, and Torrey.) New
York University's Hall of Fame was also helpful. Out of a total of
eighty-six distinguished Americans so far elected to the Hall of Fame,
nineteen are scientists. Their names are:

John James Audubon	(1785–1851) elected 1900 by 67 votes		
Benjamin Franklin	(1706–1790)	1900	94
Robert Fulton	(1765–1815)	1900	86
Samuel F. B. Morse	(1791–1872)	1900	82
Eli Whitney	(1765–1825)	1900	69
Asa Gray	(1810–1888)	1900	51
Maria Mitchell	(1818–1889)	1905	48
Louis Agassiz	(1807–1873)	1915	65
Joseph Henry	(1799–1878)	1915	56
Elias Howe	(1819–1867)	1915	61
William T. G. Morton	(1819–1868)	1920	72
Matthew F. Maury	(1806–1873)	1930	66
Simon Newcomb	(1835–1909)	1935	78
Walter Reed	(1851–1902)	1945	49
William C. Gorgas	(1854–1920)	1950	81
Alexander G. Bell	(1847–1922)	1950	70
Josiah W. Gibbs	(1839–1903)	1950	64
Wilbur Wright	(1867–1912)	1955	86
George Westinghouse	(1846–1914)	1955	62

In this preliminary search I even included the nineteen scientists
honored on United States postage stamps; namely:

John J. Audubon	William C. Gorgas
Alexander G. Bell	Elias Howe
Luther Burbank	Crawford W. Long
George W. Carver	Cyrus H. McCormick
George Eastman	Samuel F. B. Morse
Thomas A. Edison	Walter Reed
John Ericsson	Eli Whitney
Benjamin Franklin	Harvey W. Wiley
Robert Fulton	Wilbur Wright

Orville Wright

With the above sources serving as leads, I read widely in the fields
of the history and biography of science, turning especially to a large

number of original papers. Out of this reading grew another list which I discussed, either in person or through correspondence, with several eminent scientists. The discussions were illuminating, and often led to further investigations and new revampings of the list. Even at the very close of this exploratory period, wide differences of opinion remained in some cases. The inclusion of Franklin, Gibbs, and Henry found general acceptance. Sectionalism entered into the question of whether to select Dr. Morton of Massachusetts or Dr. Long of Georgia. Here the difficulty was easily resolved because the story of anesthesia is the story of both of these pioneers.

Rather strong personal views punctuated the discussions over the inclusion of Agassiz as against Asa Gray. One eminent zoologist so completely debunked the importance of the Swiss-American as a creative scientist that he was willing to preserve him in the final list only because of his importance as a popularizer of scientific educa-tion. Agassiz, incidentally, was the only American scientist besides Franklin to appear in a list of thirty-five American Immortals which Dumas Malone, editor of the *American Dictionary of Biography*, "speaking as a biographer and not as a scientist," prepared about thirty-five years ago. In explaining his selection, Malone remarked, "Little can be written about the lives of most scientists because there is nothing much to say. On quantitative grounds, therefore (that is, the number of lines of biographical material which followed their names), they were eliminated from this list as were Fulton, Morse, Whitney, and Ericsson, the inventors." This is an interesting reflec-tion of what America knew about her men of science.

The inclusion of Thompson, Dana, and that triumvirate of paleon-tologists of the 1870's—Marsh, Cope, and Leidy—was also generally agreed upon. Say and Cooper were practically unknown names to most of the scientists I consulted, and for the most part still remain neglected and overshadowed. There was some difference of opinion over the choice of Rafinesque instead of Audubon. Rafinesque re-mained in the list because he was an unusual collector, systematizer, and polyhistor—a real titan among our early naturalists.

In the selection of contemporary scientists I hardly hoped to obtain universal agreement; first, because I was limited to just a few names, and secondly, because we are still too close to these men and their achievements to be able to evaluate their work with complete objectivity. The final list which appears in the Table of Contents is, of course, not an exhaustive one. The work of dozens of other men is mentioned in the story.

Before the first draft of the book had been completed, a number of interesting ideas began to emerge. Until recently, for example, the scientific contributions of America were largely in applied science and invention rather than in pure or theoretical science. American men of science had shown extraordinary ingenuity in building new tools of science and in applying pure science to technological progress. The U. S. Patent System had been created on April 10, 1790, by George Washington in the first year of the republic under the Constitution. Between the time of the establishment of our Patent Office in 1836 and the year 1860 some 32,000 patents were granted to Americans. It is no wonder that Abraham Lincoln remarked that the Patent System "had added the fuel of interest to the fire of genius."

During the next thirty years another 450,000 patents were issued, including one to Mark Twain in 1873 for a self-pasting scrapbook, a series of blank pages coated with gum. This book, one of his biographers remarked, did not contain a single word that critics could praise or condemn. Between 1890 and 1935 an additional million and a half American patents were taken out, and in the next two decades almost a million more were added. The United States has actually led the world in the number of patents registered—twice as many as Great Britain or France and four times as many as Germany. At the hundredth-anniversary celebration of the establishment of the U. S. Patent Office, which was held in Washington, D. C., in 1936, a research parade was presented. The twelve greatest inventions of the country were selected by a committee and listed chronologically as follows:

Cotton Gin .. invented 1793 by Eli Whitney of Massachusetts
Steamboat ....1809...Robert Fulton of Pennsylvania
                  and 1786...John Fitch of Connecticut
Reaper ....1834...Cyrus McCormick of Virginia
Telegraph ....1837...Samuel F. B. Morse of Massachusetts
Rubber Vulcanization ..1839...Charles Goodyear of Connecticut
Sewing Machine ....1846...Elias Howe of Massachusetts
Airbrake ....1872...George Westinghouse of New York
Telephone ....1876...Alexander G. Bell (born in Scotland)
Incandescent Lamp ....1880...Thomas A. Edison of Ohio
Linotype Machine .....1884...Ottmar Mergenthaler (born in Germany)

Commercial Aluminum 1886...Charles M. Hall of Ohio
Airplane ....1903...Wilbur Wright of Indiana and
                                    Orville Wright of Ohio

  To this list might be added at least five more:

Typewriter
  (first practical) .....1868...Christopher L. Sholes of Pennsylvania
Phonograph ....1877...Thomas A. Edison
Radio Tube
  (3-electrode) ....1906...Lee de Forest of Iowa
Bakelite ....1909...Leo H. Baekeland (born in Belgium)
Oil Cracking ....1913...William M. Burton of Ohio

  Some of these inventions were improvements, developments, or
applications of scientific principles discovered outside our own borders. The first practical steamboat, for example, was made possible
by the adaptation of the steam engine to water transportation. Other
inventions such as the telegraph, telephone, incandescent lamp, and
airplane were the results of the application of principles discovered
in the realm of pure science either wholly or in great measure by our
own scientists. Still others, such as the cotton gin, reaper, and sewing
machine, were the products of sheer mechanical ingenuity. The harnessing of the internal-combustion engine in automobiles, the development of the modern radio and of the moving-picture, television,
and electronic computer machines, the huge increase in our varieties
of metals, steel, and other alloys, the opening up of a whole new field
of plastics by the inventions of celluloid and bakelite; our advances
in new rocket fuels, the refining and cracking of petroleum and our
first-rate contributions to the new chemical world of synthetic rub-
bers, fibers, dyes, insecticides, drugs, vitamins, and hormones—all are
but a few examples of our leadership in the practical utilization of
scientific principles. Eli Whitney's introduction of the use of interchangeable parts in the manufacture of machines and tools was another revolution which may well be credited to America. The assembly line, automation in petroleum refining and other processes, our
huge, intricate, uncannily efficient continuous-process machines such
as those used in the manufacture of glass and steel, are further examples of America's superior role in applied science.
  The reasons for this tremendous output of practical applications of

science lie in the nature of the social forces which have been at work in the building of the United States. From the beginning, our people were engaged in subduing a land of great area, a land rich in natural resources and, in the early years, low in man power. We were a new country. Immense forests waited to be stripped. Mountains of iron, copper, silver, gold, and other metals had only to be mined. Enormous deposits of coal and bursting reservoirs of petroleum needed but to be tapped to yield a steady flow of power. Fertile fields, vast prairies, rich forests smiled graciously on the pioneers, waiting to be peopled and exploited. But mountain barriers, rushing rivers, arid plains, and burning deserts had to be crossed. The mind, the labor, and the energies of our forebears were occupied for two hundred years with the immediate problem of conquering a country and holding dominion over it. The inventive genius of our people was challenged to produce new and swifter means of transportation and communication as well as labor-saving devices to accomplish this prodigious task. The inventive capacities and the technological skills of America were stimulated to a fever heat.

A powerful native royalty emerged from this restless people dazzled by the possibilities of new conquests and new acquisitions. Railroad magnates, oil kings, coal barons, steel manipulators, and other monarchs of industry fought one another in applying the fruits of science to the piling up of huge fortunes and the building of a new country. There was little time and less thought for abstract science when every one of its values was approached in terms of exploitation, service, and function. Alexis de Tocqueville, a distinguished European who visited the United States during the Jacksonian era, wrote, "The spirit of the Americans is averse to general ideas and does not seek theoretical discoveries." Theoretical speculation and contemplative philosophy in science were engulfed in the mad rush to exploit a land bursting with colossal physical resources. In such an atmosphere the pragmatic philosophy of William James was born, and the guiding star of "learning by doing" rose under the leadership of John Dewey.

The point has frequently been made that while in applied science the United States has kept pace with and even forged ahead of our European contemporaries, we have lagged behind in the realm of pure science—the search for truth with no thought of practical application

BENJAMIN FRANKLIN

BENJAMIN THOMPSON

THOMAS COOPER

"Thomas Cooper in
Old Age in South Carolina"

THOMAS SAY

CONSTANTINE S. RAFINESQUE

WILLIAM THOMAS GREEN MORTON

JOSEPH HENRY

Henry's electromagnet engine (1837), recognized as the first type of electric motor.

Courtesy, Dr. H. D. Smyth, Princeton University

MATTHEW FONTAINE MAURY
*Courtesy, Naval Academy
Museum, Annapolis*

LOUIS J. R. AGASSIZ

JAMES DWIGHT DANA

OTHNIEL C. MARSH

Mounted skeleton of *Stegosaurus ungulatus*, 19½ feet long and almost 12 feet high.

JOSIAH WILLARD GIBBS
Courtesy, Sloane Physics Laboratory, Yale

Skull of *Triceratops*, 6 feet long.
Courtesy, Carl O. Dunbar, Director, Yale's Peabody Museum

Samuel P. Langley observing an eclipse of the sun in 1900.
Courtesy, Smithsonian Institution

The first successful flight of an airplane, with Orville Wright at the controls. *N. Y. Sun photo*

Albert Abraham Michelson with the octagonal steel mirror which shot a beam of light 82 miles from Mt. Wilson to Mt. San Jacinto.

University of Chicago photo

THOMAS HUNT MORGAN

HERBERT M. EVANS and ERNEST O. LAWRENCE

Carl D. Anderson at the machine with which he discovered the positron.

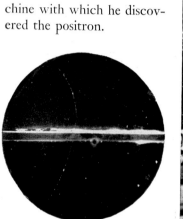

The discovery plate of the positron. Below the center of the plate a positron strikes a lead plate 6 mm. thick, passes through it and emerges much weakened, as shown by the greater sharpness of its curve. This positron resulted from cosmic ray bombardment. Photo taken August 2, 1932.   *Courtesy, Wide World and Carl D. Anderson*

The bevatron at the University of California's Radiation Laboratory.
Courtesy, University of California Radiation Laboratory

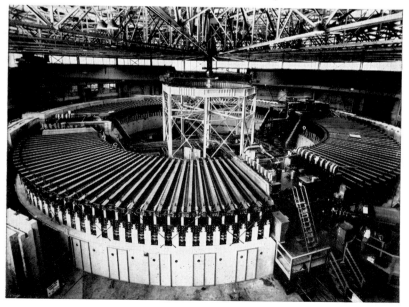

The observatory housing the new 200-inch telescope on Mt. Palomar, California.
Photo, O. K. Harter

The velocity-distance relation for extra-galactic nebulae. The arrows above the nebular spectra point to the H and K lines of calcium and show the amounts these lines are displaced toward the red end of the spectra. The comparison spectra are of helium. The direct photographs (on the same scale and with approximately the same exposure times) illustrate the decrease in size and brightness with increasing velocity or red-shift.

NGC 4473 is a member of the Virgo cluster and NGC 379 is a member of a group of nebulae in Pisces.

EDWIN POWELL HUBBLE

	KH	VELOCITY	DISTANCE
NGC 221		−200 km/sec	250,000 parsecs
GC 4473		+2,300 km/sec	1,800,000 parsecs
NGC 379		+5,500 km/sec	7,000,000 parsecs
bula in sa Major luster		+15,400 km/sec	26,000,000 parsecs
ula in ni Cluster		+23,000 km/sec	41,000,000 parsecs

ENRICO FERMI
Courtesy, University of Chicago Press

or pecuniary reward. We have been reminded that in our annals of science there is no Darwin, whose scientific genius shaped the cumbersome mass of data in the world of biology into a theory which revolutionized man's idea about his place in the scheme of living things. Biographers have fruitlessly searched, we are told, in our magnificent universities for an American-born peer of Einstein, who introduced into modern science as sweeping a synthesis of physical phenomena as did Newton before him in England. They cannot find, they insist, an American counterpart of James Clerk Maxwell, who with rare insight enunciated the electromagnetic theory of light and successfully predicted the discovery of wireless waves. We have given the world, they claim, no equal of Pasteur, who proved the germ theory of disease which forever destroyed the demoniacal conception of illness and launched a momentous new era in medicine.

Does the record of scientific achievement in the United States bear out this generally accepted point of view? Let us examine the ledger. American science had its birth in the electrical researches of Benjamin Franklin. About two hundred years have gone by since those immortal experiments were performed in Philadelphia. What was happening in the scientific laboratories of the rest of the world during this same period? Said Millikan, a generation ago, "If I were asked to list the most influential scientists who have lived during the eighteenth and nineteenth centuries, I should bring forward the following eleven names:

Benjamin Franklin	1706–1790	American
Pierre Laplace	1749–1827	Frenchman
Michael Faraday	1791–1867	Englishman
James Clerk Maxwell	1831–1879	Englishman
Charles Darwin	1809–1882	Englishman
Auguste Fresnel	1788–1827	Frenchman
Louis Pasteur	1822–1895	Frenchman
Karl F. Gauss	1777–1855	German
Hermann Helmholtz	1821–1894	German
Alexander Volta	1748–1827	Italian
J. Willard Gibbs	1839–1903	American."

In this top-ranking group are three English men of science, three French scientists, two Germans, one Italian, and two native Americans. This list would seem to indicate that among the most eminent scientists who worked during the less than two centuries which followed the birth of theoretical science in America, we produced at least a small number who were the equal of some of those in Europe.

Another list could be presented which would give a less favorable, yet equally interesting, picture. Of the eighteen scientists of this same period who were chosen by our National Academy of Sciences for bas-relief bronze portraits to decorate their Washington building, we find the following distribution:

2 Americans ......Franklin and Gibbs
2 Germans ....Helmholtz and Gauss
6 Englishmen .....Darwin, Faraday, Galton, Joule, Lyell, Maxwell
6 Frenchmen ......Bernard, Carnot, Cuvier, Laplace, Lavoisier, Pasteur
1 Austrian ....Mendel
1 Swede ....Linnaeus

America did make at least a modest contribution to conceptual science in spite of the many forces which were working against the burgeoning of acute scientific thinkers during the years of the building of our republic. Is this because master theoreticians need no particular humus in which to blossom; because among large literate populations great minds are inevitably born and make their influences felt? We must not forget that famous men of science have sprung up in the most unexpected places, without cultural forebears, special training, or exceptional encouragement. Witness the lives and achievements of Benjamin Franklin, who started as a printer's devil; Benjamin Thompson, as a poor schoolteacher; Joseph Henry, son of a day laborer; Matthew Maury, child of a struggling frontier farmer; James Dana, clerk in his father's store; Albert Michelson, whose father operated a drygoods shop in California; and Isidor Rabi, whose Austrian immigrant father ran a small grocery store in Brooklyn, New York.

It is a fairly general opinion that American men of science have almost completely ignored the social scene and have been content to follow their scientific pursuits undisturbed by the storms about them. The chronicle of American science, however, does not bear out this belief in the utter detachment of our scientists.

The social and political activities of Franklin, which made him the first citizen of his day, are too well known to need repetition here. Thompson, in accordance with his own beliefs, spent a good part of his life in the service of the impoverished masses of Europe. We may disapprove of the methods he tried for the solution of unemployment and mendicancy, but we cannot deny his deep preoccupation with socioscientific problems. Cooper, a refugee from the political and religious intolerance of Europe, held public office in the young republic for many years, fought the undemocratic Alien and Sedition Acts of President Adams, and took an active part in the struggle against religious bigotry on this side of the Atlantic. David Rittenhouse brought testimony against the slave trade and openly sympathized with the motives of the French Revolution. Thomas Say was led by the beckoning utopian socialism of his day to throw in his lot with the New Harmony venture of the 1820's. He spent the remainder of his life in the New World Utopia on the shores of the Wabash in an effort to discover whether this was the answer to the many problems arising from the abuses of the emerging factory system.

That strange, erratic genius, Rafinesque, spent many years of his busy life concocting schemes for social betterment. In his own way he tried, with some degree of success, to improve the lot of the little man by establishing a bank where the citizen of small means could borrow money at reasonable rates and without too heavy collateral. Fate played a cruel prank on Rafinesque, for he was buried in a pauper's grave. Dr. Morton, all through his fight to commercialize ether anesthesia and reap the reward which he felt was justly his, never forgot his duty to mankind. His method and skill were offered to the hospitals and armies of the world free of charge. Joseph Henry turned down offers to exploit his discoveries—offers which would have made him rich—to accept the directorship of the newly founded Smithsonian Institution. He spent half his life in the service of America as disseminator of knowledge and consultant to the government on scientific problems.

Simon Newcomb entered the field of economics, wrote on financial subjects, and is said to have been the first to formulate accurately the quantity theory of money. Louis Agassiz in his own way tried to solve the problem of slavery in this country of his adoption. He became interested in many kinds of projects directed toward raising the level of public education in the United States. Othniel Marsh not only spent his own inherited fortune to advance the science of paleontology in America, but also fought bravely against the corruption of the agents appointed to deal with the American Indian. Marsh lobbied in Washington because he felt that this fight was just as much his duty as a citizen as was his purely scientific work a service to his country.

The social awareness of American men of science, an awareness which became even more marked with the sudden advent of the nuclear era and the age of outer-space flight, is not difficult to explain. American science is to a great extent the fruit of men who were themselves victims of Old World intolerance and bigotry, political or religious refugees who found freedom in the United States. Others were the descendants of men and women who had left the oppressive life of Europe to breathe the purer air of a free country. Few of these men were rich, many were self-taught, intelligent, alive to the meaning of the rights and obligations of free men under a democratic government.

Franklin's father, a dyer in England, left for America because of his nonconformist principles. Cooper was a refugee from the blind political and sectarian intolerance of Europe. Rafinesque was the son of a French merchant victimized by the innumerable wars on the Continent. Say's father was a Congressman whose Huguenot ancestors had escaped from France after the revocation of the Edict of Nantes. Thompson tried hard to forget that his impoverished ancestors had come over to New England with Governor Winthrop in 1630 to find a more endurable economic life. Dr. Patrick K. Rogers, after taking part in the Irish rebellion against England, escaped to America in 1799. Later he became Professor of Natural Philosophy and Mathematics at the College of William and Mary.

Since the days of these pioneers of American science, more particularly within the last sixty years, there have been two significant changes. These are an acceleration in the tempo of scientific discoveries and a noticeably greater emphasis on theoretical science. One of the reasons for these changes is the final disappearance of the territorial frontier. Restless, adventurous, imaginative men have been compelled to find new outlets for their energies in the new and never-closed frontiers of knowledge. Men with keen mathematical minds, for example, were no longer snatched up in large numbers by pioneering business enterprises for their numerous surveys. Instead, they are exercising their mathematical and theoretical powers in the research laboratories of our universities and industrial organizations.

Also, with the establishment of graduate and postgraduate universities and institutes based to some extent upon European models, such as Johns Hopkins, the University of Chicago, Stanford University, the California Institute of Technology, and the Institute for Advanced Study, opportunities for higher learning and research have been made available to many who would otherwise have been compelled to go to foreign centers. By expansion of a new system of part-time teaching, our university professors have been relieved of some of their routine pedagogy and can spend a little more time in basic research. In the earlier years, practically all of the fundamental research done in our colleges was accomplished between classes, so to speak. Further emancipation from the load of teaching and the treadmill of class routine will make available clearer heads and longer hours for philosophic contemplation and scientific exploration. The story of Joseph Henry's life would have been quite different had he been given the opportunity for greater leisure and more time for "dreaming" in his earlier productive years when he was obliged to spend most of his time in the classroom.

Another important development in American science was the relatively recent rise of many large private foundations such as the Carnegie Institution of Washington, Carnegie Corporation of New York, Rockefeller Foundation, Commonwealth Fund, Guggenheim Memorial Foundation, W. K. Kellogg Foundation, Sloane Foundation, and Ford Foundation. Tens of millions of dollars have been made available for scientific laboratories such as those of the Rockefeller Institute for Medical Research, opened in New York City in 1904 with Simon Flexner as Director. The Bamberger and Fuld gift of $5,000,000 made possible in 1930 the establishment of the Institute for Advanced Study at Princeton, New Jersey. Additional funds have also been provided for the salaries of thousands of research men and women, and for the best equipment available for many large-scale research projects which our universities could not possibly undertake alone. The two-hundred-inch telescope atop Mount

Palomar, largest in the world, and the cyclotron of the University of California are but two of the many products of the philanthropy of great foundations.

Partly as a result of this, scientists from all over the world were attracted here to work side by side with our own research men. Here in an atmosphere of freedom and serenity they exchanged, pooled, and enriched each others' ideas, skills, and learning. To the Rockefeller Institute for Medical Research came Hideo Noguchi from the mountains of Northern Japan to fight yellow fever, and Max Theiler from South Africa to develop a vaccine against this same disease which won him the Nobel Prize in 1951. To the Institute for Advanced Study came two very young Chinese theoretical physicists, Tsung Dao Lee and Chen Ning Yang, to further develop the theoretical work which led to the overthrow of the principle of parity and their sharing of the Nobel Prize in Physics in 1957. And, of course, here, too, the footsteps of the great Einstein were heard for the last twenty-two years of his life.

Of great importance, too, has been the establishment of very large and elaborate, up-to-the-minute research laboratories by some of our powerful industrial organizations. The first of these laboratories of any great effect was that of the General Electric Company established in 1902 at Schenectady, New York. Others followed, such as those of Eastman Kodak Company, Westinghouse Electric and Manufacturing Company, the Gulf Oil Company, Allied Chemical and Dye, Pfizer, American Cyanamid, and E. I. du Pont de Nemours and Company. The great impetus for these private laboratories started about 1916. World War I taught us quickly and dramatically that we were altogether too dependent on the Old World for many essentials such as scientific instruments, synthetic chemicals, and dyestuffs. This situation was not only dangerous but unworthy of a young and vigorous nation. By 1920 our industrial laboratories were already employing 6,000 scientists, and twenty years later this figure rose to 36,000. Billions of dollars were poured into research. Furthermore, revolutionary discoveries in science offer a constant threat to even the most substantial industries. Almost overnight some chemical or physical discovery may throw into the scrap heap a flourishing business—a fate which overcame the indigo, wood alcohol, and, to some extent, the silk and natural rubber industries. Industrialists have consequently found it necessary to subsidize generously the best research available in order to safeguard the continued profits of their immense organizations. Research laboratories have come to be regarded as no less essential than insurance—no wide-awake industrial organization could dare ignore either need.

Out of this new development in America have come scientific advances both fundamental and fruitful. From two such research establishments, in fact, came five recipients of the Nobel Prize in science: Irving Langmuir of the General Electric Company, and Clinton J. Davisson, John Bardeen, Walter H. Brattain, and William Shockley of the Bell Telephone Laboratories. The first two of these men won their honors for researches in pure science, and the other three for the development of the transistor.

American science is also being served by more than forty federal research agencies and units. Some were established during the nineteenth century, such as the Naval Observatory, Coast and Geodetic Survey, Geological Survey, and the Department of Agriculture. The first decade of the twentieth century witnessed the creation of the U. S. Bureau of Mines, the U. S. Bureau of Standards, the National Institute of Health, and the United States Public Health Service. Their scientists have made magnificent contributions in the fields of pellagra, yellow fever, typhoid, amoebic and bacillary dysentery, Rocky Mountain spotted fever, malaria and mosquito control, and industrial hygiene. They did creditable work in basic physical science, too, such as the discovery of deuterium by F. G. Brickwedde of the National Bureau of Standards, and the delicate meson experiments successfully carried out in the same laboratories in 1957 to help disprove the principle of parity.

With the establishment of the United States Atomic Energy Commission in 1946 a new and most powerful agency for scientific research came into being in this country. Whereas the other Federal agencies scraped along on scanty budgets, billions of dollars continue to be poured into this huge organization to keep us ahead of the rest of the world in nuclear weapons and atomic power development. Part of the enormous treasure used by the Atomic Energy Commission has happily been applied to basic science projects.

Another reason for the changes in American science may well have been the gradual realization by gifted young people that research in science offers a new, a beautiful, and an exciting field for a useful career. No longer are the ministry, law, medicine, engineering, and business pre-empting the brains of this country. Some of our youth have found new values—a deep appreciation of the creative and esthetic values of hard fundamental research in pure science. The tempo of advance here, in spite of setbacks, is steadily increasing. This can be measured in a sense by the rapidly growing number of Americans who are being honored with the Nobel Prize in science. Among 205 recipients of the science awards during the period from 1901, when the first one was made, through 1958, forty-nine have been Americans. In the first decade after the establishment of these awards only one went to an American. In the next decade, two Americans were honored; in the third ten years, three were chosen; in the fourth decade, nine; and in the fifth, fourteen. During the last eight years as many as twenty Americans became Nobel science laureates—this is half the total awards made in the sciences.

Here is the list of Americans who received Nobel prizes for pioneer achievements in physics, chemistry, and medicine and physiology.

1907	Albert A. Michelson (born in Poland)	physics
1912	Alexis Carrel (born in France)	medicine
1914	Theodore W. Richards	chemistry
1923	Robert A. Millikan	physics
1927	Arthur H. Compton	physics
1930	Karl Landsteiner (born in Austria)	medicine
1932	Irving Langmuir	chemistry
1933	Thomas H. Morgan	medicine
1934	Harold C. Urey	chemistry
1934	George R. Minot	medicine
	William P. Murphy	medicine
	George H. Whipple	medicine
1936	Carl D. Anderson	physics
1937	Clinton J. Davisson	physics
1939	Ernest O. Lawrence	physics
1943	Edward A. Doisy	medicine
1944	Isidor I. Rabi (born in Austria)	physics
1944	Joseph Erlanger	medicine
	Herbert S. Gasser	medicine
1946	Hermann J. Muller	medicine

1946 Percy W. Bridgman ....physics

{

Wendell M. Stanley ....chemistry ⎫

John H. Northrop ....chemistry ⎬

James B. Sumner ....chemistry ⎭

}

1947 { Carl F. Cori (born in Czechoslovakia) ....medicine ⎫

Gerty T. Cori (born in Czechoslovakia) ....medicine ⎬ }

1949 William F. Giauque (born in Canada) ....chemistry

1950 { Philip S. Hench ....medicine ⎫

Edward C. Kendall ....medicine ⎬ }

1951 { Glenn T. Seaborg ....chemistry ⎫

Edwin M. McMillan ....chemistry ⎬ }

1952 Selman A. Waksman (born in Russia) ....medicine

1952 { Felix P. Bloch (born in Switzerland) ....physics ⎫

Edward M. Purcell ....physics ⎬ }

1954 {

John F. Enders ....medicine ⎫

Frederick Robbins ....medicine ⎬

Thomas Weller ....medicine ⎭

}

1954 Linus Pauling ....chemistry

1955 Vincent du Vigneaud ....chemistry

{ Willis E. Lamb ....physics ⎫

Polykarp Kusch (born in Germany) ....physics ⎬ }

1956 { Andre F. Cournand (born in France) ....medicine ⎫

Dickinson W. Richards ....medicine ⎬ }

{

John Bardeen ....physics ⎫

Walter H. Brattain ....physics ⎬

William B. Shockley (born in England) ....physics ⎭

}

1958 {

George W. Beadle ....medicine ⎫

Joshua Lederberg ....medicine ⎬

Edward L. Tatum ....medicine ⎭

}

America's inferiority to Europe in the field of abstract science had already become a thing of the past even before World War II started. The tide of young people seeking graduate work and advanced training in the sciences had already turned from Europe, where research had become widespread in the late nineteenth century, to our own centers of culture. We were producing research on a greater scale, and of a quality as high as that originating in the laboratories abroad. At the California Institute of Technology, Thomas Hunt Morgan, aided by Alfred Sturtevant and a group of minds as original as can be found anywhere in the world, had worked out a brilliant theory of inheritance. Morgan's theory of the gene, a conception which may yet rank with the monumental contributions in thermodynamics of J. Willard Gibbs, has carried science a long step forward in unraveling the mysteries of evolution and heredity.

In Pasadena worked another brilliant theoretical scientist, Richard C. Tolman, who, until World War II sent him to Washington, was busy interpreting the data furnished by Edwin Hubble and other observers at the one-hundred-inch telescope on Mount Wilson. He constructed new cosmologies so compelling that Einstein himself gave up his own static model concept of the universe in favor of the nonstatic conceptual model of Tolman. Hubble, who abandoned law for astronomy, not only furnished, first at Mount Wilson and later at Mount Palomar, the bulk of the international output of cosmological data but, with a genius which matched that of the European giants of theoretical science, lifted men's minds to heights never before dreamed of with his penetrating conception of an expanding universe.

In Berkeley, on the campus of the University of California, Ernest O. Lawrence, as a young research worker, made a daring attack on the inner citadel of the atom with a weapon never before conceived of and opened up an entirely new and ever challenging world of investigation. His cyclotrons, or atom-smashing machines, were so effective that more than a score of other American universities quickly constructed similar apparatus with his help; and European and Asian laboratories soon followed suit.

Here, too, Glenn T. Seaborg and his associates, using this new revolutionary machine, took on the role of Creator and synthesized a whole new group of chemical elements which had never before been found in the heavens or on earth. And still another Nobel laureate, working here in the field of low temperatures, completed a classic piece of research which enabled scientists to reach the coldest temperatures ever attained to that time—less than one one-hundredth of one degree above Absolute Zero, corresponding to 459.6° below zero on the Fahrenheit scale. This was the Canadian-born chemist, William F. Giauque.

At the Rockefeller Institute for Medical Research, the Indiana-born biochemist Wendell M. Stanley discovered in 1935 a crystalline protein with all the characteristics of a disease-producing virus. He isolated the pure chemical from leaves infected with tobacco mosaic, a virus disease. This crystal could produce tobacco mosaic in healthy plants. Though not alive, it could increase its own chemical substance from some of the compounds found in living cells. Stanley's invasion of the borderland of physics, chemistry, biology, and medicine electrified the world and renewed man's hope of conquering human virus diseases such as measles and infantile paralysis.

In a laboratory of Columbia University in New York City, Harold C. Urey, with masterly technique and a theoretical approach of the highest order, developed a hitherto unexplored field of study with his discovery of one of the two heavy isotopes of hydrogen and his separation in appreciable quantities of other isotopes such as those of carbon and nitrogen. With these and other new chemical tags which thus became available, a fresh attack upon physiological problems affecting vital questions of human health was begun.

At this same university Isidor I. Rabi, Polykarp Kusch, and others kept probing the interior of the atom's nucleus, extracting new data and propounding new theories as to its innermost structure and behavior. Felix P. Bloch, at Stanford University in Palo Alto, and Willis E. Lamb at the same university belong to this same breed of men playing with subnuclear particles of strange design and power. They are but a few of the scores of nuclear scientists wrestling with the atom's core in the many atomic-energy research centers around the country, such as those at Brookhaven, Long Island; Argonne National Laboratory, outside Chicago; Arco, Idaho; Los Alamos, New Mexico; and Oak Ridge, Tennessee.

Carl Anderson, working under the inspiration of Robert A. Millikan on the mysterious cosmic rays, discovered a new unit of matter, the *positron*, and stumbled also over the curious particle called the *meson*. Across the campus from Anderson's laboratory in Pasadena, California, Linus Pauling, an unusual combination of brilliant theoretician and bold experimentalist, applied quantum mechanical reasoning to the interpretation of chemical behavior and clarified some of the problems of crystal structure and molecular stability. Then, with the daring of a conquistador, he plunged into the dark continents of the chemical architecture of proteins and the nature of molecular medicine. And again in both of these new areas of exploration this Nobel laureate in science made outstanding contributions.

Selman A. Waksman, who came here in 1910 as a young man of twenty-two from Kiev in the Russian Ukraine, worked for years in microbiology at Rutgers University in New Brunswick, New Jersey. In 1943 he discovered a new antibiotic, streptomycin, which did a spectacular job in combating serious kidney infections and other diseases of man. Then he and his associates continued to search successfully for new chemicals at the Institute of Microbiology, which was built with money accumulated from royalties received from the sale of his streptomycin.

At Harvard University Percy W. Bridgman, philosopher-physicist, worked with enormous pressures approaching those found in the interior of the earth to study the structure of crystals and other effects of massive weights. Here, too, young Robert B. Woodward was not afraid to attack some of the most complicated organic molecules to learn their structure and succeeded in synthesizing for the first time such chemicals as cortisone, strychnine, quinine, and the tranquilizer reserpine. And in another laboratory of this same institution George Wald after a quarter of a century of effort continued to unravel the mysteries of the chemistry of vision.

At the Washington University School of Medicine in St. Louis a husband-and-wife research team set out to answer some of the questions about what happens in the body to sugar and starch taken in as food. Drs. Carl F. and Gerty T. Cori came here from Prague, Czechoslovakia, in 1922 as a young couple and were naturalized six years later. They cleared up some of the problems connected with insulin and cheered millions of diabetics around the world.

The laboratories of this same school of medicine witnessed the pioneer work also of two other American winners of the Nobel Prize in science. Edward A. Doisy was honored for his work on vitamin K, and Joseph Erlanger for his unusual investigation of the conduction rates of various nerve fibers closely related to pain reactions.

And then, after long years of research by scores of investigators, came the electrifying announcement that an effective protective vaccine had finally been developed against the scourge of infantile paralysis. Jonas E. Salk of the University of Pittsburgh Medical School, who completed this epic of medical history, obtained part of the money needed for his brilliant researches from the National Foundation for Infantile Paralysis.

American science today is still vigorous, imaginative, and potentially creative to a measure unbelievable. All over the country there is a fresh excitement for science. American scientists are silently engaged on many crucial fronts and in many lonely outposts. But the university, government, and industrial laboratories are not the only centers where science is being cherished and cultivated as never before. When I traveled about the country gathering data, talking to scientists and trying to weave together the many threads of the fabric of science in America, I found the spirit of our early naturalists still alive. As I drove along part of the route of Lewis and Clark or followed the trails of old Bartram and Rafinesque, I found the prototype of the old-fashioned naturalist still with us. Out in the colorful bottom of the Death Valley National Monument, where John C. Frémont had picked up some interesting new plants a century before, I came across one of those men who still "likes live things."

In the beautiful valley between the high Panamints and Funeral Range I met M. French Gilman, who more than a half century back started botanizing around Banning, California. In 1931 he came into the valley to work for the National Park Service as desert nurseryman. Today his name is synonymous with Death Valley botany and ornithology. Unschooled, like so many of our early naturalists, without even a faint knowledge of Latin, Gilman won recognition as a careful collector. *Gilmania luteola* and several other flowers were named after him. He and his nimble company, too, are part of America's exciting excursions into science.

CHAPTER ONE

THOMAS HARRIOT
(1560-1621)

BRINGING THE SEEDS OF SCIENCE TO AMERICA

T HEY ARE a people clothed with loose mantles made of deere skinnes, and aprons of the same round about their middles, all els naket, of such a difference of stature only as wee in England, having no edge tooles, or weapons of yron or steele. . . . Their houses are made of small poles, made fast at the top in round forme. . . . They seem very ingenious. For although they have no such tooles, nor any such crafts, Sciences and Artes as wee, yet in those things they doe, they shew excellencie of wit. . . . Most things they saw with us, as Mathematicall instruments, sea compasses, the virtue of the load-stone in drawing yron, a perspective glass whereby was shewed many strange sights, burning glasses, wilde fireworks, gunnes, hookes, writing and reading, spring clocks that seemed to go off themselves, all were so strange unto them, and so far exceeded their capacities to comprehend that they thought they were rather the workes of God than of men (this made them listen to us about our God and our religion)."

These were among the very first observations printed in the English language on the science of what is now the United States of America. Harriot's *A Briefe and True Report of the New Found land of Virginia* referred to the Indians of Wingandacoa, in a region named Virginia in honor of Elizabeth, the Virgin Queen of England. More specifically the book described the natives of Roanoke Island, North Carolina, on whose shores a party of English explorers landed in 1585. Sir Walter Raleigh, recipient of a patent or license from his Queen, had sent the party out to "discover, search, find out, and view such remote, heathen, and barbarous lands, countries, and territories not actually possessed by any Christian prince, nor inhabited by Christian people." In return for all proprietary rights over all the territory that was to be occupied by his men, Raleigh would pay Elizabeth twenty per cent of the precious metals from all the mines found and exploited there.

Raleigh was interested in more than the soul of the heathen. The newly discovered world was rich in natural resources. That was the report brought back by Amados and Barlow, whom he had sent out in two ships the previous year to reconnoiter the coast from Florida to Newfoundland for a suitable spot for colonization. On their return, his two captains had brought back Manteo and Wanchese, two "savages" who were to help in further expeditions, and also a glowing account of the teeming riches they had seen. The New World was to free England from the exorbitant prices it had to pay to the Baltic states for potash and naval stores, and from dependence on the faraway East for essential dyes, spices, and niter. England needed desperately to become self-sufficient in these commodities.

Raleigh looked around for a man of science who could make a careful survey of the dominions over which he planned to take possession. He might have approached William Gilbert, pioneer in electricity and magnetism and physician to the Queen, but Gilbert was wanted at home. Besides, he wanted an even younger man, one who could endure the hardships of a seventy-five-day voyage on a scarcely charted sea, as well as the rigors of life in a new and perhaps hostile country. He was seeking a natural philosopher of wide knowledge, keen judgment, and youthful enthusiasm. There was one at hand. Oxford-born Thomas Harriot had been his mathematical tutor for the five years since Harriot had been graduated, at the age of twenty, from Oxford University. Raleigh had taken the already distinguished student into his household and had allowed him a handsome pension. Patronage to promising men of science by wealthy individuals was quite general in those days. The English nobleman and member of Parliament found young Harriot a faithful, trustworthy, and close-mouthed servant, a likable and witty companion, a capable and patient teacher. Raleigh was not his only pupil. Many came from Oxford University to study under him; Raleigh's sea captains, too, were instructed in navigation and impressed with the need of "uniting profitably theory with practice."

On April 9, 1585, seven ships set sail from Plymouth Harbor under the command of Sir Richard Grenville, acting as admiral in the name of Raleigh. Master Harriot was among the one hundred and seven men in the command. He was entrusted with the job of making a statistical survey of the new land, of acting as historiographer and geographer, and of bringing back a detailed account of the mineral resources, the plant and animal life of the region, and as much as he could learn of the heathen. Grenville headed his craft along the route Columbus had taken. The winds bore the ships first to Santo Domingo and finally to the northern end of Pamlico Sound, where the island of Roanoke, twenty miles long and six miles broad, lay in the waters between Pamlico and Albemarle Sounds.

Here a fort was built. With Manteo and Wanchese acting as guides and interpreters, Harriot proceeded to map the area and to note carefully everything he saw so that he might "set down all the commodities which the country doth yield for victuals and sustenance for man's life . . . of such other commodities besides for those that shall inhabit and plant there, with a brief description of the nature and manners of the people."

The numerous explorations of the period had brought back to Europe both specimens and tales of strange plants and animals, and a new stimulus was given to scientific interest in and study of living things. The old tomes of Aristotle were dusted off and the newer information was examined in the light of his teachings. About the middle of the century some of the universities revived the study of botany and zoology. Botanical gardens and zoological parks sprang into being at the golden touch of wealthy collectors who hunted eagerly for novel plants and animals with which to amuse their friends. It was a variegated and curious collection of birds, beasts, and flowers which found its way to Europe. To this growing list of newly discovered species of living things Harriot brought his own report and specimens.

From the New World Harriot brought strange mammals never before seen in Europe, such as the opossum and raccoon, the American gray squirrel and black bear, the otter and the marten, the cony, the American variety of wolf, and the biologically fascinating skunk which, he said, he needed no eyes to observe. Among the birds, he introduced the New World parrot, falcon, marlin hawk, stock dove, partridge, crane, swan, goose, mockingbird, woodpecker, bluebird, towhee, bluejay, and the cardinal or redbird. The American mockingbird, the bald eagle (which later became the national emblem of the new country), and the turkey (which had previously been brought to Europe by Spanish explorers) were singled out for special interest by European zoologists. Animals as well as plants were painted and drawn by John White, a member of the expedition.

Harriot described how the natives speared many of the fish or caught them in reed weirs. He told of his fishing for sturgeon, herring, trout, rays, the oldwife or menhaden, the porpoise and the mullet, and of his finding the sea crab, the oyster, the gar pike, the horseshoe crab, mussel, scallop, and tortoise.

And the region around Roanoke was filled in due season with an abundance of chestnuts, walnuts, acorns full of oil, crab apples, summer grapes, fox grapes, and strawberries (as good, Harriot noted, as ours in England). Of the trees he did not fail to describe the oak, cedar, cypress, maple, mulberry, holly, willow, the beech, elm, and ash, and the witch-hazel shrub, as well as the sassafras tree from which was obtained an oil which "cured many diseases." Then there were roots of many kinds, "silke of grasse" (*Yucca filamentosa*), hemp, and flax. His "mineralman," or geologist, reported many building materials such as sandstone and limestone, as well as iron and copper ores, chemicals such as alum and sodium carbonate, and pearls from oysters.

The scientists of Europe were not the only men interested. To the merchants of England the Roanoke Island fir trees meant sturdy masts for ships, the ash meant cask hoops, the cedar would yield furniture, the pine trees spelled pitch and tar, rosin and turpentine. The woad plant would yield blue indigo, the root of the madder plant a red dye, the sumac would give a black dye; sweet gums and other apothecary drugs could be extracted from some of the other native plants. Wintergreen (methyl salicylate) was just one of the drugs known to the Indians for their curative powers. And Harriot noted that "to the dealing therein there will rise in short time great profit." This essentially was the reason for Raleigh's attempt at colonization.

Raleigh was unusually enthusiastic over two products which Harriot brought back to Europe. The first was corn (*Zea mays*), called by the natives *Pagatour*. The Spanish explorers had already seen this remarkable plant, first grown in Peru, which had been cultivated throughout most of South America since the days of the Incas. It had eventually found its way to the North American Indians. Harriot had watched them place shad or menhaden in each hill of corn as fertilizer and had seen them harvest the many-colored kernels of corn. The Indians also cultivated melons, peas, squash, pumpkins, gourds, and lima beans which they mixed with maize to form their *sauquaquatash*.

The second product which aroused Raleigh's enthusiasm was "an herbe which is sowed apart by it selfe, and is called by the inhabitants *Uppowoc*." (This "herbe" had been brought back to Europe earlier by the Spaniards and cultivated as a garden plant.) "The leaves thereof being dried and brought into powder, they used to take the fume or smoke thereof, by sucking it thorow pipes made of clay, into their stomacke and head, from whence it purgeth superfluous flames and other grosse humours." After smoking the plant with the natives of Roanoke Island, Harriot reported "many rare and wonderful experiments of the virtues

thereof, of which the relation would require a volume by itself."
While his scientific accounts were generally accurate and reliable, unfortunately this cannot be said about his observations on
this strange weed.

Harriot was the world's first great publicity agent for the smoking habit. His patron, Raleigh, after being shown how to smoke
tobacco the Indian way, began to sing its praises and soon made
pipe smoking fashionable at court. No modern merchant of the
cigarette could have been more effective in spreading the use of
tobacco. It actually became a medium of exchange; it is reported
that a fairly good wife could be purchased for a hundred and fifty
pounds of American tobacco. Harriot, steeped in the crude and
quack medicine of his day, praised among the virtues of tobacco
its great medicinal value, for it "openeth all the pores and passages
of the body whereby the bodies are notably preserved in health,
and healeth many grievous diseases, wherewithall we in England
are often times afflicted."

Some of the natives were won over to Harriot; they sang at his
prayer meetings and kissed his Bible, especially when their corn
began to wither during a drought. The Indian leader Pemisapan,
however, suspected the designs of the white intruder and determined that his people would not be robbed of their land. This
was the beginning of the relentless struggle that was to follow—
the Indians driven ruthlessly back across the continent until what
was left of them were finally huddled into narrow reservations.
Pemisapan counseled his people not to trade skins and victuals for
the white man's trinkets, tin dishes, and copper kettles. He robbed
the Englishman's weirs at night, set fire to his huts, and then con-
spired to get rid of him by assassination.

Ralph Lane, who had been left in charge, soon found starvation
facing his colony. He sent his men in small groups to Croatoan,
Hatorask, and other near-by places to live off the land on fish and
mollusks and whatever animals they could kill, and to keep a sharp
lookout for boats of the English fleet which might be passing. The
Indian chief finally fought it out with the white men and was

killed only a few days before Sir Francis Drake, returning from
some private looting of gold and silver in Santo Domingo and St.
Augustine, sighted the colony. Hungry, weary, and despondent,
the colonists decided at once to return to England.

On June 19, 1586, the "first colonie," less only four who had
died during the year, set sail for home not knowing that fourteen
days later Sir Richard Grenville was to return, as he had promised,
with abundant supplies and more colonists. Of the latter, a small
number remained on Roanoke Island to retain possession of the
territory. But they were never heard of again. The mystery of
this Lost Colony has never been completely unraveled. We know
that among them were Virginia Dare, the first white child of
English parents born in the New World, her father, and her
mother, the daughter of Governor John White of Virginia. This
tragic episode in the early history of our country has been depicted
for the last several years on Roanoke Island in what has been
called "America's patriotic Oberammergau." It was during its
first performance in 1937 that President Franklin D. Roosevelt
said, "We do not know the fate of Virginia Dare. We do know,
however, that the story of America was largely a record of that
spirit of adventure."

Back in England, Harriot delivered his glowing report of the
new land to Raleigh, who made another unsuccessful attempt the
following year to colonize the region around Chesapeake Bay.
His sailors refused to go any farther than Roanoke. But Raleigh
planned still another expedition. Then on July 20, 1588, the In-
vincible Armada of Spain, 134 ships carrying 30,000 men, risked
the gamble of invading England. After an eight-day battle the
invasion was repulsed and all but fifty-three of the ships were lost.
Soon after, Raleigh resigned his rights to the land in the New
World to a company of merchants for a nominal rent and one
fifth of all the gold mined there. Harriot never returned to America.

In the Old World, meanwhile, scientific research was pushing
ahead in new fields and scientific discoveries were opening up a

different kind of unexplored territory. Simon Stevin was experimenting with falling bodies in Bruges; Galileo Galilei was demonstrating the fundamental laws of falling bodies at Pisa; William Gilbert, after seventeen years of investigation, was finally publishing his classic *De Magnete*. Zacharias Jansen and Galileo were independently inventing the compound microscope; John Kepler in Prague was demonstrating the inversion of an image on the retina of the human eye; Sanctorius Sanctorius was constructing the first clinical thermometer; and Francis Bacon was writing his *Novum Organum* (New Methodology) on the inductive method of science.

Harriot, too, threw himself into scientific research. In 1607 he studied what was later known as Halley's comet and compared his own observations with those of Kepler. Two years later he was using a telescope, or "perspective truncke," which he himself had devised without knowing of its invention the previous year by three Hollanders, Zacharias Jansen, James Metius, and Hans Lippershey, all of whom had made it independently. He made several of these "cylinders" for his friends and studied the sunspots which had fascinated Galileo. The leading English astronomer of his day, Harriot attacked the errors of Aristotle, such as the belief that the earth of the tropics was completely scorched by the sun and thus uninhabitable. He kept up a correspondence with both Kepler and Galileo.

In addition to investigations with light, color, refraction of light by oil, and the center of gravity of bodies, Harriot was carrying out studies in algebra which have led some historians of mathematics to acclaim him the originator of the solution of quadratic equations by factors, among other mathematical achievements. In his book *Artis Analyticae Praxis*, published ten years after his death, he set the standard for modern textbooks in mathematics; he introduced certain changes in symbols and notations still used by millions of schoolboys. Like Berzelius of Sweden, who introduced the symbols of modern chemistry two centuries later, Harriot was the first to use the dot to indicate a multiplication sign, as well as the first to use the two signs of inequality: $>$ greater than, and $<$ less than. He was also one of the first to represent power by an exponent; for example, XXX as X^3.

Harriot was the leader of a small circle of amateurs who dabbled in science and mathematics and did not hurry to publish their discoveries or innovations. This resulted later in a great deal of controversy over priority, especially among mathematicians. In a running battle between English and French mathematicians from which Harriot stood aloof, attacks were made on the stature and reputation of such men as François Vieta, the lawyer-mathematician Pierre de Fermat, and René Descartes, who is credited with the invention of analytical geometry. The American historian of mathematics, Florian Cajori, after a careful study of all the available facts concluded that Harriot "brought the theory of equations under one comprehensive point of view. . . . He was the first to decompose equations into their simple factors. . . . Algebra was now ready for Descartes to make a great milestone, the application of algebraic analysis to define and investigate the properties of algebraic curves."

During the busy years of his mathematical and scientific investigations Harriot, who never married, found time to visit his erstwhile patrons, Raleigh and Henry Percy, Earl of Northumberland, now languishing in prison. They played anagrams together and performed chemical experiments at the furnace and still that had been installed in Raleigh's prison room. Harriot helped Raleigh with his *History of the World* and was a solace to him to the very end. On the night before his execution Raleigh dictated to Harriot the "Note of Remembrance" for his speech *On the Scaffold*.

The tragic death of his friend was a severe blow to the now ailing Harriot, who sought forgetfulness in his telescope and his mathematics. A month after the execution of his patron, Harriot was making his famous observations of the comet of 1618 at the observatory built for him by Percy at Sion, near London. Three years later, on July 2, 1621, six shillings and eightpence were paid for his knell, and four pounds were paid as his legacy to the poor of the parish. His death was due to cancer of the lip, which, it was rumored, he had developed through holding his brass mathematical instruments between his teeth. Harriot was buried in London; today the Bank of England gardens built around the churchyard of St. Christopher's cover his remains. Eight volumes of his manuscripts were guarded in the subterranean vaults of the British Museum against enemy planes during World War II.

Raleigh, who had spent more than $40,000 in his various attempts to form a permanent colony in the New World, finally came to believe that to be successful such an undertaking would have to be executed by more than one man. Groups were soon formed to exploit America. In 1606 two such companies were organized. They were essentially stock companies in which gentlemen of wealth and members of the nobility and clergy, as well as the butcher, the baker, and the tailor, bought stock in the hope of fat dividends from profitable mining ventures and other activities. High-pressure salesmen, with the help of every agency, including the pulpit, raised money and colonists for the London Company, which established the first permanent English settlement in North America at Jamestown, Virginia, on May 13, 1607. Among the writers of promotion for the colonization companies was John Smith, head of the Jamestown colony in 1608, and author of a description of the plants and animals of Virginia. The London Company alone spent five million dollars, but corporate ownership proved a failure. Private landowning and individual trade were introduced in 1629.

Motives other than the hope of profit soon impelled men from England to come to the New World. At Plymouth, Massachusetts, there landed from the *Mayflower* a group of Pilgrims, members of a separatist sect who had first migrated to Holland and were still seeking religious liberty. In 1628 the Massachusetts Bay Company founded a colony made up of Puritans, who wanted to simplify the ceremonies of the Church of England, and of others interested primarily in bettering their economic standing. Catholics suffering under the harsh laws of England found asylum in Maryland under Lord Baltimore. Rhode Island had its birth when Roger Williams, the great liberal preacher, political philosopher, and member of the Royal Society, was banished from the theocratic commonwealth of Massachusetts. The cruel restrictions of this same theocracy sent a handful of men, led by Thomas Hooker, to set up quietly a self-governing colony in the Connecticut wilderness under the first written constitution of modern democracy.

Swedish traders settled Delaware in 1638, just a year before New Hampshire was founded. Adventurers, religious dissenters, poor folk fed up with the feudal aristocrats of Virginia, and Huguenots driven out of France peopled the proprietary colonies of the Carolinas. Dutch and English traders added New York to the list of American colonies. English Quakers trickled into New Jersey, while others came to Pennsylvania to be joined by Irish Quakers and refugee Mennonites from the German Rhineland. Finally, in 1733 the last of the original colonies was founded in Georgia by James Oglethorpe, who pictured America as a better place for debtors than the damp, dark prisons of England.

Out of the immigrants who gave birth to these colonies, out of the political and religious refugees, and the unemployed of England who sold themselves for as long as seven years as indentured servants in the new land; out of the dispossessed and dissatisfied of Europe, the adventurers, the debtors, the proprietary officials, the soldiers, the kidnaped, and even the criminals—from these tough roots sprang the men and women who were to make American science. The Pilgrim Thomas Clark, mate on the *Mayflower*, was the ancestor of Alvan Clark, maker of famous American optical apparatus. Josiah Franklin, a nonconformist in religion, left Northamptonshire for Boston in 1682. He was the father of Benjamin Franklin. Philip Welch, kidnaped from Ireland by soldiers of Cromwell and sold in Boston Harbor as an indentured servant, gave us our great pathologist, William H. Welch. Thomas Hale, an English farmer, impoverished and disillusioned, sold his last possession to come to Massachusetts in 1640, and through his descendants gave the United States its eminent solar authority and foremost builder of telescopes, George Ellery Hale.

From the original settlers and their children came also our early American naturalists, the men who continued the work of discovering, describing, and classifying the multitude of animals and plants of the new continent. Among them were simple, uneducated men who loved nature deeply, rich planters who spent their leisure hours collecting, as well as physicians, clergymen, lawyers, and other college-trained men who, tied to the culture of Europe, became a link in science between the two worlds. The collection of botanical and zoological specimens was the main field of their scientific efforts.

For fifty years the Reverend John Clayton, a clerk in Gloucester County, Virginia, spent his spare time botanizing, corresponding with Carl Linnaeus, the most famous European botanist of his day, contributing his observations on the culture of tobacco to the newly founded Royal Society of London, and finally helped J. V. Gronovius to write his *Flora Virginica*, which was edited in Leyden with the help of Linnaeus. John Banister, clergyman, made important collections in Virginia for a generation and added to entomological knowledge at least fifty-two new species of insects, including the mud wasp, the seventeen-year locust, the firefly, the spring beetle, and the tobacco moth. He drew and described much of the life history of the ichneumon fly, added mollusks to his collection, and printed his *Catalogus Plantarum*, the first systematic paper emanating from America. Banister might be called the first American martyr to science, for in 1692, while on one of his scientific excursions among the rocks of the falls of the Roanoke, he was accidentally killed by his companion.

The Virginia physician, John Mitchell, also corresponded with Linnaeus and sent a paper to the Royal Society describing thirty new genera of plants which he had found around his home. He made pioneer physiological studies of the opossum, wrote a treatise on the principles of science, and dabbled in physics. A chief justice of Massachusetts, Paul Dudley, wrote on the moose deer, the bee, the whale, and the rattlesnake, and sent to the Royal Society a paper describing a new method of getting sugar from the maple tree. James Logan, private secretary to William Penn, and later governor of the Colony, contributed the first investigation in physiological botany when he experimented with Indian corn, and recorded in 1735 the union of the pollen of the tassel with the silk of the ear.

Among these early collectors none did more or is better known than the Quaker farmer boy, John Bartram, who went in for plants almost as instinctively as he breathed. Peter Collinson, a Quaker merchant in London, England, took a fancy to Bartram and became his patron. For over half a century the American colonist sent the English merchant every botanical specimen he could find. In return he received not only funds but seeds, roots, plants, and tree cuttings with which to experiment in his own garden. Lord Petrie, who boasted the most famous gardens and hothouses in England, also gave him an allowance to enable him to carry on further botanical expeditions. The more Bartram sent to his English patrons the more they asked of him. They wanted specimens of birds and their eggs, turtles, insects, snakes, shells, bulbs, even fossils. To satisfy his own burning desire to learn more about nature and to get necessary funds from his foreign patrons for new botanical books, Bartram tramped widely not only through his native Pennsylvania but also through Maryland and the Blue Ridge Mountains. In Georgia, he came across a new species of plant which he named *Franklinia* in honor of his friend, Benjamin Franklin. He covered thousands of miles on foot from Lake Ontario to Florida, usually alone, for he once complained that "Our Americans have very little taste for these amusements. I can't find one that will bear the fatigue to accompany me in my peregrinations."

On the west bank of the Schuylkill River at Kingsessing, now within the city limits of Philadelphia, Bartram converted five acres of land into the first great botanical garden in America.

Here he planted all manner of plants, and from here he sent large numbers of specimens to the botanical leaders of Europe. George Washington and other amateur horticulturists of the colonies visited his garden and took away with them not only seeds and cuttings but the best botanical advice available on this side of the Atlantic. For had not Linnaeus pronounced Bartram "the greatest natural botanist in the world"? He was also something of a scientific botanist, for he used the microscope and carried out some experiments on the cross-fertilization of flowers to "improve the beauty of the florist's garden."

His son William followed in his parent's footsteps. At fourteen he began tramping through the Catskills with his father. He, too, became enamored of the wilderness. John Bartram had been forced to struggle through a Latin grammar by himself rather late in life when he discovered that most of the botanical knowledge of his day was locked up in treatises in that language. He saw to it that William was sent to school at an early age to learn Latin and French so that he could read the botanical works of Europe. William tramped more widely than even his father. His book of *Travels*, published in 1791, made a tremendous impression not only at home but even more so in Europe, where French and German translations appeared. The poetry of Wordsworth was greatly influenced by this book which came out of the American wilderness. Southey, Coleridge, and Thoreau also read it and saw the promise of a new America.

These early naturalists found plenty to interest them in our wooded hills, our broad meadows, and on the floors of our virgin forests. Hundreds of new species of plant and animal life were discovered, described, and classified to the best of their ability.

The work of these descriptive botanists and zoologists and the efforts of these early collectors did not exhaust all the scientific curiosity of the men and women of the original colonies. The mysteries of the heavens, too, beguiled them. John Winthrop, Jr., eldest son of the autocratic first governor of Massachusetts Bay, studied the heavens with a three-foot refractor telescope and in a communication sent to the Royal Society predicted the discovery of the fifth satellite of Jupiter. The actual discovery of this celestial body had to wait almost two and a half centuries for better instruments which finally revealed the satellite to the American astronomer, Edward E. Barnard, in 1916.

Thomas Brattle, Harvard graduate and successful merchant, sent his observations of the famous comet of 1680 to the Royal Society. Both Newton and Halley acknowledged the use of this data. Solar and lunar eclipses, as well as the first observations in this country of the variations of the magnetic needle, also occupied Brattle's leisure hours. Another Harvard graduate, Thomas Robie, practiced medicine and followed astronomy. In his article *A Wonderful Meteor that Appeared in New England, December 11, 1719*, he actually described an aurora and was instrumental in allaying the public dread of calamity by showing that it was a perfectly harmless natural phenomenon.

James Logan was another disciple of Newton, whom he had met at the Royal Society of London in 1724. He had already obtained in 1708 the first copy of Newton's *Principia*, which had been published thirty years earlier. It was the first copy to be found in the colonies and became part of Logan's collection of mathematical and scientific books which in 1792 was incorporated with the Library Company of Philadelphia and still functions today as the Loganian Library. Logan sent four papers which were published in the *Transactions* of the Royal Society. One of these (1738) expressed *Some thoughts concerning the sun and moon, when near the horizon, appearing larger than when near the zenith*. It was an attempt to study the moon's motion on the basis of the new Newtonian laws of motion. Logan also wrote on lightning darts and streaks.

While in many quarters of Europe the discovery of Copernicus that the sun and not the earth was the center of the universe was not accepted, here in America the newly demonstrated scientific fact was taught at Harvard College and easily received. Even Cotton Mather, foremost Puritan preacher, witch-burner, and

bigot, preached this new fact from his Boston pulpit. Like many of
the clergymen of his period, Mather used some of the newly discovered facts of science to show the glory of God and His mysterious handiwork. He even preached a sermon on the microscope.
Mather was a typical example of the scientific enthusiasts of his
century, who mingled pseudo-science, superstition, and a child-
like acceptance of the queerest "facts of nature" with their keen
curiosity of all natural phenomena. Scientific truth sometimes led
them into dangerous paths which they trod unafraid. Cotton
Mather, for example, boldly championed the practice of inoculation against smallpox, about which he had first read in the *Transactions* of the Royal Society, defying a scurrilous pamphlet
attack and a howling mob outside his door who shrieked that this
was the work of the Devil because it would banish Providence
from the lives of men. Even some of the physicians of Boston opposed inoculation, and a lighted bomb was thrown into the great
preacher's study. But Mather stood firm and threw safeguards
around Zabdiel Boylston, the self-educated physician who, during a serious smallpox epidemic in 1721, inoculated his own son,
another boy, and two colored servants.

Early American science was, in general, no better than that of
Europe. This was especially true in the field of medicine. No
medical school existed here, so that most practicing physicians
had to obtain their training and education by the apprentice
method. A few went to European schools for a medical degree.
Dissection as part of medical training was seldom practiced,
human anatomy being taught by uninspiring college professors
from the anatomical works of Aristotle. Even the best medical
knowledge of the time was crude.

The first American patent medicine, "Tuscarora Rice," was
manufactured in 1711 and sold as a cure for tuberculosis, to be
followed by a flood which is still inundating the land. Doctors and
their apprentices concocted strange medicines and elixirs of their
own. William Penn's *Book of Physick* prescribed as a cure for a
pain in the eye "a white shelled snail pricked and its liquid dropped

in the eye." For bruises to the body the patient was to take "a con-
coction of butter, snails, rosemary, lavender, elder, new cow-
dung and half as much new hen dung and frankincense *in a pretty
quantity as often as you please*." There was a widespread belief
in sympathetic remedies which prescribed useless medicines containing elements similar to those in the diseased or pain-producing
parts of the body. Among the most frequently used prescriptions
was the following: "For all sortes of agewes pare the patient's
nayles when the fever is coming on, and put the parings into a
little bagge of linen, and tye that about a live eele's necke in a
tubbe of water. The eele will dye and the patient will recover."

Bacterial infection was unsuspected, the modern knowledge of
nutrition had not yet been born, and the human body with its
functionings was still much of a mystery. It is no wonder that
the death rate was appalling, as epidemics of smallpox, brought
over by the Spaniards, dysentery, malaria, yellow fever, which
was first brought in from the West Indies, and other diseases
swept over the land. The real wonder is that so many survived.
Of 14,000 colonists sent out before 1624 by the London Company,
13,000 died of disease and exposure, on land and at sea; during one
voyage in 1711, 859 out of 3086 passengers succumbed. Children
seldom survived the grim conditions of these crossings, when
hunger drove passengers to fight for rats and mice, and even in
some cases to cannibalism. Nor were the chances of survival much
greater on land. Of Cotton Mather's sixteen children, nine died in
infancy; four had smallpox, three died of measles, several had
scarlet fever. Life expectancy at birth was only about twenty
years as compared with the present sixty-nine years.

Some investigation and thought were also given to the realms
of physics and chemistry. John Winthrop, Jr., colonial governor
of Connecticut, imported apparatus for both physical and chemical experimentation, assembled a chemical library, and presented
at least one chemical paper before a scientific society. As an industrial promoter, he also attempted to establish a chemical industry here, and in 1644 started the manufacture on a small scale

of glass, salt, saltpeter, and several other products. From England came Charles Morton, to assume the presidency of Harvard College. He did not secure the position but managed, however, to bring the new science of Robert Boyle, Isaac Newton, William Harvey, and Galileo to the colonists of America. His *Compendium Physicae* was used at Harvard as a textbook in science for forty years. While it was inaccurate in part and clung rather too strictly to the Aristotelian classification of physics, it did, nevertheless, open the eyes of the new country to the tremendous discoveries in the world of science which were stirring the Old World.

Somewhat later, in 1721, Cotton Mather summarized the scientific knowledge of the time for his colonial friends in a book which was published in London and read widely in New England. It was called *The Christian Philosopher, a collection of the best discoveries in Nature with religious Improvements*. Under this ambitious title, the book contained the first elaborate explanation of Newtonian philosophy in America, as well as many of Mather's own observations on plants, birds, snakes, medicines, earthquakes, thunder, rain, lightning, and other natural phenomena, many of which were distorted to fit into his anthropomorphic concept of God.

It was during this early period that the Royal Society of London was established. The founding of this scientific institution in 1662 almost occurred on the soil of the American colonies. Robert Boyle, pioneer of chemistry, had talked it over with Winthrop before the latter sailed for Massachusetts. Winthrop went ahead with plans for setting up the Society to aid in the exploitation of the wealth of the new land. But pressure from the King changed this plan and the scientific academy was established in London.

One of the chief aims of this society of scientists was to study a number of practical problems of which the solution was made imperative by the rise of the new merchant economy. More efficient methods of mining were demanded to supply larger quantities of metals for machinery and artillery. New sources of power had to be found. Many of the great advances in theoretical science made by the Society's members stemmed from this utilitarian need. Much of the work of Boyle, Hooke, Huygens, and Flamsteed was concerned with immediate practical questions. Robert Hooke told of pressure brought upon him to undertake an investigation of the improvement of clocks. This resulted in his classic experiments with springs and the discovery of the law bearing his name, to the effect that stretch is proportional to the stretching force.

Even Newton's world-stirring advances, often cited as examples of the work of an individual genius isolated from the practical problems of the society in which he lived, can be traced directly to this trend. Newton's contributions came at a time when other men of science were making other useful discoveries. He was not a lone, inexplicable genius who had little if anything to do with the social background of his day. The change from feudal economy to merchant capital and manufacture presented European scientists with many problems. Among the most imperative were the development of more adequate means of marine transportation to settle and exploit the new colonies successfully, and swifter modes of communication to make possible a vigorous trade with distant parts of the world. This meant studies in the determination of latitude, longitude, and exact time, and in the cause of tides. Many of the problems intimately connected with the heavenly bodies were taken up by Newton and his contemporaries as a direct or indirect result of social and economic pressure. Newton was a member of a parliamentary committee appointed in 1713 to stimulate the study of longitude. His greatest discoveries, such as the universal law of gravitation, mirrored the needs of the rapidly changing times in which he lived.

"The New Found Land of Virginia" which Harriot had surveyed and described was a virgin area where practical experimentation had to be encouraged. The Royal Society had a number of members among the early colonists. Nine were from the Massachusetts Bay Colony, three from Pennsylvania, three from Virginia, and one each from Connecticut, Rhode Island, and the Carolinas. John Winthrop, Jr., was among its founders. Cotton Mather became a Fellow in 1713. John Winthrop, grandson of John Winthrop, Jr., was admitted to the Royal Society in 1734. So were Paul Dudley; Colonel William Byrd II, writer on the plants and minerals of Virginia, who was elected a Fellow in 1696 at the age of twenty-two; John Clayton of Virginia, who wrote a description of the lightning bug; and the physician-botanist, John Mitchell. Through these men the Royal Society stimulated scientific investigation here, printed the communications of the colonists in its *Transactions*, and influenced Parliament and the various colonial governments to make grants and offer bounties for such efforts. Early American science was primarily English science transported to the new land.

John Winthrop, Jr., was requested by the Royal Society to conduct experiments in brewing beer from corn; the American scientist reported the results of his investigations. Ten years later John Clayton presented a paper to the same society on experiments he had performed to determine the best soil in which to grow tobacco. The Lord Proprietors of Carolina sent a naturalist to Barbados to obtain "cotton seeds, indigo seeds, ginger roots, some canes and other seeds to make experimental plantings" and to determine the best soil and the best time for planting. The actual experimental work was left to "a man or two," who after two years of work reported that the Carolina winters were too cold for the profitable cultivation of either sugar cane or cotton. Dr. Wigglesworth of Harvard College began raising silkworms in 1727 in the hope of promoting sericulture in New England.

When in 1733 James Oglethorpe established at Savannah the first settlement in Georgia, he saw to it that an experimental garden of ten acres was planted "for improving botany and agriculture." For five years a trained botanist was employed in the West Indies and Central and South America to collect plants for this garden. Between 1733 and 1743 the English Parliament made grants of about half a million dollars for the establishment there of an indigo industry. The Society of Arts in London offered prizes to the colonists for the best products of potash, pearl ash, hemp, logwood, saltpeter, cochineal, and sarsaparilla. The Reverend Jared Eliot, Yale graduate, preacher, farmer, physician, and botanist of Connecticut, received a gold medal for discovering a new method of extracting iron from certain black sands on his land. He also introduced the growing of clover and chicory in Connecticut and wrote *Essays upon Field Husbandry*, and an anonymous two-volume work entitled *American Husbandry*.

The naturalists of the first century and a half after Harriot's arrival on Roanoke Island played an important role. They added a great deal to the growing knowledge of new species of plants and animals, and prepared the way for the new scientific classification of living things so essential to further progress in both botany and zoology. When Linnaeus, in 1737, published his *Genera Plantarum*, modern systematic botany was born. The Linnaean botanical and zoological binomial system of classification and nomenclature was accepted here even more avidly than in England. Harriot had brought back descriptions, specimens, or John White's drawings of twenty-eight species of mammals, eighty-six species of birds, and a larger number of new plants. About two hundred years later, in 1766, the great Linnaeus could describe no more than 210 species of mammals from all over the world; of these, seventy-eight came from the observations of American naturalists. Of the 790 species of birds which he catalogued, the descriptions of at least one third had been contributed by our early naturalists.

The names of several flowers still recall some of these pioneer naturalists. *Bartramia*, a moss found in the Berkshire Hills, was named for John Bartram. *Mitchella repens*, the name of a little trailing vine, keeps alive the burning interest of John Mitchell in the life of the forest. The delicate, crimson-pink spring beauty, *Claytonia virginica*, commemorates John Clayton, while the *gardenia* has kept fresh the name of Dr. Alexander Garden, physician and botanist of Charleston, South Carolina. *Tradescantia virginiana*, the common spiderwort, recalls to the historian of American botany the work of John Tradescant, gardener to King Charles I, who sent him here to collect plants, shells, and flowers.

The first century and a half of American science was in large part the story of our early naturalists, intoxicated by the wealth of new botanical and zoological material. Yet it was really more than that. True, we produced no eminent scientific theoreticians, no great experimenters in the physical sciences. But this was to be expected. In those years only a mere handful of men were stirring on the narrow fringe of a new continent. They were preoccupied with physical existence and held in check by the superstitions and pseudo-science of the Old World. And they were in a real sense isolated from one another and from the rest of the world.

Yet science was already finding a new sanctuary in America, which was not altogether inhospitable to its spirit and flowering. What Harriot surveyed in those months of 1585 was not simply so many acres of virgin land which awaited the exploitation of trade and industry, but part of a new country in which the pursuit of science was to flourish in due time and in whose fertile soil its seeds were to germinate with increasing vigor and fruitfulness.

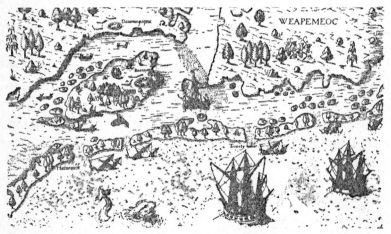

From Harriot's *Narrative of the First English Plantation of Virginia.*

CHAPTER TWO

BENJAMIN FRANKLIN
(1706-1790)

THE FIRST FRUIT OF AMERICAN SCIENCE

FOR ALMOST one hundred and fifty years after Harriot had begun the study of the natural history of America, his successors were lone spirits. Their main contact with the rest of the world of science was the Royal Society of London and a few eminent scientists, like Linnaeus and Gronovius, on the continent of Europe. True, some of our early naturalists and natural philosophers carried on a desultory correspondence with men of kindred interests in other colonies. Some of them even met occasionally to exchange notes and experiences or carried on scientific projects together. The establishment of Harvard College in 1636, of the College of William and Mary in 1693, and of Yale College a few years later added something to a more integrated effort toward the extension of scientific knowledge. Yet there was an urgent need for better facilities for the frequent meeting of the minds of our natural philosophers.

This need was soon met. Benjamin Franklin had just returned from a nineteen-month sojourn in England. The nineteen-year-old boy had made several unsuccessful attempts to see Sir Isaac Newton, who was then in his eighty-third year. He had, however, met several members of the Royal Society of London. In the autumn of 1727, the year in which Newton died, Franklin "united the majority of well-informed persons of my acquaintance into a club which was called the Junto." Every Friday evening, in tavern, home, or in the open, the members met to improve their minds. Each scientist in turn would present some question on natural or economic philosophy which the group would investigate and discuss. "Whence comes the dew that stands on the outside of a tankard that has cold water in it in the summer?" was one such question. The need of a paper currency was another topic introduced. In 1729 Benjamin Franklin published *A Modest Inquiry into the Nature and Necessity of a Paper Currency*, which attracted wide attention. He advanced the theory that *labor*, not silver, was the measure of value. Unknown to Franklin, this idea had been stated back in 1622. Later the theory was adopted by Adam Smith in his famous *Wealth of Nations*.

Actually the Junto was not the first scientific society started in this country. In 1681 Increase Mather had organized a number of men interested in "adding to the store of natural history," but the group was short-lived and of no great consequence. Out of the Junto, however, developed a powerful institution. In the very beginning it was a small group of only eleven men. To keep the club free from the obstacles of prejudice, prospective members had to affirm that they loved their fellow men regardless of what religion or profession they followed, and that they would see that no person was harmed in body, name, or goods for holding any speculative opinion. Finally, they had to declare that they loved truth for truth's sake and would endeavor impartially to find and receive it and communicate it to others. These four qualifications, so civilized, intelligent, and modern in spirit, bore the stamp of the founder of the club, Benjamin Franklin.

Members of the Junto brought their own books to the meeting room and all shared in their use. Franklin obtained contributions, and sent to London for other books to add to this collection. A permanent circulating library was thus established which became "the mother of all North American subscription libraries." We have no printed record of the early activities of the Junto, but it is safe to say that no great discovery was lost by that lack. The original members were apparently as much interested in the political problems of those years as they were in science.

Four years prior to the founding of the Junto, Benjamin Franklin had fled from the bigotry of Boston to the more tolerant and cosmopolitan Philadelphia. In Boston his half brother, James, had edited the *New England Courant*, the first militant newspaper in America, and through it had dared to attack Cotton Mather and his declining Calvinistic regime. A violent press battle between the Mathers and James Franklin's Hell Fire Club of young men culminated in the imprisonment of James. At the age of seventeen Benjamin took his half brother's place in the editor's chair. Although the Mathers were attacked for their consistent reactionary acts, one of the points at issue in this battle of words was inoculation against smallpox. Strangely enough, the Mathers approved and James Franklin opposed the practice.

During the year following the formation of the Junto, Benjamin Franklin entered the printing business in Philadelphia. He soon purchased the *Universal Instructor in All Arts and Sciences: and Pennsylvania Gazette*, which he renamed *The Pennsylvania Gazette*. Within a few years this weekly rose from a total circulation of only ninety to a subscription list of ten thousand, the largest at that time in America. Now as then finding profit in advertisements, it has continued to the present day as *The Saturday Evening Post*, "Founded A.D. 1728 by B. Franklin."

On the side, Franklin ran a shop where Deborah Read, whom he married in 1730, sold everything from codfish to lottery tickets. He also wrote and published his *Poor Richard's Almanack*, which sold by the thousands, bought tons of linen rags for several paper mills which he was helping to establish throughout the colonies, obtained from Governor Keith of Pennsylvania a government contract to print paper money, and established branch printing offices in New York City, Charleston, and Kingston, Jamaica. At twenty-six Franklin was elected grand master of the Freemasons of the colonies. Four years later he was elected clerk of the Pennsylvania Assembly and shortly afterward was appointed postmaster of Philadelphia, a position which gave him the inside track in the race against his rival publishers.

Franklin's unusual versatility, excellent common sense, keen wit, and extraordinary ability to get along with people built up profitable business connections for him all over the colonies. This very active business life left little time for scientific work, but he did manage to read to the Junto a paper on fires and to invent a stove. This, his first invention, was inspired by the needs of the colonists, by Franklin's eye to thrift and his hatred of waste. Most of the heat of the burning logs in the fireplace of his day never entered the room but was lost up the chimney. Some of the Dutch and German immigrants had brought stoves from Europe, but these, although they prevented the heat from leaving the house, kept warming up the same stale air. Franklin's stove, which was constructed of cast iron, was set inside the fireplace and made use of the principles of ventilation. The governor of Pennsylvania offered Franklin a patent on this invention, but he declined, saying "That as we enjoy great advantages from the inventions of others, we should be glad of an opportunity to serve others by any invention of ours."

In 1743, a year after this invention, Franklin took time off from his numerous activities to revive the somewhat somnolescent Junto. He drafted and printed *A Proposal for Promoting Useful Knowledge Among the British Plantations in America*, which urged that a new "society be formed of virtuosi, or ingenious men, residing in the several colonies, to be called *The American Philosophical Society*, who are to maintain a constant correspondence, and that Philadelphia, being the city nearest the center of the continental colonies, and having the advantage of a good growing library, be the center of the Society." The reorganized society, with Thomas Hopkinson as president and Franklin as secretary, included several of the original members: William Coleman, associate justice of the Supreme Court of Pennsylvania; Philip Syng, silversmith; William Parsons, geographer; and Thomas Godfrey, glazier and self-taught mathematician. He was a close friend of Franklin and lived for a time with his wife and five children in the latter's home. Godfrey, who died in 1749 at the age of forty-five, was well versed in the contributions of Newton and employed his work in optics in inventing in 1730 a reflecting quadrant. Because Hadley in England had independently completed the same instrument a few months earlier, it is generally referred to as Hadley's quadrant or sextant.

One of the six new members was Dr. Thomas Bond, the physician who, with Franklin, was responsible for the establishment in 1751 of Pennsylvania Hospital, the first hospital for the insane in America. Others were the botanist John Bartram; the scientist Phineas Bond; and Samuel Rhoads, a mechanic. Robert Morris, Chief Justice of New Jersey; James Alexander, defender of Peter Zenger in the famous trial; and several others were later recruits. It was modeled after the Royal Society of London.

Throughout his life Franklin was a most inquisitive person, alert to every business opportunity which presented itself and insatiably curious about every natural phenomenon around him. Hardly had the reorganized club met when he gave its members his theory of the origin and direction of northeasters, those turbulent storms which often batter the New England coast. He had been waiting to watch an eclipse in Philadelphia which was completely obscured by a storm. When he later read an account of the same eclipse by an observer in Boston, four hundred miles to the northeast, and learned that the gale reached the Massachusetts city after having struck Philadelphia, he made a search for other data on storms. He analyzed all of the available facts and reached the correct explanation of the source and general direction of storms. Northeast storms, he showed, come from the southwest. They travel in the direction opposite to that from which they blow—a neat generalization from a man who was both unschooled and untrammeled by science.

A much more difficult and fundamental scientific question was tantalizing men of science at that time. Just what was electricity? The question was a very old one. It had vexed more than one inquiring mind ever since Thales of Miletus had noticed that amber when rubbed would attract light objects, such as pieces of dry leaves and bits of dry straw. True to legend, "The Greeks had a

word for it": amber was called *elektron*. Others discovered that
such friction-induced electricity could be obtained in other ways.
Sealing wax when rubbed with fur, and glass when rubbed with
silk, also attracted light objects. Men wondered whether there was
any difference between the electricity associated with glass and
that connected with sealing wax.

Some experiments were tried to settle this point. A rod of sealing wax which had been rubbed with fur was brought near a tiny
pith ball suspended by a silk thread. The pith ball was mysteri-
ously pushed away; it was *repelled*. Then a glass rod which had
been rubbed with silk was brought close. The pith ball was *attracted* to the glass. These observations told the experimenters that
they seemed to be dealing with two kinds of electricity. Charles
Du Fay of Paris called them *vitreous* (glass) and *resinous* (amber)
electricity. This was the two-fluid theory of electricity.

In the meantime large glass frictional machines were constructed which could produce fat sparks and electrify various objects. Many became interested in them as toys for the amusement
of their friends. Itinerant amateur scientists contrived all kinds of
gadgets to show the spectacular effects of this static electricity,
and peddled their bundle of tricks throughout Europe before gaping crowds. A new device, invented almost simultaneously by E.
von Kleist, a clergyman of Pomerania, and Pieter van Musschenbroek of Leyden in 1745, proved a great boon to these showmen
and a still greater contribution to science itself. In the early months
of 1746 the new invention, known today as the Leyden jar, was
applied to experiments with frictional electricity. A fresh collection of even more spectacular demonstrations soon added to the
profits of professional amusement vendors.

The Leyden jar was charged with electricity from frictional
electrical glass tubes. The large quantity of electricity thus stored
up in the bottle was discharged in long fat sparks or sent through
human conductors who jumped when they received the shock.
Chickens were electrocuted, steaks were roasted, alcohol was set
afire, flames were blown out, shocks were transmitted across

streams, and mysterious lights were produced in the dark. These demonstrations made a great impression on the public. The colonies, where the chief amusements until then had consisted of fairs, tea parties, horse racing, and an occasional peep show, were sold on this new type of entertainment, and numerous electrical machines found their way over here.

During one of Franklin's frequent business trips to Boston he stopped to watch the electrical performance of a Dr. A. Spencer who had just arrived from Scotland. His bundle of tricks was not very successful because the damp air of Boston made these demonstrations difficult. Franklin was, of course, interested, but in much more than just the tricks. Here was something which demanded scientific exploration. He had heard that William Claggett, a clockmaker of Newport, Rhode Island, had come to Boston with an electrical machine to give a free demonstration to the poor of the city. On his way home from Boston, Franklin stopped at Newport to see Claggett and discuss the experiments with him.

Franklin was now forty years old. He had made a considerable amount of money out of his rag-paper factory and his printing and newspaper ventures. He was wealthy enough to give up some of his business and devote more time to scientific investigation. The fascination of the problem of electricity could no longer be resisted. He wrote to Peter Collinson, the London cloth manufacturer who had become the patron of the naturalist John Bartram and the book buyer for Franklin's circulating library. In the next bundle of books which Collinson sent him was included an electrostatic tube for rubbing with silk—"a straight three-foot glass tube as big as your fist."

On March 28, 1747, Franklin wrote to Collinson from Philadelphia, "For my own part, I never was before engaged in any study that so totally engrossed my attention and my time as this has lately done; for what with making experiments when I can be alone, and repeating them to my friends and acquaintances who, for the novelty of the thing, come continually in crowds to see them, I have, during some months past, had little leisure for anything else." He made no secret of his activities. He even persuaded other members of the American Philosophical Society to undertake similar investigations. Fortunately for Franklin, the atmosphere of Philadelphia was not only intellectually clearer than the stuffiness of Boston, but it was also drier, enabling him to produce powerful sparks from his machine.

Franklin, just an ordinary amateur, began to make some exciting discoveries. By July 11 of that year he was already writing to Collinson that he "observed some particular phenomena, which we looked upon to be new. . . . The first is the wonderful effect of pointed bodies, both in drawing off and throwing off the electrical fire." This fundamental discovery came to him after he and Thomas Hopkinson had thought out a rather ingenious experiment. Franklin suspended a cork from a long silken thread attached to the ceiling of his room. The cork was brought near a metal ball, three inches in diameter, which he had set on an insulated body. The cork was repelled, as he expected. Then he brought a metal needle (or bodkin, as he called it) near but not in contact with the metal ball. The cork began to move nearer to the metal ball. Trying a needle with a blunted point, he found that this time he had to bring the needle closer to the metal ball before the electricity of the metal would be drawn off and the cork would approach the metal ball. "The less sharp the point," he reported, "the nearer you must bring it to observe the effect." Then he added, "If you present the point in the dark, you will see, sometimes at a foot distant or more, a light gather upon it like that of a firefly."

Franklin's next experiment, with its interpretation, is probably, according to Robert A. Millikan, "the most fundamental thing ever done in the field of electricity." He was trying to answer the question as to whether the friction of the glass and silk actually created electricity *de novo* or whether the electricity was really taken from the silk and communicated to the glass. He knew that wax would not conduct electricity. Standing on a cake of wax, therefore, he rubbed a glass tube with his hand vigorously. Then he got rid of the electricity produced on his body by this action by touching another object connected with the ground. He then placed two of his friends on two cakes of wax. One of them rubbed the glass tube which became electrified, and the other insulated person drew electricity from it. In this case both subjects became electrified and could attract light objects. A third person, standing on the floor, received a spark on approaching each of the other men with his knuckle. Furthermore, when the first two experimenters, still insulated and electrified, touched each other, a stronger spark was produced, whereupon all signs of electricity disappeared.

Franklin felt certain now that he had the answer. Electricity *was not created de novo* but was simply transferred from one body to another during the process of rubbing. To Franklin all matter contained electricity, or, as it was then called, a subtle fluid. Normally, bodies were electrically neutral. When, however, an object such as glass was rubbed with silk, the ordinary distribution of this subtle fluid was disturbed. The glass received more than its normal share of the electric fire and gave evidence of electrical properties. The silk (or hand) used to rub the glass, having lost some of this subtle fluid to the glass, also became electrified. If the glass was touched to the ground, this excess of subtle fluid was immediately taken away by the ground. The glass became electrically neutral again and showed no electrical properties.

Franklin performed all of the above experiments and reached his conclusions before the fall of 1747. He then wrote in part as follows: "The electric fire [electricity] is not created by friction but collected, being really *an element diffused among matter.* The electrical matter consists of particles extremely subtle. . . . Hence have arisen some new terms among us: we say B is electrised *positively*; A *negatively*. Or rather B is electrised *plus*; A, *minus*." Franklin was the first person ever to use these modern terms in referring to electricity. His one-fluid electrical theory was not altogether correct, for he believed that if a body possessed too much electricity, it was charged +; if it had not enough electricity, it was charged —; if it had just the right amount, it was electrically neutral.

Yet in spite of this error, his reasoning and terminology were much more modern than those of any other eighteenth-century scientist. So deep and clear was Franklin's creative imagination that he came very close to arriving at the modern conception of the electrical nature of matter, with its electrons (negative particles of electricity) and protons (positive charges of electricity) —a point of view reached only after some hundred and fifty years of further and more elaborate experimentation. Said Sir J. J. Thomson, Nobel laureate in physics and discoverer of the electron, "A collection of electrons would resemble in many respects Franklin's electric fluid, the idea of which was conceived in the infancy of the science of electricity." Had Franklin never contributed another piece of scientific thinking and experimentation, he would still have won a place among the clearest and most provocative scientific minds of all time.

To Franklin, the theoretical and the practical were equally important. They were the two feet upon which science strode forward. They were both essential in man's struggle to understand and control nature. He had already made up his mind to give up his active work in business and devote himself completely to science and to the political service of his country. He was only forty-two years old, but the income from his business would be sufficient to keep his family and himself in fair comfort. On September 29, 1748, he turned over his active interest in the printing business to a partner, David Hall. This done, he turned his attention to the problem of the possible relationship between electricity and the lightning flash which destroyed life and property—a phenomenon which for centuries had been regarded by many as God's answer to the wicked.

More than one natural philosopher had already noted similarities between these two phenomena. Sir Isaac Newton had likened the electric spark produced by a friction machine to the lightning from the sky. The Abbé Jean Nollet, teacher of natural history to the French royal family, had also pointed this out. Winkler in Germany, in the year before Franklin undertook his first electrical investigations, went so far as to declare that the thunderstorm and the artificial spark differed only in intensity, and that the thunderstorm was actually produced by friction of air particles with the water vapor which rose from the large bodies of water on the earth. But none of these men could produce evidence of the truth of their assumptions.

In a letter dated November 7, 1749, Franklin drew up a list of the similarities between the two phenomena. He had already performed those highly important experiments which showed the attraction of electricity to points and noted that while this had been definitely established, yet *"We do not know whether this property be in lightning."* Then he concluded that since the two phenomena "agree in all the particulars on which we can already compare them, it is not improbable that they agree likewise in this." Scientific evidence had to be found, however, to settle the matter. "Let the experiment," he wrote, "be made." He devised a method and proceeded to carry out his best-known experiment.

Franklin's plan was to fly a kite as high as possible and by its means to reach an electrified cloud, thus bringing the lightning flash down to earth for examination. He made his kite by stretching a piece of silk cloth over two sticks placed crosswise. He then attached to one of the sticks a pointed metal wire, connected also to the hempen cord which was to be used to fly the kite. To the lower end of the cord was tied a piece of silk string holding a metal key.

Out in a field Franklin waited under a shed with his twenty-one-year-old son William. When the sky grew dark and the clouds looked ominous, the kite was sent up. Suddenly Franklin noticed that the loose ends of the fibers of the hempen cord had begun to spread out. They were repelling each other. He quickly brought his bare knuckle to the metal key. A strong spark was seen and felt. The proof was literally in his hand. There could be no doubt that lightning, too, was attracted by metallic points.

To learn more about the nature of the electricity in clouds, Franklin decided to draw the lightning down into his room by means of an iron rod which he extended about nine feet above the chimney. To save time, he rigged up an ingenious device. "From the foot of the rod was attached a wire. On the staircase opposite to my chamber door the wire was divided, a little bell on each end, and between the bells a little brass ball, suspended by a silk thread, to play between and strike the bells when clouds passed with electricity in them." As the bells became charged with electricity from the clouds, the brass ball would be attracted to them and the stroke of the bell would notify Franklin that the experiment was ready for his observations. With the help of these electric chimes he was enabled within a few months to determine that the clouds were most often charged negatively but occasionally showed positive electrification.

Now it was time to determine whether lightning and the electric spark had other properties in common. For these experiments Franklin made use of the Leyden jar, which he called "Musschenbroek's wonderful bottle." He had made a thorough study of it and had accurately discovered the principle of its operation. He correctly concluded that its effects were due to opposite electric charges on the inner and outer coats of the glass jar. When connected by an electrical conductor, these produced a spark and the jar discharged itself. He successfully tried charging the Leyden jar with lightning flashes and found he could get all of the effects which he was able to obtain when the jar was charged from a rubbed electrical tube. Therefore, he wrote, "the sameness of the electric matter with that of lightning is completely demonstrated."

Franklin did not realize at the time the great danger of these experiments. He knew that wet objects are better conductors of electricity than dry objects, but he did not know that had the hemp cord of his kite been thoroughly wet he might have been electrocuted. This actually happened to Professor G. Rikhman, a Swedish scientist of the Imperial Academy of Sciences in St. Petersburg. Rikhman was trying to repeat Franklin's Philadelphia experiments when he was killed by a flash of lightning which reached him through a wire he was holding in his hand.

Franklin, the theorist and experimenter, had proved his point. Franklin, the practical utilizer of scientific facts and principles, saw an immediate and important application of his work. This was a time when men of science were beginning to effect closer ties between theoretical science and the technology which was just being born. Science, Franklin knew, could be applied to safer and better living. Why could not homes, barns, public buildings, and ships at sea be protected against the fire and destruction of lightning? Why could not the flash of lightning, which he had proved was nothing more than a stream of electricity, be controlled, and thus destroy man's fear of the lightning bolt and banish the superstition of a vindictive power punishing man for his sin?

The conception of the lightning rod to protect life and property came to Franklin during those days when he was discovering the effect of pointed metal rods in drawing off and discharging electricity. Early in 1750 he wrote to Collinson about his ideas on lightning rods. Two months later, on July 29, he again wrote to the Quaker merchant proposing to the Royal Society an experiment which would carry the lightning down the side of a ship into the water, which would act as the ground wire. English men of science were not impressed, but Franklin went about constructing a lightning rod on his own house. He placed an upright metal rod, sharp as a needle and gilded to prevent rusting, along the roof of his house from which it was carefully insulated. To the rod he attached a wire which extended down into the earth where the ground was moist. Lightning in its attempt to discharge itself would seek the best conducting medium on its way to the ground and hence take the path of the metallic rod and wire and leave the rest of the structure untouched.

Then he thought of an improvement. At intervals along the metal rod pointed strips of metal were added. The lightning rod would not only conduct the destructive lightning flash to the ground but would also, by means of the many pointed strips, slowly and quietly draw off the static electricity of the air or cloud and prevent it from piling up until it was strong enough to produce a destructive flash. As Franklin expressed this thought back in 1750, "Would not these pointed rods probably draw the electrical fire silently out of a cloud before it came nigh enough to strike?"

Franklin was a modern in more ways than one. He made a publisher's scoop out of his double-barreled discovery of the nature of lightning and his invention of the lightning rod. To accomplish this he apparently waited for the publication of his almanac—almost four whole months—before he announced his invention to his fellow countrymen. Otherwise, it is difficult to explain his silence between June, 1752, when he raised his famous kite, and October 19 of the same year, when he flashed the news by means of an advertisement in his own *Pennsylvania Gazette*. The "ad" referred to the forthcoming 1753 edition of his almanac, *Poor Richard Improved*, which contained his first positive statement of the lightning-rod invention. On the second page from the end of this thirty-six-page almanac, tucked away between notices of the mayor's courts dates, Quaker meetings, and numerous fairs, appears Franklin's eighteen-line article on *How to Secure Houses, etc. from Lightning*.

The almanac, of which several were published in the colonies, was a sort of potpourri which entertained thousands during the long evenings at a period when books and newspapers were scarce. Franklin's almanacs contained much scientific information, such as articles on whirlwinds, earthquakes, planting, and hygiene, and astronomical tables or ephemerides of the motions of the sun and moon, the lunations, conjunctions, eclipses, "The Anatomy of Man's Body as Governed by the Twelve Constellations," judgment of the weather, "together with entertaining remarks."

Franklin did not delay publishing this article because he wanted to keep his experiments secret. His friends and even acquaintances knew all along what he was doing. To his friend and collaborator, Ebenezer Kinnersley, teacher and minister without a congregation, he had reported everything he knew regarding electricity when he had launched him on a lecture tour through several of the colonies. Kinnersley included in his talks on electricity many of the latest discoveries in the field. Nor did Franklin hold back because he hesitated to publish a theory or invention before he was absolutely certain of its truth and effectiveness. Referring to his experiments on the effects of sharp points on the electric fire, Franklin once wrote that he published his findings even though he had some doubts about them because "even a bad solution read, and its faults discovered, has often given rise to a good one in the mind of an ingenious reader."

But if Kinnersley knew about the lightning-rod invention he made no public announcement of it until after Franklin had published the information himself. Then the lecturer's traveling show in science added a few more new demonstrations in the field of electricity and he hastened to assure his audiences that attaching a lightning rod to one's home was not really sacrilegious. He pointed out that at one church in Philadelphia exactly this had already been done. The colonists adopted the new invention in large numbers. There were no patent costs to pay and almost any house owner could equip his home with the new device without calling in a specialist or paying for expensive equipment.

The news soon reached England. On October 19, 1752, Franklin wrote a letter to Collinson, who was a member of the Royal Society, telling him about his lightning rod. This was the only way in which a scientific communication could be transmitted to the Society by a nonmember. The letters which the American wrote to his English friend were not just personal notes but scientific articles to be read before the scientific body of England, in the hope that they would reach a much wider audience by publication in the *Philosophical Transactions* of the Royal Society.

On December 21, 1752, this letter finally was read before the members of the Royal Society, who were at last impressed. They promptly made amends for their treatment of the American about two years earlier, when they had laughed at his paper describing experiments showing the similarities between lightning and elec-

tricity and had refused to print it in their *Transactions*. The new
paper was immediately published in their official organ and the
Royal Society elected Franklin a member without going through
the technicality of asking his permission. They even dispensed
with the customary subscription paid by new members, and in the
following year they presented him with the highest scientific
honor then available, the Copley Medal. In America, Harvard and
Yale lost no time in honoring him with degrees.

England followed the example of the colonists in introducing
the lightning rod at once. However, some of its men of science
still doubted the superiority of the pointed rod over the rounded
rod as an attractor of electricity from the air. The question was
argued in the halls of the Royal Society, in courts and in taverns,
until the government in 1772 requested a final decision on the matter. New powder magazines were to be built at Purfleet; the construction officials wanted to know which lightning rod would best
protect the explosives from lightning bolts. A committee was appointed to investigate and decide. Four of its members—Henry
Cavendish, the wealthy eccentric who discovered hydrogen and
proved the compound nature of water for the first time, William
Watson, John Robertson, and Franklin—recommended the
sharply pointed lightning rod. Benjamin Wilson, scientist and
painter, who was the other member of the committee, entered a
minority report in favor of the rounded or knobbed lightning rod.
"The battle between the sharps and the flats," as J. J. Thomson
had called it, soon entered the field of politics.

Benjamin Wilson was a close friend of the King of England.
George III was, moreover, annoyed at the militancy of the French
and his own American colonists. In his eyes Franklin was a rebel.
The King joined the battle and privately asked Sir John Pringle,
president of the Royal Society, to support the knobbed school of
thought. As a scientist, Pringle politely explained to His Majesty
that he would like very much to please him but he "could not re-
verse the laws and operations of nature." It is said that the King
became so enraged over this impertinent reply that he told Sir

John, "You had better resign." Pringle did resign. Then to show those stubborn, recalcitrant men of science that he meant business, George had the pointed lightning rods removed from Kew Palace and replaced with the round, knobbed type. Franklin, who could not afford to antagonize the King and yet would not compromise with the truth, withdrew to the background. The incident gave birth to the following lines:

> *While you, great George, for knowledge hunt,*
> *And sharp conductors change for blunt,*
> *The nation's out of joint;*
>
> *Franklin a wiser course pursues,*
> *And all your thunder useless views,*
> *By keeping to the point.*

Franklin never entered into any open controversy in defense of his scientific opinions. "I leave them to take their chance in the world," he wrote, adding, "If they are right, truth and experience will support them; if wrong, they ought to be refuted and rejected. Disputes are apt to sour one's temper and disturb one's quiet. I have no private interest in the reception of my inventions by the world, having never made, nor proposed to make, the least profit by any of them."

Within the space of less than six years (1746-1752) Franklin, now only forty-six years of age, had made several classic contributions in the field of electrical research. During the remainder of his life, he made no further contributions in this field and no additional scientific discovery of equal magnitude. But his practical and philosophical disposition and his original mind continued to roam the vast world of natural phenomena. Wherever he approached a baffling problem, he left it less mysterious. Hardly a year after he had so brilliantly dabbled in electricity, he devised and constructed the first flexible catheter recorded in American medicine. He had made this long, thin tubular instrument to reach the bladder and relieve a pain from which his brother

John was suffering. That same year witnessed his pioneer experiments on the relative heat conductivity of wood, silk, silver and other metals, and chinaware. His observations led him to the conclusion that "a silver teapot must therefore have a wooden handle," since wood is a poor conductor of heat. Parenthetically he remarked that "perhaps it is for the same reason that woolen garments keep the body warmer than linen ones, equally thick; woolen keeping the natural heat in, or in other words, not conducting it out to the air." He may not have known at this time of similar experiments that were made in Europe.

Two years later Franklin contributed some unusual observations on the causes and structures of whirlwinds. While out riding with a company of friends one afternoon in Maryland, he rested on his horse while following close to the side of a whirlwind "for about three-quarters of a mile, till some limbs of dead trees, broken off by the whirlwind flying about and falling near me, made me more apprehensive of danger."

In England four years later with his son, he dropped all other work to visit John Hadley, professor of chemistry at the University of Cambridge. Together they spent some time performing a number of experiments dealing with the loss of heat during the evaporation of liquids. Hadley placed a piece of cloth soaked in alcohol around the bulb of a mercury thermometer which he swung through the air to increase the rate of evaporation of the alcohol. The temperature dropped to zero. Franklin substituted ether for the alcohol and succeeded in causing the temperature registered on the thermometer to drop to a reading of 25° Centigrade below zero. As he watched the results of these experiments and began to see cause-and-effect relationships and possible uses (the electric refrigerator of today is based on this same principle), he wondered whether "negroes stand heat better because they sweat more than white men." He believed that the evaporation of sweat lowered the temperature of the body. He also noted that reapers in Pennsylvania were known to drop dead during very hot weather when they did not drink freely, thus raising the temperature of their bodies because of the lack of evaporation of sweat. He even experimented on himself to make sure of this conclusion. He showed that clothes dried more quickly in a wind than on a calm day because the wind hastened the evaporation of water.

In 1761 Franklin wrote to Polly, daughter of the Mrs. Stevenson who ran a boardinghouse in England which he frequently patronized. He informed her of some experiments he had conducted back in 1729 on the effect of heat on objects of different colors. "I took a number of square pieces of broadcloth from a tailor's pattern card, of various colors. I laid them all out upon the snow in a bright sunshiny morning. In a few hours the black, being warmed most by the sun, was sunk so low as to be below the stroke of the sun's rays; the dark blue almost as low, the lighter blue not quite so much as the dark, the other colors (green, purple, red, yellow, and white) less as they were lighter; and the quite white remained on the surface of the snow, not having entered it at all."

Then he added, "*What signifies philosophy that does not apply to some use?* May we not learn from hence that black clothes are not so fit to wear in a hot sunny climate or season as white ones? That soldiers and seamen, who must march and labor in the sun, should in the East or West Indies have a uniform of white? That summer hats for men and women should be white, as repelling the heat which gives headaches to many and to some the fatal stroke that the French call the *coup de soleil*?" It took almost a century for this advice to be generally followed by millions of people around the world.

When Franklin was fifty-three years old, news of the tragic death by fire of Richard Puckeridge reached him. This Englishman had invented a musical instrument consisting of a number of glasses of different sizes in which water was placed. The production of musical sounds by rubbing with the moistened finger the edge of drinking glasses containing different quantities of water had been known for a century. Franklin had witnessed a demonstration of this instrument at a meeting of the Royal Society. He now got the notion that he might be able to get a greater number of tones in a more compact arrangement. He had glasses blown in the shape of hemispheres which he mounted on an iron spindle running through openings in their centers. As the revolving spindle moved the glasses, he would touch them with his fingers and produce tones covering a range of three complete octaves. He called this invention the *armonica* and learned to play it with great skill. Beethoven and Mozart wrote music for it. Franklin also found time to learn to play the violin, harp, and guitar.

Franklin studied the effects of oil in smoothing the surface of water, and would often carry oil in the hollow of his walking stick for these experiments. At sixty-two he was investigating the deadly effects of lead poisoning, which he discovered was due to the poisonous nature of lead compounds. That same year he reported to Sir John Pringle the results of some experiments he had undertaken to discover why boats move more slowly in low water than in deep. He thought out the principle of hydrodynamics involved and then constructed model boats and a model canal to test his theory. He even found time that same year to write some interesting thoughts on *A Scheme for a New Alphabet and Reformed Mode of Spelling*.

The nature and origin of the Gulf Stream occupied Franklin's mind during the next year. His interest in this subject was aroused when he learned that the Board of Customs at Boston had complained to the Lords of the Treasury in London that boats sailing between Falmouth, England, and New York were generally two weeks longer in their passage than merchant ships sailing from London to Rhode Island. The official at Boston proposed that in the future ships should be ordered to Rhode Island instead of to New York. Franklin was consulted in the matter. It appeared to him that "there should not be such a difference between two places scarce a day's run asunder."

He talked the problem over with his cousin, Timothy Folger, a sea captain from Nantucket who hunted whales along the Gulf

Stream. Folger explained that the Rhode Island mariners made use of the Gulf Stream, a current which was rather vaguely defined . and about which the English shipmasters knew nothing. They would cross it directly or run with it rather than against this stream. At Franklin's request, Folger proceeded to make measurements and observations of this stream. His chart was sent to the British Post Office to be used by the masters of mail packets in an effort to shorten the passage from England to America. During his many crossings of the Gulf Stream thereafter, Franklin himself made measurements of its width, depth, temperature, and velocity, data which he continued to gather as late as 1785, when he was almost eighty years of age.

Franklin was no cloistered professional scientist or research worker. His many contributions to science were made in the midst of a very active public life. Intelligent, alert, civilized, courageous, and a keen judge of men, he took a leading part in the struggles of his day on the side of liberty and individual rights. He was a citizen-scientist to whom social responsibility was as much his business as trying to discover whether the ant possessed some system of thought transmission or to understand how sea shells could be found embedded in the rocks of mountains a mile above the surface of our oceans.

In 1748 Franklin was elected to the city council of Philadelphia; two years later was voted a member of the Pennsylvania Assembly and was re-elected to that office for fourteen consecutive years. His diplomatic career, which was to continue almost to the end of his long life, began in 1757, when the Pennsylvania Assembly sent him to London to try to settle the dispute over taxation between the Penn family, the Proprietors of Pennsylvania, and the British government.

Franklin's part in the struggle against the proprietary family is an interesting one. It shows an unusual relationship between the political struggles of the day and the fortunes of the American Philosophical Society, the most powerful scientific body in the colonies. The heirs of William Penn, conveniently forgetting the ideals of the founder, looked upon the province of Pennsylvania simply as a rich source of revenue. They manipulated officials so that they paid no taxes on the land. This and other abuses led to a division among the people into two political parties. The Proprietary Party was led by James Hamilton; that which might be called the Popular Party was championed by Franklin. Various means were taken by the Penn family party to weaken the Popular Party. They tried to win Franklin over by having him elected to the Royal Society and by arranging to have his son, William, at the age of thirty-one, appointed governor of New Jersey. Franklin was too principled a man to behave as they schemed. As a further measure they decided to take over the American Philosophical Society(of 1743) by packing its membership with their own candidates. The situation finally reached a point where the unprejudiced thinking of science flew out of the window and scientific and philosophical discussions were drowned out by the bitter political quarrels of its members.

Franklin and his friends stepped out of the organization and began to reorganize the old Junto. More active liberals were corralled; a call was sent out to men of learning and independence regardless of whether or not they were citizens of Philadelphia. The Junto became the American Society Held at Philadelphia for Promoting and Propagating Useful Knowledge, with Franklin as president. As a result of this shakeup there existed in December, 1766, two scientific societies where formerly there was one. Governor John Penn, grandson of the founder of Pennsylvania, saw an opportunity to oppose Franklin, whom he hated intensely. He became the wealthy patron of the other American Philosophical Society, now controlled by members of the Proprietary Party. In this way he hoped to starve out Franklin's scientific organization and weaken the prestige of the Philadelphia printer. A good deal of confusion resulted. Some scientists were members of both societies and attended meetings of the two bodies. Annoyed by this scientific duality, they looked for a solution of the difficulties.

After two years of private sessions, proposals, and counterproposals, compromise terms of formal union were agreed upon by both organizations meeting jointly.

Under the title by which it still functions today, the American Philosophical Society Held at Philadelphia for Promoting Useful Knowledge held its first meeting and first election of officers on the evening of January 2, 1769. In a heated contest Franklin won over James Hamilton, who had been president of the American Philosophical Society. This was definitely a victory for the democratic element in Philadelphia and was a portent of what was to come very soon in a larger arena. When John Penn received the news with an invitation to become the patron of the new and only scientific society, he shouted in a rage that he would not give aid to any group whose president was "the greatest enemy of my family." That happened to be true, but it was also true that Franklin was the most creative scientist in the colonies and the only American man of science who measured up to the greatest scientific luminaries of Europe.

It was not alone his scientific discoveries and inventions which enriched America; his tremendous influence also shaped the cultural interests of the colonies. Franklin was in the center of almost every cultural ripple which appeared on this side of the Atlantic. His curiosity and enthusiasm were infectious, and he encouraged many in their pursuit of science. Throughout the history of the American Philosophical Society he brought the energetic minds of the colonies together on common problems of nature through meetings, visits, projects, correspondence, and financial aid. In 1771 the American Philosophical Society had 157 members from Pennsylvania, eleven each from New York and New Jersey, ten from Massachusetts, five each from Maryland and South Carolina, four from Virginia, three from Delaware, two from Rhode Island, and one from Georgia. Ten of its members lived in the West Indies and another twenty-five had their homes in Europe.

Through the Royal Society of London, of whose executive

council he was four times a member, Franklin brought the scientific quests and discoveries of Europe to the attention of America. He sponsored the membership of many Americans in the Royal Society and made the Old World aware of the scientific awakening of the New. Through his influence many of the illustrious names in the world of European science, including Linnaeus, Lavoisier, Buffon, and Banks, were added to the roster of the American Philosophical Society. In 1758 Franklin met Matthew Boulton, owner of a large factory in Soho, England, who together with William Small, Scotch physician and mathematician, had helped James Watt draw up the design for the steam engine, one of the greatest inventions of all time. Through Franklin's intervention, Small was appointed professor of natural history at the College of William and Mary, where he exerted a great influence upon Jefferson, according to the statement of the future President. Another American, Christopher Colles, was encouraged by Franklin to investigate the steam engine as a means of pumping water. The agricultural experiments of Jared Eliot, the astronomical studies of Rittenhouse, and the botanical work of Colden were all aided by Franklin. To John Bartram in 1770 he sent the first Chinese rhubarb, Scotch cabbage, and kohlrabi seed to be planted in America.

In a sense Franklin directed the career of Joseph Priestley, the English dissenting minister who discovered oxygen in 1774. Franklin had met him earlier and had interested him in electricity. From this start Priestley then turned to the study of chemistry. Franklin helped to sell the Englishman's scientific writings in the colonies. In Lavoisier's laboratory in Paris, Franklin had met E. I. du Pont de Nemours, who later emigrated to America and in 1802 established a small powder mill which was the beginning of the powerful Du Pont Company of Delaware. Franklin built the bridge which joined the worlds of science of the two hemispheres.

A number of other scientists were active in the colonies during

Franklin's lifetime. Perhaps no other was more important than John Winthrop, born in Boston of a merchant father. At the age of twenty-four he was appointed professor of mathematics and natural philosophy at Harvard College, a position which he held to his death forty years later. Both Franklin and Benjamin Thompson, who attended some of his lectures, owed much to Winthrop. He established the first laboratory of experimental physics in an American college, where he demonstrated the laws of mechanics, falling bodies, heat, and light according to the best Newtonian knowledge of his day. He reached out of his classroom to help educate those who stood in terror of natural phenomena. When in 1755 an earthquake terrorized New England, Winthrop calmed the people by giving a public lecture in the college chapel in which he explained that the condition was caused by the expansion of liquids and vapors in underground caves. "Earthquakes," he admonished the terror-stricken, "are neither objections against the order of Providence nor tokens of God's displeasure, but necessary consequences of natural laws." When Halley's comet returned on April 3, 1759, as predicted by scientists, and hundreds again were frightened, the Harvard professor returned to the lecture platform to explain that it was a perfectly natural occurrence and brought no terrors with it.

Winthrop co-operated with the American Philosophical Society, of which he was a member, in various astronomical projects, such as studies of the transits of Venus in 1761 and 1769. In the course of the latter project the first observatory in the United States was erected in the State House yard in Philadelphia at public expense at the request of the American Philosophical Society. David Rittenhouse built a transit telescope and clock for this observatory. Winthrop, too, persuaded the Massachusetts Assembly to send him on a sloop to Newfoundland where he could better observe and study the transit, a study which might give American scientists a more accurate determination of the distance between the sun and the earth. Rittenhouse also made many observations of the new planet Uranus discovered by William Herschel in 1781. Twelve years later the American discovered a new comet.

With the exception of Franklin's contribution to electricity, no single fundamental discovery marked the period in America between the founding of the Junto in 1727 and the death of its founder in 1790. Yet the volume of scientific investigation was increased, more abstract and broader problems were approached, and America began to feel her growing powers.

For example, the astronomer David Rittenhouse, descendant of William Rittinghuysen, who in 1690 opened the first paper mill in North America, also made some important contributions to physics. In 1781 he proposed a theory of magnetism which is still true in the light of our newer knowledge. Rittenhouse wrote, "I suppose that magnetical particles of matter are a necessary constituent part of iron. . . . These magnetical particles have each a north and south pole, and retain their polarity however the metal may be fused or otherwise wrought. In a piece of iron which shows no sign of magnetism these magnetical particles lie irregularly, with their poles pointing in all possible directions, they therefor mutually destroy each others' effects. By giving magnetism to a piece of iron we do nothing more than arrange these particles, and when this is done it depends on the temper and situation of the iron whether that arrangement shall continue, that is, whether the piece of metal shall remain for a long time magnetical or not." He devised a metal thermometer and a hygrometer, and built an orrery— a mechanical model of the solar system with a range of five thousand years. He constructed a diffraction grating in 1786 which he attempted to explain in terms of Newton's theory of the nature of light. This was thirty years before the work of Joseph Fraunhofer, the German physicist who is usually credited with this invention.

Other serious students of natural philosophy began to inquire about the fundamental problems of the nature of light and heat, and the structure of celestial bodies. Cadwallader Colden, physician, botanist, and friend of Franklin, wrote two papers on *Light and Colors, an Inquiry into the Principles of Vital Motion* and *Explication of the First Causes of Motion in Matter, and of the Cause of Gravitation.* In the latter he propounded a theory which Jacob Bernoulli had advanced almost a century before. Newton's disciples in Europe read these papers with great interest and Franklin reported that they were eager to learn more from "us Americans." Franklin and some of his friends even dared question the accuracy of Newton's corpuscular theory of light. "It is well we are not as poor Galileo was, subject to the Inquisition for philosophical heresy," wrote Franklin.

In 1776 Franklin was sent to France by the new Congress of the United States to secure treaties with that country. During his nine years in France his eminence as a scientist was of no small help in keeping the two countries on better than friendly terms. He joined in the discussions of the meetings of the French Academy of Sciences where he read a paper on the nature of the aurora borealis. He correctly interpreted the cause of this spectacular display as a discharge of electricity through the upper regions of the atmosphere where the thinness of the air provides the partial vacuum necessary for this phenomenon. To the *Journal of Paris* he recommended daylight saving as a means of diminishing the cost of light.

The American ambassador was placed by the King of France on a committee with Lavoisier to investigate the claims and method of Mesmer, pioneer in hypnosis. He became very much interested in aeronautics, after witnessing in 1783 the first ascent of Dr. Charles' hydrogen-filled balloon, and subscribed money to further experiments with balloons. Franklin thought this new invention might convince "sovereigns of the folly of wars . . . since it will be impracticable for the most potent of them to guard their dominions." He explained the proper use of water-tight bulkheads in ship construction. He continued to play with and devise new

200	217	232	249	8	25	40	57	72	89	104	121	136	153	168	181
58	39	26	7	250	231	218	199	186	167	154	135	122	103	90	71
198	219	230	251	6	27	38	59	70	91	102	123	134	155	166	187
60	37	28	5	252	229	220	197	188	165	156	133	124	101	92	69
201	216	233	248	9	24	41	56	73	88	105	120	137	152	169	184
55	42	23	10	247	234	215	202	183	170	151	138	119	106	87	74
20	214	235	246	11	22	43	54	75	86	107	118	139	150	171	182
53	44	21	12	245	236	213	204	181	172	149	140	117	108	85	76
205	212	237	244	13	20	45	52	77	84	109	116	141	148	173	180
51	46	19	14	243	238	241	206	179	174	147	142	115	110	83	78
207	210	239	242	15	18	47	50	79	82	111	114	143	146	175	178
49	48	17	16	241	240	209	208	177	176	145	144	113	112	81	80
196	221	228	253	4	29	36	61	68	93	100	125	132	157	164	189
62	35	30	3	254	227	222	195	190	163	158	131	126	99	94	67
194	223	226	255	2	31	34	63	66	95	98	127	130	159	162	191
64	33	32	1	256	225	224	193	192	161	160	129	128	97	96	65

Fig. 1. One of Franklin's Magic Squares.

magic squares—numbers arranged in a square in such a manner that the sum of the horizontal, vertical, and diagonal rows is constant.

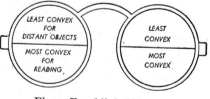

Fig. 2. Franklin's Bifocals.

At the age of seventy-eight, after wearing ordinary glasses for twenty-five years, he invented the first *bifocals*.

During his last years Franklin complained to Priestley of his lack of leisure and strength to search "into the works of nature." Later, after he had returned to the United States in 1785, at the age of seventy-nine, he wrote to another famous European scientist, John Ingenhousz, that at last he was "a freeman" ready to resume his experiments. But his continued interest in science did not dissociate him from further participation in public matters. In 1787 he was appointed delegate to the Constitutional Convention to which he gave his last great service to his country.

Three years later, after a short illness, Franklin died in Philadelphia at the age of eighty-four. The United States House of Representatives officially mourned his passing. When the news of his death reached the French National Assembly, Mirabeau rose to exclaim, "Antiquity would have raised altars to the mortal who knew how to subdue both thunder and tyranny." Posterity did, but they were different altars.

CHAPTER THREE

BENJAMIN THOMPSON (1753-1814)

SCIENCE FACES THE TUMULT OF THE AMERICAN REVOLUTION

HALF A CENTURY was to pass after Franklin's work in electricity before the next epochal advance in science was made by an American. This second fundamental addition to pure science was made, strangely enough, not in the colonies but in Europe. Its author, however, was born in Woburn, Massachusetts, about twelve miles from the birthplace of Franklin, and did not leave America until he was twenty-two years old. The explanation of this unusual circumstance is tied up with the political events of the stormy second half of the eighteenth century.

When the Frenchman Turgot wrote about Franklin that "He snatched the lightning from the sky and the sceptre from tyrants," the American replied, "I left the lightning where I found it; but more than a million of my countrymen joined me in reaching after the sceptre." Of fundamental importance to an understanding of this struggle is the study of the philosophy and practice of *mercantilism*, the theory which shaped the actions of the British Empire for more than a century. Mercantilism was a pseudo-scientific and shortsighted policy which cost England her American colonies.

Under this system colonies were regarded merely as sources of raw materials and as markets for the finished products of the mother country. This policy, it was argued, would insure for England a favorable balance of trade, and thus enhance the prosperity of the British Empire. As mercantilism worked out, however, the merchant class of England was favored by the Crown at the expense of the corresponding class in the American colonies.

From the beginning, agriculture was the basis of colonial economy. New York and the other middle colonies grew wheat and vegetables and also supplied dairy products, beef, and pork to Europe. Rice and indigo were harvested in the Carolinas and Georgia; tobacco, first successfully raised by John Rolfe in 1612, was the great staple of Virginia and Maryland. All of these agricultural efforts fitted in with the demands of mercantilism. Colonial capitalist activities were restricted to land speculation, the fur trade, and shipping.

The English Parliament passed laws closely governing the trade of the colonists. The first of these restrictive measures were the Navigation Acts of 1651, under which only British or colonial boats could ship goods to and from America. Ships carrying goods from the European continent destined for the American colonies had to stop at an English port, pay a tax, and transfer the cargo to a British or colonial boat which would carry the goods across the Atlantic.

The colonists were not allowed to manufacture many articles but had to purchase most manufactured products from England. Stringent measures were passed to stifle any expansion of colonial manufacturing. In 1750 the English Parliament passed the Iron Act, which forbade the further expansion of American ironworks making nails, sheet iron, iron plate, and tools. The colonists were, however, permitted to manufacture pig iron for exportation to England, which needed it badly.

For decades the colonists did not abide by these restrictions. England needed the good will of the colonists during her struggle with the French for control of North America. By a policy of "salutary neglect"—shutting its eyes to infractions of its laws—the British government countenanced much prohibited manufacturing and trade expansion. The iron industry, for example, spread out into the production of more and more wrought iron and steel. By 1760 there were four steel furnaces in the colonies. Augustine

Washington, father of George Washington, was one of the owners of the Principio Company, which operated furnaces in Virginia and Maryland.

In 1763, however, England won the French and Indian War, and by the Treaty of Paris received Canada and all French territory east of the Mississippi River. She began to feel now that the colonies ought to pay for her expensive wars, which had incidentally benefited them. It was also time to end the policy of salutary neglect; the help of the colonies against the French was no longer needed. The old restrictive laws were taken down and dusted off. New teeth were put into them by King George III and his Tory ministers. Smuggling was stopped, and strict enforcement of the old navigation and trade acts began to irritate the colonists. New taxes were imposed. In 1765 the Stamp Act ordered the colonists to place stamps on their newspapers, pamphlets, and legal documents. Two years later, by the Townshend Acts, new duties were imposed on tea, glass, paint, and paper. Then came the offer of "cheap tea" to the colonists, who refused the tea on the principle of "no taxation without representation." They showed their displeasure by dumping a cargo of this tea into Boston Harbor on December 16, 1773.

In 1774 came the five Intolerable Acts, which closed the port of Boston, changed the government of Massachusetts, provided for the trial of royal officers in Great Britain, prescribed the payment of British colonial troops by the colonists, and extended the boundary of Quebec to the Ohio River to prevent Americans from settling the Northwest. Americans retaliated swiftly by calling the First Continental Congress, which demanded the immediate repeal of these acts and announced the suspension of all trade with the British until these wrongs were redressed. In his *Common Sense*, published in Philadelphia in December, 1776, Thomas Paine, friend of Franklin, who in London had advised him to come to America, boldly called for complete independence. This pamphlet sold by the thousands, and made a tremendous impression on the colonists. At the December 17, 1774, meeting of the American

Philosophical Society, the secretary, Benjamin Rush, noted that "the members of the Philosophical Society were obliged to discontinue their meetings until a mode of opposition to the said Acts of Parliament was established."

The following April, British troops marched on Concord to seize the ammunition of the Minute Men and shots were fired at Concord and Lexington. A second Continental Congress was called in May of 1775, the Revolutionary Government organized a Continental Army under George Washington, and a committee set to work to draft the Declaration of Independence. The Declaration with its famous principles of equality and of government by the consent of the governed, drawn up by Jefferson, was revised and signed by Benjamin Franklin. The great scientist, businessman, and patriot also offered all of his wealth to the Congress for the conduct of the war.

It was during these exciting days that the life of Benjamin Thompson, a schoolteacher of Concord, New Hampshire, was abruptly and radically altered. Thompson's scientific curiosity developed at an early age, and was to result in many substantial contributions to science and technology. Born into a middle-class family, Thompson lost his farmer father when he was only a few months old, and he was brought up in poverty. His schooling ended at the age of thirteen and he was apprenticed to a Salem merchant, spending several years as a drygoods clerk. He attended some of Winthrop's lectures at Harvard and struggled to enter the medical profession but had to abandon this career because he was penniless.

While on his third teaching job at Concord in 1772, Thompson met the wealthy widow of a Colonel Rolfe. Not long after that he wrote, "I married or rather was married at the age of 19." Benjamin was handsome, had a wide knowledge, and was a brilliant conversationalist. He liked good clothes, pomp, and ceremony. Before long he was being pushed into the circles of the rich and mighty. Through his wife he won the attention of the governor, who offered him a commission as major in the local militia. The townspeople did not like the uppishness of this parvenu who had married wealth to gain social prestige. In trying to forget the difficult days of his youth, Thompson became an aristocrat by adoption, and frequently showed his dislike of the common people. The people in return distrusted his sympathies at this perilous hour.

The small farmer, blacksmith, carpenter, seaman, and artisan had felt the pinch of the economic depression which set in after the end of the French wars, leaving business stagnant and unemployment widespread. Many of this class were Scotch-Irish and German settlers who felt no loyalty to the English. The common people had another reason for taking an active part in arousing the colonies against England. Principles of liberty and equality were involved. By means of meetings, handbills, and demonstrations they functioned effectively. Many of them, as members of the Sons of Liberty, which counted in its roster such men as Paul Revere, an artisan, and Samuel Adams, the political agitator, did heroic work among the colonists, especially in Massachusetts. Some of the merchant class were incensed, too, for the English attitude interfered with their business. Even the Southern planters, who did not feel the economic barriers so much as the Northern merchants, were inflamed by the addition of tobacco to the enumerated list of products which could be sold only to Britain, and by the English proclamation closing the western lands to them. They had been in the habit of working their land to death with tobacco and rice crops, and then, instead of fertilizing their fields, moving on into virgin territory.

Even with all these economic restrictions, some method might have been worked out for patching up the troubles between the motherland and the colonies. While opposing the British policy, the American Philosophical Society, for example, had declared in 1774 that it hoped some way would be found "to restore the former harmony and maintain a perpetual union between Great Britain and the American Colonies." "But for a blustering ministerial imperialism that challenged this nascent liberalism," wrote

Parrington, "the colonies would have written a different story."

But other forces were at work. A spirit of individual worth and liberty had begun to spread among the common people. The meaning of democratic ideals was being preached by the radicals of the day. The people, especially those outside the merchant class, listened breathlessly to their words. The decline of the early theocracies, the rumbles of the "natural rights" of man which echoed the Age of Reason, and the widening of man's horizons by the new discoveries in world science made the common man more receptive to dissenters if not altogether sympathetic to political separatists.

A stupid group in London, believing it could depend on American Tories, gave the radicals in the colonies every opportunity to set the temper of the people against the British government. Yet the break with the mother country by no means won the unanimous consent of the colonists. There were those aristocrats who sided with England for no other reason than hatred of the "mob." Others would not join up with Samuel Adams and Thomas Paine because of conservative make-up and royal favors received or hoped for. There were some who honestly felt that the English Parliament was within its rights in imposing restrictions, and that harmony could be reached by negotiations. Besides these appeasers, there were many whose allegiance to England was stronger than their interest in their fellow countrymen. These "fifth columnists" whispered that the British system of government was far better than any so-called democratic system which the American political upstarts could possibly devise.

Persons who were known to be Whigs (the liberals of that day) were reported to the British authorities. The Whigs, too, published lists of "Protesters"—rich merchants, officials of the crown, wealthy landowners, and others suspected of aiding the British. There was much searching after subversive acts, a welter of suspicions, gossip, taletelling, and even the settling of old scores with personal enemies. Committees of Correspondence formed by the patriots listened to the evidence of every spy and eavesdropper.

Benjamin Thompson was swept into the net. In the summer of 1774 he was brought before one of these tribunals for "being unfriendly to the cause of liberty." He was found innocent of the charges, but several months later it was noised about that he had been in communication with General Gage in Boston. A mob surrounded the Rolfe mansion in Concord where he was staying. Thompson escaped to Woburn, where he wrote to his father-in-law that he "never did or ever will do any action to injure the true interests of my native country." On May 16, 1775, however, he was again arrested and sent to prison for two weeks. Through the influence of his friend, Loammi Baldwin, he was again acquitted by the Woburn Committee of Correspondence, which failed to find evidence of any overt unpatriotic act.

Now sick of the patriots, Benjamin Thompson went to Boston secretly to enlist in the British army. When on March 24, 1776, Washington forced the British to evacuate that city, Thompson boarded a man-of-war and left for England. Massachusetts confiscated his property just as he received a position in the office of the British Secretary of State in London. Soon afterward he was promoted to an undersecretaryship of state. In 1782, he returned for a while to America as Lieutenant Colonel of the Kings Dragoons and saw some inconsequential service against the patriotic citizens of Flushing, Long Island. Before the final disbanding of the British forces in the colonies, he left his native land for the last time.

Benjamin Thompson was not the only scientist who was a Loyalist. Joseph Galloway, vice-president of the American Philosophical Society and member of the Continental Congress, left for England, where he acted as spokesman of the exiled American Loyalists. Dr. William Wells, the physician who had propounded the correct explanation of the formation of dew, returned to the mother country as a Loyalist. Dr. Alexander Garden, botanist and zoologist of Charleston, South Carolina, followed in 1784, never forgiving his son who served in the Continental Army. J. L. McAdam, inventor of macadamized roads; Dr. Samuel Bard, professor of medicine at Kings College; Reverend Thomas Barton, Philadelphia botanist and mineral collector; and William Byrd of Virginia were Loyalist sympathizers who managed to stay in the colonies. Another was the Irish immigrant, Cadwallader Colden, who wrote on botany, medicine, physics, and mathematics and served as lieutenant governor of New York for fifteen years. He died in September, 1776. The plant *Coldenia* was named after him.

The rank and file of American men of science, however, knew the meaning of liberty. They were convinced that science could make greater progress in a land freed from the shackles of the reactionaries of Europe. Almost in a body American scientists followed the patriotic example of Franklin, Rittenhouse, and Winthrop. When Franklin was appointed to a committee named by the Second Continental Congress to confer with Washington on measures to support the Continental Army, he wrote to Priestley in England, "Tell our good friend, Dr. Price, who sometimes has his doubts and despondencies about our firmness, that America is determined and unanimous. . . . Britain at the expense of three million has killed 150 Yankees this campaign, which is £20,000 a head. During the same time 60,000 children have been born in America. From these data his mathematical head will easily calculate the time and expense necessary to kill us all and conquer our whole territory."

The war was won by the courage of Americans who knew they were fighting for freedom. Many factors added up to the final victory. Of some importance was the use by our troops of the Pennsylvania rifle. This firearm had been developed by Swiss and German immigrant gunsmiths who settled near Lancaster, Pennsylvania. It could be loaded easily. Instead of a tight-fitting bullet they used a smaller bullet wrapped in greased cloth. It had a longer barrel (40 to 44 inches) than the rifle used by the British, and its smaller bore (less than one-half inch) enabled our soldiers to outshoot the enemy by about fifty yards. Another contribution of Yankee ingenuity to the war effort was a huge iron chain thrown across the Hudson River just below West Point to help bar the upper river to the British fleet. This chain, made by New York ironmasters, was 1500 feet in length, with links two feet long and each weighing one hundred pounds. The chain rested on a series of log rafts in the river.

After his brief service with the British army in America, Thompson had gone to the Continent to serve with the Austrian army against the Turks. Late in 1783 he found himself in Bavaria. He made a great impression on the reigning Duke, who offered him an appointment as colonel of a cavalry regiment and as his general aide-de-camp. The former American could not hide his excitement at this flattering invitation and rushed back to King George III in England for permission to enter a foreign service. He soon returned not only with the King's personal permission to serve Charles Theodore of Bavaria, but also with an English order of knighthood conferred upon him in February, 1784. A palace in Munich was placed at his disposal. Here, surrounded by his military staff and a retinue of servants, he served his Elector faithfully for more than fifteen years.

Munich turned out to be a very busy place for Thompson. The greatest scientific discovery that came out of Munich in the eighteenth century was a new explanation of the phenomenon of heat and a brilliant experiment by Thompson which proved the truth of the new theory. This milestone in the history of science was reached while Thompson was connected with the Bavarian army.

More than once military needs have been both the stimulus and mainspring of investigations which had led to major contributions in pure science. Back in the seventeenth century, for example, the flight of war projectiles led to a study of trajectories, which gave us our first precise knowledge of the laws of falling bodies.

During our War of Independence, while he was still in the service of England, Thompson's interest naturally turned to studies in gunpowder and projectiles. To measure more accurately the explosive force of gunpowder, he invented, in 1778, the Rumford apparatus. This was a small steel cannon or mortar mounted on solid masonry and containing a small cavity in which powder was exploded. The gases formed by the exploding gunpowder were forced to leave through a small hole in the mortar plugged with well-greased leather. Over this hole were placed different weights which when finally heavy enough just balanced the explosive force of the gases attempting to escape. This weight became a measure of the effectiveness of the explosive force of the powder used. These experiments added to our knowledge of the science of internal ballistics. One of the facts Thompson discovered was that the force of the explosion was due not only to the volume of gas produced but also to the rapidity of combustion of the explosive.

The factors which determined the velocity of bullets also engaged his interest. He investigated different types of gunpowder, various methods of firing the charge, and different vents for escaping gases in the firearms. To check his laboratory observations he went on a three-month cruise with the British fleet in 1779 and persuaded the commander of the ships to fire all kinds of shells from every type of cannon while he made fresh observations and collected new data.

Thompson's scientific curiosity was stimulated by a problem which had baffled man for centuries: the nature of heat. In spite of innumerable attempts to explain and countless experiments to track down this elusive entity, heat was still nothing more than a word, *caloric*. Caloric was conceived of as a mobile fluid which was present in varying amounts in the pores of all bodies. Caloric could be squeezed out of such bodies in the form of heat, or added to them by the agency of flames. Observation showed that objects expanded when heated and that metals increased in weight when burned. Such data seemed to add weight to the theory, and the theory of caloric prevailed for more than a century.

The question as to whether caloric actually possessed weight was studied by Hermann Boerhaave of Leyden in 1732. He made careful determinations of the weight of a five-pound mass of iron both before and after heating it to a red heat but reported no change in weight. Buffon in 1775 weighed a fifty-pound mass of iron while white hot. Then, after cooling it to the freezing point of water, he weighed it again and insisted that the iron suffered a loss in weight of nearly two ounces. The following year John Roebuck, an English scientist, repeated these experiments using both gold and iron. His results were contradictory. Sometimes he obtained an increase in weight; at other times, the balance showed no change at all, and some of his readings even showed a loss of weight.

Was caloric really material? No one had as yet satisfied stubborn men of science on this question. Thompson saw obvious errors in the procedures of the other scientists who had attempted to clear up the matter of caloric. He planned to avoid these pitfalls and worked out a series of beautifully controlled experiments. He took two identical thin glass flasks, one of which he filled with carefully distilled water and the other with a dilute alcohol solution. The flasks were then sealed and hung, one from each arm of a very sensitive balance in perfect equilibrium. The temperature of the room in which the balance was placed was regulated at exactly 61° Fahrenheit. The apparatus was then moved into another room where the temperature was regulated to remain at 29° Fahrenheit, three degrees below the freezing point of water.

At the end of forty-eight hours the water in the first flask was frozen solid. The solution of alcohol, which has a freezing point lower than 29° Fahrenheit, remained liquid. Thompson also noted that the equilibrium of the balance had been disturbed and that as much as 0.134 grains of metal had to be attached to the side of the balance carrying the pure water before this equilibrium could be re-established. This disturbance apparently pointed to the conclusion that some caloric had leaked out of the flask containing the water. But to check the accuracy of this conclusion he removed the added grains of metal and carefully returned the whole apparatus to the room where the temperature remained at 61° Fahrenheit. The ice in the flask thawed out, the balance returned to its original equilibrium. Apparently the "lost" weight had been "recovered" without adding anything material to the flask. Confusion was worse confounded. Thompson checked the balance and the apparatus once more and could find no change.

Thompson reasoned that if caloric could be squeezed out as heat, then it ought to be possible to demonstrate this during the process of boring cannon. The gun metal strips or turnings which came out of the center of the cannon during the boring process should show less heat capacity than the same original weight of gun metal before it was gouged out. Calorimetric methods had already been devised to determine the heat capacity of metals. Thompson set to work to determine the heat capacity of the cannon before boring began, and then the heat capacity both of the metal turnings which came out of the cannon and of the finished cannon itself. He made very careful measurements and found absolutely no loss of heat. Not an iota!

The next step was clear to him. In 1797 he planned to rotate an unfinished solid cannon, a gun metal six-pounder ready for boring, against a steel borer. He devised a method of measuring the amount of heat liberated during this operation. The cyclindrical mass of metal was placed in a wooden box holding 18¾ pounds of water. By means of several teams of horses the cannon was rotated against the steel cutting tool. At the end of 2¾ hours of boring, the heat liberated raised the initial temperature of the water from 60° Fahrenheit to 212° Fahrenheit, and the water began to boil. This was indeed a spectacle even for Thompson. "It would be difficult," he wrote, "to describe the surprise and astonishment expressed in the countenances of the bystanders on seeing so large a quantity of water heated, and actually made to boil, without any fire." Strange that this should have been so great a surprise, for the old Indian method of striking a fire was exactly that—rubbing one dry object with another and reaching the burning point of the wood by friction.

Thompson began to feel more certain now that the heat generated was the result of mechanical action only. But where did the heat really come from? How could he pin down the answer to this question? Could the heat have come from the action of the oxygen of the air combining with the metal of the cannon? That was impossible, since the cannon was under water. Was the heat which was generated inexhaustible? That he could find out by means of another experiment. He repeated the boring process. More water kept boiling off. Apparently the heat was inexhaustible. The experimenter wrote in conclusion, "It is hardly necessary to add that anything which any insulated body, or system of bodies, can continue to furnish without limitation cannot possibly be a material substance. It appears to me to be extremely difficult, if not quite impossible, to form any distinct idea of anything capable of being excited and communicated in these experiments *except it be motion*."

Thompson had established the fact that heat was a form of energy due to vibration of the particles of matter. This is now an accepted truth. He next wanted to learn just how much heat was liberated during a boring operation and devised experiments to find out. Using wax candles of ¾-inch diameter he showed that "the quantity of heat produced by the boring [of a weighed quantity of metal] was greater than that produced by the continuous burning of nine such candles."

His next step was a bold and fundamental one. He attempted to discover the *exact* relationship between the *exact* amount of energy employed in the boring operation and the *exact* amount of heat generated during the boring process. This mathematical relationship, which is known as the *mechanical equivalent of heat*, was of basic importance in technology and was a prerequisite to any theoretical consideration of the conversion of one form of energy into another. After some very careful experimentation, Thompson found that this mechanical equivalent of heat was equal to 847 foot-pounds; that is, the work done in lifting a weight of 847 pounds a distance of one foot. This mechanical energy was equivalent also to the heat required to raise the temperature of one pound of water one degree on the Fahrenheit scale.

About forty years later, in 1842, the German scientist Julius R. Mayer employed a different experiment to establish the principle of the conservation of energy, one of the most significant determinations in the whole history of science. He measured the heat developed during the compression of air and showed that heat and mechanical energy are mutually convertible. Unfortunately, the work of this overshadowed genius was neglected by the world of science. At about the same time, the Englishman James Prescott Joule performed similar experiments which proved conclusively that the mechanical equivalent of heat is equal to 772 foot-pounds. (The figure accepted today is 778 foot-pounds.) When we consider the forty-year span between the experiments of Thompson and Joule, the less than ten per cent error of the American-born scientist was not a bad one. Joule's work earned for him immortality in the unit *joule*, which is equivalent to 0.738 foot-pounds.

At the realization of his great discovery, Thompson began to think of another matter closely related to the principle of the transformation of energy. He wondered whether the energy of the horses which he had used to bore the cannon and which had been converted into heat might not itself be the result of the burning of the fodder inside the animals. Franklin, writing about heat as early as 1757, had remarked, "As by a constant supply of fuel in a chimney you keep a room warm, so by a constant supply of food in the stomach, you keep a body warm." Lavoisier in 1774 had discovered that burning was the rapid union of the burning substance with oxygen, and for the first time asserted that in the process of food assimilation in the body the food was oxidized. This slow oxidation in the body produced the heat which kept the body temperature at 98.6° Fahrenheit regardless of the outside temperature.

Thompson now declared that his "computations showed how large a quantity of heat might be produced by proper mechanical contrivance, merely by the strength of a horse, without fire, light, combustion or chemical decomposition; and, in case of necessity, the heat thus produced might be used in cooking victuals." His practical mind, however, saw the difficulties. He added, "But no circumstances can be imagined in which this method of procuring heat would be advantageous; for more heat might be obtained by using fuel than fodder necessary for the support of the horse." He had definitely brought the living animal into the category of heat engines.

Thompson wrote up his experiments in a paper entitled *Inquiry concerning the Source of the Heat Which is Generated by Friction* and in 1798 sent it to the Royal Society, of which he was a member. The paper, one of the classics of science, was written in a clear, short, beautiful style, for Thompson was a meticulous author. "Too much pains," he declared, "cannot be taken by those who write books to render their ideas clear, and their language concise and easy to understand. Hours spent by an author in saving minutes and even seconds to his readers is time well spent." The paper was read and discussed, yet many were not convinced of the mechanical nature of heat until the mathematical determinations of Mayer and Joule finally destroyed every vestige of the caloric theory.

A beautiful, ten-foot bronze statue was erected in Thompson's honor in the city of Munich. It was raised not to Benjamin Thompson, the scientist, but to Count Rumford, the philanthropist and humanitarian. In 1791 he had been created a Count of the Holy Roman Empire, and nostalgically chose the title of Rumford, the original name of Concord, New Hampshire. On the statue was placed an inscription which read, "To him who routed out the most scandalous of public evils, Idleness and Mendicity, who gave to the poor help, occupation and morals, and to the Youth of the Fatherland so many schools of culture."

The Elector of Bavaria wanted the world to remember how Thompson, soon after his arrival in Munich, had rounded up hundreds of beggars and indigents and set them to work in his Home of Industry. This was an industrial institution founded by Thompson where men, women, and children who had roamed the city as beggars were given food and shelter together with some small payment in return for making clothes for the army and other useful work. Here hundreds of the impoverished of Munich baked their own bread, made their own mattresses and shoes, and in this quasi-communal life soon gained enough skill and confidence to find employment outside this labor camp.

As head of the Bavarian army, Thompson changed a corrupt, idle, and hated soldiery into a more wholesome organization by improving the quarters of the men, raising their pay, introducing schools for them, and setting them to work on state projects such as draining swamps, building roads, and raising potatoes and vegetables in their military and home gardens.

What were the motives which led Thompson to this work? Georges Cuvier, the eminent French scientist, knew him well. It was his opinion that "His services to his fellow men were rendered them without loving them or even thinking well of them. He felt that the common people could not be trusted with the care of their own well-being. He loved slavery, and China seemed to him to have a nearly perfect government because its common people were absolutely in the power of its intelligent men." Cuvier understood that Thompson was no democrat. His motives sprang from different sources. Poverty and economic distress revolted him because, aesthetically, he was repelled by them. Furthermore, he feared the dangers inherent in such depressing conditions. They might ultimately lead to rebellion and bloodshed.

If his long attempts at the salvation of the poor by organized charity proved only a temporary palliative rather than a sound and long-range solution, they had at least the virtue of leading Thompson into an extended series of experiments in the science of heating, cooking, and lighting. In the interest of economy in his relief work, this expatriate Yankee made a number of significant improvements in cooking utensils and methods. The modern pressure cooker, the gas range, and the fuelless cooker are all developments of his innovations. He showed that coating the bottom of a pan with lampblack increased its absorption of heat and caused liquids to boil more quickly in such containers. In connection with this experiment he made another important discovery. He found that "all the heat which a hot body loses when it is exposed in the air to cool is not given off to the air, but a large proportion of it escapes in rays which do not heat the transparent air through which they pass, *but, like light,* generate heat only when and where they are stopped and absorbed."

He also investigated the transfer of heat through liquids and found that this transfer was due chiefly to convection currents formed during the heating. The water in the bottom of the kettle is heated first. Warm water, being lighter than cold water, rises; the colder water at the top sinks to take the place of this warm water. In this way, a current of water is set in motion and the heat is distributed throughout the contents of the kettle until the temperature of all the liquid becomes the same.

Thompson determined the heats of combustion of various fuels and invented a new *calorimeter* for this purpose. The principles of heat radiation were also investigated. He found that the loss of heat from steam pipes could be reduced by covering the pipes with such poor conductors of heat as paper or wool. He invented an alcohol *thermoscope* which could detect very slight differences in temperature between two bodies. He tackled the problem of the most economical way of heating buildings, devised and improved fireplace and stove, and planned a steam-heating unit. The lighting of buildings also occupied his attention. During some experiments in lighting a military workhouse in Munich, he devised his famous *shadow photometer*, an instrument which measures the relative intensities of different lights.

After an absence of eleven years on the Continent, Thompson returned to London to publish some of his writings and to introduce some of his economies. Both in England and in Ireland he assisted in the establishment of soup kitchens, workhouses, and hospitals, and introduced his inventions, none of which he had patented. He also cured scores of smoky chimneys. He welcomed publicity in connection with these efforts at philanthropy, economies, and popular science education. The publicity which came, however, did not please him, for it ridiculed his attempts. The liberal element in England disliked his patronizing and overbearing attitude in feeding the poor. The conservatives thought it definitely unwise to emphasize the class differences which Thompson's program brought out. Dr. John Wolcot, physician and satiric poet of the day, writing under the pseudonym of Peter Pindar, added his own observations on Count Rumford's doings:

> Knight of the dish-closet, whereso-er I walk,
> I hear thee, Rumford, all the kitchen talk:
> Note of melodious cadence in my ear
> Loud echoes, "Rumford" here and "Rumford" there.
> Lo! every parlor, drawingroom, I see,
> Boasts of thy stoves, and talks of naught but thee.

The following year Thompson was back on the Continent, mulling over a plan which first came to him while he was helping a member of the Society for Improving the Condition and Adding to the Comforts of the Poor. The world was in urgent need, he thought, of some institutions where inventions and discoveries could be made and exploited for the benefit not only of the poor but also for the rest of mankind. A number of plans began to crystallize in his mind. The two objects of the new institution were to be the diffusion of knowledge about new inventions and improvements and the teaching of the application of scientific discoveries for the increase of domestic comfort and convenience. A research laboratory was to be set up to investigate various problems, such as a further study of heat and fuel. Lectures were to be given, and the science of mechanics was to be taught to a small number of worthy young men. A permanent exhibition of working models of all new mechanical inventions was also to be included in this Royal Institution.

Funds for this new scientific organization were raised by the Society for Improving the Condition and Adding to the Comforts of the Poor. Rumford also appealed to the wealthy men of England for more money, assuring them, "When the rich shall take pleasure in encouraging such mechanical improvements as are really useful, good taste, with its inseparable companion, good morals, will revive."

In 1800 the Royal Institution was chartered by the King. Thompson superintended the work of constructing a building and organizing the installation for active work. It was formally opened the same year. Thomas Young was chosen as lecturer in physics. In 1801 Humphry Davy was selected by Thompson as assistant lecturer in chemistry, director of the chemical laboratory, and assistant editor of the *Journal* of the new institution. Davy, who was already attracting fashionable London to his lectures, was soon to make first-rate contributions in chemistry through his isolation of the elements sodium, potassium, calcium, and barium. Thompson made another great discovery in the person of Michael Faraday, for whose appointment at the Royal Institution he was responsible. Faraday's classic researches in electricity were to mark the Royal Institution as one of the most fertile research centers of all time.

As an administrator, Thompson was a very active and efficient individual. His one weakness was his dictatorial, opinionated, and unbending attitude. He quarreled with Dr. Thomas Garnett and with others of the administration. "He assumed the character of absolute controller as well as projector of this establishment and conducted himself with a degree of hauteur which disgusted its patrons," wrote one English paper. He soon learned that London was not Munich, where he had been virtual dictator and where his subjects were the poor and the cowed soldiery of the Elector. He was dealing with men of better education and greater courage. Difficulties piled up and he left the Royal Institution. He also sold his home in Brompton Row in London and went to Paris.

Thompson's American wife, whom he had never seen after leaving the then Colonies, had died in 1792. Now in Paris he met the widow of the great Antoine Laurent Lavoisier, who had been guillotined during the Reign of Terror of the French Revolution. He fell in love with this very wealthy and vivacious lady, and in

1805 they were married. On hearing of this event, the Elector of Bavaria raised his pension to about $6000 a year.

For a while, Thompson went back to further researches in science. In an attempt to improve the lighting devices of his day he constructed as many as fourteen different types of lamps. He experimented, too, with the chemical effects of light on a film made of a ribbon covered with a thin layer of gold, but the successful development of chemical photography had to wait for later investigators.

The lively pace of his popular young wife proved too strenuous for the scientist. She was constantly inviting to their home the social and intellectual elite of Paris. Thompson abominated what he considered the idle conversations of her salon and declared himself bored by the skepticism and spirit of the Age of Reason. He usually spoke little, but when he did get the floor he monopolized the talk and often insulted the guests by correcting their mistakes with the "facts" as he knew them. He was very fussy about every detail of the household, and introduced into every room of their establishment every scientific innovation and mechanical improvement he could think of in heating, cooking, and ventilation, to the annoyance of his wife. A friend, De Candolle, wrote, "Rumford was cold, calm, obstinate, egotistic, and prodigiously occupied with the material element of life and with the very smallest inventions in detail. He wanted his chimneys, lamps, coffee pots, and windows made after a certain pattern, and he contradicted his wife one thousand times a day about the household management." In 1809 this incompatible couple separated for good.

Tired, sick, lonely, and disillusioned, Thompson retired to the quiet little village of Auteuil near Paris. Here he lived for five years the life of a country squire, grubbing around in his garden and doing some research work. In trying to ascertain whether narrow-rimmed or wide-rimmed carriage wheels were more economical, he invented a spring dynamometer. This was attached to the carriage and registered the pull of the horse. From these experiments he was convinced that a wheel having a four-inch rim was better than wheels of either 1.75- or 2.25-inch rims. He would ride about in his funny wide-rim-wheeled carriage to convince his neighbors of the truth of his discovery. He attended meetings of the French Institute and read papers on a new portable lamp and a new calorimeter. In another essay entitled *On the Excellent Qualities of Coffee and the Art of Making It in the Highest Perfection,* he described the drip coffee pot.

Some scientific friends such as Cuvier or Lagrange would occasionally drop in for a talk. His daughter, Sally Thompson, now Sarah, Countess of Rumford, came to visit him late in 1811, but she returned to America and he was left alone for long stretches of time. Sir Humphry Davy, Lady Davy, and Faraday, on their way to Paris in 1813, dropped in on him and they dined together.

Thompson's health became worse; after an illness of only three days he died almost alone on August 24, 1814. Cuvier read an éloge which emphasized how, through his scientific experiments, he had helped mankind in its fight against cold and hunger. Lafayette was one of the three witnesses to his will, in which he described himself as "Benjamin Thompson, Count of Rumford, Knight of the Illustrious Orders of the White Eagle and of St. Stanislaus, Lieutenant General in the Service of His Majesty, the King of Bavaria."

Thompson left an annuity to his daughter and his gold watch to Davy. To America, land of his birth, he gave the remainder of his estate. His books, plans, and designs relating to military affairs were bequeathed to the government of the United States. To Harvard College went the rest of his possessions, including a fund to found a professorship "to teach the utility of the physical and mathematical sciences for the improvement of the arts and for the extension of the industry, prosperity, happiness, and well-being of society." Eighteen years before, he had presented to the American Academy of Arts and Sciences, of which he was an honorary member, a cash gift of $5000 for endowing the Rumford Medal to be given alternate years for the best contribution of the two previous years in the fields of heat and light. (He made a similar gift to the Royal Society of London; he himself was the first recipient of the Society's Rumford award in 1802.)

It is not difficult to understand Thompson's spiritual return to America. Much as he tried to forget his self-imposed exile, he was not completely happy in Europe. He was often overcome with a nostalgia for the land he had left. It has been said that about 1799 he thought seriously of returning to America. He sounded out the United States ambassador in London on the subject of helping in the establishment of an American military academy at West Point, such as Washington had proposed. It is even reported that President Adams was ready to offer him the superintendency of this military establishment. Nothing came of this project and he made no further attempts to return.

Although Thompson's work was done in Europe, many regard his scientific contributions as belonging to America. Today his grave in Auteuil, France, is cared for jointly by Harvard University and the American Academy of Arts and Sciences of Boston. A replica of his Munich statue now stands in Woburn, Massachusetts, the town of his birth.

While Thompson was experimenting and inventing in the Old World, new chapters were being added to the story of American science. The period between the struggle to establish a nation and the close of the eighteenth century was marked by a number of interesting events. In 1780, even before our liberties were won on the battlefield, men of science, with the help of John Adams, founded the American Academy of Arts and Sciences. Two years later, when Joseph Priestley in England was elected an honorary member of this scientific body, he wrote, "I rejoice that after so noble and successful a struggle for your liberties, you are now attending to matters of science."

An attempt to teach scientific agriculture was begun. The New Jersey Society for the Promotion of Agriculture, Commerce and Art was organized in 1781. The South Carolina Society for Promoting and Improving Agriculture was started in Charleston four years later. During the same year the Philadelphia Society for Promoting Agriculture, foster child of the American Philosophical Society, was also founded. Its object was "to promote greater increase of the products of the land within the American states." Many prominent Americans, including George Washington, became associated with this organization, which stimulated a renewed interest in the science of agriculture. The Chemical Society of Philadelphia was organized in 1792, long before Europe had a single chemical society. Its first president was James Woodhouse, friend of Priestley and vigorous proponent of the French Revolution.

The Charleston Library Society started a modest natural-history museum in 1773. Twelve years later the first independently established public museum in the United States was founded by Charles W. Peale, the artist who painted George Washington. Peale's Philadelphia Museum grew out of his private collection of portraits and natural-history specimens such as stuffed animals and fossils. In 1794 the museum, which included a huge fossil vertebrate, was transferred to the Hall of the American Philosophical Society.

Americans began to write their own science textbooks to replace those prepared in England. Jedediah Morse in 1784 published a geography; four years later Nicholas Pike published an arithmetic textbook in Massachusetts. Caspar Wistar prepared the first American textbook on anatomy, and in 1812 Benjamin Rush published his *Medical Inquiries Upon Diseases of the Mind*, which approached the insanities as diseases, and pioneered in occupational therapy.

The first Federal Patent Act as provided in the Constitution was passed by Congress early in 1790. Jefferson recommended and helped administer it, and wrote that "it has given a spring to invention beyond my conception." On July 31 of that year Samuel Hopkins of Vermont was granted the first patent, for an improved method of making pure pearl ash from wood ashes. This was the beginning of a flood of patents. The Patent Act was to serve as a vigorous stimulus to new scientific advance. In 1791 John Fitch, an itinerant clock and gun repairer, took out his steamboat patent and in the same year James Rumsey also received a patent for a steam-propelled vessel. Three years before, John Fitch had built the first steamboat and sailed it down the Delaware River. Franklin saw the invention and was asked to contribute funds to its development, but for once, at least, the American genius, who was then eighty-two, could see no future in a newfangled contraption and would not help the unfortunate Fitch.

In 1797 the *Medical Repository* was established in New York City by Samuel L. Mitchill, professor of natural history at Columbia College. It was the first scientific journal in the United States outside of the scientific transactions of scientific organizations. This medical journal became for a time another focal point around which American science continued to grow. Two years later the Connecticut Academy of Arts and Sciences was organized at New Haven. In 1804 Dr. Barton's short-lived *Philadelphia Medical and Physical Journal* appeared.

While experimental work was for the most part pushed aside during those fateful years, American men of science took a leading role in the prosecution of the War of Independence. Doctors John Morgan, William Shippen, and Benjamin Rush organized the medical branch of Washington's army and used all the scientific knowledge of that period to shape it into an effective weapon. In 1775 Morgan was elected by Congress to the post of director general of the military hospitals and physician in chief of the Continental Army. Others took an active part in what Franklin described in a letter to Rochefoucauld as "experiments in politics." Among the signers of the Declaration of Independence were Franklin, Rush, and Francis Hopkinson; some of the scientists elected to Congress and other public offices were Mitchill, Williamson, Morgan, Seybert, Maclure, and Cutler. Rittenhouse was appointed by Washington the first director of the United States Mint in 1792.

The new age of experiment and empiricism and the spread of scientific knowledge helped shape the American Constitution.

When the members of the Constitutional Convention of the new republic met in Philadelphia in 1787, they faced a basic struggle. On the one side there was the fear of domination by a small minority in whose hands too much power might prove disastrous to the growth of the new country. On the other, the danger to the young republic of the tyranny of the many was also keenly felt. By separating the powers of the legislative, executive, and judiciary branches of government, it was hoped that the country would possess a safeguard against the assumption of complete power by any group. It was also believed that the setting up of checks and balances and the overlapping of some powers of the three branches of government would insure a stable and successful nation.

The lawyers and statesmen of the infant country had heard of Newton and his theory of the universe. They believed that natural laws kept opposing forces so regulated that the physical universe became a sort of self-regulating mechanism, each part of which worked harmoniously with every other part. They thought that these principles of science could be applied directly to government. Franklin, however, challenged the concept as a practical scientist. He could see that the Newtonian principles of opposing centrifugal and centripetal forces, of action and reaction, and of delicate balances in the physical world could not be so easily applied to a complex system of human government. But when the Constitution was finally drawn up, for the sake of national unity he affixed his signature to the document, which he realized was the best compromise which could be established.

The thirteen colonies were now a nation of four million people launched on a great adventure in self-government. The science of America, freed at last from its necessary preoccupation with a great war effort, was again ready to march forward. At the moment when the military struggle was just over, Jefferson replied to the charge of the French Abbé Guillaume Raynal that America had not produced a good poet, an able mathematician, a single genius either in art or science. He pointed to Franklin the scientist, and added, "When we shall have existed as a people as long as the Greeks did before they produced a Homer, the Romans a Virgil, the French a Voltaire, the English a Shakespeare, should this reproach still be true, we will inquire from what unfriendly cause it has proceeded."

CHAPTER FOUR

THOMAS COOPER
(1759-1839)

SCIENCE ADVANCES SLOWLY IN
THE NEWBORN REPUBLIC

Not long after America lost Benjamin Thompson to Europe, it gained two eminent scientists and political philosophers who migrated here from England. One of them was Joseph Priestley, the discoverer of oxygen; Thomas Cooper was the other. Around these two immigrants most of the scientific activities of the young republic were centered. Priestley already had an international reputation. Cooper was to become, according to Thomas Jefferson, "the man who is acknowledged by every enlightened man who knows him to be the greatest man in America in the powers of mind and in acquired information, and that without a single exception."

Cooper began life in a fairly prosperous middle-class family of London. At nineteen he matriculated at Oxford University, where he studied the classics, law, medicine, and the natural sciences. He balked at reciting the religious creed at the university, and left without taking a degree. Soon after, he married a young woman who inherited a considerable fortune. For three years he practiced law; at twenty-six he became an active member of the Literary and Philosophical Society of Manchester. This scientific body, of which he became vice-president, counted among its members John Dalton, the Quaker schoolteacher who propounded the atomic theory of matter.

Cooper soon showed a decided interest in political affairs. He read a paper before the Manchester society *On Propositions Re-*

specting the Foundations of Civil Government. A zealous believer in the principle of the natural rights of man, he agitated for social changes which would improve the condition of the common man and insisted that "the right of exercising political power is derived solely from the people."

Joining the liberals who were sympathetic with the French Revolution, Cooper incurred the enmity of Edmund Burke, influential member of the House of Commons. The latter, in his *Reflections on the Revolution in France*, attacked those who supported the revolution on the Continent. The thirty-one-year-old pamphleteer reminded Burke that his unsanctioned correspondence with the rebel, Benjamin Franklin, in 1781 was infinitely more reprehensible than that of the Revolution Society of England with the French National Assembly. He also recalled that Burke himself had sided with the American Revolution, calling it not a rebellion but a justifiable resistance. Cooper defended the English dissenters who had supported their King on all critical occasions, but now had to oppose Burke because of his open hostility to the French Revolution. He concluded with the embarrassing question, "If they abhor Slavery and Wooden Shoes, is our Constitution built upon so rotten a foundation that the people may not proclaim that abhorrence?"

Sympathy Clubs were formed in England and engaged in active correspondence with the so-called Constitution Clubs of France. Cooper and his young admirer, James Watt, Jr., son of the inventor of the first practical steam engine, who happened to be in France in 1792, were designated by their fellow members of the Manchester club as delegates to the Jacobin Club in Paris. Cooper and Watt read an impassioned address before the Paris body, condemning the despotic powers of Europe for attempting to ignore man's natural rights to liberty. Cooper joined the Girondists and quarreled publicly with the fiery Robespierre, leader of the more radical Jacobins. Only a timely warning saved Cooper's head from the basket of the guillotine.

Escaping to England, Cooper was met by a smashing attack

against him in the House of Commons. Burke accused him of plotting with an "infamous band of French regicides" to destroy the English Constitution. Cooper quickly replied in kind, calling the famous orator's words "mere Burkisms, accusation without proof and invectives without arguments." "Is there any impropriety," asked Cooper, "in the philosophical societies of London, Paris, or Stockholm corresponding for the improvement of chemistry? Why then should societies instituted for the promotion of *political* knowledge be debarred from the common means of improvement?"

Raising the fundamental questions of the origin of government and the duties of rulers, he called loudly for a liberal code of national education. "The God of Nature," he reminded Burke, "has given to man not merely hands to labor, but a head to think; he has given him the capability of obtaining knowledge, of mental improvement, and of social intercourse. One great use of society is to bring these capabilities into action." He flayed the rottenness of rule by aristocracy and hereditary nobility, reminding the common people that "some years ago there was a toast in vogue among this fashionable world to this purpose, 'May elegant vice prevail over dull virtue.'" Six thousand copies of this pamphlet were quickly bought up; the Attorney General stepped in to stop the printing of a cheap, popular edition.

The government regarded Cooper as a dangerous man. He was shunned even by the scientists of the Royal Society who, in spite of Priestley's recommendation, turned down his application for membership. Priestley was furious. "The Dissenters," he declared, "have been defeated not only in the House of Commons but in the Royal Society also." Disgusted with the governing group in England, opposed to the Reign of Terror in France because he was not "an advocate of propagating liberty by the bayonet or terrifying a nation into freedom by the guillotine," Cooper decided to try the political climate of the United States.

Cooper left England in August, 1793. After a voyage of ten weeks he arrived with part of his family and a son of Priestley. He made a very careful and extensive investigation of the social, political, and economic life of the infant nation. In February of the following year he returned to England and soon issued a report, entitled *Some Observations Concerning America*, for the benefit of his friends and others who were seriously considering emigrating to the United States.

Very sensibly, Cooper warned immigrants to be prepared for a seven- or eight-week voyage, and to "take care that the captain has a filtering stone [for purifying water]. Should your water smell offensive, add powder of charcoal. If there is no filtering stone, the water will be cleared by adding a solution of alum." This was scientifically sound advice. He also advised voyagers, "Take care to provide yourself with lemons, apples, or any other fruit that will help sickness. . . . You will soon get tired of ship biscuit, therefore, provide yourself with rusks, or slices of bread baked over again, which you will be obliged to Dr. Franklin for having recommended."

Cooper had a number of significant things to say about the type of immigrant who would be most welcome in the new land. "It is inadvisable," he said, "for a person to go thither who has no other quality to recommend him than his birth. In Europe, it has, indeed, its value; but it is a commodity that cannot be carried to a worse market than to that of America where people do not inquire concerning a stranger, What is he? but What can he do? The husbandman is in honour there, and even the mechanic; because their employments are useful. The people have a saying that God Almighty is himself a mechanic, the greatest in the universe; and He is respected and admired more for the variety, ingenuity, and utility of His handiworks, than for the antiquity of His handiworks. America is a land of labour, and by no means what the English call Lubberland where the streets are said to be paved with half peck loaves, the houses tiled with pancakes, and where the fowls fly about ready to be roasted, crying, come eat me."

Immigrants were interested in other facts, too, and Cooper supplied some of them. He informed his readers of the climate and fertility of various sections of the country. Among other practical observations, he warned them not to settle in New Jersey because "Musquitoes and agues are more troublesome in this than in many of the other States." He wrote also of the price of land and about land speculation in the United States. "Rich unimproved land is sold at 30 shillings an acre. . . . Within the last three years the purchases of land in Pennsylvania and New York have increased at least threefold on the average, and I have little doubt of their continuing to increase."

Some hints about the price of food were also included. "Provisions," he wrote, "(Milk and butter excepted) at Philadelphia and southward are a full third cheaper than in similar places in Great Britain. . . . Coffee costs 14 pence per pound, refined sugar 1 shilling 6 pence per pound, and the best cognac 7 shillings per gallon. . . . In every part of America the common beverage is cyder (beer and porter are too expensive). In New England rum is the common drink from the molasses brought from the West Indies. In New York and Pennsylvania the spirit used is generally rye," he noted, adding that he did not believe the use made of them had any perceptible effect unfavorable to the health of the Americans. On the contrary, he offered the very questionable opinion that, "In hot weather it is extremely dangerous to quench great thirst with water alone, without spirit."

With respect to manufacturing ventures Cooper also had something to say. "While land is so cheap and labour is so dear, it will be too hazardous a speculation to embark a capital in any branch of manufacturing which has not hitherto been actually pursued with success in this country. . . . I think no one will as yet succeed in establishing a profitable manufacture of woolen, linen or of cotton goods (stockings, perhaps, excepted), neither does it appear to me that the time is yet come for any branch of pottery to succeed. I have no doubt, however, of the success of a glass manufacturer, a gunpowder manufacturer, a paper maker, a paper stainer, a letter founder, a manufactory of all the heavy kinds of iron work such as castings from the ore, pig iron, cast iron, bar iron, rolling mills, slitting mills, and the making of nails. I believe that no soap boiler, hatter, gunsmith, tallow chandler, whitesmith and blacksmith, brass founder, wheelwright, cabinet maker, carpenter, mason, bricklayer, taylor, showmaker, cooper, tanner, currier, maltster, brewer, distiller, sailmaker, printer, bookbinder can miss of employment there."

These recommendations were based on the fact that several chemical enterprises had already been started in the United States. The manufacture of glass was the dean of American industries. The first glass factory had been set up near Jamestown as early as 1621, to make glass beads for the Indians. The first glass bottles and hollow-ware were made in Salem, Massachusetts, in 1638, and while window glass was practically unknown in the colonies for a long time, a plant for making crown glass for windows was started in Boston in 1789. The previous year the New York Assembly, in order to encourage this new industry, voted an appropriation of $15,000 to the owners of a glass factory near Albany.

The manufacture of iron in this country was also started very early in its history. In 1628 some iron ore found in bogs and swamps was converted into pig iron at Saugus near Lynn, Massachusetts. In 1641 John Winthrop, Jr., went to England to form "A Company of Undertakers for the Iron Works," which he established in Saugus, and to bring back machinery and some workers skilled in the making of both pig iron in blast furnaces and wrought iron in bloomeries. By 1700 about a dozen ironworks were in operation in the colonies, turning out iron pots, stoves, skillets, and wire for nails. In 1725 the first American steel was made. Samuel Higby of Connecticut manufactured steel by packing iron bars with coal in a furnace and heating the mixture for as long as a week. By 1775 eighty blast furnaces turned out 30,000 tons of cast iron or about 15 per cent of the world's output for that year.

Brick was also manufactured in America at an early date. The first brick kiln was built in Salem in 1643; it produced the bricks for the first brick house built in the colonies that year. By 1793 many of the houses in the large cities such as Philadelphia, New York, and Boston were of brick and stone. By 1760 there were seventeen spermaceti candle factories built by Jewish refugees from Spain, Portugal, and Jamaica who came to Newport, Rhode Island, ten years before.

Glue was made here from the horns of animals. Salt was prepared as early as 1623 by evaporating sea water. The first paper manufacturing plant was established in Germantown, Pennsylvania, ten years before the close of the seventeenth century. The first potash (crude potassium carbonate) for soapmaking was produced in 1609 by eight Poles and Germans sent over here by the London Company. By 1788 the number of potash works in Massachusetts alone was two hundred and fifty. The plants were, of course, very small, and Cooper reported that it took 700 bushels of field or fireplace ashes to make one ton of potash, worth at that time $120. More than half of the expense of clearing land in New York at that time was repaid by the proceeds of the potash obtained by burning the wood.

Other chemicals were also manufactured in small amounts. Gunpowder was made from the saltpeter extracted from dung. (Eight years after Cooper's arrival Eleuthère I. du Pont de Nemours came here from France to start his first gunpowder mill near Wilmington, Delaware.) Even dyes were made in small quantities. Long before the colonists arrived in America, the Indians had made vegetable dyes from various roots, barks, and seeds. The colonists copied and improved upon these methods. In 1643 Winthrop started a primitive dye industry in Massachusetts and made the first experiments on the manufacture of indigo in the United States. The indigo plant is indigenous to South Carolina, and cultivated varieties giving a large yield of dye were introduced. In 1775 South Carolina grew and exported to England more than one million pounds of indigo. The industry flourished for many years until European competition began to stifle it. The chemical synthesis of indigo in 1868, one of the milestones in organic chemistry, finally gave natural indigo its deathblow.

Sericulture was tried early in the life of the country. Hundreds of mulberry trees were planted for the silkworms which were introduced. As much as ten thousand pounds of raw silk were exported from South Carolina to England in 1759. Between 1770 and 1775 there was much discussion at the meetings of the American Philosophical Society over the desirability of asking the state legislature for funds to establish filatures in Philadelphia. The industry never prospered for any great length of time, in spite of the many attempts to revive it. Even as late as sixty years ago the eminent American entomologist, Leland O. Howard, head of the Bureau of Entomology, dreamed of establishing sericulture in the United States. He purchased a reel and brought over two expert reelers to teach the art of manufacturing silk. The project proved a failure, for we could not compete with the Orient, and Congress refused to place a tariff on so-called "raw" silk.

In addition to reporting business opportunities in America, Cooper was also an eager observer of social conditions. "You ask me," he wrote, "what appears to me to be the general inducements to people to quit England for America? In my mind, the first and principle feature is the total absence of anxiety respecting the future success of a family. . . . The wages of journeymen are somewhat higher than with you, and the money of a poor man can certainly go farther. . . . The master has not the same kind of command over his men; the men have the alternative of becoming farmers and look forward to becoming independent by investing their savings in the land. . . . You see nowhere in America the disgusting and melancholy contrast so common in Europe, of vice and filth and rags and wretchedness in the immediate neighborhood of the most wanton extravagance, and the most useless and luxurious parade. . . . They have very few taxes to pay, they have no animosities about religion; it is a subject about which no questions are asked."

Then Cooper introduced a sentence which was later made immortal by Abraham Lincoln. As a young man, he may have read Cooper, who had also written on the law. "The government," said

Cooper, "is a government *of* the people and *for* the people." Another significant fact about his guide for his English friends was its inclusion of the Constitution of the United States, a document which at the time of the book's publication was only about five years old.

Cooper made a special point of impressing on his English friends the fact that Americans were not ignorant, since newspapers were plentiful and book societies were everywhere. "Night school for young men and boys who are employed at labour or business in the day has been long and beneficially supported. Free schools for both sexes have been increased. There exist nine colleges or universities."

Impressed by the scientific contributions of the United States, he reported, "The people of the United States are ingenious in invention, and prompt and accurate in the execution of mechanism and workmanship for purposes in science, arts, manufactures, navigation, and agriculture. David Rittenhouse's planetarium, Franklin's stove, and machine for taking levels, electrical conductor and fireplaces, Thomas Godfrey's quadrant improved by Hadley, James Rumsey's and John Fitch's steam engines (which propelled boats), Leslie's rod pendulum and other horological inventions, the wire cutter and bender for card makers (invented by Oliver Evans in 1777), Folsom's and Brigg's machinery for cutting nails out of rolled iron, Mason's engine for extinguishing fire, the Connecticut steeple clock which is wound up by the wind, Anderson's threshing machine, Donaldson's balance clock are a few of the numerous examples." Cooper forgot to mention one of the greatest inventions of them all—Eli Whitney's cotton gin. Whitney also introduced the methods of mass production by a system of interchangeable parts. Vice-President Jefferson signed a contract with him several years later for 10,000 muskets.

When Cooper arrived here on his preliminary visit late in 1793, Washington had already been unanimously re-elected President of the United States. Hamilton was still his Secretary of the Treasury. Jefferson, who had been his Secretary of State, resigned his cabinet post because of his differences with Hamilton, who was getting stronger support from Washington. Hamilton believed in the rule of the rich, the well-born, and the able. He had contempt for the common people. He wanted a strong centralized government to safeguard the interests of the rich merchants and traders. Jefferson, on the other hand, favored the agrarian element, and believed in the rule of the common man. The rural, back-country people, who were afraid of too strong a federal government which might take away some of their individual liberties, supported Jefferson.

Cooper sized up the political situation in America rather clearly. "The Americans," he wrote, "are republicans but of two classes; the one leaning to an extention of the power of the legislative and executive government; rather leaning to the British than to French politics; inclining to introduce and extend the funding, the manufacturing and the commercial systems. In this class rank almost all the executive officers of government, the majority of the members of the Senate, and the greatest part of the opulent merchants of the large towns. This party is denominated the Federalists. . . . The other party are called Anti-Federalists, not because they are adverse to a Federal government, but in contradistinction rather to the denomination of the other class. The Anti-Federalist Party, among whom may be ranked the majority of the people and the majority of the House of Representatives."

Early in 1794 Cooper returned to the United States, bringing his wife and four children. He was followed a few weeks later by his friend, Joseph Priestley. The Coopers and the Priestleys had planned a large colony for a group of liberty-loving people, but the project, in which the English poets Coleridge and Southey were also interested, fell through. The two scientists settled, instead, in the same house in Northumberland, Pennsylvania, on the shores of the Susquehanna. They preferred this little town of three hundred wooden houses to the "bustling" city of Philadelphia with its 43,000 inhabitants.

A year after his arrival, Cooper became an American citizen.

He dabbled in chemical experimentation with Priestley, and interested himself in the chemical and other scientific work of fellow Americans.

In 1792 Benjamin Rush had founded the Chemical Society of Philadelphia. At this time a great chemical revolution was shaking the world of science. Lavoisier, father of modern chemistry, had explained for the first time the real nature of burning, dealing a deathblow to the mischievous theory of phlogiston, and had reformed the nomenclature of chemistry. America, following these changes with intense interest, took kindly to the new chemistry. Dr. Samuel L. Mitchill brought the new chemical nomenclature to Columbia College, where he was serving as professor of chemistry. His *Medical Repository* served as the battleground between those few in America, including Priestley, who still clung to the phlogiston theory, and the larger number who accepted the revolutionary findings of Lavoisier. John Maclean of Princeton College, Robert Hare and Benjamin Rush of the College of Philadelphia, John Griscom of Rutgers, Lyman Spalding of Dartmouth, Adam Seybert and James Woodhouse, all helped the new chemistry to find a warm welcome in America.

In addition to his interest in chemistry, the versatile Cooper, who had also studied medicine, ministered to the sick of the neighborhood free of charge, edited for a while the *Northumberland Register*, and practiced law. Before long he was also actively involved in the political life of his new home. A great battle was raging between the Federalists under Hamilton and the Republicans led by Jefferson. (This is not the present Republican Party, which was founded in 1854.) In the summer of 1798 the Federalists passed the Alien and Sedition Acts. The Alien Act was introduced to get rid of foreign "agitators," especially French and Irish, who were criticizing the administration of President John Adams. The Sedition Act was aimed at the Republicans, who were the radicals of that day.

Cooper was one of ten Republican editors and printers who fell victim to this act. Accused of writing and publishing "a false, scandalous and malicious writing against President Adams" in the *Reading Weekly Advertiser*, he was arrested and placed on trial before Judge Samuel Chase, a bullying, highhanded member of the United States Supreme Court. He pleaded his own case, was found guilty, fined $400, and put in jail. Priestley tried hard to get his friend released, but Adams would not act. The President wrote to Jefferson, "Scarcely anything has made a deeper impression upon me than that such a learned, ingenious, scientific and talented madcap as Cooper should have influence enough to make Priestley my enemy." After serving six months in prison, Cooper was released. He continued the fight against the Sedition Act on the ground that it was unconstitutional, since it violated the first article of the Constitution, which guaranteed freedom of speech and press. He petitioned for restitution of the fine he had been forced to pay. This was finally returned with interest to his heirs by Act of Congress ten years after Cooper was in his grave.

In 1796 Jefferson had become the third president of the American Philosophical Society, a position he held for eighteen years. During this period he gave, through his talents and the prestige of his high office, great encouragement to the development of science and mathematics in this country. He had the conviction that the young republic needed science above everything else. To President Willard of Harvard College he wrote, "The botany of America is far from exhausted, its mineralogy is untouched, and its zoology totally mistaken. We have spent the prime of our lives in procuring your students the precious blessing of liberty. Let them spend theirs in showing that it is the great parent of science and of virtue, and that a nation will be great in both ways in proportion as it is free."

Jefferson was more than just an enthusiast and dilettante in science. "Nature intended me," he wrote to a friend, "for the tranquil pursuits of science, by rendering them my supreme delight." In 1781 he had prepared his *Notes on the State of Virginia* (first printed in Paris in 1784), which gave a detailed treatment of the topography, natural history, and natural resources of the country.

He did not hesitate to point out to the most eminent world authority in zoology, the Frenchman Buffon, that he had made a few errors concerning certain American animals. Later, when Jefferson was minister to France, the two men discussed one of their differences—the size of the American moose. Buffon had made the assertion that among those animals found in both the New and the Old World, the smaller species always lived in the New World, because the animal had degenerated and grown smaller there. They argued long and earnestly, but there was no moose in Paris to settle the question. Jefferson wrote to ask his friend General John Sullivan for the skeleton of a moose. The general transmitted the request to some friends in Durham, New Hampshire. A hunting party was organized and a moose was soon captured and shipped to France. Buffon was flabbergasted. "I should have consulted you before publishing my *Natural History*," he admitted to Jefferson. "Then I should have been sure of my facts."

In 1801, five years after Jefferson became president of the American Philosophical Society, he went to Washington to be inaugurated third President of the United States. The campaigns between the two political parties had been very bitter. Jefferson was the constant target of scurrilous newspaper attacks. "You know," he wrote to Cooper, "if I wrote as a text that 2 and 2 are 4, it serves to make volumes of sermons of slander and abuse." But the Federalists were beaten by a Republican revolution. His rival, Aaron Burr, received the same number of electoral votes as Jefferson. The House of Representatives had to decide who was to be named President.

During these critical days Jefferson took time to write to Dr. Caspar Wistar of the College of Philadelphia, the first American vertebrate paleontologist, about some mastodon bones that had been dug out of the ground of Shawangunk, in Ulster County. Though Jefferson never dug out fossil bones himself, he helped collect and finance fossil expeditions for the American Philosophical Society. He also helped write in 1797 the first American paper on paleontology for the American Philosophical Society on the fossil claws, toe bones, and other bones of an ancient slothlike animal found in Greenbriar County, Virginia, by workers excavating for saltpeter in the floor of a cave. Jefferson presented the bones to the American Philosophical Society and Wistar made a scientific study of them. This species of animal is known as *Megalonyx Jeffersoni*.

Jefferson's interest in science was used by his enemies as another means of discrediting him. His political opponents, who feared his liberal views, charged, "He has refuted Moses, dishonored the story of the Deluge, and speculated in the primary causes of the difference between whites and blacks. Think of a foreign minister," they sneered, "surprising him in the act of anatomizing the kidneys and glands of an African to find out why the Negro is black and odoriferous!" They laughed at his attempts to invent all sorts of things such as a mold-board for ploughs—the first application of science to agriculture in America—a dumbwaiter, a whirligig chair with writing arm, a pedometer, and a machine for beating hemp into fiber. He patented none of his inventions.

When during Jefferson's second administration, Napoleon blockaded England and Britain retaliated by blockading France, Congress passed the Embargo Act in 1807 to avoid the danger of being drawn into war. This was a hard blow to our shipping, and Jefferson was blamed for the depression which followed. Even Nathaniel Bowditch, whose shipping interests suffered, became a violent anti-Jeffersonian. William Cullen Bryant, at the age of thirteen, was prompted to write *The Embargo*, a satirical poem which contained the stanza:

> *Go, wretch, resign the Presidential chair;*
> *Disclose thy secret measures, foul or fair.*
> *Go search with anxious eyes for horned frogs*
> *'Mid the wild waste of Louisianian bogs,*
> *Or, where the Ohio rolls his turbid stream*
> *Dig for huge bones, thy glory and thy theme.*

While Jefferson was President, the world-famous scientist Alexander von Humboldt, with whom he corresponded on mathematics and astronomy, came to visit him in Washington. Humboldt found on Jefferson's desk a newspaper full of abuse of the chief executive of the land. Surprised, the German asked, "Why are these libels allowed?" "Put that paper in your pocket, Baron," was Jefferson's reply, "and should you hear the reality of our liberty or the freedom of the press questioned, show this paper, and tell where you found it."

Priestley died in 1804, during Jefferson's first administration. Cooper was present at his deathbed. For many years Cooper continued to use the laboratory which Priestley had built for chemical experimentation. Priestley's will had bequeathed to his friend his apparatus, including the burning glass with which he had made his historic discovery of oxygen in 1774. In addition to his chemical researches and geological investigations—he was seldom without hammer and acid for the examination of new rocks—Cooper also kept very busy politically. In 1806 he received a judgeship in Pennsylvania and for five tumultuous years he dispensed justice with a liberal mind and a stern hand.

His liberal views brought him many enemies, who preferred charges of official misconduct against him and petitioned the legislature to remove him from office. Among the fifty-three charges filed against Cooper were those of drunkenness, appearing in court with loaded weapons to intimidate peaceful citizens, browbeating of both counsel and witnesses, and unjust imprisonment of an innocent citizen for wearing his hat in court. Priestley's family testified that Cooper had never been drunk during the ten years that he and his family had lived under the same roof with them. It was also shown that the hat wearer whom Cooper had fined a dollar was a cocky Quaker who had deliberately hidden his reason for refusing to doff his hat, an action which was against Quaker principles. In spite of the trumped-up nature of the charges and in the face of a dissenting opinion submitted by several fellow judges, Governor Snyder, by order of the legislature, was forced to remove Cooper from the bench on April 3, 1811.

Two days later Thomas Cooper became a professor of chemistry. Through the influence of Benjamin Rush, he was chosen to occupy the chair of chemistry and mineralogy at Dickinson College in Carlisle, Pennsylvania, which Rush had helped to found. Within two days of his appointment, Cooper delivered a lecture in which he sounded a new and progressive note in the teaching of science in America. He believed that the teaching of chemistry should be tied up more closely with other cultural studies. Chemistry was to have social worth not only because of its practical value but also because of its cultural contributions. "It appears to me," he maintained, "that the history of an art or science is a proper introduction to the study of it; especially of chemistry as containing areas of discovery intimately connected with controversies yet unsettled and therefore worthy to be known; as giving a clear and concise view of the manner in which improvements have been effected; as furnishing due caution against future errors by exhibiting the mistakes of superior minds of olden times, and as rendering merited honor to those who have benefitted mankind by their discoveries." This was one of the earliest chemical lectures printed (1812) in the United States, and Jefferson complimented the author for its wisdom. Unfortunately this phase of science teaching is still underemphasized.

Cooper taught at Dickinson College for five years. His laboratory took care of about eighty students, each of whom paid a fee of ten dollars a semester. Among his students, who were taught the chemistry of milk, bread, soap, beer, wine, cheese, glass, brass, and iron, were the sons of Du Pont de Nemours. He also taught his classes the story of early chemistry, the alchemy of the Hindus and the Chinese, as well as the new chemistry of his contemporaries. He was a potent force in bringing the new chemistry of Lavoisier to America. He revised and brought up to date Accum's *System of Theoretical and Practical Chemistry*. He also carried on chemical experiments of his own, edited and revised Coxe's *Emporium of Arts and Sciences*, a scientific periodical first started in Philadelphia in 1812, and wrote *A Practical Treatise on Dyeing and Calico Printing*. As a young man in Manchester he had experimented with the newly discovered chlorine gas and had established a large but unsuccessful cotton-goods bleaching factory in that city.

The law also continued to occupy some of Cooper's attention. During these years at Dickinson College he introduced the study of Roman law by translating the *Institutes of Justinian*, adding to the original manuscript a quantity of notes of his own equal in volume to the original book. He was still the same old Cooper, expressing unorthodox ideas and making enemies. He was accused of spending the Sabbath in his laboratory with some of his students and was finally forced to resign from the college. Cooper turned over to the college the historic burning glass which Priestley had bequeathed to him and which now is housed in a fireproof vault in the new Bosler Library of Dickinson College.

A year after his resignation Cooper was back in the classroom, this time as professor of chemistry at the University of Pennsylvania. This was the educational institution which grew out of Franklin's attempts in 1749 to start a new college, free from the evils of sectarianism which were warping the development of Yale, Harvard, William and Mary, and the College of New Jersey. Franklin had hoped to get away from the overemphasis on Latin and Greek and the classics, and to stress history, economics, and political economy. He visioned a college for the mechanic as well, and had dreamed of developing the individual abilities of skilled artisans and agricultural workers with studies in mathematics, navigation, accounting, and the physical and biological sciences.

At this college William Smith, a noted clergyman who had come to America from Scotland, had taught chemistry in 1756 and had seen in the new liberal institution a new era for science in

America. Turning for a moment to poetry, he had sung of science and labor:

> *It comes! at last, the promis'd Aera comes.*
> *For lo! her azure Wing bright Science spreads.*
>
> *Oh Science! onward thus thy Reign extend*
> *O'er Realm yet unexplor'd till Time shall end.*
>
> *Not trackless Deserts shall thy Progress stay;*
> *Rocks, Mountains, Floods, before thee must give Way:*
> *Sequester'd Vales, at thy Approach shall sing*
> *And with the Voice of Cheerful Labor ring!*

But the path of scientific progress was not altogether rosy. Hardly had Cooper assumed his new duties when he found himself in the center of another tempest. The question of the place of chemistry in the medical school came up and was violently opposed by Dr. Charles Caldwell of the medical faculty. Caldwell ridiculed the importance of pure chemistry to medical students. "Shall I be told," he asked, "that chemistry aids in the explanation of any of the phenomena or laws of the living body? That it sheds light in physiology, pathology or therapeutics? As far as chemistry has mingled in discussions of this nature, it has not only darkened them but filled them with error." This was a strange pronouncement from a teacher of science. He must have forgotten that three centuries before, Paracelsus, the Swiss scientist, had wedded chemistry to medicine in a fruitful union.

Dr. Benjamin Rush had been the first to teach chemistry as a required subject in the same medical school. And now chemistry was being taught by Dr. Robert Hare, the celebrated inventor in 1801 of the oxyhydrogen blowpipe which won him the Rumford Medal of the American Academy of Arts and Sciences. He had also improved the voltaic cell, or electric battery, which had recently been invented in Italy. In spite of the fact that he had had no training in medicine, Hare had been selected to teach chemistry in the medical department. Cooper, who had had medical training,

persuaded Hare to confine himself to the purely chemical part of
the young medico's examination for the medical degree while he
himself, with a knowledge of both medicine and chemistry, would
pass upon the other medical qualifications of the medical students.

Then, answering Dr. Caldwell's protestations, he delivered a
lecture *On the Importance of Chemistry to the Medical Man*,
pointing out how essential was the teaching of chemistry in the
training of all physicians. He advocated a four-year training period
for medical students instead of the prevailing three-year period,
and proclaimed that "medical chemistry has only just commenced
its career." Cooper's opinions were accepted. His words were
prophetic, for he had inaugurated a new advance in the teaching
of medicine in America.

During that same year Cooper advocated the replacement of
the thirteen hundred oil street lamps that lighted the city of Philadelphia with new lamps burning coal gas. He considered gas a safer
and better system of illumination. No gaslight system had as yet
been introduced in America, although the city of Baltimore had
one house lighted by coal gas as early as 1802. In Cornwall, England, William Murdock had lighted his own house with coal gas
even earlier, in 1792, and twenty years later the city of London
introduced this new method rather widely. In 1816, Rembrandt
Peale lighted his museum on Holliday Street in Baltimore with
coal gas which was prepared on the premises; four days later the
City Council of Baltimore signed a contract for lighting the whole
city with coal gas. On February 17, 1817, the first gas street lamp
was lit in Baltimore. At this time Cooper wrote an important book
to meet the public interest in this new system of illumination:
Some Information Concerning Gas Lights. Someone pointed out
that "The dealers in oil, and the makers of candles, may be somewhat affected eight or ten years hence by the general introduction
of gas lights, but no improvement can be introduced which will
not partially interfere with former articles of consumption and
modes of manufacture."

Cooper was also active in the American Philosophical Society, to which he contributed articles on bleaching, platinum alloys, iron ores of New Jersey, and tests for arsenic. In 1818 he edited four volumes of Thomas Thomson's *A System of Chemistry*, adding to this English textbook copious notes of his own and a full explanation of the recently propounded atomic theory of John Dalton. That same year he also revised the very popular American chemistry textbook, *Conversations in Chemistry*. This book, written by Jane Marcet, had a profound influence on the career of many a young American scientist. Cooper even found time to publish a book on medical jurisprudence which received high praise.

His old malady of bumptiousness broke out again, however, and he was forced to resign from the College of Philadelphia. With every resignation, Cooper enriched another center of learning. This time the gainer was the newly established University of Virginia, the crown of Jefferson's educational system. Cooper had been consulted by Thomas Jefferson in the planning of this university, where mathematics was to be given a prominent place, and the practical sciences were to be taught to all students. Jefferson, its founder, prevailed upon the trustees of the college to appoint Cooper to the chairs of chemistry, mineralogy, and the law. There was the usual opposition to Cooper, but the personal endorsements of two other Presidents of the United States, James Madison and James Monroe, could not be ignored. Cooper got the job, but did not last there very long. Such violent opposition soon developed that even Jefferson was powerless to help him. After serving only a few months, Cooper sent in his letter of resignation to avoid embarrassing some of his friends.

After the North had rejected him and Virginia, too, had accepted his resignation, an offer for Cooper's services came from another Southern state. The College of South Carolina called him in 1819 to fill its chair of chemistry. Later the departments of mineralogy and geology were also placed in his care. Within a year he became president of the college, and for the next thirteen years he guided the institution to new leadership in the South. He abolished the teaching of metaphysics as a waste of time, and banished the teaching of oratory, which he declared to be "little else than the art of cheating the understanding of a gaping populace." He further modernized the curriculum by introducing the first course in political economy in the United States, maintaining that "we teach our youth in vain unless we enable them to keep pace with the improvements of the day." Cooper, like Franklin and Rush, advocated the extension of free elementary, high-school, and college education, because they were stanch believers in free public education as a bulwark of democracy.

Even as president of the college, Cooper continued to teach chemistry. He was an outstanding schoolmaster. La Borde, one of his colleagues, wrote, "He gave the first great impulse to the cause of physical science in South Carolina, and it was he who first made known to our people the names of Watt, Cavendish, Black, Scheele, Davy, Lavoisier, and Priestley. . . . He had mingled intimately with the most remarkable men of the Old World and the New. With wonderful art he could weave a dinner with Priestley, a glass of wine with Robespierre, or a race for the convention with the Duke of Orleans, into a lecture on asbestos, soda or magnesium." He was a science popularizer in the highest sense of the term. One of his students quoted him in his lecture notebook: "Don't be afraid of a little dirt. What is dirt? Why, nothing at all offensive when chemically viewed. Analyze it. It will separate into very clean elements. Dirt makes corn, corn makes bread and meat, and that makes a very sweet young lady that I saw you kissing last night. So after all, you were kissing dirt. There is no telling, young gentlemen, what is dirt."

As a citizen-scientist Cooper was certain that he had something to contribute to the solution of political, economic, and social problems. He jumped into the stormy waters of his day and championed the doctrine of states' rights because he mistrusted the centralized power at Washington. "The President of the United States," he said, "is a very wise man; so are all our senators and representatives, all wise men; and the city of Washington contains the congregated wisdom of the nation. But none of them can instruct me whether it would be more advantageous to purchase a chemical article for my laboratory than to make it there. Every man is the best judge of his own business. Therefore the laws of the community interfere imprudently when they direct the industry of individuals."

Cooper struck telling blows at the manufacturers of the North who clamored for a high tariff while the interests of the agricultural South called for free trade. He was a fighter to be reckoned with. Even Daniel Webster, in his memorable reply to Senator Robert Hayne of South Carolina on the issue of states' rights, branded Cooper and his states' rights group as an anticonsolidation force against the Federal Union.

Yet in spite of his recognized leadership in the educational and political life of the South, his heterodox religious views finally dislodged Cooper from the presidency of the College of South Carolina. The storm had been gathering over his head for some years. In translating Broussais' book, *Irritation and Insanity*, Cooper added two essays of his own on materialism. That was anathema to many. Then, in commenting on Sir Humphry Davy's *Elements of Agricultural Chemistry* for *The Southern Review*, he again boldly aired his materialistic views. He pricked the most eminent chemist of his day with the barb, "Davy seems to think it necessary to combat the notion that vegetables are possessed of life in the same sense as animals, whose life he seems to consider as emanating from a superior immaterial principle. We only observe here that a man may be an excellent chemist and a miserable physiologist."

Finally, in 1833, Cooper opened the gates to the flood which was to engulf him by publishing his pamphlet *On the Connection Between Geology and the Pentateuch*. He was teaching geology from the only textbook then available, an American edition of Bakewell's *Geology* which contained a copious appendix of the lecture notes of Benjamin Silliman the Elder. Silliman had written, "Respecting the deluge there can be but one opinion . . . geology fully confirms the scripture history of that event. . . .

Geological research clearly proves that the earth was gradually redeemed from the universal dominion of water *under which it lay at its first creation*, and that there is decisive evidence that no further back than a few thousand years a universal deluge (Noah's flood) swept the whole surface of the globe."

Now Silliman was one of the most eminent American scientists of his day. He had at first practiced law, but then turned to the sciences. He had taught at the medical school of the College of Philadelphia, where he had met Hare, Rush, Priestley, and Cooper. He was called to Yale, where his lectures in chemistry and his chemical laboratory attracted many students. He founded *The American Journal of Science*, which became the most famous repository of American science and for many years the most potent organ of the spread of scientific research in the United States.

Cooper's students in geology could not adjust the fundamentalist statements of Silliman to the newer ideas expressed by their teacher. Cooper had read and accepted the modern geological theory of the earth first printed by James Hutton of Edinburgh in 1785 and 1795. Hutton believed that the earth was molten at one time, and as it cooled, granite and other rocks were formed. Convulsion after convulsion upturned the crust of the earth, and long periods of erosion between these cataclysms formed new strata of rock. Charles Lyell in England, who had studied rock formations, continued the ideas of Hutton in his *Principles of Geology*, which he had published in 1830-33. Cooper had read in Lyell's book a denial that the present surface of the earth was formed by any sudden cataclysm such as a tremendous flood, but rather that the face of the earth had been altered by slow, uniform, and continuous evolutionary changes extending over millions of years.

Cooper wrote to Silliman, whom he admired as a sincere man. He told him how his "theories and geological reputation were in jeopardy with my young men, and I found it absolutely necessary to stand upon my defense. I hold that the Old as well as the New Testaments were by no means meant as infallible guides in mineralogy and geology." Silliman respected the opinions of Cooper,

and no great fuss would have resulted from this honest interchange of scientific theories. But the belligerent Cooper was not
satisfied to stop at letter writing. He made it plain to his pupils
and to others who questioned him where he stood on the scientific
accuracy of the Biblical story of the earth's creation. Calumny and
abuse were heaped upon his old head, and the state legislature was
petitioned to remove him from his college position. Cooper presented a heroic and brilliant defense before the South Carolina
House of Representatives and was actually exonerated of all
charges. He continued to teach chemistry at the college, but the
battle for his expulsion continued to rage until he was forced to
resign in 1834. He was then seventy-four years old.

Cooper's broad scholarship was recognized in the South. He
was appointed to revise the statutes of South Carolina, a job which
kept him busy for five whole years. As he approached the end of
his life, his asthma and dropsy grew worse, he became half blind
and could scarcely walk about. But his mind maintained its vigor
to the very end. Even at eighty he amused himself by translating
Spanish ballads.

More than a century has passed since this physical caricature of
a man, less than five feet high and looking like a huge head set
upon a wedge—a perfect taper from the side of his head down to
his feet—stirred the troubled waters of his time on two continents.
What can we say today about this dynamic figure in American
science? We can be certain of several things. Cooper was indeed
a rare and well-rounded intellect, eminent not only in science but
in law, education, political economy, and philosophy. He was a
superb teacher. He gave a mighty push by pen and lecture to
scientific education. Had his heterodox utterances and acts not
antagonized polite society, he might have graced the halls of Yale
or Harvard, where his teachings would have spread to wider and
more influential circles.

Cooper was a man whose political and philosophical outlook
was, in certain respects, generations ahead of his time. He was another Franklin in the breadth of his interests, his social-minded-

ness, his versatility, his modernity. There was nothing mean, small, selfish, or sordid in his life. He was a warmhearted father and husband, an excellent companion, sincere in his beliefs, righteous in his own free way, sensitive to the feelings of men whom he admired. How otherwise could he have shared the home of Priestley for ten years, differing fundamentally as he did from the minister-scientist on religious questions? "Theology," he wrote, "was a subject in which we had agreed to differ; a difference which, though a mutual source of regret, was to neither of us a source of offense."

Cooper was a reformer—aggressive, courageous, tenacious, frequently tactless and bellicose. He followed his reason wherever it led him. There were moments when he was the firebrand variety of reformer who trampled on authority and "walked roughshod over men's opinions." Coupled with this peppery temperament was an eccentricity which led the English geologist, G. W. Featherstonhaugh, who studied the public lands of the Ozark Mountain region, to report that his host was "a most remarkable man some of whose screws were uncommonly loose."

Cooper once wrote to Jefferson, "Perhaps I do not know exactly myself what my religious creed may be." Yet his religious views were the cause of many of his troubles. Even in death he was not forgiven. The story is told that his old white mule, Blanche, balked as she approached the gates of the graveyard where her master was to be buried. The mule's act was explained for many years after by a Negress who witnessed it. It was due, she said, to another Balaam's ass who had confronted Blanche with flaming sword to keep the infidel Cooper out of the burial ground of the Episcopal Church of Columbia, South Carolina.

When a simple tombstone was erected over the mound that covered Cooper, it bore the inscription:

ERECTED BY A PORTION OF HIS FELLOW CITIZENS TO THE MEMORY OF THOMAS COOPER, M.D. AND LL.D., FORMER PRESI-DENT OF THE SOUTH CAROLINA COLLEGE

The other portion wanted to forget him forever, and in the hurrying years of the last century he has been neglected. So completely has this outstanding American been forgotten that in 1939, on the hundredth anniversary of his passing, not a single commemorative exercise was held anywhere to mark the event. Yet Thomas Cooper needs to be remembered for the great part he played in the cultural development of our country.

CHAPTER FIVE

CONSTANTINE SAMUEL RAFINESQUE

(1783-1840)

AMERICAN SCIENCE VENTURES OUT
ACROSS NEW FRONTIERS

A MERICA HAD BEGUN to move westward even before Jefferson took office in 1801. A light trickle of pioneers had already crossed the mountain barriers of the Alleghenies and the Appalachians. By 1792 Kentucky had a large enough population to be admitted into the Union; Tennessee joined the young republic four years later, and in 1803 Ohio became a state.

Beyond these new borders there still stretched a vast continent. All of the region between the Mississippi River and the Rockies belonged to Spain. In 1800 Spain secretly ceded this land to Napoleon, who soon after found himself desperately in need of money to carry on his expensive wars on the Continent. He was tempted to sell this territory because his imperialistic adventure in the New World had not been a success. Haiti had managed to throw his soldiers into the sea and liberate herself. Napoleon had another reason for wanting to turn his American possessions over to the United States. England was still his greatest enemy. To embarrass further this "nation of storekeepers," as he derisively called them, he thought of creating a new enemy of Great Britain by arranging a land deal with the Americans.

In 1803, therefore, this territory called Louisiana was turned over to the United States for the sum of about $15,000,000. The future corn fields of Iowa, the wheat lands of the two Dakotas, the pine forests of Minnesota, the copper deposits of Montana, the cattle land of Wyoming, and the fabulous oil fields of Oklahoma were sold at the ridiculous price of less than a nickel an acre.

To the science-conscious Jefferson came the opportunity which he had been awaiting for almost twenty years. He had nursed the hope that some day he would be able to explore the virgin continent beyond the Appalachians for new scientific data. Now in the White House, he made plans for the first exploring expedition ever to be attempted by the government of the United States. He selected two young Virginians to head the expedition, Captain Meriwether Lewis and Lieutenant William Clark. Lewis, who had been Jefferson's private secretary, was a studious young man who knew the flora and fauna of his own surroundings and had had some scientific training in mathematics and in the rudiments of physics and geology. He had also had some fighting experience. He saw action during the first test of Federal power in the Whisky Rebellion of 1794, when the farmers of western Pennsylvania revolted against Hamilton's tax on whisky. Clark had been in the United States army, too, and had had frontier and Indian fighting experience. He was an excellent hunter and trapper, and could draw birds, fish, and plants with meticulous care.

Lewis and Clark were intelligent men—able, courageous, and resourceful. They were not, however, professionally trained scientists. In order to overcome this deficiency in the leaders of the expedition, Jefferson called upon his friends of the American Philosophical Society. For a year Lewis was instructed at Philadelphia in the use of mathematical and astronomical instruments. Jefferson himself spent many weeks with Lewis and Clark instructing them concerning their scientific duties. They were to make topographical surveys and take daily astronomical and meteorological observations. They were to note the dates at which different plants flower or lose their flowers and leaves. The times of appearance of the many different birds, reptiles, and insects were also to be watched. And they were to make further reports on the plants, animals, and minerals of this huge new backyard of America. They were to confer with whatever Indians they might meet and bring back information on their numbers, customs, habits, religions, diseases, and agricultural and other pursuits. Jefferson gave them whatever information was available about this unexplored territory, and supplied them with a map containing all the geographical data then known concerning the land embraced in the Louisiana Purchase.

The expedition started by boat from St. Louis on May 16, 1804, and with extreme difficulty reached the Great Bend of the Missouri River after five and a half months. In one of the villages of the Mandan Indians near Bismarck, North Dakota, they found Toussaint Charbonneau, a half-breed, and his slave wife of sixteen, Sakajawea. The girl, who was with child, wanted to return to her people and was glad to be engaged as guide by Lewis and Clark. She knew the pass over the Bitterroot Mountains of the Rockies to the headwaters of the Columbia River. The hardships endured by the expedition might have been too great had not Sakajawea, the Bird Woman, with her newborn baby, Pomp, obtained the aid of the Shoshone Indians from whom she had been abducted as a child. Their chief, who turned out to be her long-lost brother, sold them supplies with which to reach the Pacific. Seldom has so dramatic an episode intervened so opportunely to save an expedition from disaster.

Across heavily timbered and snow-covered mountains the explorers first tasted of the waters of the great Columbia River. They followed it to its mouth in the Pacific Ocean before returning to St. Louis, which they reached on September 23, 1806. Lewis and Clark and their twenty-seven men, including a Negro whom Clark took along as his servant, had been away for two years and four months. For eighteen months they had not been heard from at all. Yet for almost three months after their return hardly a word of the expedition appeared in the newspapers. The first mention in most newspapers came when, in his special message to Congress, Jefferson took occasion to praise Lewis and Clark for achieving "all the success which could have been expected." He was thinking of the niggardly $2500 which he had finally squeezed out of an economy-conscious Congress to defray the expenses of this scientific expedition, undertaken in the guise of a war project.

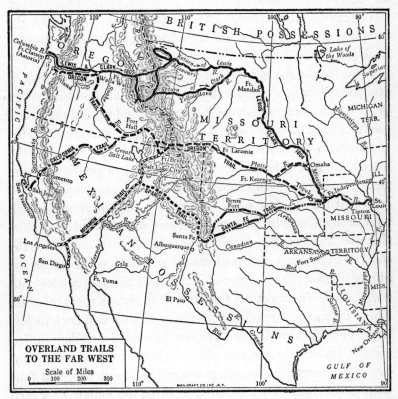

Fig. 3. Overland Trails to the Far West (Courtesy of Harper & Brothers, from *America: Its History and People*).

This appropriation permitted the purchase of only $217 worth of mathematical instruments, while $696 had to be spent for four-teen bales containing such things as gilt braid, red trousers, medals, flags, colored handkerchiefs, mirrors, beads, paints, and toma-hawks to be used as gifts to obtain the co-operation of the Indians.

Both Lewis and Clark kept individual diaries, as did some of the other members of the expedition. From these and from the official journals much material of scientific interest was brought forth. The explorers had found the continent much wider than had been supposed. They found the two mountain ranges, the Sierras and Cascades, separated by 400 miles of valleys. They saw the interior drainage of the Columbia River and noted the summer rains of the Great Plains, the torrential rains of the Pacific Coast, and the comparative aridity of the Columbia Plateau between the Rockies and the Cascades.

They fought the ugly grizzlies, which they were the first to describe to science. They killed several, weighed and measured them, cut them up to examine their organs, and studied their food habits. The black-tailed fallow deer, the mule deer, the sewellel or mountain beaver, the tiger cat or lynx of the Columbia, the Rocky Mountain sheep, the barking squirrel or prairie dog, the sage grouse of the Plains, and the steelhead salmon trout were all described for the first time. Other zoological specimens which were brought back by the expedition included the wild goat of the Cascades, the "pack rat" which lives in holes in the rocks, the cowardly coyote, a species of ermine perfectly white except for a bit of black at the extremity of its tail, the California condor with a wingspread of almost ten feet, as well as various types of snails. These were in addition to specimens previously sent back to Jefferson in the White House—"a variety of articles including stuffed animals, skeletons, elk horns, peltries, plants, tobacco seed, Mandan corn, insects, a burrowing squirrel, a prairie hen, and four magpies all alive." Their journals reported the finding of several fossil fish and other fossil animals which were later turned over to the American Philosophical Society. They also described the alkali salts which covered the riverbanks, and collected many mineral deposits, rocks, sandstones, pumice, granite, and geodes. In the night, sleeping under the cottonwoods, they would often hear the noise of some cracking geodes—hollow, crystal-lined rocks.

In 1814, five years after Lewis died either by murder or suicide, his book describing the expedition was first published. In addition to much scientific data, the book included new information about various Indian tribes. The expedition noted in particular the three types of Indians they had met: those who lived on fish, those whose main diet consisted of roots, and those whose needs were supplied by the huge herds of buffalo. Some Indians used the seed of the sunflower for their bread; some used buffalo dung for fuel. The explorers noted that the Chinook Indians flattened their heads to distinguish themselves from other tribes. The Indians of the Columbia River, they found, suffered gravely from bad teeth and soreness of the eyes. All this was written down in their notebooks even as they rested from their narrow escapes or thrilled at the first sight of new mountain peaks such as Mount Hood and other breath-taking scenes.

At the time Lewis and Clark were preparing for the expedition, there lived in Philadelphia a young man of twenty-one who had come to this country from Italy two years earlier. He had already done a number of interesting things in the field of natural history, and he was known to Thomas Jefferson. But not satisfied with the progress he was making in the new land, he was thinking seriously of returning to Europe. "I hesitated, however," he wrote, "when I was told that I might be admitted as botanist in the expedition which Lewis and Clark were then preparing." The famous William Bartram had turned down an invitation to join the Virginians as official botanist, but Rafinesque was never approached by those in charge of the expedition. Instead of applying for the position, he waited until it was too late. Disappointed, he sailed on New Year's Day, 1805, for Leghorn, Italy, to remain away from the United States for ten years. It was a misfortune that Rafinesque was unable to accompany Lewis and Clark. He would have added immeasurably to the scientific contributions of this important expedition.

Picturesque and grotesque are words, said someone, which rhyme with the name Rafinesque, and these two words also describe the man. Constantine Samuel Rafinesque was the offspring of an unusual marriage. His father, G. F. Rafinesque of Marseille, France, was in charge of a branch office of a business firm in Constantinople. Constantine's mother, Madame Schmaltz, was a German woman born in Greece. Constantine was born in 1783 in a suburb of Constantinople called Galata. The child was brought to France, but in 1792 the terrors of the French Revolution drove his parents to Leghorn, Italy.

Nature and exploration were the two passions of this boy. In Pisa he began a botanical collection at an early age. "It was among the flowers and fruits of that delightful region," he wrote later in life, "that I became a botanist. Afterward the first prize I received in school was a book of animals, and I became a zoologist and a naturalist." The constant movements of his family, however, prevented any advanced formal education. He studied Latin by himself, as John Bartram had done, to learn the language in which the botanical knowledge of his day was locked up. In his book, *A Life of Travel and Researches in North America and South Europe*, which was published when he was fifty-three years old, Rafinesque boasted, "I never was in a regular college nor lost my time on dead languages. I have undertaken to learn Latin and Greek as well as Hebrew, Sanskrit, Chinese, as well as fifty other languages, as I felt the need or inclination to do so."

At eighteen the youth was living in Leghorn, Italy, hiking, exploring, studying the flowers, the trees, and the birds as he roamed the woods and fields. He also made a topographical map of the region of Calci in the Apennines. Then tragedy came to his family. The ship on which his father was sailing around the Cape of Good Hope on a business voyage was chased by an English cruiser. Forced to change its course, the ship landed him in Philadelphia, where he died of yellow fever. His family's fortune soon disappeared. Strange stories had come to young Rafinesque of this fabulous country with its untouched riches of natural history. He started out with his younger brother, Anthony, and after forty-two days on the water reached Philadelphia on April 18, 1802. A year later another young naturalist also came to this country to escape the dragnet of the Napoleonic wars—Audubon, who was to become America's best-known ornithologist.

In the summer of Rafinesque's arrival another epidemic struck Philadelphia. This city had been visited by a series of yellow-fever epidemics against which the medicine of that day was helpless. Constantine fled to Germantown, where he obtained employment with a horticulturist. For the next two years he was part of the woods and the meadows, making a number of foot journeys and botanical excursions into the still virgin botanical world around him. "I never was happier," he noted, "than when alone in the woods with the blossoms, or resting near a limpid stream. I enjoyed without control the gifts of Flora and the beauties of Nature."

It did not take Rafinesque very long to seek out the most active of the country's botanists. He corresponded with many of them, visited several, and joined a few on botanical excursions. America was literally covered with amateur and professional botanists. Public and private herbariums and botanical gardens flourished everywhere. The search which Thomas Harriot had begun more than two centuries back was still in full swing.

Humphry Marshall, a cousin of John Bartram, had written in *The American Grove* descriptions of our forest trees and shrubs. Dr. Benjamin Smith Barton of the College of Philadelphia (after whom the cactuslike *Bartonia* was named) had published his two volumes of *Elements of Botany* in 1803. Dr. Manasseh Cutler, a minister of Ipswich, Massachusetts, had already described 370 species of plants in his *Account of Some Vegetable Productions of America*.

In Lancaster, Pennsylvania, the Reverend Gotthilf Heinrich Muhlenberg, son of the Patriarch of the Lutheran Church in America, was building an excellent herbarium and planning a new catalogue of plants of the United States. He visioned a co-operative enterprise sponsored by the American Philosophical Society and engaging the work of many botanists in as many different sections of the country as could be included. Muhlenberg was to cover his own neighborhood. André Michaux, who in 1785 had been sent here from France by royal decree to collect trees, shrubs, flowers, and game birds, was to work in South Carolina and Georgia. Dr. David Hosack, professor of botany and medicine at Columbia College (and physician to Burr and Hamilton on the day of their fatal duel), also promised to join in the project. William Bartram, who was the first botanist to study the flora and fauna of Florida and who had traveled through the Great Smokies and knew the botany of North Carolina and Tennessee, was also to contribute his knowledge. This project was never completed, although a great deal of work was accomplished.

Besides these college professors, ministers, and physicians, there was a host of amateur botanists who searched the untrodden paths of the wilderness for new species of American plants. The greatest of these lone wolves of botanical investigation was Rafinesque.

When Rafinesque, failing to join up with Lewis and Clark, went back to Europe in 1805, he did not plan to return to America. He took back to Italy rocks, shells, plants, and seeds, and traded his stock of specimens with the colleges, gardens, and museums of Europe. He worked for a time with William Swainson, an English ornithologist stationed in Sicily. He resumed his scientific exploration during the hours when he was not working as secretary to the United States consul at Palermo, Sicily, or engaging in the manufacture of whisky and the sale of drugs and medicinal squills. He sent several papers on American plants to the *Medical Repository* in New York, and started his own natural history journal, *Specchio delle Scienze*. When, however, his business ventures failed and his request for a professorship of botany at the University of Sicily was turned down, he set sail again for the United States.

The return of Rafinesque to America was not an auspicious one. Ninety days out of Palermo his ship sighted the shores of Long Island. Just then a thick fog rolled in and the boat ran aground against the underwater rocks between Long Island and Fisher Island. In the shipwreck he lost all of his possessions—fifty boxes of botanical and other scientific material, the fruit of ten years of labor in Italy, as well as drawings and unpublished manuscripts. He managed to get safely to shore and reached New London, Connecticut, in a state of utter despair. As soon as he could pull himself together he journeyed to New York City to call on his friend Dr. Samuel L. Mitchill, with whom he had corresponded from Italy for many years. Mitchill, who had married a wealthy lady, had given up other work and was now devoting all of his time to science. He had a wide acquaintance among scientists and other learned men. Through his recommendation, Rafinesque, who was thirty-two years old, was engaged as tutor to the three daughters of a Mr. Livingston of Clermont, New York.

This association was not altogether to the botanist's liking. It only helped to remind him of his own children. Just as he left for the United States, his wife, whom he had married in 1809, ran off with an Italian comedian. His daughter Emily was then only four years old and his other child, Charles Linnaeus, had died as an infant. Even the rich library of his employer could not console Rafinesque. He felt cramped in his new surroundings, and the urge to roam and lose himself in the woods overcame him. Back to New York City he went to join Mitchill in a field trip through New Jersey.

Having tasted the outdoors once more, he took to the field again in earnest. He botanized in Flatbush, Gravesend, Jamaica, and Oyster Bay, while he made his home for a short time in Brooklyn, New York. He also explored the Hudson River valley, taking the steamboat to Albany and then traveling on foot to Niagara Falls, Lake George, the mineral springs of Saratoga, and Ticonderoga. When he came home, umbrella in one hand and notebook in the other, his back was weighed down by a mountain of plants, shells, fossils, and minerals. He seldom rode a horse during these expeditions, for, he wrote, "I never liked riding horses and dismounting for every flower; horses do not suit botanists."

Between his many scientific excursions Rafinesque found time to help Mitchill, Cooper, and James E. DeKay establish the Lyceum of Natural History of New York, to become a member of The Academy of Natural Sciences of Philadelphia, to send contributions to the *American Monthly Magazine* and to other publications. In May, 1818, he walked across the Alleghenies and then proceeded to botanize all the way to Hendersonville, Kentucky. Here he looked up an artist who was eking out a living in a little grocery store while he spent his leisure hours hunting and sketching birds. This man, John James Audubon, was fast becoming the greatest painter of American birds and the best-known ornithologist of the United States.

Audubon was born near New Orleans in 1785, when Louisiana was still French territory. His mother was a Creole of Haiti and his father an admiral in the French navy. His mother was killed during a native uprising in Santo Domingo, and father and son escaped to France. At the age of seventeen, young Audubon was sent to take charge of his father's Pennsylvania estate at Mill Grove. Here he began to paint birds from life, and married a neighbor, Lucy Bakewell. In 1808 financial reverses sent him to Kentucky.

On March 19, 1810, a total stranger walked into his store at Louisville. It was Alexander Wilson, the Scottish farmer, weaver, peddler, poet, and political refugee, who had come to the United States in 1794 to devote himself to the study of American ornithology at the suggestion and with the help and encouragement of William Bartram. Wilson showed Audubon the first two volumes of his now classic *American Ornithology* and asked for a subscription. Audubon in turn took out some of his bird drawings in water color and crayon. They hunted birds for a few days and Wilson left Audubon without a subscription. Three years later Wilson died at forty-seven of overwork and dysentery, but not before he had given a great impetus to American science by placing American ornithology on a firm foundation. He has rightfully been called the father of American ornithology, even though others had been working in this field before him. A few of the forty or more new species of American birds which he was the first to describe were named after him, including the warbler *Wilsonia*, Wilson's snipe, Wilson's thrush, and Wilson's phalarope. The American ornithologist, just as Jefferson had done thirty years earlier, attacked Buffon's fantastic theory that the animals of the New World had degenerated. With his characteristic sarcastic humor Wilson declared that the Frenchman's theory "would leave us in doubt whether even the *Ka-te-dids* of America were not originally Nightingales of the Old World degenerated by the inferiority of the food and climate of this upstart country."

When Rafinesque, looking like a tramp, walked into Audubon's store eight years after Wilson's historic visit, he handed the Frenchman a letter of introduction from a common friend in Philadelphia. Audubon laughed long and loud as he read in this letter a description of his visitor as "an odd fish, which might not be described in the published treatises." He carefully scrutinized this queer bird who had come down from the East to perch on the steps of his grocery store in "an exceedingly remarkable attire," as Audubon later wrote. "A long loose yellow nankeen, much the worse for the many rubs it has got in its time, hung about him loosely like a sack. A waistcoat of the same, with enormous pockets and buttoned up to the chin, reached below over a pair of tight pantaloons, the lower part of which buttoned down his ankles. His beard was long and his lank black hair hung loosely over his shoulders. His forehead was broad and prominent, indicating a mind of strong power. His words impressed an assurance of rigid truth, and as he directed the conversation to the natural sciences, I listened to him with great delight."

Audubon made Rafinesque welcome. They talked of plants, of birds, and of their contemplated projects. It was late when they turned in for the night. Hardly had Rafinesque gone to his room when, as Audubon reported, "I heard a great uproar. To my astonishment I saw my guest running naked holding the handle of my favorite Cremona violin the body of which had been battered to pieces in attempting to kill the bats which had entered the open window! I stood amazed, but he continued jumping and running around and around until he was fairly exhausted, when he begged me to procure one of the animals for him, as he felt convinced that they belonged to a new species."

New species happened to be Rafinesque's great obsession. He was always searching for the new and the unknown among living things. At one time, he described, amid great laughter, two species of fossil jellyfish. It was this almost insane desire to announce new species that at times led him to make hasty and inaccurate reports based, in a few cases, on the words of others. At one time he offered in his *Atlantic Journal and Friend of Knowledge* (a quarterly magazine which lasted two years) a prize of twenty-five dollars in books for a synopsis of "all native plants in the United States, provided that *not a single one already described in America or Europe be omitted!*" This weakness of his made him the victim of more than one hoax. Audubon, for example, showed Rafinesque some drawings of fishes he had seen "down the river." These fictitious pisces were called *Pogostoma* and *Pilodictis* by the French and English settlers of the region, Audubon informed him. Rafinesque copied this information in his notebook, and later published the data in one of his numerous papers. For many years students of ichthyology were puzzled at their inability to locate fishes that resembled in any clear way the *Pogostoma* or the *Pilodictis*, which swam out of the mischievous head of Audubon.

Rafinesque, at this time, was living from hand to mouth. He wanted desperately to get some position in a college where he might earn a modest salary teaching science. This would free him from the constant fear of poverty and enable him to continue with his botanizing and other natural-history collecting. It would also give him the prestige necessary for a number of ambitious projects that were hatching in his head. He had already applied for the chair of botany and natural history at the University of Pennsylvania. His memberships in the Literary and Philosophical Society of New York, the Academy of Natural Sciences of Philadelphia, the History Society of New York, and in two scientific societies of Italy were not impressive enough. He was turned down. It was pointed out by the trustees of the college that he had no college degree and that he was queer.

Rafinesque had found a very good and influential friend in a successful businessman whom he had met in Philadelphia. John D. Clifford was an amateur scientist who owned a private museum of fossils and antiquities in Lexington, Kentucky. He was a trustee of Transylvania College, which had been created by the state of Kentucky in 1780. Through his influence, Rafinesque was appointed professor of botany, natural history, and modern languages at this college in the spring of 1819. Free board and lodging with "casual emoluments" were his pay. He began his lectures to a handful of "ladies and students" early in the fall of that year and remained at this college for seven years.

These years were very productive ones for Rafinesque. Soon after this appointment—his one and only college connection—he published at Lexington, Kentucky, at his own expense, a pamphlet of ninety pages entitled *Ichthyologia Ohiensis*. This described the natural history of the fishes of the Ohio River and its tributaries. Many of these were new to science. It was dedicated to his friend, Samuel L. Mitchill, who had already described the Atlantic fishes of New York, and to Charles A. Leseur, who was the first to explore the fish life of the Great Lakes. A scientific society of Bonn, Germany, presented Rafinesque with an honorary certificate for his contributions. (This apparently was his reason for adding the Ph.D. title after his name in 1824.)

These were not the only pioneers in the study of American fish. Dr. John D. Schopf, a surgeon who had come over with the Hessian troops during the Revolutionary War, was another. In addition to studying medicinal plants, which grew all along the Eastern seaboard, Schopf wrote one of the first papers on the fishes found in New York. Another pioneer was William D. Peck, a graduate of Harvard who became interested in natural science after reading a book he had picked up on the seashore among some washed-up wreckage. In 1794 he wrote one of the first papers in systematic zoology in America—*A Description of Four Remarkable Fishes Taken Near the Piscataqua, N. H.* William Bartram and Lewis and Clark had also contributed new data on American fishes.

Rafinesque was living in a time of great activity in the systematic collecting and naming of new species of plants and animals. Realizing that much information could be obtained from the common folk who lived near rivers which he could not explore, Rafinesque made a popular appeal through magazines and through his books for further information on the fish life of the United States. He hoped to do for the fishes of America what Wilson had done for the birds, and what others were attempting to do for the mammals.

On the title page of his *Ichthyologia Ohiensis*, Rafinesque wrote, "The art of seeing well, or of noticing and distinguishing with accuracy the objects which we perceive, is a high faculty of the mind, unfolded in few individuals, and despised by those who can neither acquire it, nor appreciate its results." He described here for the first time one hundred species of Ohio River fishes, ninety of which were new, as well as forty new fish species from Lake Champlain, Lake George, and the Chesapeake and Hudson Rivers. He clearly classified and named the salmon perch, golden-eyed perch, black-dotted perch, and sunfish, and described them with the aid of drawings, some of which were supplied by his friends Audubon and Clifford.

Rafinesque was very busy outside the college. During the year following the publication of his book on the Ohio fishes, he made a scientific expedition down to the mouth of the Miami River. John Bradbury, who in 1811 had traveled 2900 miles up the Missouri River from New Orleans, visited him in 1822 and they botanized together through Kentucky. Transylvania College honored him with an M.A. degree, and that same year Rafinesque became secretary to the Kentucky Institute, the first scientific society founded in Kentucky. He tried to get the state legislature to pass a bill for the establishment of a public botanic garden. When this failed, he proceeded to organize a joint-stock company to raise funds for this project. He went to see the statesman Henry Clay, and persuaded him to purchase two fifty-dollar shares in this undertaking. But this method, too, failed. He hiked to Washington to hear President John Quincy Adams plead unsuccessfully with Congress in 1825 for the erection of a government observatory which he called a "lighthouse of the sky." Rafinesque asked Adams to send out circulars through the Indian Service for the purpose of collecting information on Indian vocabularies.

He continued to teach at Transylvania College. From all accounts, he must have been an effective teacher and an entertaining lecturer. Watchful of every phase of progress in the natural sciences, alive to every new development, well informed on the work of most of his American contemporaries, highly individualistic and quite impish at times, he was an unusual professor. One of his students (Jefferson Davis, who attended Transylvania College from 1821 to 1824, may have been among them) left the following illuminating description of Rafinesque as a teacher: "His lectures on the ants were peculiarly instructive and interesting, and caused many of the students to laugh heartily, especially when he described the ants as having lawyers, doctors, generals, and privates, and of their having great battles, and of the care of physicians and nurses of the wounded."

If his students enjoyed this unusual personality, the trustees of the college were getting worried about him. Outside of his own circle of friends, where he was a delightful companion, Rafinesque had won the reputation of being impulsive, scrappy, opinionated, and even unjustly jealous of other scientists. After Linnaeus had named a flower after Kuhn, a botanist of the College of Philadelphia, Rafinesque publicly declared Kuhn to be a very poor botanist. He had also questioned the artificial system of Linnaeus and advocated the adoption of a natural system of classification. He quarreled with American botanists who showed annoyance at radical reforms he proposed in the nomenclature of plants. Rafinesque displayed real anger whenever Benjamin Silliman's name was mentioned, because the Yale professor, after publishing ten of his papers in 1818-19, suddenly put a ban on them in his *American Journal of Science* the following year. Silliman's explanation was reasonable enough. "In 1819," he wrote, "I became alarmed by a flood of communications and new discoveries by Rafinesque and being warned both at home and abroad against his claims, I returned him a large bundle of memoirs. The step was painful but necessary; for if there had been no other difficulty, he alone would have filled the *Journal* had he been permitted to proceed." As a result of this decision Rafinesque sent many of his publications to Paris, Brussels, and other European cities. Some were also published in the *Western Review and Miscellaneous Magazine*, his *Western Minerva*, and the *Kentucky Gazette*, all of which were published in Lexington, Kentucky. His greatest weakness—lack of tact—was his final undoing. In 1826 Dr. Horace Holley of Boston, president of the college, forced him to leave his position.

Rafinesque, who was now forty-three years old, again faced poverty. He sent his books and scientific collections to Philadelphia and hiked home on foot to do some more scientific exploring. He skirted Lake Erie and spent two days at Niagara Falls, which excited his wonder. After studying the geology and making maps and drawings of the formations of the Falls, he crossed into Canada. On his return Rafinesque traveled from Lockport to Rochester along the Erie Canal, which had been opened the previous year.

In Troy he stopped off to spend several days with his friend Dr. Amos Eaton, who was on the staff of a school for teachers in that city. This was the school, founded in 1824 for the purpose of instructing young men in the practical sciences, which later became the Rensselaer Polytechnic Institute. It was the first science and engineering school in the United States. In 1824 Eaton had introduced the laboratory method of teaching chemistry in America, a year before the great Justus von Liebig had opened his famous chemical laboratory in Giessen which became the mecca of many young American scientists. Before returning to Philadelphia, where he spent the rest of his life, Rafinesque went to see another of his friends, John Torrey, who was then professor of chemistry in the United States Military Academy at West Point. In 1824 Torrey, who was also a first-rate amateur botanist, had published *A Flora of the North and Middle United States*.

For a while Rafinesque was permitted to give some scientific lectures to a small class in the Franklin Institute of Philadelphia. He also managed for a short period to act as teacher of geography and drawing in the high-school division of this same institution. This work provided some meager funds, but before long he was again struggling without any professional connections. Keeping alive on salt pork and corn bread, he turned to planning the construction of steam plows, fireproof houses, aquatic railroads, and similar inventions, and to the manufacture of a vegetable compound "remedy" for consumption.

All this while, however, he never seriously neglected his botanizing and other scientific pursuits. In 1830 he wrote a series of letters to Cuvier and other European scientists, and also sent along a paper on the origins of Asiatic Negroes. For this paper (in 1832) the Geographical Society of Paris presented him with a gold medal on which were inscribed the words, "The spirit of Linnaeus he chose as his guide." He was the first American to be honored by this prize. That same year Cuvier asked him to collect fishes for him in the United States. This looked very much like salvation for Rafinesque. But Cuvier died soon after, the scheme evaporated, and Rafinesque received no money. Between 1827 and 1832 he contributed a series of illustrated accounts of dozens of plants to *The Saturday Evening Post*.

He then entered the field of economics. At the time the Second United States Bank was being attacked by Jackson and the Western farmers, he published his own plan of banking, under the title *Safe Banking, Including the Principles of Wealth*. He fought the loan companies of the day, which he called Lombard Banks of usurious pawnbrokers, charging thirty-six per cent annual interest, and he opposed the banks which were gambling in stocks. In

1835 he invited the public to become stockholders in a savings bank which was to pay good dividends, he promised, and from which loans could be made at only six per cent interest. "It is abominable," complained poor Rafinesque, "that a rich man or a speculator can obtain loans at six per cent from banks *without pledge,* and that a poor and industrious man cannot obtain a small loan at six per cent on a pledge. Is it not shameful also," he continued, "that a rich man can get six per cent or more for his large capital, while an industrious saving man who may save a few dollars monthly cannot get as much for it, but is offered only four or five per cent by the pseudo-philanthropists who manage the common Savings Banks for their own benefit and not for the poor?" Five thousand shares at $10 a share were sold to fifty subscribers, and the bank was organized in 1835 with Rafinesque as actuary. Rafinesque tells us that a nine per cent dividend was paid to the stockholders of his bank after its first year of operation, and that his ideas were so sound that others adopted them in part and ran him out of business to prevent competition.

Again he found himself without funds to continue actively his scientific collecting. The colleges would not have him, he was not wanted as a public lecturer, and no rich sponsors came to his aid. "Why should I not find protectors or enlightened patrons as were found by Audubon?" he cried out in a moment of despair. Audubon incidentally had to go to Scotland and England to get subscribers and a printer for his five volumes of *Birds of America.* His friend Torrey tried to engage Rafinesque as his paid assistant, but the funds could not be raised. For a while Rafinesque hoped that "the geological and scientific expeditions begun by the States of Massachusetts, Maryland and Tennessee might perhaps call me to another field of utility. A great field of usefulness," he said, "is now opening by these surveys." When they, too, failed him, he tried to find a way out of his economic distress by turning to literary work and publishing. He "had to become a poet," as he put it, and scribbled poems on *Despondency, Sylva Telluriana, The Western Flowers, The Universe and the Stars, Alsographia Amer-*

icana, Rivers of the Ohio (in French), and *The World, or Instability*. It was this last long and rambling poem which, written ten
years before, he now dug out of his pile of manuscripts. He published it himself and actually saw it go through two small editions
in one year.

From his pen also poured *The Pulmist or the Art to Cure the
Consumption* and *The Annals of Nature*. The following year he
continued to feed the presses but hardly his body with his *American Manual of Mulberry Trees*, and another pamphlet entitled
*Improvements of Universities, Colleges and Other Seats of Learn-
ing*. In 1840 came his *Antiken Botaniken, The Pleasures and Duties
of Wealth*, and finally, as an epilogue, *The Good Book*.

Altogether, Rafinesque managed to write and publish more than
a thousand essays, memoirs, scientific monographs, and books over
a period of almost half a century. His versatile mind spread itself
over many fields. Yet in spite of the fact that it was spread very
thin in most areas of knowledge, he managed to leave substantial
and solid contributions in more than one sector of scientific research. He was still living in the days when natural philosophers
could range far and wide without poaching too severely on one
another's territory. In those days, too, it was still possible to remain
a specialist in more than one field of scientific investigation. Science had not yet reached our present stage of development when,
for example, we have in chemistry more than a dozen specialized
branches, each of which might engage a research worker a full
lifetime.

There was scarcely a domain of human knowledge which entirely escaped this inquisitive man. His thinking and his writing
invaded the fields of archeology, architecture, banking, botany,
cartography, and conchology; he was deeply interested in economics, engineering, ethics, geography, geology, history, ichthyology, and, as though these were not enough, his restless curiosity
embraced Indian lore and languages, morals, paleontology, phil-
ology, philanthropy and philosophy, religion, sericulture, and
surveying. Near the close of his life, however, Rafinesque be-

moaned the fact that he had written so much for such an unappreciative audience. "The endeavors to enlighten, instruct, improve, are often unavailing. Truth and knowledge are not always welcome. Ignorance, poverty, and selfishness are the real banes of all improvements, and they are quite prevailing as yet. When property, rewards, and happiness shall be offered to all willing to be wise, good, and grateful, few will continue to be otherwise. But universal tolerance of opinion and unlimited scope of industry must be added to secure mutual happiness and unrestrained exertions of skill."

Cancer of the stomach and liver finally killed Rafinesque after a long illness. He died in a lonely, miserable garret on Race Street in Philadelphia. Only the intervention of some friends who secretly lowered his cold body by rope from his room in the dead of night saved his remains from a potter's field, or perhaps even from its sale to a medical school for dissection. His landlord, to whom he owed several months' rent, had threatened to take that means of collecting his unpaid rent. Rafinesque was buried in Ronaldson's Cemetery in the poor section of Ninth and Catherine Streets in the city which boasted itself the intellectual center of America.

John Torrey was one of the three executors of the naturalist's estate. When Rafinesque's will, which was drawn up in 1835, was opened, it was found that he had provided for the sale of his miscellaneous possessions, the proceeds of which were to be divided among his daughter, his sister, and an orphanage for girls which he hoped could be founded. Colored posters were printed to advertise the sale of eight truckloads of his effects. His Paris medal was sold for $16.55, a few of his notebooks and manuscripts went to the highest bidder for $5, and the rest of his papers and collections went into the furnace. The auction was so badly bungled, and interest in the work of Rafinesque was at such a low ebb, that when the sale was all over, the estate owed its administrators the sum of $14.43. Fortunately, part of his herbarium found its way to the University of Pennsylvania, the New York Botanic Gardens, and the Academy of Natural Sciences of Philadelphia.

So came to a tragic end the most colorful figure of his day in American science. Stripped of the exaggerations, the occasional flimsy reasoning, and the few hoaxes that mar his manuscripts, they retain enough real scientific value to place Rafinesque among the immortals of American science. Forget his invention of an improved stock or bond coupon system of divisible, circulating certificates (Divitial system), ignore as inconsequential his influence as a teacher in science, brush aside his hazy glimpse of the germ theory of disease half a century before the rise of Pasteur. Even minimize, if you will, his fight to introduce a natural classification of living organisms as opposed to the artificial system of Linnaeus, and we still have to examine critically his opinions on the theory of evolution, which, though ignored during Rafinesque's day, finally shook the world nineteen years after this "crazy herb doctor" breathed his last.

More than a century has passed since Rafinesque's death. Men of science have had time to forget his eccentricities, his tactlessness, his unbridled egotism, his human frailties. What can they say of his work? He was much more than a mere collector of plants, a builder of large herbariums, a keen observer of plant differences, and an unusual systematizer of living organisms. Others of his contemporaries in the United States may have equaled him in these respects. But Rafinesque was a genius who excelled them all in his penetration and in his ability to generalize. After studying thousands of living plants and animals over a period of forty years, he saw through their resemblances and differences a broad vision. This vision, in the mind of a more financially and emotionally stable man in England, Charles Darwin, matured into one of the greatest syntheses of science—the theory of evolution.

Seven years before Rafinesque died, when he was fifty years old, he wrote in his *Herbarium Rafinesquianum* that it was needless to dispute about new genera, species, and varieties. "The truth is," he believed, "that Species and perhaps Genera also are forming in organized beings by gradual deviations of shapes, forms and organs, taking place in the lapse of time. There is a tendency to deviations and mutations through plants and animals by gradual steps at remote irregular periods. This is a part of the great universal law of *perpetual mutability* in every thing. . . . Every variety is a deviation which becomes a Species as soon as it is permanent by reproduction. . . . It is not impossible to ascertain the primitive Species that have produced all the actual; many means exist to ascertain it: history, locality, abundance, etc. This view of the subject will settle botany and zoology in a new way and greatly simplify those sciences. The races, breeds or varieties of men, monkeys, dogs, roses, apples, wheat . . . and almost every other genus, may be reduced to one or a few primitive Species yet admit of several actual Species names may and will multiply as they do in geography and history by time and changes, but they will be reducible to a better classification by a kind of genealogical order or tables. . . . My last work on Botany if I live and after publishing all my New Species will be on this. . . . If I cannot perform this give me credit for it, and do it yourself upon the plan I trace."

Here he saw clearly a new truth against which the world was to battle for a long time. America and the rest of the world were not ready for such a revolutionary idea. Even a generation later, when Darwin, armed with much more data, published his theory of evolution, he found plenty of doubters in the United States. We have no record that Darwin and Rafinesque ever corresponded, but we do know that the Englishman's eyes were ever turned to the American wilderness for new species and new data. This information finally helped to destroy the belief in the constancy of species, and to prove that lower forms of life developed gradually into higher and more complex forms.

No other American scientist glimpsed this great truth of evolution as early as Rafinesque. None struggled so early for its acceptance. It may be said with a great deal of justice that, in a real sense, he was a forerunner of Charles Darwin. Had Rafinesque not been fettered by his need to eat and clothe himself and have a roof over his head, he might have been freed for the world of science. Had our colleges or our government surveys and expeditions given him opportunities for the employment of his genius, he might have escaped becoming one of the most neglected scientists of America.

Near the close of his life Rafinesque remarked, "Time renders justice to all." These words are coming true, for his scientific stature has been growing with the years. Sixty years ago G. B. Goode, the historian of American science, saw in his eccentricities only "the outcome of a boundless enthusiasm for the study of nature." Forty years ago David Starr Jordan, the eminent American zoologist, called him "the most remarkable man to appear in the annals of American science," and very recently Donald Culross Peattie, the gifted writer on science, declared, "Among all the naturalists who have ever worked on the American continent, he is the only one who might clearly be called a titan."

In 1919 Henry C. Mercer of Doylestown, Pennsylvania, placed a stone marker over the forgotten grave of Rafinesque in Ronaldson's Cemetery in Philadelphia. The headstone bore the inscription: *Honor to Whom Honor Is Overdue*. When a few years later it was learned that the area occupied by this cemetery was to be converted into a public park, the trustees of Transylvania University recalled that the great Rafinesque had been a professor of science in their institution. What greater honor could come to their college than to have his remains rest on their campus? On March 1, 1924, the bones of Rafinesque were brought from Philadelphia to Lexington, Kentucky, and placed in a vault in Morrison Hall of Transylvania College. On October 30, 1940, an elaborate Rafinesque Centennial Memorial was held at the college to pay tribute to the memory of this great American scientist. At this meeting, the only memorial ever held for Rafinesque, both the public and undergraduates attended an exhibition of his books and manuscripts and heard speakers recall the interests and contributions of this overshadowed scientist.

The first third of the nineteenth century during which Rafinesque labored saw prodigious strides in the world of science in Europe. Michael Faraday was making classic discoveries in electricity in England, Friedrich Wöhler was synthesizing the first organic compound (urea) in Germany, and in France, Joseph Laplace was enriching mathematics and astronomy with his *Méchanique céleste*.

In America, too, science was making significant advances. Joseph Henry was working in the field of electricity, Samuel Guthrie was preparing chloroform for the first time, and John R. Young and William Beaumont were studying the chemistry of digestion. Thomas Say was investigating the insects of America, and William S. Sullivant, an Ohio engineer, became interested in botany and after thirty years of work published his monumental work on the mosses of North America. Richard Harlan, professor of comparative anatomy at the Philadelphia Museum, published his most notable work, *Fauna Americana*, in 1825. Robert Fulton was building his first steamboats, and other inventors were busy. New scientific societies were being formed. The Columbian Chemical Society of Philadelphia was founded in 1811, the Academy of Natural Sciences of Philadelphia in 1812, the American Institute of the City of New York in 1828, and the Boston Society of Natural History in 1830.

In 1816 the United States Coast and Geodetic Survey was established. Four years later the first United States Pharmacopoeia was completed under the leadership of Dr. Lyman Spalding, professor of chemistry and materia medica at Dartmouth College. New botanical gardens, natural-history museums, chairs of science in the ever-growing number of colleges, public science lectures, state geological surveys, and Federal exploring expeditions—all were helping to bring scientific knowledge to more people than ever before.

The acquisition of vast new territories, our demonstration in the War of 1812 that our faster ships and better Yankee gunnery were more than an even match against a great European power, and the rise of the common man to dignity and political power in the election of our first frontier President, Andrew Jackson, gave the average American a firmer feeling of personal power and ability. This growth of individual power and of a sense of nationalism was reflected in many ways. In 1823, for example, President Monroe's Secretary of State, John Quincy Adams, wrote down the policy which came to be known as the Monroe Doctrine. Another consequence was the growth of interest in science. "In truth," wrote Dr. Amos Eaton at this time, "a thirst for the natural sciences seemed already to pervade the United States like the progress of an epidemic."

Some have wondered at this upsurge of scientific interest. Professor Charles Beard attempted an answer. "Political democracy and natural science," he wrote, "rose and flourished together. Whether in their inception there are deep connections, researches have not yet disclosed, but beyond question their influence upon each other has been reciprocal." As for reasons, he had this to say, "Democracy arrested the attention of idle curiosity, and demanded that the man of microscope and test tube come into the street and invent, relieve and serve. Science, on the other hand, helped to determine the course of democratic development. It was itself democratic in that it spurned nothing, however commonplace, in its researches. Nothing was sacred to its relentless inquiry. Before it there was neither prerogative nor privilege. . . . Finally, science gave to man revolutionary concepts of the world and of his place in the great scheme of nature, feeding the streams of thought which wore down ancient superstitions of church and state."

CHAPTER SIX

THOMAS SAY
(1787-1834)

SCIENCE CAUGHT IN THE FIRST UPRUSH OF
AN INDUSTRIAL REVOLUTION

T HE HERBORIZING RAMBLES of Rafinesque brought him athwart many important paths. None was perhaps more significant in the history of American science than that which was being traversed by a group of men on the Ohio River. A boat bound for Indiana carried an unusual collection of passengers. There on the banks of the Wabash they hoped to establish a New World Utopia far from the sweat and slavery of a new terror they foresaw—the coming machine age, spawned by the Industrial Revolution, which was already beginning to grip the East in its grimy steel fingers.

Among this motley group of idealists was part of the flower of American science, caught up in the wave of enthusiasm created by Robert Owen. At New Harmony, in Indiana, they dreamed of continuing their studies and investigations in the natural history of the United States. They hoped to prove to the world that men could live modestly and usefully without the whip of a harsh industrialism. The land was rich and beautiful; they could live in it harmoniously with the aid of science and by wise planning.

Their leader, Robert Owen, was one of the new captains of industry who appeared in England after John Kay, James Hargreaves, Richard Arkwright, Samuel Crompton, and Edmund Cartwright had made the flying shuttle, the spinning jenny, the water frame, Crompton's mule, and the self-acting loom—machines of wood and iron which could weave and spin fibers into cloth. James Watt, another Englishman, had developed and perfected the steam engine; now this new power could drive the looms. Workers demonstrated against this mechanical revolution, just as they had fought the introduction of carding machines during the previous century. But it was to no avail. Cottage manufacture was dead, and the textile industry was born.

To keep the machines running and to feed them with raw material, men streamed from farms and cottages. Women and children, too, left their handicrafts at home, and soon cities huddled around the new factories. Men, women, and children (some recruited from the foundling asylums of Scotland) who were accustomed to work from sunup to sunset on farms and in cottages were now working from thirteen to fourteen hours a day in factories. Wages were low, and working conditions ignored the health of the workers. In one factory, 500 out of the 2000 workers were children between the ages of five and seven!

Alexander Wilson, who became America's foremost bird naturalist, had cried out against this monster in an anonymous poem, *Watty and Meg*, in 1792. At first it was thought to be the work of Robert Burns, but when the truth came out, Wilson was imprisoned. He had protested against the cruel overseers of the Scottish looms and against the degrading conditions of the factory system. He had also written verses satirizing some of the civil authorities. Only after his works had been publicly burned and he had made a public apology to the men he had attacked was he released from jail. Then he fled to the United States.

The chemist Thomas Cooper had also fought the new industrialism. "I detest the manufacturing system," he wrote, "observing the fallacious prosperity it induces, its instability, and its evil effect on the happiness and morals of the people. You must in this system have a large portion of the people converted into mere machines, ignorant, debauched, and brutal."

Robert Owen, a self-made man, improved cotton-spinning machinery in Manchester, England, and piled up a fortune at an early age. He was superintendent of a cotton mill in Manchester, and later managed his father-in-law's factory at New Lanark, Scotland. When he finally became owner of the mill he set himself the task of introducing revolutionary improvements. He built a model factory, cut down the hours of labor of his 2000 workers, introduced wholesome and healthful working conditions, gave his employees schools, clubrooms, and clean cottages, and abolished the employment of very young children. By 1816 he had "made philanthropy pay." His factories were the best in the world, a hundred years ahead of his times. He was instrumental in the passage of the first British Factory Act in 1819, the Magna Charta of working children. As a result of this law, children under the age of *nine* were barred from factory employment and the working day was limited to twelve hours.

Owen's fame as a philanthropist and industrial idealist spread far. Gradually he was led to believe that men would be happier if they lived and worked together in a community of interest. He became a Utopian socialist, dreaming of a great experiment to determine whether such a world could be made to function successfully. A large area was needed for his project, a virgin land where nature would be lavish in its gifts. There was no such place in England, and his eyes turned to America. He had learned that beyond the Alleghenies a tract of 30,000 acres was available which would suit his purpose.

In the village of Harmonie, or Harmony, a group of religious reformers had settled under the leadership of George Rapp, who had come to Pennsylvania in 1803 from Württemberg, Germany, in search of religious freedom. He had organized the Rappist colony of 600 industrious and agricultural Germans who shared their work and possessions. The colonists had prospered for a while, but soon their neighbors became hostile and there was a slump in the sale of their textiles. They, therefore, planned to come East again to found the city of Economy, near Pittsburgh, where they intended to raise silk and make handkerchiefs. In December, 1824, Robert Owen purchased the Indiana property and all of the colony's equipment for $180,000.

During February and March of the next year he made a lecture tour around the United States to explain his plan and to gather recruits for his ambitious undertaking. He addressed members of the House of Representatives in Washington, spoke to college faculties, newspapermen, scientific societies, to miners in Pennsylvania and to workers in New York. Everywhere Owen was enthusiastically received. The ugliness and abuses of the English factory system had already reached the United States. Some years previously Samuel Slater, an apprentice to a partner of Arkwright in England, had sailed for America, where, he learned, they were having difficulty with textile machinery. Since it was against the law to take plans of such machines out of England, he drew them from memory for a spinner of Pawtucket, Rhode Island. In 1791 they opened a factory housing the first successful spinning machine in America, operated by water power. Two years later saw the invention of Eli Whitney's cotton gin. Textile factories began to spring up. In less than nine years after Whitney's invention, the production of cotton for cotton cloth jumped from 2,000,000 pounds to 50,000,000 pounds.

Francis Cabot Lowell in 1813 opened, at Waltham, Massachusetts, the first cotton factory that handled the whole textile manufacturing process. Mill conditions here in the beginning were no better than those in England. Children and grown girls made up the bulk of the workers. In 1830, forty per cent of these New England factory workers were children under sixteen. Wages were small, hours of work long. New cities began to appear. Lowell, Massachusetts, which did not exist in 1820, had a flourishing cotton mill in 1822, and by 1840 was a city of 20,000 inhabitants, most of whom worked in the cotton mills.

The abuses of the early factory system led many to yearn for a better sort of life. Some workers went West. Many others, with large families and strong home ties, could not move away, and began organizing labor groups for self-protection. The years between 1815 and 1840 saw the rise of the common man. Local labor unions reached flood tide in 1828 when a democratic revolution elected the frontier candidate, Andrew Jackson, to the presidency of the United States. In 1828 the Workingman's Party was born in Philadelphia. Eight years later Jackson established the ten-hour work day in Federal shipyards.

In addition, a new humanitarianism had sprung up. America, as Emerson wrote to Carlyle, was "a little wild with numerous projects of social reform. Not a reading man you meet but has a draft of a new community in his waistcoat pocket." Transcendentalism, under the leadership of Emerson, Thoreau, and Hawthorne, emphasized the dignity of the human spirit. The temperance movement was getting under way and, in the 1820's, Frances Wright was calling for political equality for women. The first public hospital for the insane was established by Dorothea Dix in Massachusetts. Many colleges were founded, among them Colby, Amherst, Mount Holyoke, and Oberlin, the first coeducational college.

William Maclure, president of the Philadelphia Academy of Arts and Sciences, saw in Owen's scheme an opportunity for testing out some ideas of his own on education. Among them was the welding of science and letters. Maclure was a wealthy and cultured Scot who had come here in 1782 at the age of nineteen, gone to England to make a fortune as a merchant, and returned in 1796 to become an American citizen. By the publication in 1817 of his *Observations on the Geology of the United States*, the first attempt at a geological survey of the country, he became known to many as the Father of American Geology.

Maclure invested $150,000 in Robert Owen's New Harmony venture. As an active and wealthy scientist he persuaded many of the best minds of America to join him in the new social experiment. Among these scientists were three of his colleagues of The Academy of Natural Sciences of Philadelphia, and the American Philosophical Society: Dr. Gerhard Troost, Charles Alexander Leseur, and Thomas Say. (Rafinesque intended to join Maclure but never did.) Troost was a Hollander by birth who had become an American citizen. He established an alum manufacturing plant at Cape Sable, Maryland, became the first president of the Philadelphia Academy of Sciences, and was later professor of chemistry at the College of Pharmacy in Philadelphia. Although he had a medical degree from the University of Leyden, he turned to mineralogy and geology and did important work in those fields. Leseur was an artist and zoologist whom Maclure had persuaded in Paris to come to the United States in 1816. Say, the third of this triumvirate, had already distinguished himself in zoology. On the *Boatload of Knowledge*, the name given to the ark which floated down the Ohio from Pittsburgh in January, 1826, were also Joseph Neef, a Pestalozzian educator; John Speakman, a Philadelphia druggist, with his wife; and John Chappelsmith, artist and engraver.

Thomas Say's background and early struggles made him a natural convert to the Owen experiment. He was descended from Huguenots who, after the revocation of the Edict of Nantes by Louis XIV in 1685, fled France to escape religious persecution. Some settled in England, others came to America. Thomas's great-grandfather, William Say, was a Philadelphia harnessmaker. His grandfather, Thomas Say, without benefit of medical degree became a chemist-apothecary and physician and cured patients by sympathetic healing. He removed "wens and indolent tumors dispersed in the glands of the human body by stroking his hands over his patients a few times." He also agitated for the establishment of free schools in Philadelphia for both whites and blacks.

The young scientist's father, Benjamin Say, was brought up and educated by Quakers. He became one of the fighting Quakers, however, and during the Revolution took up arms against the British. He, too, was a physician and druggist, but apparently a more scientific one than his father. He thought enough of Fitch's steamboat invention to subscribe to its promotion. As one of the founders of the College of Physicians of Philadelphia, he took a great interest in humanitarian work. He was also a founder of the Pennsylvania Prison Society and one of the incorporators of the Humane Society of Philadelphia, which was established to prevent "sudden death by drowning, suffocation, burning charcoal, stroke of the sun, drinking cold water, damps of wells, and thunder." He married the granddaughter of the famous botanist, John Bartram, entered politics, became a state senator and later a member of the Congress of the United States.

Thomas Say was born in Philadelphia in 1787. Six years later his mother died and he was sent to a school conducted by the Society of Friends. He did not like his schooling and at the age of fifteen was apprenticed in his father's drugstore. When the biologist William Bartram showed him some beetles and butterflies, Say became extremely interested in natural history. To steer his attention away from this passion, his father contracted a partnership between the boy and John Speakman, another apothecary of Philadelphia. But Speakman, too, was interested in science, and Thomas Say found this Quaker a very agreeable partner. The business arrangement, however, turned out to be an unfortunate one, for neither partner was a businessman. The two would sign notes for needy friends without stopping to find out how much money was available for such commitments. The drugstore languished and expired; Say dropped everything else and devoted himself completely to science.

Philadelphia was at that time the wealthiest city in the United States. Its rich citizens were snobbish, but "it was the fashion to be scientific." In 1795 Dr. Caspar Wistar inaugurated a series of informal parties among the elite, who would gather at his house to discuss literature and science. When Wistar died in 1818, the meetings continued at the homes of friends. Speakman moved in the center of this scientific whirl, and occasionally the back of the partners' drugstore would be the meeting place. Here Say met many American and European scientists, among them the ornithologist Alexander Wilson and the naturalists Barton, Muhlenberg, and Troost. One night Speakman suggested an organization of scientists; in 1812 the new association was born as The Academy of Natural Sciences of Philadelphia.

Three months later the United States declared war on England. The New England merchants were not keen on this drastic action, but the new Congress counted many frontiersmen, including

Henry Clay of Kentucky and John C. Calhoun of South Carolina, who wanted to fight. Britain was accused of supplying arms to the Indians who were massacring Americans in the West. England was also tampering with our merchant shipping and forcibly impressing American seamen into her service. Once again our independence was at stake. Two days before our declaration of war, Great Britain moved to refrain from these provocative acts. Had there been an Atlantic cable, war might have been averted. But war came; England invaded our shores and set fire to our Capitol in Washington, D. C.

Thomas Say became so enraged over this act that he enlisted in the First City Troop of Philadelphia and served for three and a half months, receiving the usual private's pay of two dollars a month. He saw no active service, and continued to botanize and hunt insects while in uniform. Peace was declared in December, 1814, but the news was so slow in reaching the United States that Andrew Jackson fought the bloody Battle of New Orleans two weeks after the declaration.

Soon after the establishment of The Academy of Natural Sciences of Philadelphia, Say was admitted to membership and made curator of its tiny museum. He was also called upon to give a few lectures in zoology, with special emphasis on entomology. In 1813 his father died, leaving him, as his entire legacy, seven eighths of a house at 64 North Second Street and the lot on which it stood. Without a salaried position at the Academy and with no other source of income, Say struggled three years against poverty. He lived in the Academy building, sleeping under the skeleton of a mounted horse. A diet of bread and milk enabled him to live on about twelve cents a day for many months.

Then two splendid opportunities for scientific work came to him. In 1817 William Maclure became president of the Academy. He donated a library of 15,000 scientific books and made liberal cash contributions to the Academy. He also undertook an expedition to gather geological data for his own research project and other scientific information for the society. George Ord, friend of

Alexander Wilson, and Thomas Say were invited to join Maclure. Say took along Bartram's *Travels* and followed his "excellent and ingenious relative, Bartram," as far south as Florida.

The expedition first roamed along the coast and then penetrated the wild lands of Florida. Say was in an entomological heaven, from which he brought back many specimens. He might have gathered a larger collection but for the Florida Indians, who became very unfriendly to the scientists. Nevertheless, Say was sympathetic toward them, blaming the United States government for the "most cruel and inhuman war which our government is unrighteously and unconstitutionally waging against these poor wretches whom we call savages." That same year, upon his return, Say published his first paper on entomology in the *Journal* of the Philadelphia Academy.

The second good fortune for science and Say was his appointment as zoologist on a new government expedition organized by John C. Calhoun, Madison's Secretary of War. A number of professional and amateur naturalists were included in the more than twenty men who were chosen to discover the sources of the Platte, Red, and Arkansas Rivers, the principal tributaries of the Missouri, and to explore the regions around them. In addition to Say, the party included Dr. William Baldwin as physician and surgeon, Augustus E. Jessup as geologist and mineralogist, Samuel Seymour to paint Indians and western landscapes and as assistant naturalist to sketch and prepare the skins of animals. Dr. Edwin James, who had studied under Torrey and Eaton and knew his botany and geology, joined later.

The leader of the expedition was Major Stephen H. Long, graduate of Dartmouth College, instructor of mathematics at West Point, and army engineer. His party left Pittsburgh on May 5, 1819, and descended the Ohio River on one of the first steamboats ever built. It was a seventy-five-foot stern-wheeler, the *Western Engineer*. Painted on the boat was a large serpent whose mouth belched clouds of steam from the boilers. The steamer was described by the inhabitants along the river as a boat which "neither

wind nor human hands are seen to help; and to the eye of ignorance the illusion is complete that a monster of the deep carries
on his back smoking with fatigue and lashing the waves with violent exertions."

The *Western Engineer* reached St. Louis in a little more than
a month, and on June 22, 1819, started its trip up the Missouri
River. This was a very slow voyage, for the boat traveled upstream
at the speed of about three miles an hour. It finally managed to
reach Council Bluffs, Iowa, the first steamboat to go so far. On
August 31, Dr. Baldwin died, and Say was asked to take over the
work of chronicling the expedition. He begged off, saying he was
not competent for such an important journalistic task.

For more than a year the men collected mineral specimens, skins
of animals, shells, plants, and insects, and studied the geology and
weather conditions of the broad region over which they roamed.
In spite of the suffering the group endured not only from weather
but also from swarms of blowflies, intermittent fever, stomach ailments, ticks, and fatigue, the scientific contributions of the expedition were considerable. These included sixty skins of rare and
previously unknown animals, five hundred undescribed plants,
fossils of many kinds, minerals and rocks in a wide variety, as well
as thousands of insects of which several hundred were new to
science. The insect contributions were mostly the work of Say,
who, despite his almost constant illness, made prodigious efforts
to bring back a complete report of the entomology of the region.
In white beaver hat, with a double-barreled gun in his hand and a
hunting knife in his belt, Say set his eyes not so much for the lurk-
ing Pawnee Indian in the hills or the ponderous buffalo on the
prairies, but rather for some strange new plant or swiftly flying
insect. Once while sitting in front of a chief and his tribe with
whom the white men were palavering, Say suddenly jumped up
to chase a *Blaps suturalis,* much to the amazement of the Indians.

Say investigated the habits of various Indian tribes, especially
those living in Kansas and Omaha. With the aid of notes supplied
by Dr. Samuel Brown of Transylvania College, he also studied

various Indian vocabularies. Unfortunately, some of his manuscripts containing notes on the habits and vocabularies of the Indians were stolen by three soldiers who deserted the party.

The *Account of the Expedition from Pittsburgh to the Rocky Mountains* was written by James, Say, and Long, and published in 1823. The expedition was not altogether successful. It failed to discover the sources of either the Platte or Red River. It mistook the peak later named Long's Peak for Pikes Peak. Lieutenant Zebulon Pike in 1806 had first discovered Pikes Peak, in what is now the state of Colorado, while on a military and semiscientific expedition through the territory acquired by the Louisiana Purchase. Some of the blame for the failure of Long's expedition may justly be laid at the door of the government, which showed a foolish and crippling parsimony.

A second expedition was sent out by Calhoun in April, 1823, for the same general scientific purposes. Information was wanted, too, about the extent of the fur trade carried on by the British and American trading companies. Long was again the leader of the expedition, which included Professor William Keating of the University of Pennsylvania as geologist, and Thomas Say, who this time went along as zoologist and antiquarian.

The party traveled from Philadelphia to the Mississippi River by way of the present site of Chicago. The men ascended the river to Fort St. Anthony, and thence to the source of the St. Peter's River. Long's company completed the exploration of the land between the Missouri River, the Mississippi River, and the northern boundary of the United States, an area of about 200,000 square miles.

On August 8, 1823, Long reached the intersection between the Red River and the forty-ninth parallel of latitude. The American flag was hoisted, and Long issued a proclamation establishing the northern boundary line of our country and declaring the territory he had explored to be the soil of the United States. The party returned in a few months by way of the Great Lakes and the Erie Canal.

Thomas Say brought back copious notes. In the *Narrative of an Expedition to the Source of the St. Peter's River*, published in 1825 (in London), about one hundred pages of its two volumes were filled with Say's notes on insects alone. A few pages were devoted to his observations on the shells, birds, and fossils of this area. Say also acted as botanist for this expedition and brought back a large collection of plants and flowers. This he turned over to the botanist Lewis David von Schweinitz at Bethlehem, Pennsylvania. Von Schweinitz was especially interested in fungi; in 1831 he presented to the American Philosophical Society his *Synopsis of North American Fungi*, which included more than 1200 new species and seven new genera of these growths.

Long reported that the area they had explored "is almost wholly unfit for cultivation. However, viewed as a frontier it may prove of infinite importance to the United States, inasmuch as it is calculated to serve as a barrier, to prevent too great an extension of our population westward, and secure us against the machinations or incursions of an enemy that might otherwise be disposed to annoy us in that part of the frontier." Dr. Edwin James, a member of the first expedition, described the same area as a sandy waste containing cacti and stunted sagebrush. James wrote that "the traveller who shall at any time have traversed its desolate sands will, we think, join us in the wish that this region may for long remain the unmolested haunt of the native hunter, the bison and the jackal."

Say, too, on his return to Philadelphia wrote, "The country within five hundred miles of the mountains is destitute of timber and miserably poor, thus furnishing us with an excellent frontier in that direction which is totally unfit for the tillage of civilized man and which may for ages afford an asylum to the cruelly persecuted Indian and its immense herds of bison at present so numerous there." One might have expected a better prophecy from an engineer, a geologist, and a naturalist. But Long, James, and Say could not foresee the iron horse galloping across these hundreds of miles in a few hours. Nor could they vision a rush of Americans from the East, and Scandinavians and Germans from Europe, who with dry farming, irrigation, and other methods of scientific agriculture were to transform this "wasteland" into a fabulous granary.

This discouraging picture halted for a while another wave of the westward movement which had begun about the close of the War of 1812. In addition to the tens of thousands of Scotch-Irish and Germans who went there from Europe after the Napoleonic wars in search of cheap land and work, there were thousands who migrated from our Eastern states. In the five years between 1816 and 1821 five states—Indiana, Mississippi, Illinois, Alabama, and Missouri—were added to the Union. (Florida and the coastal territory west to the Mississippi River were sold to us by Spain in 1819.)

The East was beginning to worry over the loss of its farm and factory hands. The reports of the Long expeditions removed for a while the threat of further westward migration. But even the official reports of scientists engaged by the government could not permanently discourage this movement. The expansionists called it Manifest Destiny. In 1836 and 1837 Arkansas and Michigan were admitted as states, and by 1840, five and a half million people were living between the Alleghenies and the Rockies.

When Thomas Say returned to the Philadelphia Academy in 1823 he resumed the task of building up its museum of scientific collections. He also went back to his insects. In addition to the thousands which he had caught, hundreds of other specimens were coming in from friends and amateurs. Thaddeus W. Harris, a Massachusetts physician, offered him his collection of five hundred insects. Charles Pickering of Salem and Joseph Barabino of New Orleans sent him many specimens. Say wrote to many collectors encouraging them to study "the manners, lives, and conversations of insects" in addition to the color of their hair, eyes, number of bristles, and other details of their structure.

He also undertook a thorough study of the insect work of other Americans before him. "It is certainly of the first importance to a naturalist," he wrote, "to know what has been done by others in his particular science in order that his researches may be directed to proper objects and that he may not do over again what has been better done by his predecessors. I am determined to be as cautious as I can in this respect." Some work in entomology had already been accomplished by Americans, especially in the field of economic entomology. Paul Dudley of Massachusetts wrote a paper on bees in 1723. John Bartram's son, Moses, published his observations on the seventeen-year cicada in 1767. Colonel Landon Carter of Virginia wrote a paper the following year on "the fly weevil that destroys wheat," which appeared in the *Transactions* of the American Philosophical Society. John Bartram had studied wasps, May flies, and dragonflies; five of his short articles on insects were printed in the *Transactions* of the Royal Society. In 1795 Dr. W. D. Peck of Harvard had discussed the cankerworm and other injurious insects. In 1792 the American Philosophical Society appointed a committee, consisting of Jefferson, Benjamin Smith Barton, James Hutchinson, and Caspar Wistar, to study the Hessian fly, which was also ravaging wheat fields. They turned in a full report of the history of this insect. Isaac Chapman had described the blister beetles in 1798, the year after the first book on American insects appeared. This volume was compiled from notes and drawings of John Abbot of Georgia.

Europe actually knew more about American insects at this time than we did. Our amateur collectors of bugs, flies, and beetles sent their specimens to English, French, and German entomologists for identification and classification. Europe had been busy for many years with insect study, a branch of science which had received a great impetus from the publication, between 1734 and 1743 of René Réaumur's *History of Insects* in six volumes. Say made it his business to become familiar with much of this European work. He corresponded and exchanged insect data and specimens with the leading entomologists of Europe, including Comte Pierre Dejean, one of Napoleon's generals.

Thanks to Say's efforts, American entomology came into its

own. American collectors began to send their specimens and questions to Say in Philadelphia rather than to the bigwigs of insect knowledge in Europe. Say worked hard to untangle the chaos of names and classifications of the thousands of American insects which reached his workroom. He respected the feelings of his collaborators and gave credit wherever it was due. When he had to make corrections in names, he made them because he was "very anxious that the vanity that induces many naturalists to change specific names unnecessarily should be discountenanced, for, besides introducing much confusion and adding exceedingly to the labor of the study, it is undoubtedly robbing the first describer of his just rights." Say was no scientific prima donna. He accepted corrections and criticisms graciously, asking his friends to correct his printed errors and "to teach me to do better when they perceive the way open to amendment."

So absorbed did Say become in this titanic job that even eating, which he regarded simply as a bothersome necessity, was frequently forgotten. He remarked that he would have preferred a hole in his side into which he could slip nourishment from time to time just as one tosses wood into the opening of a furnace. His work taxed his eyes, too. Writing to the son of Reverend Frederick V. Melsheimer, amateur entomologist and president of Franklin College in Lancaster, Pennsylvania, Say said, "It gives me much concern to learn that you have been afflicted with an ophthalmia, a disease perhaps more truly distressing to an Entomologist than to almost any other person, and although Rumplius continued his observations in total blindness, and in our own day Huber made extraordinary discoveries although deprived of vision, yet it falls to the lot of but few persons to extend the boundaries of science even when blest with all their organs of sense in full perfection. Do, my dear Sir," he cautioned him, "*have great care of your eyes; but I am giving you council that I have great need of myself. Lamarck I am told is quite blind.*"

Within a year after his return from his second Western adventure, Say was ready with the first volume of his *American*

Entomology, or Descriptions of the Insects of North America.
Charles Alexander Leseur did the frontispiece and drew the insects. The book was published in Philadelphia in 1824 by Dr. Samuel L. Mitchill, who also published the second volume the following year. In the preface to the first volume Say modestly explained the significance of the work. "The author enters upon the task without any expectation of pecuniary remuneration, and fully aware of the many obstacles by which he must inevitably be opposed. . . . Whatever may be its merits or its defects, we must observe, that it is the first attempt of its kind in this country. It is an enterprise that may be compared to that of a pioneer or early settler in a strange land. . . . If our utmost exertions can perform only a part of a projected task, they may, at the same time, claim the praise due to the adventurous pioneer, of removing the difficulties in favor of our successors."

Say's pioneer contribution to American entomology was dedicated to William Maclure, munificent patron of the natural sciences. Soon after the publication of the second volume of *American Entomology,* Maclure asked Say to join him in the New Harmony experiment. Say would be permitted to continue his work on the third and last volume of this book and would give some of his time to teaching science in the college which would be founded there. Say needed no coaxing. He saw in the new venture an opportunity to continue his scientific contributions in an atmosphere of quiet, intellectual companionship without the dread of poverty and with the money and equipment which would facilitate the completion of the many scientific projects he had in mind.

Maclure's party arrived at New Harmony on January 26, 1826. A large scientific library was placed at Say's disposal. He went on a number of important explorations with Maclure and other scientific members of the community as well as with several European visitors who dropped in at New Harmony. One of these trips with Maclure took him in the fall of 1827 as far south as Mexico City and Vera Cruz. Bernhard, Duke of Saxe-Weimar, whom he

had first met in Philadelphia at one of the Wistar parties, came to
New Harmony soon after Say's arrival. The Duke, in his *Travels
through North America*, which was published in 1828, wrote, "I
renewed acquaintance here with Mr. Say whose hands were covered with huge lumps and blisters." Say had been working in his
new garden, where he was cultivating many of the interesting
plants brought back from botanical excursions.

Even with all his scientific preoccupation Thomas Say, who
was tall and handsome, apparently found time to court one of the
"handsomest and most polished" young ladies of New Harmony.
On January 10, 1827, the *New Harmony Gazette* printed the announcement that "Say was married to Lucy Sistaire the other day.
They ran off by themselves to a place beyond Springfield and
were married by a squire somebody who doubtless thought the
party a queer set from the account they gave of it." The men of
the New Harmony colony wore wide pantaloons buttoned over
a boy's collarless jacket, while the women affected coats reaching
to the knee and pantaloons such as little girls then wore.

In 1828 the third and final volume of Say's *American Entomology* was published. There were fifty-four colored plates, all
of them beautifully executed, in the three books. Plate 37 in Volume III was a picture of the *Spectrum* (walking stick); Say's remarks about this insect throw some light on his thinking. He
fought ignorance and superstition, wherever they appeared, with
the weapons of scientific knowledge. "We are told," Say wrote,
"that there was a time when a piece of wood was transformed to
a serpent, and even in the present age of knowledge, a hair fallen
from the mane or tail of a horse into a stream of water. . . . Dead
sticks were said to sprout legs, to move from place to place and
perform all the functions of a living body. These, and a thousand
other equally ridiculous tales were at one period or another more
or less generally admitted as indisputable truths, and to contradict
them would only be to expose oneself to the imputation of ignorance or criminal faithlessness. And although at present the possibility of making a living serpent out of wood, and the story of

animated leaves and sticks would be despised as absurd, yet many are to be found, both in Europe and America, who firmly believe in the reanimation of a horsehair."

Entomology took up the greatest part of Say's scientific attention. Conchology, or the study of shells, was also enriched by his work. He began collecting and studying shells at an early age. When he came to New Harmony he already owned a considerable collection which he had classified. Boxes of insects and shells came pouring in to New Harmony from people all over the United States. After Say had made the final selection of the shells which were to be included in his new book, *American Conchology*, Leseur engraved the plates. Mrs. Say, who helped take charge of the numerous school children at New Harmony, also found time to hand paint the engravings of the book. The New Harmony School press, which Maclure had set up, undertook the work of printing this pioneer work. In 1830 the book finally appeared. Enough copies of both the *American Entomology* and *American Conchology* were distributed to give these branches of study a new impetus in America. Europe was astonished at this achievement. Say had definitely earned for himself the respect of men of science all over the world, as well as the title of Father of American Descriptive Entomology.

Say's hope of working serenely in an atmosphere of deep contentment was far from realized. The nine years he spent at New Harmony were years of much excitement, some of which was not due to the thrills of creative accomplishment and scientific discovery. It came from another source. Among those who joined the colony in Indiana, which numbered a thousand by the middle of 1826, were men and women from all walks of life. There were scientists, amateur natural philosophers, skilled laborers who came to work in the colony's brewery, tannery, hat, soap, and shoe factories; cotton and wool hands, pedagogues, artists, silk-stockinged ladies, and starry-eyed idealists. Many were highly individualistic, and expressed themselves loudly and often when the general rules laid down by the administration interfered with their philosophy or freedom of action. Some were adventurers, others were lazy or emotionally unstable. The usual lunatic fringe found in all reform movements was not absent here. One of Owen's sons, who was left in charge of the experiment while his father went East to lecture, found the situation very difficult. "We have been much puzzled," he wrote, "to know what to do with those who profess to do anything and everything; they are perfect drones and can never be satisfied here. We have got rid of a good many such although we still have a few left."

Quarrels and dissensions broke out, cliques developed out of jealousies or honest differences of opinions. Several aristocratic young ladies under the wing of the brilliant Madame Marie Fretageot, wife of a colonel in Bonaparte's army, refused to dance with partners chosen by lot. Living in close quarters as the colonists did, petty annoyances cropped up and grew into sharp feuds. Seven different new constitutions were adopted by as many different groups. In two years from the time of the first settlement, ten splinter groups had broken away from the parent tree.

Matters were made infinitely worse by a break between Owen and Maclure. Dissatisfaction with the way things were going, and a growing feeling that drastic changes were needed to save the life of the experiment, ended in a quarrel over property rights between the leaders. Maclure had invested $150,000 in the venture, but had stipulated that his liability was not to exceed $10,000. When money began to be used up at an alarming rate, Maclure demanded an accounting, which Owen refused. Much heated discussion ended in the posting of a public notice by the Scot that he would no longer be responsible for Owen's financial transactions. The happy marriage was on the rocks. Maclure went to the courts and sued Owen for $40,000. In return, Owen took out a writ against Maclure for twice this amount. On May 26, 1827, Owen left New Harmony in high dudgeon, and a year later he admitted the failure of his experiment in communal living. An earnest visionary, Owen, before he died in 1858, made several other unsuccessful attempts to establish co-operative communities. New Harmony was later divided and sold to individuals, and eventually became an incorporated town.

Maclure stayed on for a while at New Harmony, and then took Say with him to Mexico City in the winter of 1828-29. Later he started a trade school for boys and girls and a manual-training school for orphans. Ten years later he founded the Workingmen's Institute, to which he donated a large library. When he died near Mexico City in 1840 he left $80,000 for the endowment in the Middle West of dozens of free public libraries to help educate workingmen in Indiana, Illinois, and other Midwestern states.

In 1827 Troost left New Harmony to become professor of chemistry, geology, and mineralogy at the University of Nashville, in Tennessee. Leseur stayed on with Say for two more years; then he, too, left for France to devote himself to painting. The four sons of Owen, all of whom became American citizens, continued to live at New Harmony. The eldest, Robert Dale Owen, edited the *New Harmony Gazette* for a while; David Dale Owen became a well-known geologist; and Richard Owen, state geologist of Indiana, lived at New Harmony until his death, in 1890, at the age of eighty-one.

When Maclure was away from New Harmony the colony was left in the care of Say and Madame Fretageot. Say was modest, scrupulously honest, and faithful to every trust imposed upon him. He was, however, not equipped for administrative duties, and in money matters he was like a child among thieves. In addition to this work and his scientific projects he was persuaded in 1830 to accept an assignment as editor of New Harmony's *Disseminator of Useful Knowledge from the School of Industry*. These duties sapped his already weak body and left him sickly during the last years of his life. Frequent attacks of dysentery and fever finally carried him away in 1834 at the age of forty-seven. He was buried in the heart of New Harmony; in 1846 a brick vault was built for Say's remains and a new tombstone erected by Alexander Maclure. Say's widow died forty years later at the age of eighty-six.

Many scientists from America and Europe came to visit New Harmony and to observe its scientists and educators at work. Constantine Rafinesque, Leo Lesquereux, Joseph Leidy, and Sir Charles Lyell were among the eminent men who went to Indiana to watch the experiment. Maximilian, Prince of Wied, spent four months with Say during the winter of 1832-33 before publishing his *Travels in the Interior of North America*. Before the New Harmony episode was closed, it exerted a tremendous influence on the progress of science and public education in America, especially in the Middle West. From New Harmony came Josiah Warren's invention of the continuous roller press, the first regular weather reports, and one of the first trade schools in America. Here Say's important books on American entomology and conchology were printed; here the plates of Michaux's famous botanical book, *North American Sylva*, were colored and the book reprinted. Here the United States Geological Survey moved its staff of mapmakers and engineers when David Dale Owen in 1835 began his geological survey of Indiana.

The importance of Thomas Say in the story of American science is not based on any great original contribution. It is based, rather, on the impetus he gave to neglected areas of biological investigation and to his own accurate reporting of the largest collection of insects ever made by a single man up to his time in America. He was a superb describer of the insect world. Five years after Say's death, Erichson in Europe wrote, "In brevity I see that no one excels the American Say who published descriptions so concise that they hardly go beyond the extent of a diagnosis, nevertheless, so clear that you will hardly ever find doubtful a form exhibited by him." He helped immeasurably to lessen the confusion in the naming of the myriad denizens of the insect world.

It is difficult to give an exact reckoning of all the different insects Say described during the twenty years of his entomological labors. Among them he described 1150 new species of Coleoptera,

225 species of Diptera, 100 Hemiptera, and at least 100 other species.

Dr. Thaddeus W. Harris worked on Say's insect collections, which were in a very bad state of deterioration when he received them. He called himself "a second Hercules doomed to clean the thousand stables [Say's insects] of Augeas [Philosophical Society] from filth." It took him several years to get some of the insects back into a tolerably good condition for mounting and cataloguing. Some of these may be found at the Boston Society of Natural History. Only a single specimen, *Chionobas semidea*, remains with The Academy of Natural Sciences of Philadelphia. Dr. John Lawrence Le Conte, twenty-five years after the death of Say, published in France his entire work on insects, in two volumes comprising 1226 pages.

Say also did some work with American birds. He prepared for the press Charles Lucien Bonaparte's *Natural History of Birds Inhabiting the United States*, which continued the story told in Wilson's *American Ornithology*. Scientists of the British Museum acknowledged his contributions by naming the genus *Sayornis* after him, and Bonaparte named the pewee, *Sayornis sayus*, in his honor. Actually Say did very little original work with American birds, but in the Museum of Banff, British Columbia, one can still view a number of stuffed birds labeled Say's orange-crowned warbler, Say's long-billed dowitcher, and Say's band-tailed pigeon. Say was known very well not only in England, where he was a member of the Linnaean Society of London and the Zoological Society of England, but also in France as a correspondent of the Société Philomathique of Paris.

During Say's time, others were busy with the biota of America. High in the list of these naturalists was Thomas Nuttall, one of the most lovable characters in the history of early American science. Nuttall was a journeyman printer who had come here from Yorkshire, England, in 1808, at the age of twenty-two. Professor Benjamin Smith Barton, his neighbor, turned his interests to botany, and William Maclure helped finance some of his botanical excursions. In 1809 he joined John Bradbury to the Platte and Mandan regions, where he almost lost his life. In 1817 he became a member of the American Philosophical Society at the same meeting when Thomas Say and Lewis David von Schweinitz were admitted. His two-volume *Genera of North American Plants* was published in 1818. During this year he was traveling, with the financial assistance of Maclure and Zaccheus Collins, through dangerous Indian territory in Arkansas never before explored by scientists. He studied not only the botany but the geology and bird life of this region. Five years later Harvard College called him to teach botany. After remaining there eleven years, during which he produced two volumes of an illustrated *Manual of the Ornithology of the United States and Canada,* he left Cambridge to join Captain Wyeth's second expedition. John K. Townsend, who was to bring back many new birds from Oregon and Washington, accompanied him on this trip. He was very shy. His bedroom was over his study, and he "put a trapdoor in the floor of an upper connecting closet, and so by a ladder could pass between his rooms without the chance of being met in the passage or on the stairs."

The rest of this description is so reminiscent of the famous chemist, Henry Cavendish, the eccentric millionaire misanthrope of England who discovered hydrogen, that it is worthy of note. "A flap, hinged and buttoned in the door between the lower closet and the kitchen, allowed his meals to be sent in on a tray without the chance of being seen. A window he cut down into an open door, and, with a small gate in the board fence surrounding the garden, of which he alone had the key, he could pass in and out safe from encountering any human being." After botanizing here for thirty-three years, Nuttall returned to his native land. An estate had been bequeathed to him on condition that he reside in England.

Nuttall is said to have discovered more new genera and species of plants in North America than any other single scientist with the possible exception of his young contemporary, Asa Gray.

Gray was the son of an Irish tanner in New York. After receiving a medical degree he was diverted to botany by the influence of Dr. John Torrey, another New York physician, botanist, and chemist. In the year of Say's death, Gray read his first paper in botany before the New York Lyceum of Natural History. Four years later appeared the first two parts of the *Flora of North America*, written by Torrey with Gray's assistance. The material was organized and systematized according to the natural system of Jussieu rather than that of Linnaeus. Gray joined the staff of Harvard College in 1842, and became the greatest authority of his day on the flora of the United States.

The labors of Say and his contemporaries, long and arduous as they were, did not by any means complete the record of the flora and fauna of the United States. The work of these men had no widespread dramatic appeal and, as a result, they were little known to the general public. Nevertheless, the contributions of these naturalists were important. They helped not only to illuminate many of the hidden biological corners of the continent, but also to pile up information which helped in the creation of a new and fundamental biological synthesis. Say was followed by many others who, even today, are searching in the most inaccessible crannies of America for new scraps of biological knowledge.

CHAPTER SEVEN

WILLIAM T. G. MORTON
(1819-1868)

AMERICA MAKES MEDICAL HISTORY

UNTIL ABOUT the beginning of the third decade of the nineteenth century the story of medicine in the New World was one of dependence upon Europe, especially upon the University of Edinburgh, the leading medical school in Great Britain, for instruction and inspiration. Since medical advance throughout the world was slow even in the foremost centers of Europe, little of any great consequence was accomplished here. But coincident with and resulting from the burgeoning of Yankee inventiveness and the emergence of the rugged individualism of the frontier came a series of discoveries and inventions in medicine which turned out to be of world importance. Individual courage based on self-reliance, sheer necessity when lone doctors found themselves on the fringes of the wilderness with only their daring to save a life, and the lure of invention with its pot of gold at the end of a rainbow, all contributed to this new development.

Physicians healed as best they could with laxatives and purgatives such as tartar emetic and calomel, and with medicinal concoctions many of which were of doubtful value. Druggists came here from Europe and opened the first drugstore in Boston in 1646. Bloodletting, a heritage from Europe, was practiced by most doctors even on patients who needed a blood transfusion. George Washington, suffering from a severe cold and possibly a septic sore throat, was bled four times in twenty-four hours, and thus hastened to his death two days later. Benjamin Rush, professor of medicine at the medical school of the College of Philadelphia and foremost physician of his day, called it the sovereign remedy; he himself was bled to death in 1813 by his own doctor, Philip Syng Physick of Philadelphia, "Father of American Surgery." Pus around wounds was considered "laudable," and blisters were brought on to help fight disease.

Before the outbreak of the Revolutionary War only two medical schools existed in the colonies. The first was established in 1765 at the College of Philadelphia, now the University of Pennsylvania. Two years later King's College (now Columbia) opened a medical school in New York City. Harvard established a medical school in 1782. The first medical journal in the United States was founded in 1797. Most of our practicing physicians never attended a medical school either here or abroad. They received their training as apprentices to other physicians, with whom they made the rounds and prepared salves and medicines. They then received medical certificates from their masters. Some never even served their apprenticeship, for there were no laws regulating the practice of medicine, and quacks abounded like locusts.

When the Revolutionary War broke out, Dr. John Morgan was appointed Director General of the military hospitals and Physician-in-chief of the Continental Army, succeeding the traitor, Benjamin Church. Morgan had been a brilliant student at the medical school in Edinburgh, where he showed, for the first time, that pus came from the blood vessels and not from the solid tissues. During the Revolution, sanitary conditions in army camps and hospitals were almost primitive. Even in the mansions of the rich there was no plumbing. Rush ordered troops not to be quartered near swamps because it was believed the "miasmas" from marshes brought disease. He also ordered soldiers to cut their hair short because he believed that perspiration when it dried in long hair had a tendency to cause illnesses. Our soldiers, too, were inoculated against smallpox. But other diseases, such as typhoid, dysentery, and typhus, took heavy toll. Lack of sufficient medical supplies, the backwardness of medicine, inefficiency, and the many squabbles between Drs. John Morgan, William Shippen (another graduate of Edinburgh), and Benjamin Rush helped to pile up a frightful record of military deaths. Nine of our soldiers died of disease to every one killed by British bullets. At one time Benjamin Rush told John Adams that "The present management of our army would depopulate America if men grew among us as speedily and spontaneously as blades of grass!"

However, a few bright chapters in this dismal picture of medicine and surgery were soon to be written. The first great moment for American surgery occurred on Christmas day in 1809 at the end of the Wilderness Trail in Danville, Kentucky. Here lived Dr. Ephraim McDowell, whose Scotch-Irish father had become a judge in Kentucky. Judge McDowell was an active liberal who campaigned for universal manhood suffrage and against slavery. He presided over nine territorial conventions in Kentucky, fought against those who wanted to join up with Spain, and finally won the battle for the admission of Kentucky into the Union in 1792. His son, Ephraim, had gone to Edinburgh to win his medical degree, and had married the daughter of Isaac Shelby, the famous Revolutionary general who later became the first governor of Kentucky.

In 1809 a Mrs. Crawford, who was suffering from a huge ovarian tumor, came to Dr. McDowell for advice. The tumor had to be removed or she would die. The physician explained the dangers of an abdominal operation. No one had ever performed such surgery. Even his eminent teachers at Edinburgh, John Bell and William Hunter, taught that opening of the abdominal cavity would be fatal. McDowell's own life, too, was at stake. The inhabitants of that frontier village would hang him if he failed in this "impossible operation." The woman, however, consented to the operation. McDowell strapped her to a plain wooden table and cut. The patient survived and made a complete recovery. It was seven years before he published an account of this operation in the *Eclectic Repository*. Others followed his example, very slowly, of course. But operations for appendicitis, kidney, liver, gall, and spleen disorders were no longer considered fatal, especially after the introduction of anesthesia. The frontier, bolder and less shackled than the hoary universities of Europe, showed the world a new step forward in medicine.

In 1822 American medicine reached another milestone in another of its outposts. At a remote trading post on Mackinac Island, between Lake Huron and Lake Michigan, a bullet from an accidentally discharged musket tore a hole in the side of a young French-Canadian *voyageur*, Alexis St. Martin. Dr. William Beaumont, a Connecticut army surgeon attached to a near-by fort, was called. He found that the bullet had passed through the wall of the victim's stomach. He managed to patch him up, but despite great skill and patience it was impossible to get the wound to close completely. On healing, a fleshy flap was left which covered the opening into St. Martin's stomach. A strange idea came to Beaumont. Perhaps only a man accustomed to the dangers of frontier life and enjoying the leisure of a frontier army post might have thought of it. The freak "lid" over the hole in St. Martin's stomach would enable the doctor to reach directly into the stomach and perform some interesting experiments. At least a dozen cases of gastric fistula had been previously reported in medical literature, but no one before Beaumont had dared to execute such a plan.

The American doctor talked it over with the young lad, who agreed to co-operate in a series of experiments to determine the nature of the digestive action of the juices in his stomach. The soldier-scientist tied pieces of food to strings, inserted them into St. Martin's stomach through the flap, and after several hours removed what was left of the food. These experiments lasted over a period of several years, during which the often rebellious human guinea pig revolted and ran away only to be brought back by tempting offers of higher wages and better operating conditions. Finally, in December, 1833, Beaumont, then stationed at Plattsburg, New York, published at his own expense a cheap edition of one thousand copies of his report on these classic experiments. He supplied science with accurate facts concerning the relative digestibility of different foods as well as the composition of gastric juice. Beaumont found that the gastric juice in his subject contained a small amount (about 0.3%) of hydrochloric acid, which aided in the digestion of certain nutrients, especially proteins. He also observed that fatigue and emotional strain reduced the flow of gastric juice. And so, out of the American wilderness, came another medical discovery by a man untrained in scientific research and equipped with only the most primitive apparatus for such an important project.

So inadequate was the dissemination of scientific information in those days that Beaumont was unaware of the fact that back in 1803 another American had performed similar experiments. John Richardson Young, born near Hagerstown, Maryland, son of an Irish physician, also worked on the chemistry of digestion. He tied different kinds of food on pieces of string, and had bullfrogs and snakes swallow them whole. His frogs and snakes also swallowed other foods wrapped in bags. Young contrived to have larger frogs swallow the hind legs of smaller frogs, which continued to live with their heads sticking out of the mouths of the bigger frogs and their legs in the others' stomachs. The animals and food were withdrawn from the stomachs of his hungry test animals, and the results of digestion were then studied. Young even used himself as a human beaker, following the same procedure he had used on his frogs and snakes. From these experiments he concluded in his medical graduation thesis that an acid in the gastric juice (he erroneously thought it was phosphoric acid), and not some mysterious vital spirit or innate heat, was responsible for digestive action. This pioneer physiological chemist died in 1804 of tuberculosis at the age of twenty-two. One hundred and thirty-five years later his alma mater, the medical school of the University of Pennsylvania, unveiled a plaque to his memory.

Out of the sparsely settled Middle West came another important medical contribution. It was a monumental work called *Treatise on the Principal Diseases of the Interior Valley of North America,* written by Dr. Daniel Drake, and published in part in 1850. It contained the climate, botany, topography, and social conditions of the inhabitants of the whole region between the Alleghenies and the Rockies, as well as the diseases met there. The book, several thousand pages long, has been called the greatest addition to medical geography since Hippocrates.

Drake was born in 1785 of poor New Jersey farmers who soon after his birth migrated to Kentucky. He, too, studied medicine under Rush at the University of Pennsylvania Medical School. In 1820 he organized the Medical College of Ohio, in Cincinnati, which at that time had a population of about 2500. John L. Richmond, pioneer of Caesarean operations in America, attended this institution. Drake also published the *Western Journal of Medical and Physical Sciences*, the first medical journal west of the Alleghenies. He founded a museum in Cincinnati of which Audubon was for a while curator. He was the center of the intellectual life of the Middle West for many years. Abraham Lincoln, worried about his frequent fits of melancholia, heard of Drake and wrote to him asking advice. "I cannot prescribe in your case," came back the answer, "without a personal interview." Drake was very much interested in the social aspects of medicine and regarded "medicine not only as a physical science, but also as a social profession."

The wilderness and the frontier of America had no monopoly of bold experimenters and keen scientific philosophers. Boston was the scene of another important contribution to medicine. Oliver Wendell Holmes read a paper in 1843 before the members of the Boston Society of Medical Improvement. It dealt with puerperal fever, an illness which through the centuries had carried off millions of healthy mothers during childbirth. Poor and rich alike succumbed, and medicine was helpless against this scourge. Holmes, essayist and practicing physician, wondered about the causes of this disease. Antisepsis and the germ theory were still in the future, yet Holmes saw the real cause of puerperal fever as contamination of the victim by the attending doctor. For centuries physicians never hesitated to go directly from post-mortem examination of puerperal-fever cases or from the morgue to the confinement room.

In his paper, *On the Contagiousness of Puerperal Fever*, the Harvard physician warned doctors to stop this deadly practice. He told them to change their clothes, wash up thoroughly, and wait at least twenty-four hours after leaving a puerperal-fever patient before approaching the bedside of an expectant mother. Holmes, father of the very eminent Justice of the United States who bore his name, closed his historic paper with the statement, "Whatever indulgence may be granted to those who have heretofore been the ignorant causes of such misery, the time has come when the existence of a private pestilence in the sphere of a single physician should be looked upon, not as a misfortune, *but a crime.*"

There was a good deal of eyebrow raising among the professors of obstetrics at the medical schools of the University of Pennsylvania and Jefferson Medical College. Holmes, it was whispered, was not even connected with a hospital at the time and drew his unorthodox conclusions not from bedside experience but from mental cogitations, perhaps with his literary circle of Hawthorne, Emerson, and Longfellow. However, there were many physicians who remembered the prize essay he had written in 1837 on *The Utility and Importance of Direct Exploration in Medical Practice*, in which he urged the introduction of Laënnec's stethoscope, which the French physician had invented in 1819. These men accepted his warning advice, and many mothers were saved.

Three thousand miles away, in Vienna, no one had heard of the American physician Holmes and his new theory. But four years later, just as Holmes became professor of anatomy at Harvard College, the same conclusion about the causes of puerperal fever was reached by a young doctor, Ignaz Semmelweiss. This Hungarian physician did more than Holmes, however. He actually carried out a series of rigorous experiments to test the accuracy of his theory of the contagiousness of this fever. Using chlorine as a disinfectant, he convinced himself that when the proper sanitary precautions were taken, the number of deaths from puerperal fever was cut down dramatically. He shouted to the medical world to stop carrying the fatal disease from one bed to another. But Semmelweiss, too, was laughed at. He experimented further, repeated his warnings, and fought his opponents until they called him a madman. Yet his message was heard, and a new era dawned for those who at home or in a hospital were at the mercy of midwife and obstetrician.

Even for many years after this great triumph of medicine, general asepsis was not understood. Margaret Leech, in *Reveille in Washington*, gives a vivid description of surgery during the Civil War: "The surgeon rolled up his sleeves, gave his knife a last flick on the sole of his boot, and the operation began. The probe carried the infection deep into the torn tissues. If one of the sponges happened to drop on the floor it was squeezed in water and used at once. In threading the needle for the stitches, it was customary to point the silk by wetting it with saliva and rolling it with the fingers. Blood poisoning, tetanus, secondary hemorrhage and gangrene were familiar visitors."

Four great medical advances marked the nineteenth century. Three of them were European contributions: Virchow's cell doctrine, Pasteur's germ theory of disease, and Lister's practice of antisepsis. The fourth fundamental advance was the introduction of anesthesia. This was accomplished in America. Seldom has so much tragedy touched the lives of so many people intimately connected with a single scientific discovery.

In the city of Boston, in 1842, William Thomas Green Morton, son of a well-to-do farmer and shopkeeper of Charlton, Massachusetts, had turned his Yankee inventiveness to the problem of devising an economical dental plate. This "shy and strange" lad had turned out to be a clever mechanic. He had invented a solder for fastening artificial teeth to dental plates, he could handle dental bridge work, and even did some plastic surgery. His new plate was a great improvement. The public was ready to welcome it with enthusiasm. But there was one serious drawback. For this plate to fit comfortably and snugly in the mouth, the roots of old teeth had to be removed and even healthy teeth had to be extracted. If he could only find some way of preventing pain during dental extraction, the false teeth which he was manufacturing on a large scale would sell by the thousands, and he could easily make a fortune. The get-rich-quick bee was buzzing around the land, and the Patent Office in Washington bore testimony to the tremendous activity in the field of invention.

Morton had been in the first graduating class (1842) of the first dental school in America, the Baltimore College of Dental Surgery. Here he heard much discussion of the agelong struggle to find a painkiller. The ancient Egyptians had produced temporary insensibility by applying pressure to the carotid artery in the neck, thus stopping the flow of blood to the head. The Chinese had used an anesthetic known as Ma Fat powder, a sort of hashish which they discovered in the second century. The juices of mandragora and other plants were used for centuries to allay pain. South American Indians chewed coca leaves and lime and spat in the wound as they operated. Paracelsus, the Swiss medical reformer, gave crude opium and laudanum to the world during the sixteenth century. In 1805 Sertürner extracted morphine from crude opium and gave mankind another great pain destroyer. Some doctors in Paris, Edinburgh, and Calcutta even used hypnotism (animal magnetism or mesmerism) to produce temporary anesthetic effects, and it is said that the French surgeon Dupuytren would deliberately insult ladies to throw them into a fainting spell prior to an operation.

But mankind continued to suffer pain and cried out for deliverance. The hoary wise men of Europe, the great Pooh-Bahs of the most celebrated universities of England and the Continent, saw no hope. There was no point, they insisted, in putting a patient into a state of unconsciousness and expecting the surgeon to do a good job of operating. Give up the search, they counseled. Only three years before Morton invented his plate, the noted French surgeon, Alfred Velpeau, declared, "The abolishment of pain in surgery is a chimera. It is absurd to go on seeking it today. *Knife* and *pain* are two words in surgery that must forever be associated in the consciousness of the patient. To this compulsory combination we shall have to adjust ourselves."

But the long arm of medical conservatism did not stay the ambition of the American dentist. A way must be found to make his dental plates sell in gross lots. Meanwhile, another young dentist from Hartford, Connecticut, was dreaming the same dream. He, too, was searching for a method to produce temporary anesthesia for his dental work. Horace Wells, in December, 1844, read an advertisement in the Hartford *Courant* announcing a lecture and demonstration by Gardner Q. Colton, an itinerant entertainer. Among the demonstrations listed was one on the effects of *laughing gas*. "The gas will be administered," read the advertisement, "only to gentlemen of the first respectability to make the entertainment a genteel affair."

Laughing gas was not really new. It had been discovered by Joseph Priestley in 1772, even before oxygen. Twenty-three years later Humphry Davy, then seventeen, had inhaled some of it to relieve the pain of his inflamed gums. Davy also noted the effects of this gas, nitrous oxide (N_2O), on animals, and reported, "As nitrous oxide in its extensive operation appears capable of destroying physical pain, it may probably be used to advantage during surgical operations in which no great effusion of blood takes place." For three years, while Davy was assisting Thomas Beddoes, a physician of Shropshire, England, who had founded a Pneumatic Institute at Clifton, the gas was used against asthma, catarrh, and hysteria. Beddoes' system of treating certain illnesses by the inhalation of gases such as oxygen, carbon dioxide, and nitrous oxide was short-lived. However, the physiological effects of inhaling laughing gas interested professional entertainers, and its use for this purpose spread to thousands of towns and villages throughout Europe and the United States. As a young man, Samuel Colt, as Dr. Coult, made enough money, by demonstrating laughing gas in sideshows, to get his new revolver patented in 1836. This "revolving gun" played a part in the winning of the West.

Wells and his wife watched Colton administer the gas to several volunteers, who definitely lost their sense of pain for a considerable length of time while under the influence of the gas. He saw in this gas a possible painkiller for dental operations. After the show he persuaded Colton to administer the gas to him and then had a tooth extracted from his own mouth without feeling any pain. He was so convinced that this was the painkiller he was searching for that he managed to arrange a public demonstration of its powers before the medical faculty and students of Harvard. Something went wrong during the demonstration, and the audience was not convinced of its effectiveness. Wells tried the gas on one of his patients, who died while under the influence of the anesthetic. He gave up dentistry, tried several other business ventures, such as selling shower baths, purchasing paintings in Paris, and touring Connecticut with a troupe of singing canaries. All of his ventures failed. He began to deteriorate mentally, and finally, in a fit of melancholia, he committed suicide on January 24, 1848, in his thirty-third year.

In the meantime great things were happening to William Morton, with whom Wells had for a short time in 1842 been in dental partnership in Boston. Morton had assisted Wells in the unfortunate Boston demonstration. After Wells had failed to show the effectiveness of nitrous oxide as an anesthetic, Morton looked around for some other agent. Perhaps ether would do the trick? This colorless, volatile liquid had been known for several centuries. Valerius Cordus in 1540 had described its method of manufacture by treating grain alcohol with sulfuric acid. Both Cordus and Paracelsus knew of its pain-relieving properties, and of its ability to render certain animals, such as chickens, temporarily unconscious. Michael Faraday, the famous English experimenter, had studied the liquid and had contributed a paper on its properties to the *Journal of Science and Arts* in 1818. Faraday noted in this paper that "When the vapor of ether is mixed with common air and inhaled, it produces effects very similar to those occasioned by nitrous oxide." But Faraday's findings made no impression on European doctors. A few years later John D. God-man, an American, also experimented and called attention to the pain-relieving effects of ether. American doctors paid no heed, either.

Morton decided to test out the properties of ether for himself. At his country place in West Needham he tried ether first on various insects, green worms, fish, chickens, and on his spaniel. It worked. Then he decided to try its effects on himself. He seated himself in a chair, poured some ether on a handkerchief, and, holding a watch in one hand, applied the moistened handkerchief over his mouth and nose. He soon lost consciousness and did not come to for seven full minutes. This was long enough to extract not one but as many as three teeth, he told himself. Morton called upon a friend to extract one of his healthy teeth while he was under the influence of this chemical. Again it worked. Morton felt no pain at all.

That evening a man named Eben Frost called at his dental office with a terrible pain from an infected back tooth. He asked Morton to hypnotize him before extracting the tooth to save him from the dreadful pain. Morton told him he had a new chemical which would put him to sleep. Frost agreed to let Morton perform the extraction by this new method. That same evening, September 30, 1846, Morton extracted a "firmly rooted bicuspid," and the man suffered no pain.

Morton had Frost sign an affidavit attesting to the facts of the operation. The following morning the Boston *Daily Journal* made a very modest announcement of the event: "Last evening a man had a tooth pulled without experiencing any pain. He was thrown into a kind of sleep by inhaling a preparation whose effects lasted about a minute, just long enough to pull the tooth." Boston shook its head and would hardly believe the news. But Morton's dental practice began to show an immediate improvement.

Morton was not satisfied with his method of inhalation. He drew plans for a more efficient device which he had an instrument maker, Chamberlain, construct for him. It consisted of an eight-inch glass globe fitted at one end with a sort of hose and at the other with a hole plugged by a cork stopper. It now occurred to Morton that he could spread the blessings of ether anesthesia into the whole field of surgery, and incidentally increase his business. If he could succeed in getting some eminent surgeon in Boston to try it, Morton and the whole pain-racked world would be the beneficiaries.

At the Massachusetts General Hospital Morton found two eminent men who were willing to make the trial. Dr. John C. Warren was the leading surgeon of New England and professor of surgery at the Harvard Medical School. He consented to perform an operation on a patient in the surgical amphitheater of the Massachusetts General Hospital on the morning of Friday, October 16, 1846. Morton ordered a new inhalator and on the morning of the appointed day rushed into the amphitheater somewhat late. Dr. Warren had almost given up hope of seeing him face the public test. The patient, Gilbert Abbot, a twenty-year-old book printer, was brought in. He had a vascular tumor just under the jaw, on the right side, which was to be removed. Morton approached the patient and removed the cork from the glass inhalator. Abbot took the tube in his mouth and in three minutes was asleep.

Warren, who was almost seventy, worked quickly and skillfully with the knife. The tumor was cut away. The patient still breathed heavily. In five minutes he came out of his stupor. Warren asked if he had felt the pain. No, there was only a slight scratching sensation, was the reply. Turning to Dr. Henry J. Bigelow and the other assembled medical men, and addressing, too, the students on their benches, Dr. Warren exclaimed, "Gentlemen, this is no humbug." Deafening applause followed, the patient was wheeled out, and Dr. Bigelow remarked, "I have seen something today that will be heard round the world." And October 16 is still celebrated at the Massachusetts General Hospital as "Ether Day."

One month after the historic trial in Boston, Dr. Bigelow published an article in the *Boston Medical and Surgical Journal* announcing the great event to the whole medical world. A new day had dawned. England's famous medical journal, the *Lancet*, wrote, "The discovery of Dr. Morton will undoubtedly be placed high among the blessings of human knowledge and discovery. That its discoverer should be an American is a high honor to our transatlantic brethren; next to the discovery of Franklin, it is the second and greatest contribution of the New World to science." Surgery at one clip plunged forward with seven-league boots. No longer would operating rooms shake with the agonies of men and women. No longer would surgeons fight, often hopelessly, against time while shackled patients disturbed their skillful fingers as the scalpel cut through living flesh. For the first time, surgeons would dare perform operations which seemed hopeless before ether anesthesia. Animal experimentation, too, received a new and refreshing impetus. Before the close of 1846 surgeons in London and Paris were using ether anesthesia, and in the opening month of the following year Germany and Austria took hold of the new weapon of medicine. Dr. Piragoff brought the new deliverer to the Russian soldiers wounded in the Caucasus.

Among those who read of the great event was Dr. James Young Simpson, chief of the lying-in wards of the Edinburgh Infirmary. He quickly introduced the use of ether as a new boon to motherhood. A number of bad effects from ether, however, led him to look around for a substitute anesthetic. He tried chloroform. This volatile liquid had been made for the first time by Samuel Guthrie, an American army surgeon stationed in a remote region on the shore of Lake Ontario. Born in Prinfield, Massachusetts, of Scotch-Irish parents in 1782, Guthrie made the painkilling chemical late in 1830 by treating chloride of lime with grain alcohol. He did not publish his results, however, until 1832, when his account appeared in the *American Journal of Science*. Two other chemists, Soubeiran in France and Liebig in Germany, made independent discoveries of the same chemical at about the same time. In his original article Guthrie showed that he was not unmindful of the possible use of this new chemical, for he wrote, "During the last six months a great number of persons have drunk the solution of chloric ether [later named chloroform by Dumas] in my laboratory, not very freely but frequently to the point of intoxication . . . to discover its probable value as a medicine." Guthrie gave chloroform to his daughter when she was almost suffocated by the fumes of a charcoal fire—the "first human being that ever used it in sickness."

Dr. Simpson tried the effects of chloroform on rabbits and other small animals. When the results seemed promising, he and two of his friends inhaled the vapors of the liquid and were convinced that it was a safe and effective anesthetic. He took the next step in November, 1847, and introduced chloroform as an anesthetic during childbirth. The Scotch theologians fought the introduction of this method on the ground that it was against the will of God. The conflict raged for more than five years. Simpson went to the Bible and picked out the twenty-first verse of the second chapter of Genesis. He confronted the theologians with the Biblical account of the removal of the rib of Adam out of which Eve was made. Simpson pointed out that God caused a deep sleep to fall on Adam before removing the rib, and offered this to prove that the Lord was not opposed to painkilling operations. The controversy ended in April, 1853, when Queen Victoria gave birth to her seventh child, Prince Leopold, under chloroform.

While ether, nitrous oxide, and chloroform were beginning to dull the pains of mankind and to save lives, a heated controversy was raging over priority of discovery and patent rights concerning ether. The so-called Ether Controversy is worth recounting. It could have happened here at almost any time, but the get-rich-quick fever of this period and the weakness of our laws protecting patent holders made such an incident especially possible then. It was a turbulent period in American history, covering the "fabulous forties" when wealth from the rich lands of the West and from a booming merchant marine was beginning to roll into the purses of poor men. This was the period when Yankee inventiveness was in high gear, and new inventions were popping up daily. Every mechanic dreamed of a fortune for every gadget he fashioned in his woodshed or attic. Money was being made quickly, and there were men ready to snatch wealth from ingenious inventors.

It is not a simple matter to unravel the tangled skein of the ether affair. In conflict with the above story as told by Morton there is a somewhat different one involving Dr. Charles T. Jackson. From the most reliable sources one can piece together the following composite story. While Morton was engaged in his dental business he took some courses at the medical school of Harvard College. Here he met Dr. Jackson, in whose home he lived for some time while in Boston. Jackson was an all-around science man who had a chemical laboratory of his own, engaged in geological work, and played around with numerous inventions. When Morton told him of the failure of nitrous oxide as an anesthetic in dentistry, Jackson mentioned that he might try ether. He further suggested that he could supply Morton with some pure ether if he cared to experiment with it. Jackson also stated that he had used this chemical to counteract the effects of an accidental chlorine gas inhalation.

Morton listened intently to every bit of information regarding the use and properties of ether, but was loath to enter into any partnership or agreement with Jackson, who had a none too savory reputation. He had his fingers in many a scientific pie, and his fingers were not always clean. He had corresponded with Dr. William Beaumont, from whom he managed to get a vial of gastric juice taken from the stomach of his French-Canadian guinea pig. He had tried but failed to get Beaumont and St. Martin to go on a tour of the country under his showmanship. It was this same Jackson, too, who had talked with Samuel Morse about some electrical experiment he had witnessed in Paris. Jackson showed Morse a small electromagnet he had brought back with him and set the painter to thinking of what finally became the first successful electric telegraph. Jackson later attempted to wangle some money out of Morse for his doubtful part in the great invention, and had been dismissed as an "intolerable nuisance."

Morton suggested that a successful public demonstration of the use of ether as an anesthetic in surgery would bring instant success.

Jackson thought that Morton ought to get in touch with Dr. Warren of the Massachusetts General Hospital. However, before this step could be taken he suggested that Morton patent his ether under some trade name. Morton applied for a patent on Morton's Letheon (the mythical waters of Lethe obliterated all painful memories) in his and Jackson's names. He agreed to give Jackson ten per cent of the profits which would be derived from the use of the ether and the ether inhalator. Jackson agreed to the arrangement, but later, fearing a possible failure of the public demonstration of ether anesthesia, he asked for a cash payment of $500 for "advice given" to Morton and renounced all claims to any royalties.

After Dr. Warren had told the world that ether anesthesia was no humbug, Morton continued to keep the nature of the liquid he was using secret. However, on November 12, less than a month after the historic trial, Patent No. 4818 was granted. Morton divulged the secret to Warren and to Bigelow, who wrote up the great news in the Boston *Medical and Surgical Journal*. This news was to be dispatched on a steamer sailing for Europe on December 19. Jackson, in the meantime, dispatched a letter by the same boat to a friend, Elie de Beaumont, a member of the French Academy of Sciences, advising him to claim priority of the discovery of ether anesthesia on his behalf at once.

Jackson was apparently determined not to let this gold mine slip through his fingers. On March 2, 1847, at a meeting of the Boston Academy, he declared himself sole discoverer of the new anesthesia, without so much as mentioning the name of Morton. Horace Wells, too, decided to horn in on any profits. Morton had written to him asking him to help push the ether patent for him in New York. Instead, Wells inserted his own claim to the discovery in the Hartford *Courant* of December 7, 1846.

Morton was planning a world-wide sales campaign for his anesthesia. Rich financial returns from the discovery, however, never materialized. When Dr. Warren wanted an ether inhalator for his hospital and said that Morton should be paid for its use, the Massachusetts Medical Society cried "unethical." Morton sent the inhalator free of charge to this and many other hospitals. He offered the American government inhalators at cost price for the Army and Navy, and volunteered to teach without pay the use of ether anesthesia. The Army and Navy used ether anesthesia during the Mexican War, which was then being fought, but Morton received no compensation from the government. Private surgeons, dentists, and hospitals all over the world used ether anesthesia without bothering to pay him royalties. Some salved their consciences on the ground that they were not using Morton's inhalator, but employed sponges soaked in ether.

Morton's financial situation, instead of improving, actually deteriorated rapidly. In 1849 he petitioned Congress for a monetary award in lieu of royalties which had never been paid. Senator Stephen A. Douglas spoke in favor of such a grant. Great Britain had bestowed a gift of $100,000 upon Jenner for his medical boon of smallpox vaccination. Why should not the United States do the same for one of its own sons? Morton might have received the money had it not been for Jackson, who claimed priority, adding that he had disowned the patent because he refused to make any profit out of the suffering of mankind. He branded Morton as a quack doctor and "an infamous character."

The suicide of Horace Wells at this moment only added to Morton's difficulties. The widow of the Hartford dentist petitioned Congress to recognize the claim of her dead husband, and Senator Truman Smith used this claim as a further argument against the granting of any money to Morton. Dr. Bigelow supported the petition of Morton on the ground that he was entitled to full recognition as the sole, rightful discoverer of ether anesthesia. "Had the patient died in a stupor," argued Bigelow, "as could easily have happened, Morton is the one who would have been responsible. Since the patient did not die the glory belongs to him." The staff of the Massachusetts General Hospital told Congress they felt the same way as Bigelow. There was a great deal of Congressional investigation, and the affair bordered on a public scandal.

Europe, too, showed an interest in the Ether Controversy. In February, 1850, the Montyon Prize of 5000 francs from the French Academy of Sciences was to be divided evenly between the two "benefactors of mankind," Morton and Jackson. The French Academy believed that "Mr. Morton and Mr. Jackson were both indispensable. Had it not been," said the French scientists, "for the persistency, the far-reaching vision, the courage, nay, the audacity of Morton, Jackson's observations would probably have passed unnoticed and unapplied; but for the observations of Mr. Jackson, on the other hand, it is likely that Mr. Morton's ideas would never have been crowned with success."

When Morton angrily rejected his share of the prize money, a gold medal was struck in his honor. In England, $50,000 was collected for the American dentist. When Jackson's friends heard of this they raised such a hue and cry that the money was returned to the donors, and Morton saw not a penny of this gift. Other European capitals divided their sympathies. Orders of merit came to Morton from Russia, Sweden, and Prussia. Italy and Turkey chose Jackson for their honors.

Eight years after Morton had given ether anesthesia to the world, Congress was still debating whether to help or to ignore him. Harvard University awarded him an honorary degree; the Massachusetts General Hospital presented him with a silver bowl filled with $1000 in cash. But Jackson was still on the scene fighting his rival with every weapon at his disposal. Word reached him that a country doctor down in Georgia might be of help to him in his fight against his rival. He rushed to Athens, Georgia, on March 8, 1854. He questioned the physician about his use of ether anesthesia. Yes, it was true, admitted Crawford W. Long, that he himself had actually performed the first surgical operation under ether anesthesia. This was on March 30, 1842, more than four years before the historic ether demonstration at the Massachusetts General Hospital.

Long was the son of a plantation and flour-mill owner who had sat as a Whig Senator in the state legislature. He was descended from an Irishman who came to America in 1762 and served in the Revolutionary War. Crawford Long, born in Danielsville in 1815, attended Transylvania College in Kentucky, where Rafinesque had taught, and later was a brilliant student at the medical college of the University of Pennsylvania. He served an internship in surgery of eighteen months in New York City. He had been stimulated to thinking about anesthesia while watching a traveling science showman demonstrate the effects of laughing gas. Later the news that ether, too, gave intoxicating effects had trickled down into the back-country town of Jefferson, Georgia. Ether frolics became common. Young lads and bold damsels would gather and make merry after inhaling ether.

Crawford Long and sixteen-year-old Mary Caroline Swain, niece of the governor of North Carolina, who later became his wife, participated in some of these ether frolics. One day Long noticed that several young lads who were bruised during the ether jags showed no signs of pain. He tried the effects of ether on himself. He wondered whether its effects could be used during operations. One evening when his young friend, James M. Venable, came over to talk to him about two unsightly tumors on the back of his neck, Long suggested cutting out the growths while the patient was under the influence of ether. Venable agreed. On March 30, 1842, Long poured some ether on a towel, placed it over his friend's nostrils, waited until the patient was in a stupor, and then began cutting around the tumor. When he thought his patient was coming out of the ether, he poured a few more drops of the liquid on the towel and continued the operation. One tumor was removed, Venable came back to consciousness, and Long realized he had performed the first surgical operation under ether anesthesia in the history of man.

Neither Venable nor Long rushed to the newspapers or to the patent office. Long, who was only twenty-six years old at the time, did not even notify any medical society of the epochal event.

He wanted to try the experiment again. On June 6 of the same year Long removed the second tumor from Venable's neck, for a two-dollar fee, and the following month amputated an infected toe from a young Negro's foot under ether. Eight more minor surgical operations under ether were recorded in Long's books during the next four years.

Long was somewhat skeptical about the wider application of ether anesthesia. He did not bother to report on his ether operations until December, 1849, more than seven years after his first use of ether, when it was printed in the *Southern Medical and Surgical Journal* under the title, "An Account of the First Use of Sulphuric Ether by Inhalation as an Anaesthetic in Surgical Operations." Almost three years before, when Long read of the great Ether Controversy which was shaking America, he refused to take any part in it. But in 1853, writing in the *Southern Medical and Surgical Journal* again, he said, "I know that I delayed the publication too long to receive any honor from the priority of discovery, but having by persuasion of my friends presented my claim before the profession, I prefer that its correctness be fully investigated before the Medical Society. Should the Society say that the claim, though well founded, is forfeited by not being presented earlier, I will cheerfully respond, 'So mote it be.'"

Jackson listened intently as Long unfolded another saga of medicine written on the fringe of the American frontier. Jackson returned to Washington and reported to Senator William C. Dawson of Georgia, a member of the Senate committee investigating Morton's claim.

In the meantime, Morton went back to his farm. His dental patients had gradually left him. He could not get the ether muddle out of his mind. He wrote to President Pierce pleading for the government to buy his ether patent. Pierce turned the letter over to the Smithsonian Institution for an opinion. There were more delays. Morton brought suit against the government, naming Dr. Charles A. Davis, who was using ether anesthesia at the Naval Hospital, as defendant. Jackson turned up and rushed to the aid of Davis. Through Jackson's influence the American Medical Association attacked Morton for unprofessional conduct. The dentist's nerves began to give way. "I have become a sensitive plant," he wrote. "My nervous system seems so completely shattered that a trifling surprise or sudden noise sends a shock over me."

For sixteen years the patent struggle went on. Jackson finally prevailed and Morton's patent was officially annulled on December 1, 1862. In the meantime the Civil War had broken out. Morton volunteered his services to the North and administered ether to hundreds of Yankee wounded. Chloroform as well as a mixture of ether and chloroform were also used by the Union surgeons. Crawford Long, on the other hand, went over to the cause of the South and introduced ether anesthesia to the armies of General Lee.

Even the horrors of war were not overpowering enough to make Morton forget his personal battle. He began to suffer from a persecution complex. He kept brooding and thinking of Jackson, who was still on the warpath. In 1868 a magazine article appeared upholding the ether claims of Jackson. Morton read it one day while in New York. This last blow was too much; he suffered a stroke and died soon after in St. Luke's Hospital, leaving his wife and five children destitute. Jackson fared no better. His mind gave way under the long strain, he became violent and had to be confined in an asylum, where he died in 1880. Death had come also to the last of the principals involved in the discovery of ether anesthesia, for Long had passed away peacefully two years before.

When the dust of this tragic controversy finally settled, there was fame enough for all of the men who gave ether anesthesia to the world. The University of Pennsylvania, which claimed Long as an alumnus, placed a bronze plaque in the hall of its medical building reading: "To Long, First to Use Ether as an Anesthetic in Surgery." Monuments were raised to his memory in Jefferson and in Danielsville, Georgia, and his statue was placed in Statuary Hall of the United States Capitol. In 1940, a United States postage stamp was issued in his honor. To the eternal memory of Dr. Morton the city of Boston erected a magnificent monument. The table at which he administered ether for the first time was placed as a shrine in the cupola room of the old part of the Massachusetts General Hospital. Hartford, Connecticut, erected a memorial in Bushnell Park to the memory of Horace Wells, and a carved pew end was unveiled in his honor in the chapel of Trinity College. And in Pilgrim Hall at Plymouth, Massachusetts, is exhibited a rocking chair bearing a plate with the inscription: "Seated in this chair Dr. Charles Jackson discovered etherization, February 1842."

It was during this momentous period that America's territorial push westward finally reached the Pacific. Texas, which had torn itself free from Mexico in 1836, was admitted to the Union eight years later. In 1846 Oregon, Washington, Idaho, Montana, and Wyoming became ours when England, preoccupied with a disastrous potato famine in Ireland, agreed to the Oregon Session. Two years later our forces invaded the territory around the Rio Grande River over a boundary dispute with Mexico. Some of our soldiers were killed, and President James K. Polk called for a declaration of war. In the meantime, John C. Frémont, engaged on a topographical mission, aroused the American settlers in California to revolt against Mexico. On July 7, 1846, Commodore John Sloat, in the harbor of Monterey, formally claimed California for the United States. Nineteen months later, by the terms of the peace ending the Mexican War, present-day California, New Mexico, Arizona, Nevada, Utah, and parts of Colorado and Wyoming became American territory. Finally, in 1853 we paid Mexico the sum of $10,000,000 for a piece of land between Mexico and Arizona called the Gadsden Purchase. Our Manifest Destiny, as some called it, was at last fulfilled.

Frémont, as observer and disseminator of scientific data, had much to do with the peopling of the West. He had become interested in science through his friendship with Joel Poinsett (after whom the poinsettia was named) and with the Frenchman J. N.

Nicollet, who had a telescope in Washington, D. C. In 1842 Frémont commanded an expedition beyond the Mississippi River. He disagreed with the conclusions of Long that the region between the Missouri River and the foothills of the Rockies was arid. The following year he crossed the Sierras and came back with another report. In 1845 the Senate published his reports, ten thousand of which were sold. Newspapers printed excerpts from this book and it reached a wide audience. As a result of reading this book, Brigham Young in 1847 led his Mormons into the region around Great Salt Lake which Frémont had described with much scientific care. Others, too, came, and thousands more were soon catapulted into the new West for another reason.

Nine days before the signing of the treaty ending the war with Mexico, a tremendously important event took place at Coloma, near what is now the city of Sacramento. James W. Marshall, a New Jersey wheelwright who had crossed the continent by way of the Oregon Trail three years before, picked up on the morning of January 24, 1848, some yellow ore from the bed of the American River. He rushed back to Sutter's Fort, where John A. Sutter, his employer, found the yellow metal (now deposited in the Smithsonian Institution) to be pure gold. In spite of their efforts to keep the discovery a secret, the news leaked out. Two thirds of the male population of Sacramento scrambled into Coloma in search of gold. The American consul at Monterey sent an official notice of the event to Washington.

When the East first heard of this report, almost four months after it left California, "a delirium seized the community." Thousands of men, women, and children left their homes for the fabulous gold mines buried in the hills of California. The year after the discovery of gold, 45,000 people, including whole families, crossed the plains to get to California. Generally they traveled in small groups organized in various parts of the country. They took along whatever medicines they could find and whatever medical instructions they could get together and ministered to each other in sickness. A book called *The California Medical Companion*, quickly prepared for the use of these forty-niners, contained "Rules for the prevention of disease, and the best method for assaying or testing gold."

It was a desperate, deadly trek overland for most of the gold hunters. Extreme heat, bitter cold, insect pests, hunger, thirst, hostile Indians added more victims to the many who succumbed from disease. Five thousand died on the way. Their trails could be picked up by the deep ruts cut in the prairies by their wagons, by abandoned "prairie schooners," by the bleached carcasses of their oxen and horses, by the little mounds of earth which marked the graves of those who perished. Those who feared the overland trail went by clipper and packet ships around the Horn and up the west coast of the Americas. About 17,000 used this route. Still others were persuaded to try the path across the jungles of the Panama Isthmus. Thousands of Europeans reading about the new El Dorado in hastily prepared pamphlets rushed here to join the caravans.

So great was the migration and so eager were men to get to the mines with the greatest speed that Rufus Porter, editor of the *Scientific American,* planned a seven-ton balloon to fly the gold seekers from New York across the plains and the mountains to the Sacramento Valley in three days. Two hundred adventurers bought tickets for the voyage at $200 each, but the machine was never built. Although a practical lighter-than-air flying machine was not invented for some time, other and more important means of transportation did emerge as the boisterous, adventurous, rowdy, and riotous collection of men and women dug a billion dollars in gold in a few short years out of the California earth.

CHAPTER EIGHT

JOSEPH HENRY
(1797-1878)

THE UNITED STATES GOVERNMENT ESTABLISHES A
NEW INCUBATOR FOR SCIENCE

A S AMERICA spread westward to the Pacific, opening up new areas for settlement and exploitation, faster and more convenient means of reaching this new land became imperative. Narrow Indian trails and bridle paths were no longer adequate, and better roads had to be built. If the United States was to grow to maturity quickly it could no longer tolerate such a situation as existed during Washington's administration when legislators took two whole days to travel by stagecoach from New York to Philadelphia, and from four to six days from Boston to New York.

Private individuals were the first to take a hand in meeting the demands of farmers and merchants for new roads. They built roads or turnpikes where tolls were paid by the travelers who used them. The first of these private roads was constructed between Philadelphia and Lancaster during 1792 and 1794. It proved a financial success, and a veritable mania for turnpike building broke out. By 1811 New York alone had built 1400 miles of these stone and gravel roads. The Federal government soon stepped in; in 1806 Congress authorized the construction of the Cumberland Road, which, by 1838, stretched from Cumberland, Maryland, to Vandalia, Illinois—a distance of 834 miles.

River transportation, however, was still cheaper, more comfortable, and fraught with less danger. From earliest days our naturalists and explorers found the rivers and the lakes the most convenient paths through which to penetrate the wilderness. But canoes and flat-bottomed boats were too slow. When James Watt gave his steam engine to mankind he gave us the means of harnessing the energy of steam for the propulsion of boats. John Fitch, a clock and gun repairer of Connecticut, thought of this new tool as he struggled home one day in 1785 from an exciting trading venture into the Ohio country. When he finally reached Pennsylvania on foot, after escaping from Indians who had captured him, he set to construct, with great difficulty, a steam-driven boat, which was given a trial run on the Schuylkill River. In 1787 his second boat made its first trip on the Delaware River. This vessel, equipped with steam-propelled paddles, actually traveled up the river a distance of forty miles at a speed of four miles per hour.

Men of science, members of the Continental Congress, merchants, and other folk watched the performance, shrugged their shoulders, and did nothing to encourage the inventor. The Connecticut Yankee, however, went ahead with new plans and soon had a boat which maintained a regular passenger and freight service between Philadelphia and Burlington, New Jersey. This was 1790, and the public was still not ready. Fitch went to Europe, looking for less skeptical investors. He reached France in 1793, patented his invention, and began work on another steamboat, whose construction was halted by the outbreak of the Revolution. Back in the United States he struggled along for five more years. In 1798 he sent a bullet through his brain in Bardstown, Kentucky.

In Scotland, William Symington built a steamboat which operated on the Firth and Clyde Canal in 1802. In New York, Colonel John Stevens, who had witnessed the trial run of Fitch's boat on the Delaware, built his own boat and operated it on the Hudson River. In 1807 he built another boat, the *Phoenix*, which sailed from Hoboken to Philadelphia, and thus became the first steamboat to venture on the ocean.

Even this great feat was eclipsed by the spectacular successes of Robert Fulton, who had turned from painting and drawing to engineering. He went to England, became an authority on canal engineering, and then turned to the construction of a submarine with torpedo attachment. The French government was looking for such a new weapon to be used in its war against England. After witnessing trials of Fulton's underwater boat on the Seine, the French promised Fulton a large sum if he could sink an English vessel with his submarine. But the English fleet eluded him.

Fulton returned to the United States, where with the help of Robert R. Livingston, American minister to France, he built a boat equipped with a specially designed steam engine manufactured by Boulton and Watt in England. On August 17, 1807, Fulton's *Clermont*, "an ungainly craft looking precisely like a backwoods sawmill mounted on a scow and set on fire," left New York City for Albany with forty passengers aboard. The voyage was a complete success, making the 150 miles upstream in thirty-two hours, and the return trip in thirty hours. On the Ohio River, four years later, Nicholas J. Roosevelt launched his successful steamboat, *New Orleans*, and in 1818 Lake Erie could boast of its own steam-driven vessel, *Walk-in-the-Water*. The next year witnessed the first steamboat crossing of the Atlantic by the *Savannah*, which made the voyage from New York to Liverpool without incident. The public now accepted this new mode of travel, although sailing ships continued to hold their own for many years.

By 1830 the Federal government stopped financing road building and turned its attention to harbor, river, and lake improvements. Then came an era of canal building to save expensive haulage over land. The Erie Canal, agitated for for many years and financed to a great extent through the sale of bonds in England, was started in 1817. By 1825 this greatest engineering feat of its day was completed. It ran 363 miles from Lake Erie to the Hudson River, was four feet deep, forty feet wide, and contained eighty-three locks. This water route became the great highway to the West. The canal cut the freight-carrying time from Buffalo to New York from twenty to six days, cut the cost of shipping wheat eighty per cent, and made New York City the greatest shipping and mercantile center of the United States. Dozens of canals, totaling 3000 miles in length, were built by 1840.

But rivers and canals were not the complete answer to the transportation problem of the expanding country. There were immense
areas where waterways were absent. Something had to be devised
to take the place of the broad back of the pioneer, the pony, the
pack horse, the broad-wheeled Conestoga wagons, and the
coaches. If steam could be harnessed to the boat, why could not
the same engine serve the wagon? It soon did. As far back as 1803
the Cornishman Richard Trevitchick had constructed for a Welsh
mine a steam locomotive capable of hauling a load of ten tons of
coal. Eleven years later George Stephenson constructed his
Blucher, and in 1825 the first successful railroad, built under his
supervision, was opened for traffic between Stockton and Darlington in England. His locomotive, *The Rocket*, drew a passenger
car and attained a speed of twenty-four miles an hour.

In 1829 the iron horse was exported to America in the form of
the *Strowbridge Lion*. This locomotive, however, was found too
heavy and discarded. In the following year Peter Cooper built the
first American locomotive, the celebrated *Tom Thumb*, which
pushed a passenger car from Baltimore to Ellicott's mills and back,
a distance of thirteen miles, at an average speed of eleven miles an
hour.

Railroad construction began with rails made of wood and
plated with strap iron. Robert L. Stevens soon invented the T-rail
and the hook-headed spike. As the government could not afford
to go in for railroad building at this time, private individuals once
more jumped in. Between 1830 and 1840, 2800 miles of rails were
laid, and ten years later we passed the 9000-mile mark, in spite of
the early reluctance of the public to use the railroads for passenger
traffic. For many years passenger trains on the South Carolina
Railroad carried a car filled with cotton between the demon engine and the passenger car to allay the fears of timid travelers who
feared the engine of the locomotive might explode at any moment.
The first use of the railroad to speed news was in 1838, when copies
of a message from the President of the United States were rushed

to Baltimore and then to New York in eleven hours and thirteen minutes.

In spite of this advance in transportation, which greatly reduced the time for the transmission of messages, communication was still very backward for so vast a country as the United States. Individual inventors, predominantly men of small means, nibbled at the problem, and members of several scientific societies spoke of the need of encouraging serious experimentation in this field It is a curious reflection on the lack of social-mindedness of scientists and statesmen of the time that no effort was made to finance individual scientists or groups of inventors to tackle this huge problem. However, the need was there and this stimulated individual men of science to come to serious grips with the problem.

Fortunately, the time was ripe, because of other advances which had been made in science. Electricity was again being investigated, and several men saw the possibilities of this new power to achieve rapid communication. As in nearly all great scientific achievements, a number of significant discoveries—some made by several investigators independently and almost simultaneously—marked the prelude to the final triumph. American, Danish, English, French, German, and Italian scientists all shared in the work.

In 1790 Luigi Galvani discovered current electricity. Ten years later came the announcement of the invention by Volta of the electrical battery. In 1820 Hans Christian Oersted, a Danish scientist, noted that a copper wire carrying an electric current acted as a magnet, and rediscovered an important phenomenon first noticed in 1802 by an Italian scientist, Romagnosi. In France, André Ampère, hearing of Oersted's experiment, extended it and within a week read before the French Academy of Sciences a paper on electrodynamics in which he gave the rule showing the direction of deflection of a magnet by a current flowing through a wire. Within a few days François Arago, another Frenchman, showed that a copper wire carrying a current attracted iron filings which dropped off immediately after the current was shut off. In 1819 the German Schweigger, of Halle, showed that the deflecting effect of the coil could be increased by increasing the number of coils through which the current was passing. The following year Schweigger invented a galvanometer for detecting and measuring electric currents by wrapping an insulated wire in several turns around a suspended magnetic needle. An Englishman, William Sturgeon, lecturing and playing with these simple scientific toys in London, constructed the first electromagnet in 1825. This was the result of his observation of an increase in the magnetic strength of a bar of soft iron surrounded by a coil of wire through which a current of electricity was flowing.

Michael Faraday, working at the Royal Institution in London, repeated all of these experiments and finally reached a point where he thought he might try converting magnetism into electricity. This experiment, which reversed the usual procedure of producing a magnetic effect from an electric current, was delayed, however, for ten whole years. When the experiment was finally tried, it was performed by two men independently of each other and almost at the same time—Michael Faraday in London and Joseph Henry in Albany, New York. The experiment was a very simple one, but its implications were so tremendous that it ushered in a new era in man's progress. It brought the world to the electrical-power era—the age of motors and dynamos. This classic experiment could have been performed at least two decades earlier had a systematic attack upon the central problem of rapid communication been tackled by some central scientific academy ready to finance a long-term research into the possibilities of electrical transmission. But scientific discovery and invention ambled along in their own unplanned way, pushed ahead by man's individualistic curiosity and the slow but inevitable forces of progress.

Michael Faraday and Joseph Henry gained scientific immortality by their conversion of magnetism to electricity. Franklin, back in 1773, had failed to realize the relationship between magnetism and electricity, for he wrote, "As to the magnetism that seems produced by electricity, my real opinion is that these two powers of nature have no affinity with each other. and that the apparent production of magnetism is primarily accidental." Joseph Henry, however, fifty-seven years later actually performed the crucial experiment. Instead of rushing into print he played around with other experiments. When he finally did publish an account of his experiment, he found that Faraday, producing the same results by a slightly different technique, had anticipated him in publication by a few months. Had Henry published his results at once and been less reluctant to sell his ideas to the public, he would have snatched the honor of discovering electromagnetic induction and given American science a tremendous boost. It was a grave mistake on his part, but it was no graver than the remissness of the American public in recognizing and supporting scientific merit. America had not yet learned the value of making heroes of its scientific leaders.

But if Joseph Henry failed to win the glory of discovering electromagnetic induction, to him, at least, must go the credit of having made possible the first successful telegraphic system. In 1844 another American, Samuel Finley Breese Morse, utilizing Henry's discoveries, worked out the first successful commercial machine and code for instantaneously transmitting messages through copper wires across tremendous distances. Telegraphy was an accomplished fact. American progress was quickened overnight.

Henry's failure to patent his discoveries and capitalize on a new national utility is an interesting study in human behavior. It ran counter to what was expected of a man living in the United States at a time when men were building up huge fortunes. He was descended from Scottish Puritans originally named Hendrie. His grandparents came to America during the summer of 1775; the scientist was born in Albany twenty-two years later. His father was a tanner and day laborer, and his mother was a kindly person who was intensely religious.

Henry's father died when his son was only nine years old. The boy worked part time in a store for three years, then at the age of thirteen was apprenticed for another two years to a watchmaker and a silversmith. He attended school until he was fifteen but did not like it. His histrionic abilities and love of romance led him to join a group of young people interested in debating and dramatics. He wrote two plays, helped in producing ingenious stage effects, and acted in juvenile theatricals. Henry, who was tall, thin, and good-looking, before long became head of this dramatic group, called the Rostrum.

The following year an accident changed the course of his life completely. When an injury forced him to remain at home for some time, he picked up a book belonging to a young Scot who was lodging in his house. The book was *Lectures on Experimental Philosophy, Astronomy and Chemistry Intended Chiefly for the Use of Young People.* It was written by the Reverend G. Gregory, rector of a church near London. Henry read the book with deep interest. He had never before shown any marked interest in science, but he was an imaginative boy, and he was so kindled by the possibilities of the new world which this book revealed that he wished to own it, and the lodger presented it to him as a gift.

The book posed many questions, such as: "You throw a stone into the air; why does it not go forward in the line that you give it?" and "Why does smoke or flame always mount upward?" or "You look into a clear well of water, and see your face as if painted there. Why?" Henry read the book over and over again, trying to find the answers to these fascinating questions. When he was forty-six he wrote a memorandum on the flyleaf of this volume. "This book," it read, "although by no means a profound work, has under Providence exerted a remarkable influence on my life. It opened to me a new world of thought and enjoyment; fixed my mind on the study of nature; and caused me to resolve that I would immediately commence to devote my life to the acquisition of knowledge." No schoolteacher inspired him personally, no scientific heritage impelled him, no youthful hobby pointed the way, for he might have become a great actor instead of a great scientist. Perhaps Erwin Schroedinger, Nobel laureate in science, was right when he likened the practice of scientific investigation to an aesthetic experience such as the enjoyment of literature, art, music, or the theater.

Unable to attend school during the daytime because of lack of funds, Henry managed to get some instruction from two science teachers of the Albany Academy. He planned to prepare for a medical career, but abandoned the idea. For a while he taught school, and finally entered the Academy as a student. He did so well that the principal obtained a position for him to make sure he would stay long enough to graduate. This job involved tutoring in the family of General Stephen van Rensselaer, who as state commissioner made the first survey for the Erie Canal, and later founded the Rensselaer Polytechnic Institute in Troy.

When Joseph was twenty-seven he read his first scientific paper before the Albany Institute, a scientific body of which Rensselaer was president. It dealt with the *Chemical and Mechanical Effects of Steam*. Many of the problems of heat connected with the steam engine still called for solution. Henry investigated the effect of the sudden expansion of steam as it escaped from a boiler on the temperature of the steam, and found that a fall in temperature resulted. Sometimes the drop was so great that the steam failed to scald his hand. He then devised a piece of apparatus to show that when air is allowed to expand suddenly the temperature drops. He used this apparatus to illustrate his paper. His audience, which included many of the fashionable and scientifically uninitiated citizens of Albany, gasped as they saw him freeze water by this method in a room whose temperature was close to 80° Fahrenheit. Henry discovered nothing new here, but his demonstrations were very effective and people began to look upon him as a very capable and clever scientist.

Henry received an appointment as engineer to survey the region between West Point and Lake Erie for a road which was to be built. Upon his return he was offered a position on another survey in Ohio, where a canal was being planned, but instead he accepted an assistant teacher's position at the Albany Academy. Two years later, in 1828, he was made professor of mathematics and natural philosophy at the same school.

Before he was thirty years old, Henry had already begun his electrical investigations in what he described as "this most interesting branch of human knowledge, presenting at this time the most fruitful field of discovery." On October 10, 1827, he read his first paper in this field, remarking that popular lecturers had not availed themselves of "the many interesting and novel experiments with which it can supply them." There had been practically no new electrical experiments in the United States since Franklin performed his famous investigations. Henry, who was following the European revival of interest in this subject, deplored the fact that no serious attention was being given to electricity in our higher institutions of learning "principally because of their difficulties and expense." He, himself, could not find all the time he needed for his electrical experiments, as he was spending seven hours a day in the classroom.

Henry's first paper on electricity contained nothing startling. He had simply improved the apparatus for illustrating established facts and principles relating to the effect of the earth's magnetism on a freely moving coil of silk-covered copper wire. But Sturgeon's 1825 electromagnet haunted him. The Englishman had wound eighteen turns of bare copper wire around a varnished bar of soft iron bent in the shape of a horseshoe. When a current was sent through the coil of wire the soft iron core was capable of lifting a mass of nine pounds. This was exciting news, but Henry wanted a stronger electromagnet and kept thinking about it for a long time. One evening in 1828 as he sat absently listening to a friend, Henry suddenly rose and exclaimed, "Tomorrow I shall make a famous experiment." It was not like Joseph Henry to make such a boast, but he had thought through a method which he felt certain would work, and he could not control his emotions.

In the light of Ampère's theory of magnetism, which he had read and reread several times, Henry realized that Sturgeon's electromagnet had not been wound properly. What was needed was a winding made from insulated wire—copper wire covered with a nonconducting silk thread—to prevent short-circuiting between the turns of wire. "When this conception came into my brain I was so pleased with it," Henry told his friend Alfred Mayer in 1859, "that I could not keep from rising to my feet and giving it my hearty approbation." The next morning he wound his very thin, silk-covered wire very tightly together and almost at right angles to the axis of the soft iron core. His idea worked. The "bobbin-wound" magnet could lift much greater weights than Sturgeon had lifted with magnets of the same size. This was Henry's first original discovery and invention. Before the close of 1829 he had further improved the electromagnet to a point where, using a small current, he was able to lift more than fifty times the weight of the magnet itself. Later Professor Silliman of Yale asked him to help make a magnet which could lift a ton. Calm though he was, Henry fairly leaped from the floor when the magnet he constructed actually lifted a mass of one and a half tons.

In London Michael Faraday heard of Henry's method of winding electromagnets and constructed one on the new principles. He connected the closely packed coil of insulated wire to a galvanometer, then moved a core of soft iron in and out of the coil. Faraday noticed that the galvanometer indicated the presence of an electric current while the iron was moving through the coil. When the iron core was at rest no current was formed. The current was produced whenever the so-called magnetic lines of force in the area around the iron core were crossed. Faraday had made a revolutionary discovery—he had changed magnetism into electricity! On November 24, 1831, three months after his first observation of this phenomenon, he reported it to the Royal Society. An account of this discovery was printed in the *Annals of Philosophy* issue of April, 1832. Henry received a copy of this publication in June of the same year. The following month he published an account of his own discoveries of electromagnetic induction in the July, 1832, issue of Silliman's *American Journal of Science*. Referring to Faraday's experiments, Henry wrote, "No detail is given of the experiments, and it is somewhat surprising that results so interesting and which certainly form a new era in the history of electricity and magnetism should not have been more fully described before this time in some of the English publications."

Henry's discovery of the conversion of magnetism into electricity was made more than a full year before that of Faraday. Henry himself wrote, "Before having any knowledge of Faraday's experiment I had succeeded in producing electrical effects in the following manner: two projecting ends of a coil of wire surrounding a soft-iron armature [magnet] were dipped into two cups of mercury and connected with a galvanometer. Immersed the galvanic battery attached to the magnet into a vessel of dilute acid. Galvanometer moved." The needle was deflected in the op-

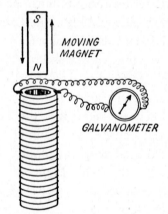

Fig. 4. Faraday's experiment of 1831 by which he converted magnetism into electricity. A hollow coil of insulated wire was connected to a galvanometer which registered a current when the magnet was in motion.

posite direction when the wires were moved in and out of the acid. This was analogous to the experiment of Faraday.

Furthermore, even before Faraday had published his discovery of electromagnetic induction, Henry had actually realized the potentialities of his own prior discovery of this phenomenon. He lost no time in trying to utilize this discovery in some practical device for generating power. He built a little electric motor which produced reciprocating motion "by a power which has never before been applied in mechanics—by magnetic attraction and repulsion." His machine consisted of a bar electromagnet resting on a fulcrum and connected with batteries placed at the two ends of the bar. Below each end of the bar electromagnet was a perma-

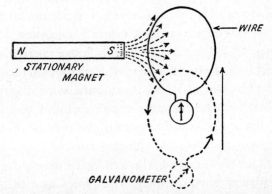

Fig. 5. Henry's experiment of 1830 by which he obtained an electric current by means of a moving magnet. As the loop of wire moved across the magnetic field of the magnet, an electric current was generated in the loop.

nent magnet with its north pole adjacent to the bar. With each temporary break in the circuit there was a reversal of current with a consequent change in attraction and repulsion. This produced a continuous oscillation of the bar electromagnet at the rate of seventy-five oscillations per minute, lasting in one experiment for more than an hour.

Henry did not jump to an exaggerated announcement of a new and full-blown revolutionary power machine. At this early stage of his invention, it was merely "a philosophical toy." But he added, "It is not impossible that the same principle, or some modification of it on a more extended scale, may hereafter be applied to some useful purpose." In 1836 a blacksmith named Thomas Davenport patented an electric motor, five years after he had seen one of Henry's electromagnets in use at the Penfield Iron Works at Crown Point, New York. In both England and the United States electric motors and dynamos, every one of which used the electromagnet of Henry, began to be built to serve the power needs of a rapidly expanding factory system.

Late in 1832 the College of New Jersey (now Princeton University), at the recommendation of Torrey and the chemist John Maclean, called Henry to a professorship of natural history. Here he continued his electrical experiments. He had found that when a long current is suddenly broken there is a momentary flash in the opposite direction. Henry's original discovery of the phenomenon of *self-induction*, and of this "extra current" produced by the induction of a current on itself, was made in the summer of 1832, two years before Faraday made the same discovery independently. When the current through a coil of wire is broken, self-induction *opposes* the dying out of the current. This so-called "extra current" added to the inducing current causes a fattening of the spark when the circuit is broken. Self-induction explains the flash that is seen when a trolley wire jumps its cable. The self-induced current plus the "extra current" produced by the sudden break of the circuit jumps the gap with a lightning flash or spark.

In February, 1837, Henry was granted a leave of absence on full pay to go to Europe, where he was eagerly awaited. Accompanying him was the great-grandson of Franklin, Alexander D. Bache, professor of natural philosophy and chemistry at the University of Pennsylvania since 1828. Bache became famous for his important experiments on the earth's magnetism in the first specially constructed nonmagnetic building on the grounds of Girard College in Philadelphia.

Henry was warmly welcomed in England, Scotland, and France, where he met many of the leading scientists of the time. He spoke on electric discharges before the British Association for the Advancement of Science. There were no discussions over priority of discovery; all agreed on the importance of electromagnetic induction; the rest did not matter. Seldom in the history of science has such complete disinterestedness over priority been exhibited. At King's College in London the great Michael Faraday, Charles Wheatstone, and John Daniell watched Henry with hot poker and block of ice try to coax an electric spark from a temperamental thermoelectric pile which had refused to operate for the others. Henry got it to work, and Faraday, seeing this experiment for the first time, could not contain himself. He jumped to his feet, shouting, "Hurrah for the Yankee experiment!"

Henry turned again to the now widely discussed problem of rapid communication. Others, too, were giving this question their attention. The conquest of this problem was finally made by two Americans. Joseph Henry laid the foundations and Samuel Morse brought the invention to full fruition. In terms of heritage, background, and interests, few men could have been farther apart. Morse, one of eleven children in the family of a Congregationalist minister, was born during the year following Franklin's death, at Charlestown (now part of Boston), within a mile of Franklin's birthplace. Although he studied electricity under Silliman at Yale, he did not become a professional scientist. He studied painting in England under Benjamin West and did portraits of Washington and Monroe as well as a large picture containing eighty portraits of members of the House of Representatives. In 1826, at the age of thirty-five, he became president of the National Academy of Arts and Design.

Returning in October, 1832, from Europe, Morse found himself discussing electricity with another passenger, Dr. Charles T. Jackson, of the Ether Controversy. Jackson had been in Paris, where he had witnessed a number of electrical demonstrations performed by the famous French scientist, Ampère. He was so fascinated by the experiments that he brought back with him a small electromagnet. Morse became extremely interested in the possibilities of this device as a means of achieving rapid communication over large distances. Many years earlier he had thought of the problem; at twenty he had written home from England, "I wish that in an instant I could communicate the information, but three thousand miles are not passed over in an instant." As early as 1798 Salva at Madrid had sent messages over a distance of twenty-six miles with the aid of a static electrical telegraph. Paul Schilling, .

a Russian baron; Peter Barlow, an English mathematician; Laplace, and Ampère had all tackled the problem. In 1828 Henry had approached the question, and three years later had been able to activate an electromagnet at the end of a mile or more of copper wire stretched around one of the rooms of the Albany Academy. He had constructed the first successful electric telegraph. He showed it to his classes and reported it in the *American Journal of Science* in 1831. This achievement convinced him that a commercially successful electric telegraph could be built on this principle.

Morse told Jackson during that conversation on the boat, "If the presence of electricity can be made visible in any part of a circuit I can see no reason why intelligence may not be transmitted instantaneously by electricity." But how? For three years after this meeting Morse continued his painting but he kept thinking about that electric telegraph. He was not doing too well in his profession, and to earn a living accepted a teaching position at New York University. Between his lessons in painting and sculpture he found time to visit the science laboratories of the college. Dr. Leonard D. Gale placed the equipment of the college laboratory at his disposal, and Morse began in earnest to tackle the problem of the telegraphic transmission of messages.

Gale knew of Henry's work and went to consult with him. Henry was very co-operative and explained his own progress in the field. He had already, while at the Albany Academy, partially solved the problem of transmitting electric impulses over fairly long distances. This was the obstacle which had discouraged both Barlow and Schilling. Henry had accomplished this by means of his *intensity* magnet and his *quantity* magnet. The *intensity* magnet, surrounded by a single continuous coil of relatively fine insulated wire of great length, had enabled the American to transmit impulses through wires three miles long. He had already been able to transmit messages by means of an electromagnet which, with swinging movement, struck a gong in uneven succession, indicating different letters of the alphabet. Henry's *quantity* magnet, made up of small multiple coils of coarse wire activated by a single battery, strengthened the electromagnet at the end of the copper wire and enabled him in 1832 to send signals from his laboratory and across the Princeton campus to his wife at home. (In May, 1830, Henry had married his first cousin.)

Morse adopted the improvement of Henry, and then successfully tackled two remaining problems. The first was that of increasing the distance over which impulses could be sent. This he did by inventing the *relay*, a device which takes a weak current from the copper-wire line through a coil of thousands of turns of wire and transmits its amplified impulses to a second circuit. Thus the original impulse can be carried along to any required distance by adding more and more relays at various intervals in the line. Then, in 1838, Morse invented the dot-and-dash or Morse code. This made it possible to translate electrical impulses into words and messages. In England Wheatstone's telegraph for railroad signaling had made use in 1837 of a deflecting magnetic needle and a cumbersome signal code which was commercially impractical. Henry showed Wheatstone how to substitute his electromagnet and the Morse code.

In 1837 Morse applied for a patent on his telegraphic system. The following year he demonstrated his invention over a ten-mile circuit before President Van Buren, members of his cabinet and Congress, men of science, and other dignitaries. He asked the government for an appropriation of $30,000 with which to build a longer line, running fifty miles, as a final demonstration of the complete practicability of the electric telegraph. Fear of the new, general inertia, political shortsightedness, and the panic of 1837 which came as the result of overexpansion in canal building, all helped to hold up final action by the Congress.

In the field of telegraphic communication things were happening in other sections of the world. Morse left the United States to take out patents on his telegraph in England. The patent was refused because Wheatstone was exhibiting his own electric telegraph, and because "America was a large country and Morse ought to be satisfied with a patent there." French scientists, including Arago and Gay-Lussac, were enthusiastic, and France gave the invention a patent. While in Paris, Morse showed his electric telegraph invention to Louis Daguerre, and the Frenchman reciprocated with a demonstration of his newly invented method of chemical photography, known as the daguerreotype. Morse obtained permission and instruction from Daguerre in 1838 to introduce his silver photography in America.

But a patent alone could not build a telegraphic system for industry, nor could it feed or clothe the inventor's family. Congress dillydallied for another five years. Morse nearly starved and almost reached the breaking point. Henry came to his help. He encouraged Morse by reminding him that "Science is now fully ripe for this application, and I have not the least doubt of the perfect success of the invention." The idea was not new, said Henry, but "the bringing it forward at the proper moment, and the devising of a plan for carrying it into practical operation, are grounds of a just claim to scientific reputation as well as to public patronage."

Finally, in 1842, a bill appropriating $30,000 for a crucial test was passed. A line of wires was strung along poles over a distance of about forty miles from Baltimore to Washington. On May 24, 1844, Morse, sitting in the Capitol at Washington, sent a message in code to Mr. Vail in Baltimore. "What hath God wrought?" came back the message instantly. The miracle of instantaneous communication had been completed.

Two days later the telegraph made a popular sensation. News of the nomination of James K. Polk for President and Silas Wright for Vice-President of the United States by the National Democratic Convention meeting in Baltimore was communicated by telegraph to Mr. Wright in Washington. Wright's declination of the nomination came back immediately, even before a committee which had been named by the convention to notify Mr. Wright of their choice could start for Washington. This incident so fired the imagination of the people that editors who until now hardly noticed Morse and his telegraph began to feature the invention as great news. The *Baltimore Clipper* published an account of

Morse's invention on May 25, 1844, and the *New York Herald's* Washington correspondent wrote on May 28, "Never before was anyone conscious that he knew with certainty what events were at that moment passing in a distant city—40, 100 or 500 miles off." Nevertheless, not until 1851 did our trains make use of this new rapid means of sending messages.

The United States government still refused to buy the invention. Thereupon private capital seized the new tool. In the hands of Alfred Vail, who had helped Morse with his experiment, the new infant grew rapidly into a lusty child. Within a few years hundreds of miles of electric wire were binding the principal cities of America. Morse and Vail piled up fortunes, while Henry went back to the service of mankind in his own way. Morse never hid his debt of gratitude to the Princeton professor, and Henry, on his side, never indulged in any priority litigation. He had refused to patent any of his inventions on the ground that he "did not consider it compatible with the dignity of science to confine the benefits which might be derived from it to the exclusive use of any individual." Years later, he said, "My life has been principally devoted to science, and my investigations in different branches of physics have given me some reputation in the line of original discovery. I have sought, however, no patent for inventions, and solicited no remuneration for my labors, but have freely given their results to the world; expecting only in return to enjoy the consciousness of having added by my investigations to the sum of human knowledge. The only reward I ever expected was the consciousness of advancing science, the pleasure of discovering new truths, and the scientific reputation to which these labors would entitle me."

When we remember that Henry carried a full teaching load and that he had practically no assistance from foundations or collaborators, we realize what a large amount of first-rate work he was able to accomplish between 1827 and 1846. At Princeton he spread out into other fields. For a while he took over Torrey's classes in chemistry and geology, and also taught mathematics, mineralogy, astronomy, and even architecture. When questions came up in class which baffled his students and himself he undertook to investigate them. He demonstrated that liquids and solids generally have the same degree of cohesion. He studied the capillary movement of liquid metals in solid metals. He worked out a new method of determining the velocity of swiftly moving projectiles and investigated the phenomena of the aurora and phosphorescence. He spent the summer of 1844 blowing soap bubbles in order to learn more about thin films and surface tension. He turned to the sun, too, and probed its surface to determine whether it liberated heat uniformly. By means of a thermopile connected with a galvanometer, he measured the heat radiated from sunspot areas and found that sunspots liberated less heat than other areas of the sun's surface. Henry encouraged P. A. Secchi, a young professor at Georgetown College and foster brother of King Victor Emmanuel of Italy, to continue with this interesting investigation. Secchi ended by making classic contributions in this field of solar physics.

Henry made a number of other discoveries which in the light of their present-day usefulness are of tremendous importance. In 1842 he independently made the discovery that the electrical discharge of a Leyden jar or a lightning flash was not of a continuous nature but rather of an oscillatory one. By arranging for a lightning flash to pass through a wire bent around a needle, he observed that the north and south ends of the needle were sometimes reversed in polarity. He calculated that the spark passed back and forth about a million times a second.

He also compared the spread of the impulse from an electric spark to the range of the propagation of light waves. This was a fact which was verified by Heinrich Hertz, who in 1886 actually demonstrated the existence of radio waves traveling through the ether. Henry showed that electric currents could be induced in coils of wire completely disconnected from the source of the electric spark which disturbed the field around the spark. He amazed his friends, who, while holding the ends of a coil of wire, were given a shock through an induced electric current from another coil operated in an adjoining room. Without grasping its full significance, Henry was expressing the electromagnetic theory of light which Michael Faraday hinted at in 1846 and which Maxwell finally announced in 1863.

During Henry's eighteen years of active research, a curious drama was being enacted on two continents. This was to make another tremendous change in his life and to transform him from a research scientist to a scientific administrator. It was to rob America of its greatest contemporary experimental investigator and, in return, was to give the country a great director of an institution which was to influence profoundly the future course of our scientific progress.

In 1829, while Henry was starting his investigations in electromagnetism, there died in London a man named James Smithson. In his will this Englishman bequeathed more than half a million dollars for the creation of an institution to be founded at Washington, D. C., "for the increase and diffusion of knowledge among men." Benjamin Thompson, an American, had founded the Royal Institution in England; now James Smithson, an Englishman, was to found the Smithsonian Institution in America. There was no connection between the establishment of these two scientific institutions or between the motives which led to their founding.

Smithson had never been in America and he knew few Americans. One of the reasons for his act was a lifelong grudge against the British nobility. Because of his illegitimacy—he was the son of the Duke of Northumberland—he was accepted only with a great deal of condescension by the dukes and duchesses to whose class he felt he belonged by birth. "My name shall live in the memory of man," he consoled himself, "when the titles of the Northumberlands and the Percys are extinct and forgotten." His interests leaned to science, in which he had done some work as a chemist (the mineral, $ZnCO_3$, was named *smithsonite* after him). He was vice-president of the Royal Society at one time, and he counted among his friends the famous discoverer of hydrogen,

Henry Cavendish, and the great French scientist, Arago. Smithson turned to America also because he believed in its institutions and in the greatness of its future.

Smithson's gift to America was contingent upon the death of his nephew without heirs; this occurred in 1835. President Andrew Jackson transmitted the news to Congress. A sharp debate ensued over the wisdom of accepting the 106 bags each containing a thousand gold sovereigns which the eminent lawyer Richard Rush, son of Benjamin Rush and former minister to Great Britain, brought from London in 1838. This was the period of Jacksonian democracy, and John C. Calhoun opposed our acceptance of the gift on the ground that it was beneath the dignity of this country to accept money from a foreigner. John Quincy Adams also opposed acceptance of the offer, insisting that America's education was our own precious obligation and should not be left to English money. The question was on the fire for ten whole years until Congress finally agreed to accept the gift. Robert Dale Owen, son of Robert Owen of the New Harmony venture, prepared the act of incorporation of the Smithsonian Institution, which was to be under the control of the President, Vice-President, Chief Justice, and cabinet of the United States. The secretary of the Smithsonian Institution was to be the executive officer and curator of this national museum.

Henry was the most distinguished man of science in America at this time. He also enjoyed an international reputation. He was in the full vigor of his health and could be depended upon to carry out both the dream of its benefactor and the plans of its beneficiary. The government asked him to become the first secretary of the Smithsonian Institution. Henry debated with himself whether to accept the honor, knowing it would mean an end to serious laboratory experimentation. He thought of Faraday and the stream of discoveries which flowed from his laboratory. He remembered Newton, who made no discoveries after he accepted an appointment as warden of the British Mint. Finally, however, exchanging "present reputation for future fame,"

Henry accepted the invitation, from a sense of public duty and with a feeling that it would be his opportunity to give American science further stimulation. He was elected secretary on December 3, 1846. Less than two years later another event of great scientific importance occurred. The American Association for the Advancement of Science was organized, with Dr. William C. Redfield as its first president. Redfield, who started as a saddler, was a student of American fossil fish, a pioneer in meteorology, and the promoter of the first barge line on the Hudson River.

For nearly a third of a century the life of Joseph Henry became the life of the Smithsonian Institution. "For the increase and diffusion of knowledge among men" were words which Henry took literally and broadly. Theoretical research for pushing back the frontiers of science was to go hand in hand with studies of practical problems and inventions. To him there was no dichotomy between pure and applied science. Remembering the obstacles which stood in the way of many capable scientists, including himself, and believing that sole dependence upon the benevolence of private patrons was hazardous and beneath the dignity of democratic men, Henry urged wider participation of the Federal government in scientific projects. "It is not enough for our government," he wrote in one of its annual reports, "to offer encouragement to the direct promotion of the useful arts through the more or less fortunate efforts of inventors; it is absolutely necessary that encouragement and facilities should be afforded for devotion to original research." Through the Smithsonian Institution Henry proposed to stimulate original research by offering promising young scientists suitable laboratory facilities and monetary grants as well as free publication of their findings.

Through the spirit of Henry, the Institution became "the incubator of American science" for almost a century. Here, aided by Arnold Guyot, he arranged for a broad system of meteorological observations transmitted by means of the telegraph. He carried out a plan to co-ordinate the work of such scientists in this field of meteorology as Coffin, Espy, and Ferrel.

James P. Espy was one of the founders of the science of storm formation. Of Huguenot ancestry, he was born in Pennsylvania in 1785, was educated at Transylvania College, and turned from law to science after reading some articles on weather by John Dalton, propounder of the atomic theory. At the Franklin Institute in Philadelphia he worked, lectured, and wrote for forty years on the theory of storms and on weather factors in general. One of his best contributions was published in the *Transactions* of the American Philosophical Society in 1843 under the title *Law of Cooling of Atmospheric Air for Various Suddenly Diminished Pressures.*

William Ferrel was another meteorologist born in Pennsylvania. During a long teaching career he carried out an important series of investigations on the physics of the atmosphere and the sea. He discovered, in 1856, the fact that terrestrial winds and ocean currents are deflected by the rotation of the earth. This fact is still taught today under the name of Ferrel's Law. He also stimulated among other Americans much thought concerning the factors of weather.

The third of the trio of meteorologists of this period was James H. Coffin, who in his *Treatise on the Winds of the Northern Hemisphere* (1853) was the first to point out clearly the existence of three important wind zones in the northern hemisphere. Later he demonstrated the same effect for the southern hemisphere. For many years, as professor of mathematics and astronomy at Lafayette College in Easton, Pennsylvania, and also under the auspices of the Smithsonian Institution, he did a great deal of fundamental work in meteorological problems.

In 1868 F. A. Armstrong, a Western Union employee at Cincinnati, got the idea of putting weather bulletins into crude maps with wind directions and temperatures. The following year Professor Cleveland Abbe of the Cincinnati Observatory used these maps as a basis for weather forecasts. Out of all of this activity in meteorological investigation was born in 1870 the Federal Meteorological Service, as part of the United States Signal Corps.

The telegraph was a vital aid to the United States Federal Meteorological Service, whose main purpose was to help shipping by the prompt transmission of storm warnings along the Great Lakes and the country's seacoast. The chief signal officer, nicknamed "Old Probabilities," later changed his daily "probabilities" to weather "indications." Finally, in 1889, these were changed to weather "forecasts."

At the Smithsonian Institution, Spencer F. Baird, organizer of the United States Fish Commission and the Marine Biological Station at Woods Hole, Massachusetts, followed Henry as secretary. Here, too, Samuel P. Langley made his classic experiments in human flight. Charles D. Walcott, who succeeded Baird, gave the world new data concerning the Cambrian fossils of the Canadian Northwest. Here, also, Charles G. Abbot, while its secretary, thrilled the world with his fascinating researches in solar heat and his discoveries concerning the relation between the solar constant and long-range weather forecasting. At the Smithsonian Institution the international system of exchange of scientific publications and the printing of an international catalogue of scientific periodicals were also inaugurated. Here the Smithsonian standard tables of physical, meteorological, and mathematical constants were prepared for world use. And here Henry started the Smithsonian *Contributions to Knowledge*, embracing a series of reports in various branches of scientific investigations, which were distributed to all parts of the globe.

From the very beginning the Federal government called upon the Smithsonian Institution for aid in the solution of scientific problems. In 1852 Henry was asked to serve as one of the members of the Light-House Board. In this capacity he undertook a series of investigations in the field of sound. He found that sound was reflected and refracted by different layers of the atmosphere of varying densities, and devised a fog signaling method which the government later instituted. This was based on the siren rather than on the steam whistle or trumpet sound. When the problem of the high cost of whale oil, which was used in our lighthouse beacons, began to bother the government, Henry suggested, after a series of experiments, that lard oil could very well be substituted for it. (Kerosene, at this time, was still not an abundant fuel.) "Lard oil was at once introduced in 1865 in all the lighthouses of the United States against all the opposition of interested dealers and prejudiced keepers." It has been estimated that for a long time this change of illuminating fuel saved the government as much as $100,000 each year.

Henry was not unmindful that such savings helped to change the opinions of many legislators regarding Federal aid to science. For himself, he was satisfied with the $3500 annual salary he received as secretary of the Smithsonian Institution. He refused salary increases, and turned down many positions which offered higher remuneration and less onerous administrative duties. Henry did not enjoy the duties of an administrative officer, but he discharged them loyally and out of a sense of public service. "Viewing the mere acquisition of wealth with philosophic indifference, he was, nevertheless, as a financier a model of sagacity." Asa Gray remembered "the blackboard where his fisc was chalked with all the exactness of an old accountant, and explained before the board of regents each year with all the nervous solicitude of a schoolboy doing his first sum."

Henry was more fortunate than most men. He enjoyed vigorous health almost to the day of his death, which occurred in Washington in his eighty-second year. A few days before he died he had discussed with the astronomer Simon Newcomb a transit of Mercury and an appropriation for a coming total-solar-eclipse expedition. In his sleep, just before the end came, he spoke of his experiments in sound.

Scientists and legislators felt the loss keenly. By act of Congress a bronze statue was erected to his memory in Washington. The man in the street, however, was not stirred as was the average Frenchman when Pasteur passed away, or as the Englishman when Faraday's work in the laboratory was ended. Henry never attained popular fame, partly because of his almost abnormal hatred for publicity, but mainly because Americans had not yet learned to look upon their scientists as great heroes.

Henry once put his finger on this tragic indifference. "In other countries," he remarked, "scientific discovery is stimulated by pensions, by titles of honor, and by various social and official distinctions. The French Academicians receive an annual salary and are decorated with the insignia of the Legion of Honor. Similar marks of distinction are conferred on the members of the Academy of Berlin and that of St. Petersburg. These modes of stimulation may be considered inconsistent with our social ideas and perhaps with our form of government. *There are honors, nevertheless, which in an intelligent democracy have been and may be justly awarded to those who enlarge the field of human thought and human power.* Heretofore," he added, "but three principal means of distinction have been recognized in this country, viz.: the acquisition of wealth, the possession of political power, and successful military achievement." In 1867, when he was seventy, Henry expressed the hope before the National Academy of Sciences, of which he was president, that "a fourth avenue for the aspiration of a laudable ambition" might be added through the recognition of great scientific contributions.

In 1875 Major John W. Powell of the United States Geological Survey, while exploring the Colorado River, named a range of mountains in southeastern Utah the Henry Mountains. Fifteen years after Henry's death, an International Congress of Electricians meeting in Chicago paid homage to the great American scientist. The assembled scientists added his name to that small roster of pioneers of electrical science—Ampère, Coulomb, Faraday, Gauss, Ohm, and Volta—after whom units of electricity have been named. They designated by the name *henry* the new unit of inductive resistance used in radio. For, long before Hertzian or wireless waves were discovered in 1886, Henry, while investigating electric sparks and electrical induction, had made some original and interesting observations in the field of radio. He obtained magnetic effects through space as far as 220 feet from the sparks, and also reported concerning his experiments of 1842 that "As these are the results of currents in alternate directions, they must produce in surrounding space a series of plus and minus motions analogous to if not identical with undulations." He was describing wireless waves. Thus through Joseph Henry, as through Benjamin Franklin almost a century before, American science had again illuminated scientific problems of broad and fundamental significance.

CHAPTER NINE

MATTHEW FONTAINE MAURY

(1806-1873)

AMERICA CONTRIBUTES TO THE SCIENCE OF THE SEA

WHEN ON April 12, 1861, the guns of Fort Sumter sounded the opening of hostilities between the North and the South and plunged the country into civil war, science, too, felt their impact. The march of science was shunted off in new directions. The meeting of the American Association for the Advancement of Science scheduled for Nashville, Tennessee, was called off, and the society's activities were not resumed until 1866. At its meeting that year no Southern scientists were present. The war also took the lives of a number of scientists. Among them was the astronomer, Ormsby M. Mitchel, who left the Dudley Observatory at Albany to command an Ohio regiment and died of yellow fever during the struggle.

The forces which brought on the irrepressible conflict were many. The burning spirit of John Brown at Osawatomie, the fighting words of William Lloyd Garrison in his *Liberator*, which aroused large sections of the country, the martyrdom of the printer Elijah Lovejoy by an Illinois mob for his espousal of the cause of abolition—all were born of spiritual drives for human betterment. But if the causes which led to the conflict had been primarily ethical, it might have been avoided, for ways may have been found to settle the question of slavery without resort to the sword.

The war, however, became inevitable because America had

been divided by the forces of deeply rooted economic changes. While the coming of the industrial revolution speeded the rapid development of business and industry in the Northern states, the South continued to carry on an agricultural economy based on the staple crops of tobacco, sugar, and cotton. Cotton had been king since 1820. Whitney's invention of the cotton gin in 1793 made possible the processing of enormous quantities of the cotton fiber for the looms of New England and the British Isles. Cotton production increased from 150,000 bales in 1815 to 4,000,000 bales in 1859. With the two economies becoming more divergent each year, the needs of the North and those of the South steadily diverged, and the struggle for control of the Federal government grew more bitter.

With the peopling of every new territory acquired by the United States came the issue of slavery. Each new slave state added to the Union meant greater representation for the South in the halls of Congress. The South, however, was losing in its attempt to corral the West. More and more territory was coming in as free states. The Western free-soiler hated slavery because the black man was his competitor. The Republican Party, organized in 1854, sponsored free homesteads and helped to finance the development of the West. It came out against slavery in the territories, but promised to leave slavery unmolested where it already existed. With the election of Republican legislators, the South feared that soon Congress would be completely controlled by Northern and Western representatives. The old cry of states' rights was raised by the South. The threat of secession became a reality late in 1860 when South Carolina left the Union. It was then that the melancholy man from Kentucky, believing that the Union must be preserved at all costs, decided to resolve the issue in blood.

Men of science, like other citizens, followed the action of their own states. In the North Joseph Henry saw the conflict as a just war for the North and stood wholeheartedly behind Lincoln. Louis Agassiz, the biologist, who seldom mixed in politics except to wangle appropriations from politicians for his scientific projects, rose in righteous indignation against the English government when he learned that it was attempting to give the South more than moral support. On August 15, 1862, he wrote to Sir Philip Egerton, "It has been agonizing week after week to receive the English papers, and to see there the noble devotion of the men of the North branded as the service of mercenaries. I can tell you that I have never seen a more generous and prompt response to the call of country than was exhibited last year, and is being exhibited now, in the loyal United States. In the last six months nearly 300,000 men have volunteered and I am satisfied that the additional 300,000 will be forthcoming without a draft in the course of the next month. . . . I am very sorry to hear such accounts of the sufferings of the manufacturing districts of England [resulting from the Civil War]." In spite of the hardships of unemployment, the English workers, sympathizing with the North, agitated to prevent their government from going to the aid of the South, for they realized that slavery in any section of the world was a threat to free labor in every other part of the globe.

The venerable scientist, Benjamin Silliman of Yale, then eighty-two years old, also called the Northern cause a righteous one. He had shown his hatred for slavery five years before at the famous Kansas-rifle meeting in the North Church in New Haven in 1856. Here a farewell service was conducted for a band of settlers going to Kansas in the interests of freedom. Silliman, in the midst of the ceremony, suggested that they be given arms to fight if need be for the Union. The suggestion was accepted, the men were given rifles, and, from then on, settlers sent out to Kansas by the New England Emigrant Company were provided with guns.

Dr. John L. Le Conte, New York entomologist and physician, served the Union Army as surgeon. His cousin, Dr. John Le Conte, born in Georgia, joined the Southern cause as superintendent of niter works for the Confederate government. Dr. St. Julien Ravenel, physician and agricultural chemist of Charleston, undertook to supervise the production of medical supplies for the Southern armies. On the other hand, the inventor, Samuel F. B. Morse of Massachusetts, then almost seventy years old, favored secession and opposed the war.

The most distinguished scientist of the South at this time was Matthew Maury, a Virginian by birth. Maury was by no means the only eminent scientist the South produced. Nor is it true, as some historians have intimated, that the South, outside of its interest in the classics, was an intellectual desert where scientific research could not thrive. While the largest and most influential scientific societies were located in the North, many of their contributors worked below the Mason and Dixon Line. Charleston, South Carolina, for many years the cultural center of the South, gave the United States its first natural-history museum in connection with its Library Society founded in 1773. The first observatory attached to an American college was erected in 1780 at the College of William and Mary, in Virginia, by its president, James Madison, who was a member of the American Philosophical Society. The Medical Society of South Carolina was founded in 1789, and the New Orleans Lyceum of Natural History in 1825.

Many Southerners, too, were inquisitive men and many of them led more leisurely lives than their colleagues of the North. Between 1780 and 1800 Virginia had fourteen members and the Carolinas eight members in the American Philosophical Society, while Massachusetts and New York had only six each. This inquisitiveness led Dr. William C. Wells of Charleston to study and advance a correct theory on the formation of dew. It made a tolerably capable entomologist and conchologist of Joseph Barabino, a New Orleans pharmacist who died as a result of one of his scientific explorations through the swamps of Louisiana in 1834. It impelled W. B. Hodgson to take up paleontology as a hobby, which resulted in his 1846 paper on certain extinct gigantic quadrupeds buried around Savannah, Georgia. Edmund Ruffin of Virginia, who fired the first gun of the Civil War for the South, was a pioneer in soil chemistry and scientific agriculture. The South was the birthplace of Crawford W. Long, the first man to perform a surgical operation under ether anesthesia. In Kentucky Dr. Ephraim McDowell performed the first ovariectomy. Among our eminent botanists and zoologists from the South were Dr. James Greenway, Alexander Garden, and John E. Holbrook, who made notable contributions to our knowledge of the reptiles of America. Dr. Edmund Ravenel of Charleston was a pioneer conchologist, and Henry W. Ravenel was an authority on American fungi.

Southern scientists were active not only in botany, paleontology, medicine, surgery, chemistry, physics, geology, and astronomy, but also in the field of practical inventions. Yankee inventiveness could more properly be termed American inventiveness, for by 1849 Southern inventors received eighteen per cent of all the patents issued by the United States Patent Office. James Rumsey of Virginia drove a steamboat up the Potomac in 1787. Cyrus McCormick of Virginia patented the first successful reaper in 1834, putting an end to hand reaping. It was a horse-drawn affair which, though still crude, embodied the six essential parts contained in the modern reaper—a knife that cut, mechanical fingers that held the stalk, a revolving reel, a platform for the grain that had been cut, a wheel which furnished power for all its movements, and a divider to separate the part of the grain which was to be cut from that which was to be left standing for the next operation. (Obed Hussey a year before had independently invented a similar machine at Cincinnati, Ohio.) By 1856 McCormick was selling more than four thousand of his machines throughout the United States, and the McCormick reaper on the fields of Indiana and Illinois helped the North to beat the South in the Civil War.

America continued to lead the world in the development of agricultural machinery. In 1857 two brothers, William W. and Charles W. Marsh, of Illinois (and John Hollister of the same state independently), devised an elevator for the reaper to carry the grain up to a bin where the sheaves could be tied first by hand

and later mechanically. The culmination of these inventions is the modern combine propelled by a gasoline tractor.

Eight days after the opening of the Civil War, Commander Matthew Maury left the United States Naval Observatory to join the forces of the Southern Confederacy. Maury was more than an eminent scientist from Virginia. He was a national figure. Born on his father's farm near Fredericksburg in 1806, he was taken as a young child on a hard trek by wagon through the Blue Ridge Mountains and down the Shenandoah Valley to better land on the new frontier near Franklin, Tennessee. His father was descended from French Huguenots who settled in Virginia in 1718, and his mother was of Dutch ancestry. The Maury family counted nine children and Matthew had to help on the farm. At the age of twelve, however, a fall severely injured his back and he was sent to Horpeth Academy to prepare himself for a career in medicine. But this plan did not materialize. An old shoemaker who spent his leisure hours doing mathematical problems lit a spark in young Maury's mind which set him on the road to a new career as hydrographer in the United States Navy.

Maury secured his midshipman's warrant from General Sam Houston, who represented his district in Congress. The arrangement was made secretly, against his father's wishes, and he had to leave for Washington on a borrowed horse. Here he was told to proceed to New York and report on board the U. S. Frigate *Brandywine*. This was the first seagoing vessel the nineteen-year-old boy had ever seen. His thrill was even greater when he learned that this was the boat that was carrying the visiting General Lafayette back to France.

Maury was five feet six inches tall, with a massive head on broad shoulders, curly brown hair, and a ruddy complexion. He was an ambitious lad. "If I went below only for a moment," he wrote, "and could lay hands on a dictionary or any book, I would note a sentence, and fix it in memory to be reflected upon when I went on deck." There were many hours of duty walking the deck, and he made use of these, too. He would chalk diagrams in spherical trigonometry on cannon balls, then place them in the rack in such a position that he could study them as he paced the ship hour after hour.

The young midshipman on his rounds took along with him the internationally known seaman's Bible, *The New American Practical Navigator*, prepared by Nathaniel Bowditch of Salem, Massachusetts. Bowditch was the son of Habakkuk Bowditch, a barrelmaker and shipowner. Even as a boy Nathaniel tried to improve shipping by making a survey of the harbor and other waters adjacent to Salem and by trying to give the mariner something better than dead reckoning to determine his position at sea. Boat captains navigated "by guess or by God" to a great extent in those days. Bowditch, who had studied Newton's *Principia* and had translated Laplace's *Mécanique céleste*, made a thorough study of celestial navigation and corrected innumerable errors in the tables then in current use. His book, prepared when the author was only twenty-nine, as a revision of J. H. Moore's work, has been kept up to date for more than a century and is still a best seller at the United States Hydrographic Office.

Maury came back from his first voyage in May, 1826, made a hurried visit to his family in Tennessee, and was ordered to report for duty on the *Macedonian*. This ship sailed to Rio de Janeiro, around the Horn, and up the west coast of South America to Lima, Peru. Here, in March, 1827, he was transferred to the *Vincennes*, the second United States man-of-war to visit China, and the first American warship to circumnavigate the earth. This world-circling voyage lasted four years, and Matthew Maury did not reach New York again until June of 1830.

It was on his next and last voyage as an officer of the United States Navy that the future fame of Maury was definitely determined. In 1831 he found himself sailing master of the sloop *Falmouth*, ordered to the South Pacific. Like every other officer before him, Maury wanted to reach his objective as swiftly and as safely as possible. To increase the speed of his boat he would have to take advantage of the most favorable winds, the swiftest ocean currents, and the most favorable sea lanes. To get the data needed, he searched all the nautical books on board the ship and questioned older and more experienced sailing officers. The only conclusion he could draw was that the data were meager, the opinions contradictory, and the attention given to this problem was totally inadequate.

While Maury even then saw the great need for scientific data concerning winds and ocean currents, it was almost ten years before he was in a position to concentrate all of his attention upon this important problem. In the summer of 1834 he married his cousin, Ann Herndon, and settled down in Fredericksburg. Two years later, the first nautical work of science by an American naval officer was published. It was in the form of a textbook for junior officers in the Navy and was titled *A New Theoretical and Practical Treatise on Navigation.* Lieutenant Maury's book was reviewed by Edgar Allan Poe, editor of the *Southern Literary Messenger,* who thought very highly of it and was "pleased to see that science was gaining votaries from the Navy's ranks."

Maury's experiences led him to conclude that the education of the midshipman in the United States Navy was both inadequate and faulty. Other matters in the Navy also called for reorganization and drastic change. To bring these faults to the attention of our legislators and to enlist the support of the general public, Matthew Maury in 1838 wrote a series of twelve articles for the Richmond *Whig and Public Advertiser.* These were followed two years later by several more articles published in the *Southern Literary Messenger* under the caption "Scraps from the Lucky Bag." Believing that he could write more freely incognito, he signed his contributions with the pen names of Harry Bluff and Will Watch.

Maury's articles called for the establishment of a Naval Academy similar to the Army's West Point. Partly as the result of these efforts, the Naval Academy at Annapolis was established in 1845. He recommended that reforms be instituted in the education of naval officers. He insisted that the education of the young naval officer be broader than it was. He wished to include in their education such areas of study as foreign languages and international law. He urged that teachers of naval officers should themselves be naval officers. He fought for higher ranks for naval officers to enhance the prestige of our naval power. He called for a larger Navy, better harbor defenses, more vigorous enforcement of the law against the African slave trade, and greater protection of our merchant shipping against the China pirates.

Maury's literary efforts to arouse officialdom to act on several necessary Navy changes were successful. When the real name of the author of the articles became known in Washington, the government began to take the suggestions more seriously. When someone whispered that Maury be made Secretary of the Navy, President Tyler was not averse to such a promotion. But Maury had made so many enemies among high-ranking naval officials that he never received this honor. Disappointed, he decided in 1841 to ask for active duty again on the high seas, a service he had not seen since 1831. Fortunately for science, this request was denied because of a stagecoach accident in which Maury had suffered a thigh-bone fracture so badly set that he was crippled for the rest of his life. This was the second accident which shaped his future career.

In July, 1842, at the age of thirty-six, Maury was made Superintendent of the Depot of Charts and Instruments at Washington, which later became the United States Naval Observatory and Hydrographical Office. Here was his great opportunity to do something for the Navy and merchant marine of his country. He was certain that science had something to offer in the way of increasing the speed of our ships. Between 1800 and 1810 the United States had been the world's greatest neutral shipper, and in the thirty-year period ending in 1860 we were exporting products valued at $335,000,000. Our shipbuilding industry reached new records. We developed the famous clipper ships, fastest boats afloat, which unloaded our cargoes in every port of the world.

Just as the country needed the railroad and the electric telegraph to bind it more closely, so our merchant marine and our fighting Navy needed faster sea lanes through the oceans. This was the problem to which Maury devoted the rest of his life.

Maury was the product of a very religious home, where his stern father made the reading and study of the Bible a daily part of his children's education. Maury, too, regarded the education of his own children as part of his duty. They were not permitted to read current novels or to play cards. Instead, he read the classics to them. They were allowed to sit at the table when distinguished guests were being entertained so that they might absorb manners and knowledge. They read the Bible together. The story has been told that one day, while Maury was lying ill in bed, his daughter read the Bible to him. She came to the eighth verse of the eighth Psalm and read, "Whatsoever walketh through the paths of the sea." Maury motioned to his daughter to stop reading. He kept repeating to himself, "The paths of the sea. The paths of the sea." Then he turned to his daughter and said, "If God says the paths of the sea, they are there, and if ever I get out of this bed I will find them."

In the old building of the Depot of Charts and Instruments, tucked away in cellar, closets, abandoned desks and attics, were bundles of old logbooks covered with the dust of decades. There must be scientific gold in the pages of these "worthless papers," thought Maury, and he went to work to dig it out. These books told the nautical stories of thousands of windjammers which had sailed through every square yard of every sea. They recorded the observations of every wide-awake sea captain who had watched every wind in the sky and every furrow in the water.

There were gaps to be filled in these old records. Maury filled some of them with the data and observations which he himself had made during the years he had sailed around the world. There were other sets of data which needed careful checking and perhaps serious revision. It was an impossible task for one man to get all the necessary information himself. He felt certain that men of the sea would welcome the chance to co-operate with him in an effort to build up a chart which would "blaze a way through the winds of the sea by which the navigator may find the best paths at all seasons." Maury printed thousands of blank charts on which sea captains were asked to mark the tracks of their ships from day to day. In exchange for this data, mariners were to be given, free of charge, pilot charts and hydrographic bulletins issued by the government. Instructions were sent out to sailing masters regarding the proper ways in which to obtain data on the direction and strength of the winds, direction and velocity of ocean currents, compass variation, temperature and pressure of the atmosphere, temperature of the water, and other marine phenomena, such as rain, fog, and the appearance of whales, schools of fish, and flocks of birds. Maury himself, in the meantime, piled up from other weather records additional information regarding wind direction and velocity of many past years. Between 1842 and 1887, 26,000,000 of these filled-in blanks were turned in at Washington.

After about five years of studying the millions of observations recorded in the old logbooks, and adding to them the data which came pouring in from co-operating sea captains, he published his first classic chart. This *Wind and Current Chart of the North Atlantic* contained proposed paths which mariners could follow with confidence. The chart pointed out lanes of the sea which would save them any number of days, and wind and ocean currents which would lessen the perils of the ocean. Five thousand copies of this chart were distributed to ships' captains with requests that they follow its courses, note down any changes, collect more data, and report back its usefulness. Maury also began issuing his *Sailing Directions*, and requested mariners to throw overboard from time to time tightly corked bottles containing latitude and longitude data and the date, and to watch out for such floating bottles dropped overboard by other sailors. Records were to be kept of the exact location and time where each bottle was picked up.

The reports which came back to Washington from the men who were using Maury's charts were convincing evidence of the scientific accuracy of the methods he was using in charting the wind and sea lanes. Days and even weeks were being cut from long voyages. The average sailing time between New York and Rio de Janeiro was fifty-five days, but captains using the paths laid out by Maury were making the same trip in 1848 in from thirty-five to forty-five days. In 1849 the mad rush for gold in California was the signal for the building of more and faster clipper ships. These, too, used Maury's charts and saved much precious time. By 1851 more than a thousand ships were using his charts.

In the winter of 1852-53 four clipper ships left New York for California by way of the Horn. Each was provided with Maury's wind and current charts. A daring and exciting sea race ensued between the *Wild Pigeon*, the *John Gilpin*, the *Flying Fish*, and the *Trade Wind*. The *Flying Fish* reached its destination in 92 days, the *John Gilpin* in 94, and the slowest of the four ships took 118 days to complete the thrilling distance race. By 1855 the average sailing time between New York and San Francisco around the Horn was cut from 180 to 133 days.

When the success of Maury's undertaking became the talk of nautical circles, recognition came swiftly. Nine years after Maury started to chart the sea lanes, President Fillmore made mention of his achievement in his annual message to Congress. The President reminded Americans that Maury had shortened the long voyage from New York to San Francisco by six weeks. Here was a great saving to the commerce of the world. A group of New York shipping merchants and underwriters presented Maury with some silverware and a purse of $5000. In 1853 Columbia University made him an honorary doctor of laws. In that year he published his *Lanes for Steamers Crossing the Atlantic*, and in the following year a vessel was named in his honor. Europe, too, began to take notice when it was learned that Maury's charts and directions were shrinking the round trip from England to Australia from 240 to 200 days.

An international conference was called to meet at Brussels on August 23, 1853. The meeting was summoned by Maury, who went to Europe as the official representative of the United States government. For seventeen days scientists from France, Belgium, Denmark, the Netherlands, Russia, Great Britain, Sweden, Portugal, and Norway discussed the many problems confronting ocean travel. Travel by sea was passing into a new phase. Steam was gradually replacing sail. Maury explained that his wind and current charts and new blanks were devised for the merchant ships and men-of-war of all the nations assembled. It was agreed that all were to continue to collect nautical and meteorological data, and that even in times of war these records were to be preserved and regarded as inviolate.

Other nations watched the proceedings, and when the conference closed, Spain, Austria, Brazil, Prussia, Chile, Sardinia, the free cities of Hamburg and Bremen, and the Papal States joined up in this great international co-operative scientific undertaking. Maury's shipping lanes were accepted by ninety-five per cent of all the commercial carriers of the world, and every ship became a floating observatory. The men who searched for new pathways of the sea knew no flag.

In 1855 Maury mapped out two ocean lanes, each twenty miles wide, across the Atlantic. The cost of this project was paid by New York insurance companies which saw in the new era Maury had inaugurated not only swifter ocean voyages but also safer ones. The Secretary of the Navy of the United States ordered all ships to follow these tracks. While the clippers at about this time were beginning to lose their position as the queens of the seas, and were gradually being replaced by steamboats, Maury's charts continued in great demand. The principal steamship companies relied upon them.

In 1855 an Act of Congress was passed to promote the efficiency of the Navy. Maury remained at the Naval Observatory and two years later was restored to active service. The following year the President of the United States promoted him to the rank of commodore.

While at the Naval Observatory Maury obtained Congressional appropriations which enabled him to improve the equipment of the institution for astronomical work. Between 1845 and 1855 he managed, in the midst of all his other work, to catalogue 100,000 stars. His fame, however, rests largely on the contributions to hydrography which made him the recognized "pathfinder of the seas," and in some measure, also, on the part he played in the construction of the first successful Atlantic cable. When Maury called upon shipmasters to furnish him with data on the winds and currents of the oceans, he also requested them to send in observations concerning sea soundings. Maury needed this data for mapping the ocean floor. Under his direction American naval officers over a period of four years made many deep-sea soundings between American ports and many of the ports of western Europe.

With the aid of all of this data, Maury constructed, in 1852, a topographic map of the North Atlantic ocean floor. This map showed, along latitude 39 between Newfoundland and Ireland, a sort of plateau rising from the trough of the deep ocean. This "telegraphic plateau," as Maury called it, offered an excellent surface over which to lay a cable for the transmission of messages between the two continents. A successful submarine telegraph could join the electric telegraph on land, and eventually messages could circle the world in the space of a few minutes.

Among the men who undertook the laying of a cable on the floor of the North Atlantic was Cyrus W. Field. He knew about Maury's "telegraphic plateau," and a correspondence between the two men about the projected cable began as early as 1853. Field came to see Maury several times, and the two kept in close touch through the years of the first two unsuccessful attempts in 1857 and 1858 to lay the cable. Maury's belief in the early solution of transatlantic cable communications never flagged.

When, in 1866, the first message was sent along the wires of the North Atlantic cable, Field showed his gratitude for the naval man's aid by unstinted acknowledgment of his indebtedness to him. Maury never received any compensation for his help and advice, and turned down an offer of $5000 for the use of his name in connection with this cable. Another chapter in man's conquest of time and space was completed, with the help of American scientists working with theoretical formulas, and engineers translating these equations into practical devices. American commerce and industry received fresh impetus for further expansion.

Maury was one of those scientists who, in addition to his work in science, felt called upon to take an active part in the solution of some of the critical social and political problems confronting the country. Just before he was born, most of the Northern States had freed their slaves, and in 1808 the African slave trade was made illegal in this country by constitutional edict. However, illegal trading went on, and the domestic breeding of slaves added further to the number of blacks in the country. When, after the invention of the cotton gin, cotton was crowned king, slavery became a powerful institution in the United States. The South defended the institution on the grounds of states' rights, the sanction of the Bible, the inferiority of the African race, the humaneness of slavery as compared with the serfdom of the whites in the factories and mills of the North, and also on the contention that the whites would not be safe in this country if the blacks were given their freedom.

The American Colonization Society was founded in 1817 to solve the slavery question by returning slaves to Liberia in Africa. But the slavery issue was not to be settled by this proposal, partly because it was too expensive to buy and ship this great number of slaves, and also because the Negro's birth rate was high. In 1849 a convention of representatives of fourteen states met in Memphis, Tennessee. Matthew Maury was president of the gathering. He proposed that Brazil be made the unloading point of Southern slaves, an expedient which he hoped would in time banish the system forever from the United States. He suggested that the Amazon River be opened to ships of foreign countries and its lush banks be peopled by American blacks. "The Southern states," he said, "may emancipate just as New York, Massachusetts and other Northern states emancipated their slaves. Large numbers of them were not set free; they, after the acts of prospective emancipation became laws, were sold to the South, and so the South may sell to the Amazons [where the institution of slavery was legal], and so get clear of them. In no other way can I see a chance for it. . . . The slaves of the South are worth about 1500 million. It is the industrial capital of the South. Did ever a people consent to sink so much industrial capital by emancipation or any other voluntary act?"

But this proposition whereby the South could get rid of its slaves and at the same time cash in on them bore no fruit. The Compromise of 1850, after nine months of debate, was passed shortly after Maury's speech. California came in as a free state, a drastic Fugitive Slave Law was enacted, and for the next four years the bubbling caldron slowed down to a simmer in an era of good feeling. But in 1853 the caldron flared up anew when Douglas, championing the Kansas-Nebraska Act, literally repealed the Missouri Compromise of 1820 which had preserved the balance of power between North and South for thirty years. Under the new Act all the territory of the Louisiana Purchase north of 36° 30' was divided into two sections, Kansas and Nebraska. The people of these areas were to decide for themselves whether they were to have a free or a slave state when they were ready to apply for admittance to the Union. The Act opened new floodgates of strife, led to the bloody Kansas episode, and brought the whole controversy to a fever heat. That same year, 1854, saw the birth of the Republican Party, which favored the Homestead Act and the building of a transcontinental railroad. The South threatened to secede if John Frémont, the Republican nominee for President, were elected. Buchanan of Pennsylvania, however, won the election of 1856.

The next four years were troubled ones. The Democratic Party split, and Lincoln was elected President on November 6, 1860, by the Republican Party. Six weeks later, South Carolina withdrew from the Union. Maury, although a Southerner and a champion of states' rights, opposed the breakup of the Union. "It will never do," he wrote, "to suffer this Union to drift into dissolution." He sent urgent letters to the governors of the border states to take action quickly to prevent the destruction of the Union. "You recollect," he told them, "that in the nullification times of South Carolina, Virginia stepped forward as mediator with the happiest results. But we are now in the midst of a crisis more alarming to the peace and integrity of the Union than those memorable times. We have the people in no less than seven of those states assembling or preparing to assemble to decide whether they will remain in the Union or not. Step forth as a mediator. Let the people, not the politicians, decide whether this Union is to be broken up. The root of the thing is not cotton or slavery, nor the election of Lincoln. But it is deep down in the human heart."

Unfortunately, Maury was wrong. The war was inevitable, for the conflict between two economic systems for survival and domination was at hand. By February 1, 1861, six more states had joined South Carolina and the Southern Confederacy was born, with Jefferson Davis as its President. Maury made another desperate attempt to save the Union. He urged the border states, Virginia, Tennessee, and Kentucky, to stay in the Union and mediate the sharp differences between the North and the South. On March 4, Lincoln was inaugurated President, and Maury wrote, "The line of duty is to me clear—each one to follow his own State. If there be no war between the sections, we must hoist the flag of reannexation, to carry the elections of '64 on that issue, bring back the seceding States, and be happier and greater and more glorious than ever."

Events were moving swiftly. The South fired upon Fort Sumter in the harbor of Charleston on April 12; three days later Lincoln called for 75,000 state militiamen, and Virginia passed an act of secession on the seventeenth. Maury, up to the last minute, tried hard to keep the Union together. But now that his own state had thrown in its lot with the Confederacy, he had no choice. On April 20 he sent to Lincoln his resignation from the Naval Observatory. He went immediately to Richmond, which had become the capital of the Confederacy, to offer his services to the South. His sons, Richard and John, joined the Confederate Army.

On June 10 Maury was made commander of the small Confederate navy, after turning down an offer from Russia to come to St. Petersburg, "where you may in peace continue your useful occupations." Maury's reply to the Russian invitation was brief. "The path of duty and of honor is plain. When the invader is expelled I promise myself a trip to Russia." The trip was never taken. A year later, Napoleon made him the same offer, and again he resolved to stay with the Southern forces.

Maury's first assignment was in connection with the defense of Richmond. He had had considerable experience for this task. In 1837 he had surveyed the harbors of the Carolinas and Georgia, where he helped improve several ports. That same year he had helped in the fortification of Pensacola, Florida, and had experimented with steam vessels. In his new duties he also assisted in the fortification of Jamestown Island in the James River, and Gloucester Point in the York River. That summer he was appointed chief of the Confederate Naval Bureau of Coast, Harbor, and River Defense.

Maury realized that the inadequate Southern navy could not cope with plans of the North to blockade the South from the rest of the world and to cut the Confederacy in half by seizing control of the Mississippi River. Only by destroying the men-of-war of the North could he hope to frustrate these plans. This he planned to accomplish by his newly devised electric torpedoes. Both Robert Fulton and Samuel Colt had previously experimented with electrical mines, but Maury was the first American to devise improved submarine torpedoes set off electrically and actually to employ this new weapon in warfare. After a demonstration of the effectiveness of his electric torpedoes, Maury was given an appropriation of $50,000 to construct them. He had a difficult time finding enough insulated wire for his devices. He employed zinc-iron Wollaston batteries to supply the electricity to set off his torpedoes. "This business of blowing up men while they are asleep," wrote Maury, "I don't glory in. I shall endeavor to pick up and save the crews from drowning." The North feared his electric mines so much that Yankee warships did not attempt to sail up the James River to Richmond until 1864.

The South had counted on winning the conflict not only with the help of Northern appeasers who opposed the war because it interfered with business, but also with the aid of England and France, which, they thought, would help break the blockade. When these hopes gradually faded, and the South realized it had to destroy the Navy of the North or perish, it accepted Maury's suggestion to build "many little ships with big guns." He was put in charge of constructing one hundred gunboats. But iron and steam engines were not easy to secure, and before his shipbuilding program had reached any considerable strength, the Confederate ship *Merrimac*, armor-clad by Maury, had fought and been neutralized by the *Monitor*. The iron ship *Monitor*, with revolving turret, was constructed in a hundred days by Captain John Ericsson, a Swedish engineer who had developed the screw propeller in 1836 three years before coming to the United States. He became an American citizen and obtained the consent of Lincoln to build, without profit, a small iron ship for the United States Navy. On the anniversary of the famous *Monitor-Merrimac* battle Ericsson died, in 1889, at the age of eighty-six.

Lincoln enlisted the knowledge of many scientists of the North to help in the war effort. In a message to Congress in 1862 he said, "Steam, telegraphs, and intelligence have brought the vastness, variety of climate and production to an advantageous combination for one united people." To stimulate further the spread and utilization of scientific knowledge for the farmer and the mechanic, the Morrill Land Grant Act was passed by Congress in 1862. By the terms of this piece of legislation 30,000 acres of the public domain were set aside for the establishment of agricultural and industrial colleges in each state in the Union either independently or in connection with state universities. The Iowa, Kansas, Oregon, and Texas agricultural colleges grew out of this. Earlier that year Lincoln had approved a bill creating what later became the Federal Department of Agriculture.

Among the land-grant colleges which resulted was the Massachusetts Institute of Technology, although its opening was delayed by the Civil War until 1865. Its first president was William Barton Rogers, who had planned the institution in 1860 in order "to secure a steady prosperity in the midst of the busy inventions . . . and to make our progress commensurate with the advances of science." Rogers had a broad view of scientific research and education, for he said, "We read in the history of social progress ample proofs that the abstract studies and researches of the philosopher are often the most beneficent sources of practical discoveries and improvements." The Worcester Polytechnic Institute and the Columbia School of Mines were also established at this time.

During this critical period still another great scientific institution came into being under Federal sponsorship. Another Act of Congress established the National Academy of Sciences, which, according to its charter, "shall whenever called upon by the Government, investigate, examine, experiment and report upon any subject of science or art." It was to stimulate scientists to further effort by conferring distinctions upon those who contributed original researches. Its first president was Alexander D. Bache, superintendent of the United States Coast Survey since 1843. Lincoln also leaned heavily upon the work and advice of Joseph Henry, who was called upon to sift innumerable scientific schemes suggested to win the war. The President was frequently seen at the Smithsonian Institution, watching Henry at work with his signaling experiments and tests. The Smithsonian, he once remarked, "must be a grand school if it produces such thinkers as Henry."

When European military observers, among them Zeppelin, came over to watch the conduct of the Civil War, they were astonished at the many scientific improvements introduced in warfare. They saw the improved electric telegraph, the electric mine, the observation balloon, repeating small arms, armored ships, Brady's pioneer field photography, canned and concentrated foods, and anesthesia, all combining to make the fighting forces of the North as well aided by science as any army of its day.

Maury's close contact with the men who were leading the Confederacy disillusioned him in some respects. He thought Jefferson Davis too haughty and self-willed, and considered most of the men around him "shallow and self-seeking." He wrote a series of articles in the Richmond *Enquirer* complaining about waste, inefficiency, and red tape. His superiors were infuriated, and to get him out of the way he was sent out to run the Northern blockade and reach England. Here he was to try to purchase matériel for the navy of the South, and to attempt to drum up some sympathy and help for Jefferson Davis. Within a few months Maury managed to purchase one steamer and another new iron screw ship of about 560 tons. This was commissioned the man-of-war *Georgia*, which in seven months of prowling succeeded in capturing nine Northern ships. While in Europe Maury also continued his experiments with the electric torpedo and electric mines.

Maury remained in England for two and a half years. When he was ready to return to America, the Civil War was coming to a close, and, soon after, Lincoln was assassinated. Young Lester Ward, who was to become the first eminent sociologist in America, wrote in his diary on Sunday, April 16, 1865, "Last Sunday General Lee was forced to surrender and to deliver his whole army into the hands of General Grant. Washington was in an orgy of joy. That night everything was afire, all the public buildings were illuminated, and rockets and fireworks filled the whole sky. All was joy then, but what a change of scene in twenty-four hours! Our noble President, the idol of the people and the savior of the

Republic, was snatched from us as in a horrible dream. Everyone is sad."

Maury was advised by his friends not to come back to the United States at this time, for the so-called amnesty did not include pardons for those Confederates who had served abroad. He sailed, therefore, for Havana and, after sending his formal note of surrender to Washington, went on to Mexico City. Maury felt the need of a place of refuge for those officers and enlisted men of the defeated Confederate forces who preferred not to return to a Union against which they had fought. He thought Mexico would be an ideal country for such a haven, for it was rich in natural resources, and large sections of it were blessed with a climate which Southerners would find congenial.

Maury broached the plan to Maximilian, Archduke of Austria, whom the French emperor, Napoleon III, had set up in 1864 as ruler of conquered Mexico. The Austrian puppet was enamored of the scheme, and issued a proclamation in September, 1865, declaring Mexico open to immigrants of all nations. Maury was made Commissioner of Immigration at a salary of $5000 a year, and was given almost unlimited powers in the execution of the project. He immediately arranged free passage for those immigrants who had no money, and gave each unmarried man 160 acres; every married man who brought his family received double this area of the public domain. Those who had money were offered government land under cultivation at one dollar an acre, as well as haciendas in which to live in plantation-owner style.

From Clements Markham, who had successfully introduced the cinchona tree into India, Maury, while in England, had obtained seeds of this tree, with full instructions on how to cultivate it for its quinine in the mountains of Mexico. He had other plans, too, to make his colonization idea attractive. He wrote letters to influential Southerners inviting them to join him in this project. He assured his prospective immigrants, "By the time those lands are paid for they will be worth $20, $30, or even $100 per acre for they produce everything under the sun, and yield perpetual harvests." Generals John B. Magruder, Sterling Price, and Edmund Kirby Smith of the Confederate Army, responded almost immediately. Maury's own son, Richard, and thirty other families also settled down in his Mexican colony. Hundreds of soldiers of the disbanded armies of the South crossed the frontier in search of this new freedom.

Most of the South, however, looked upon this plan with misgivings. It was not loyal, they thought. General Lee, asked to join in the project, declined emphatically, declaring, "We have certainly not found our system of government all that was anticipated by its original founders. I cannot, however, despair of it yet. I look forward to better days. The thought of abandoning the country is abhorrent to my feelings. I prefer to struggle for its restoration, and share its fate rather than to give up all as lost. To remove our people to a portion of Mexico which would be favorable to them would be a work of much difficulty."

Shortly after the machinery of his colonization plan had been set in motion, Maury left for England, hoping to return to Mexico in a few months. He wanted to buy scientific instruments for the astronomical observatory in Mexico City, of which he was made director, and other apparatus needed for a contemplated study of the weather conditions of the country. Soon after Maury had joined his family in England (his wife did not want to come to Mexico), an insurrection broke out against Maximilian and his Empress Carlotta. The Mexican republican army under Juarez finally captured and executed Maximilian in the summer of 1867. With the Emperor's fall went Maury's colonization scheme. Only the cinchona tree, successfully transplanted, remained as mute evidence of this tragic episode.

In England Maury now found himself a man without a country. To support his family he gave lectures, taught the use of electric torpedoes to naval representatives of France, Sweden, Holland, and wrote several elementary geography textbooks for a New York publishing house. He had already made a successful venture into textbook writing. In 1855 appeared his *Physical Geography of the Sea*, which went through many editions and was translated into several foreign languages. Humboldt, the eminent European scientist, held him in such high regard that he once declared that a new science—the physical geography of the sea—had been born, and its father was Matthew Maury.

In addition to his pioneer work in mapping the lanes of the sea and the winds over the oceans, Maury continued the study of the Gulf Stream begun by Franklin. He wrote a beautiful description of it in his textbook. "There is a river in the ocean," he declared. "In the severest droughts it never fails, and in the mightiest floods it never overflows. Its banks and its bottom are of cold water, while its current is of warm. The Gulf of Mexico is its fountain and its mouth is in the Arctic seas. Its current is more rapid than the Mississippi, and its volume more than 1000 times greater. . . . The inhabitants of the ocean are as much the creatures of climate as are those of the dry land; for the same Almighty hand which decked the lily and cared for the sparrow, fashioned also the pearl, and feeds the great whales, and adapted each to the physical conditions by which His providence has surrounded it."

Early in 1866 Maury was given a testimonial dinner in London at which John Tyndall and other eminent scientists were present. "For his disinterested service in the cause of science to the maritime nations of the world," Maury was presented with a gift of $15,000. Soon after this, when the first bitterness of the American Civil War began to be obliterated, full amnesty was talked about in Washington. Maury received an invitation to return to the United States and assume the duties of professor of meteorology at the Virginia Military Institute at Lexington. He jumped at the opportunity and came back in the summer of 1868.

The last four years of Maury's life were spent in teaching and in spreading the gospel of the need of more investigations in the field of weather forecasting, a subject which had interested him for many years. As early as 1855, in his *Sailing Directions*, he had pointed out the urgent need of more weather knowledge not only for mariners but for farmers who were interested in "the atmos-

phere as a whole." He appealed to farmers and agricultural groups
for co-operative data, and to Congress for funds to establish a
weather bureau. He agitated for an international weather conference, which was finally called at Vienna in 1873. The United
States was represented at this gathering.

The popularization of science in America was further advanced
by his textbooks, which, like the McGuffey readers, were used by
tens of thousands all over the United States for decades. McGuffey
lived only sixty miles from the home of Maury, and the author of
the famous readers died only three months after the death of
Maury.

Returning to his home from a lecture engagement in St. Louis
on October 23, 1872, Maury, ill and exhausted, told his wife, "I
am come home to die." He dismissed his physician, saying, "Don't
come any more. Leave me to the great Physician." His end came
on February 1, 1873, and he was buried in Richmond, Virginia,
between the tombs of two ex-Presidents, James Monroe and John
Tyler. His name lives today in the Maury River near Virginia's
Goshen Pass, in the Maury Highway which runs from Lexington,
Virginia, to Goshen, in the Maury Volcano off Brazil, and in the
magnificent monument erected in his honor in Richmond, Virginia.

Europe, too, knew Maury well. The University of Cambridge
recognized his contributions to science by presenting him with the
honorary degree of Doctor of Laws on the same day that it honored the great poet, Alfred Tennyson. Standing, as Maury wrote,
"all rigged up in dyed garments, in a gown and a cap and a beautiful red silk cowl," he heard himself "all done up in Latin."
This degree, translated, said that he, "Maury, by the attentive
observation of the course of the winds, the climate, the currents of
the seas and oceans, acquired the materials for knowledge which
he had systematized in charts and in a book—charts which are
now in the hands of all seamen, and a book which has carried the
fame of its author into the most distant corners of the earth."

This, in a sentence, summed up the magnificent contributions of one American to the whole world of science. His book was called by the novelist Vicente Blasco Ibáñez, in his *Mare Nostrum*, the sailor's Bible. His work has been immortalized by a sentence placed at the top of all the *Pilot Charts* issued monthly by the United States Hydrographic Office of the Navy Department. It still reads today: "Founded upon the researches made in the early part of the nineteenth century by Matthew Fontaine Maury, while serving as a lieutenant in the United States Navy."

CHAPTER TEN

LOUIS J. R. AGASSIZ
(1807-1873)

THE REPERCUSSIONS OF DARWINISM IN THE
UNITED STATES

B Y THE MIDDLE of the nineteenth century American science showed a steadily increasing growth, nurtured in more than one hundred and twenty colleges. Technical and engineering schools, such as the Rensselaer Polytechnic Institute at Troy, New York, were being founded in many cities. The demand for additional instruction for engineers and scientists prompted the founding in 1847 at Harvard University of the Lawrence Scientific School. Its first director was Dr. Eben Horsford, who had come straight from Liebig's chemical laboratory in Giessen, Germany. The American Philosophical Society, the Smithsonian Institution, the American Association for the Advancement of Science, the Academy of Natural Sciences of Philadelphia, and many other scientific associations were the mental and physical workshops for an increasing number of scientists. Scientific publications such as the *American Journal of Science*, and the *Transactions* of the American Philosophical Society were increasing in number.

Scientific information came to the average man in several ways. The growing number of newspapers and new museums helped in the educational process. The first truly public museum of science, founded in Philadelphia in 1785 by Charles W. Peale, contained only a handful of shells, rocks, stuffed birds and animals, the fossil bones of a mastodon found on a farm in Orange County, New York, in 1799 (the first fossil skeleton ever mounted in

America), and other "curiosities of nature." Now, more preten-
tious storehouses of scientific exhibits arose. Itinerant science
showmen and eminent college professors lectured widely and
demonstrated simple experiments in chemistry, physics, biology,
astronomy. The public began to see, for the first time, such instruments of science as the microscope, the gas generator, the electromagnet, the telescope, and the pure chemical elements. Professor
Amos Eaton in 1824 gave a series of lectures in chemistry to the
public all along the route of the Erie Canal. Interested in showing
the common man the real wonders of science, he was opposed to
the pseudo-scientific entertainment of the quacks and impostors,
whom he called "peddling swindlers who offer to sell tickets for
isolated lectures which ought to be despised." Professor Silliman
of Yale began his career as a public lecturer in 1831 when he and
Dr. Denison Olmsted were persuaded by a New Haven carriage
manufacturer to give an illustrated course of lectures to mechanics
and others who could not attend schools during working hours.
Dozens of geologists, botanists, zoologists, and chemists engaged
in state and Federal exploring and surveying projects all over the
country and brought back much new scientific data. Many men
took up plant, rock, insect, and shell collecting as hobbies and carried on a brisk trade with each other in specimens from their
cabinets. Workers in the factories, fields, mines, and shops were
reached by visiting scientists in lyceums and Sunday schools, at
cattle shows and county fairs.

Eminent scientists were even imported from Europe to satisfy
the growing popular demand for more education in science. It was
through a speaking engagement at one of these lecture centers, the
Lowell Institute founded in Boston in 1839, that America was
enriched by a Swiss scientist who became a fertile focus of science
and education in this country for a full generation. The scientist
was Louis Agassiz, who had first written to the great British
geologist, Charles Lyell, about lecture prospects in the United
States. "Lowell Institute," replied Lyell, "is an establishment
which pays very highly. In six weeks you might earn enough to

pay for a twelve months' tour." Lyell knew, for he had made two lecture visits to the United States, the first in 1841 and again in 1845.

Shortly after his arrival here in October, 1846, Agassiz wrote home, "A characteristic feature of American life is to be found in the frequent public meetings where addresses are delivered. Shortly after my arrival in Boston I was present at a meeting of some three thousand workmen, foremen, clerks and the like. All were neatly dressed; even the simplest laborer had a clean shirt. They were brought together for the purpose of forming a library. American science," he continued, "lacks the scope which is characteristic of higher instruction in old Europe. On the other hand, the whole population shares in the advanced education provided for all. What is wanting to all these men is neither zeal nor knowledge. What they need is leisure."

Agassiz turned his eyes toward America because at the age of thirty-nine, although one of the most celebrated scientists of Europe, he was still struggling for the opportunity to use his maximum powers. He was heavily in debt because of his scientific projects. Patrons occasionally came to his assistance—the King of Prussia contributed 1500 francs for his work—but this was at best a hazardous existence. Agassiz complained to Charles Bonaparte, "The French government takes no interest in what is done outside of Paris, and in Russia such researches, having little direct utility, are looked upon with indifference." Perhaps, thought Agassiz, America, where every citizen had his eyes to the future rather than to the past, would be a more fruitful place in which to work.

Agassiz needed no introduction to American scientists when he arrived in Boston. His contributions in several fields of scientific research were already well known here. Few, however, had heard about the hard road he had traveled to achieve them. Born in the village of Motiers in Switzerland, Agassiz showed an unusual interest in plants and animals at an early age. This led him to make up his mind to become a naturalist. His father, however, saw no future for a professional naturalist. He suggested to his son that he turn his scientific interest to the study of a respected profession, namely, medicine.

At college in Munich the lively personality of Agassiz, his interest in research, and his keen mind brought him into contact with several young men who were working in science. Among them was Karl F. von Martius, who had been sent to Brazil on a scientific mission. Among the specimens which he brought back for further study was a precious cargo of fishes of the Amazon River. While classifying these specimens, his collaborator died, and Martius picked Agassiz to continue the study. This was a turning point in the life of Agassiz, who was then only nineteen.

The young naturalist had promised to follow his father's advice to study medicine. Yet he could not turn down this wonderful opportunity for research. He decided secretly to try both, pursuing his medical studies during the daytime, and at night losing himself in the study of the fishes. As he became more deeply absorbed in the fish work, he saw himself as a great naturalist rather than as a humdrum physician. Let medicine, he thought, be reserved to those who love the doctor's art. But as for Louis Agassiz, he wanted to follow in the footsteps of Linnaeus.

In March, 1828, Agassiz wrote a letter to his father cautiously sounding him out. "If during the course of my studies," he proposed, "I succeed in making myself known by a work of distinction, will you not then consent that I shall study, at least during one year, the natural sciences alone, and then accept a professorship in Natural History with the understanding that I shall take my doctor's degree in the time agreed upon?" His father knew nothing of that fish project on which his son was then working. He thought Louis was simply indulging in a temporary infatuation with research. So why be harsh? "Let the sciences," wrote back the father, "be the balloon in which you prepare to travel the higher regions, but let medicine and surgery be your parachutes."

That year Agassiz, at the age of twenty-one, completed the first volume of his work on fishes (in Latin). This was followed the next year by the publication of the second volume, and also by his receiving the degree of doctor of philosophy in science from Erlangen in Bavaria. He sent copies of his books to the great French scientist, Cuvier, to whom he had dedicated them. Agassiz became famous almost overnight. He had done for the fishes of Brazil what Rafinesque had done for those of America. He continued, however, as he had promised, to study for a medical degree, which was conferred upon him at Munich in 1830. Late that year he returned to his home in Switzerland and began the practice of medicine. However, scientific research was still what he wanted to do more than anything else in the world.

In September, 1831, an epidemic of cholera broke out in Paris. Agassiz packed up and went there to study the disease. He met Cuvier, who was then very old and ready to give up his plan of writing a book on the history of fishes. The Frenchman recognized scientific talent in Agassiz. He turned over to the young Swiss all of his fish collections and notes made over a period of half a century, gave him a modest sum to live on and a corner of his laboratory at the Jardin des Plantes in Paris. Out of his small allowance, Agassiz had to pay his artist friend who was doing the drawings. Agassiz worked fifteen and more hours a day without relaxation. "I felt within me," he wrote, "the strength of a whole generation to work and become the first naturalist of my time." Cuvier warned him to "Be careful and remember that work kills," to which Agassiz replied, "I would gladly sacrifice my life, if by so doing I could serve the cause of science."

Upon the death of Cuvier, it seemed that Agassiz would have to give up this work, return home, and resume his practice of medicine. Just then, providentially, Humboldt sent him a letter of credit for 1000 francs, which enabled him to continue working on his fossil fish. Humboldt also succeeded in getting him a modest professorship at the academy of the little watchmaking village of Neuchâtel, in Switzerland. Here Agassiz was able to continue his work, while his artist friend remained in Paris to draw for him more pictures of fossil fishes in the Paris collections. Agassiz sent out a call to many of the museums of Europe for more information on fossil fishes, and new data began pouring into his Neuchâtel workshop.

This business of trying to ascertain from available fossils "what fishes lived in each of the geological epochs of creation, and to trace their characters and their relations with those fishes now living," became an exhilarating affair. Often the fossil material was fragmentary—a single tooth, a few scales, or a fossil spine. With these as guides Agassiz sweated to reconstruct the body of the whole living fish as it swam through some prehistoric sea. So expert did he become in this work, and so deep was his final understanding of the evolution of fishes, that once, during a meeting of British scientists, he was asked to give his idea of the appearance of a species of fish which existed during some very ancient epoch. The remains of this species of fish had not yet been discovered, he was told. Agassiz went to a blackboard and drew the outlines of this supposedly unseen fossil fish. The blackboard was then pulled aside, and behind it was the actual fossil. Agassiz had drawn it perfectly! His work appeared in printed form between 1833 and 1844 as *Recherches sur les poissons fossiles*. In all, he studied more than one thousand fossil fishes. This classic contribution gave him an international reputation, and later earned him the Prix Cuvier.

The reputation of Agassiz as a broad naturalist before he reached his American audience was based upon another important contribution. His friend, Jean de Charpentier, had been puzzled by the presence of large boulders in the plains and mountain valleys of Switzerland. These huge rocks were apparently geological strangers in the places where they were found, for they were made up of rock material different from the rocks over which they were found. These boulders were often too massive to have been carried down by running water. How they got where they were was a mystery. Charpentier advanced the revolutionary theory that these great masses of rock had been carried down from distant places by glaciers or tremendous masses of moving ice.

This theory was greeted with a storm of opposition. Into the maelstrom of conflicting views Agassiz plunged head-first. At the beginning he was skeptical about the theory. He planned, therefore, to make a careful scientific investigation of the truth of this glacial theory. Starting in the summer of 1836, he continued his investigation over eight summers in the mountains and valleys of the Swiss Alps, Scotland, and Wales. He braved the treacherous crevasses of moving glaciers, had himself lowered into some of them to a depth of 125 feet, lived for weeks in a hut erected on one of these moving masses of ice in the lower Aar glaciers of Switzerland, scrutinized markings in boulders, studied dozens of erratic rocks, obtained data on the temperatures and pressures of glaciers, and had his assistants study the flora and fauna of the ice fields. He induced his friend Arnold Guyot to join in the Alpine investigation. Guyot observed that the center of a glacier moves faster than its sides, discovered the law governing the way crevasses were formed, and found that the downward motion of a glacier takes place by the gradual displacement of its ice molecules under the influence of gravitation.

After Agassiz had collected sufficiently convincing data, he announced that Charpentier was not only right, but also that his theory did not go far enough. Agassiz declared that this movement of ice had been world-wide. His studies had convinced him that the ice had at one time extended from the North Pole to central Europe, that most of it had receded, leaving behind deposits still distributed over many parts of the earth. It was a daring theory. His friend Leopold von Buch, the geologist, laughed at the young scientist who, he said, may have been sound in the fish market and with his fish-embedded rocks, but had turned out to be a quack in a field which was not his own. His patron, Humboldt, regretted his playing with such a cosmic theory when he should have been busy finishing his work on fossil fish. "Little will it avail you," he chided the young scientist, "should I vanish from the scene of this world with your fourteenth number of your Fossil Fishes. When I am a fossil in my turn I shall still appear to you as a ghost, having under my arm the pages you have failed to interpolate."

But Agassiz had his champions, too. Lyell, on being shown a beautiful cluster of glacial moraines within two miles of where he lived, finally accepted his theory *in toto*. Charles Darwin was also enthusiastic, and the King of Prussia sent Agassiz a thousand dollars to continue his work. In 1846 appeared his *Etudes sur les glaciers*.

His sponsors in America knew of the great interest his theory had evoked. What more interesting subject would an audience at the Lowell Institute enjoy than one dealing with the earth and its life of the past? This audience represented a cross section of American life. Entrance to the Lowell lectures was free, but tickets were obtained by drawing lots, a method which ensured that workers and professional people, rich and poor alike, would hear them.

Agassiz was a born lecturer. He was a forceful speaker whose groping for English words in his own charming manner only heightened the interest of the audience in his story. He amused the listeners, too, by his almost uncanny ability to illustrate his talks with beautiful sketches often drawn with both hands at once. He disarmed opponents to his theories by his mastery of data.

If Agassiz had any thoughts of returning to Switzerland after his lecture engagements, they quickly vanished from his mind. He was now in a land which offered unusual opportunities for continued researches both in fossil fish and in glacial action. Besides, the collapse of the liberal democratic revolutions which shook the Old World in 1848 had caused the closing down of the academy at Neuchâtel. Many European scientists were turned into political refugees, some of whom came to America. Agassiz helped his friends Arnold Guyot and Leo Lesquereux to come here in 1848. He took Lesquereux and his family into his own household. Lesquereux worked on plant fossils in the coal deposits of Pennsylvania, Ohio, Kentucky, and other states, and became the leading paleobotanist of his day. Guyot, in 1854, was appointed professor of geology and physical geography at Princeton University and held this position to his death.

Hardly more than a year after his arrival, Agassiz became a member of the faculty of Harvard University by accepting the chair of natural history at its newly organized Lawrence Scientific School. He was soon drawn into the center of the intellectual life of Boston and Cambridge. He was invited to join the Saturday Club, whose members met on Saturday evenings around some hotel table in Boston and talked for hours on art, science, literature, philosophy, and politics. Sometimes Emerson would come down from Concord, and other poets and philosophers attended frequently. Oliver Wendell Holmes, scientist and essayist, was one of the club's distinguished members. Holmes described a typical scene: "At one end of the table sat Longfellow, placid, quiet, benignant, soft-voiced, a most agreeable rather than a brilliant talker, but a man upon whom it was always pleasant to look, whose silence was better than many another man's conversation. At the other end sat Agassiz, robust, sanguine, animated, full of talk, boy-like in his laughter."

At these informal meetings (of which no records were kept) could also occasionally be seen such literary luminaries as Hawthorne and Whittier, the mathematician Benjamin Peirce, the abolitionist Charles Sumner, the artist William Hunt, and the philosopher, abolitionist, and reformer, Henry Thoreau. On Emerson's land at Walden, Thoreau had built himself a crude little hut at a cost of $28. Here he wrote essays and lived the simple life. Thoreau was not a professional scientist, but he loved nature, made soundings of the pond, studied birds, the leaves of trees, and tree rings, which he said could be used for dating. He hated dissection of living things and loathed classification as Agassiz practiced it. He collected some mud turtles and fish for Agassiz but avoided his presence, for he disliked the professional scientist. Nor did Agassiz understand the militant idealism which had impelled Thoreau to refuse to pay the government poll tax because of his opposition to slavery and our Mexican War policy.

In the meantime, Agassiz' wife had died in Switzerland. She and their three children had remained in Europe when the scientist sailed for the United States. In the spring of 1850 the Harvard professor married Elizabeth C. Cary of Boston, and his children were brought over to live with him. Some of the busiest years of his active life were still ahead of him. Alexander Bache, head of the United States Coast Survey, looking for the best locations for the erection of lighthouses and signal stations, and with an eye to getting more information on the geological story of Florida, sent Agassiz on a two-month study of the Florida reefs and keys.

In between sessions at Harvard, Agassiz accepted a part-time professorship at the Medical College at Charleston, South Carolina. He also gave a series of lectures at the Smithsonian Institution at the invitation of Joseph Henry. He continued his collection of the fishes of several fresh-water systems of the United States and paid tribute to the pioneer work in this field of Rafinesque, whose fish collections he searched for in Kentucky. In their new house erected by Harvard College in Cambridge, he helped his wife direct a private school for young ladies. He also found time to complete four of a projected ten-volume *Contributions to the Natural History of the United States*—and to obtain 2100 subscriptions for the work at $120 each! He founded the great Museum of Comparative Zoology at Harvard, and engaged in laboratory studies of the medusae during his summer vacations at the seashore of Nahant, Massachusetts.

By the time he reached his fiftieth birthday, eleven years after his arrival in America, Agassiz was the best-known biologist in the United States. Longfellow was moved to write *The Fiftieth Birthday of Agassiz,* which he read before the members of the Saturday Club as the beaming hero of the simple poem sat smoking his cigar.

A few months later, Agassiz received an offer from the French Minister of Public Instruction to fill the chair of paleontology in the Museum of Natural History in Paris. Agassiz declined. To a friend he explained, "The confidence shown in me by those who have at heart the intellectual development of this country make my return to Europe impossible. Were I offered absolute power for the reorganization of the Jardin des Plantes, with a revenue of 50,000 francs, I would not accept it. I like my independence better." Nevertheless, in spite of this freedom which the United States had made possible for him, in spite of his marriage to an American, and his complete assimilation into the cultural life of the United States, in a community where Americanism was almost a religion, he took a delight in still being looked upon as a European. He continued to remain a citizen of Switzerland until 1861. Then, in the dark hours of the opening of the Civil War, he became naturalized as a token of his deep faith in the cause of Lincoln and in the future of a reunited nation.

During these years scientific advances in biology, geology, and paleontology, as well as in the physical geography of the earth, were posing a number of vital questions. The answers pointed to an intellectual revolution of shattering effect. Charles Lyell in England, after his long studies of rock formations, had published in 1830 the first of three volumes of his *Principles of Geology*. His investigations had led him to deny that the earth, as it appears today, was the result of sudden cataclysmic events such as earthquakes and Noachian floods. He had been induced to believe rather that for tens of thousands of years slow, uniform, and continuous evolutionary changes had been reshaping and transforming the face of the earth. These changes are still going on. This *uniformitarian theory* had challenged the *catastrophic theory* of the formation of the earth advanced by Werner, Cuvier, and others. Lyell's book had aroused much heated discussion and no small amount of bitterness. In our own country Thomas Cooper, of the College of South Carolina, had engaged in 1834 in a verbal controversy over this new idea with Benjamin Silliman, the eminent scientist of Yale University, who was a Wernerian.

Concurrent with this geological upheaval came another contribution from the field of paleontology, a science which had just been born in France under the leadership of Cuvier. Digging into the crust of the earth, scientists had found, embedded in different layers or strata of rocks, the remains of fossils of very ancient life. A mass of these fossils had been carefully studied in the light of the advances which had been made in the classification of plants and animals now extant. Out of this work flashed a light which seemed to reveal that the earliest and simplest forms of life were always found in the oldest rocks, that the more recent and more highly developed forms were found only in the more recently formed rocks of the higher layers of earth or in those rock strata laid down last in the geological history of the earth.

Some men wondered whether the more highly developed species of life represented forms of plants and animals which had evolved from the older and extinct species. Or were the number of different species of living things fixed at creation, some of the more primitive forms having died out during the long history of life on earth? Whether species were all created at once by fiat or whether they evolved gradually from simpler forms was more than an academic question. It touched the very foundation of man's belief in the Biblical story of creation. It also involved deep-rooted questions, as, for example, did man develop from lower forms of mammals, such as the monkey or the ape, or had he been formed separately in the first creation?

For many years such questions were generally confined to scientific circles. Europe, naturally, was the center of these controversies. But American scientists were by no means blind to their momentous significance. They, too, were thinking along these lines, and some even saw glimpses of the great truth that was soon to illuminate the world. Dr. James E. DeKay, president of the Lyceum of Natural History of New York, had expressed himself as early as 1826 thus: "It must be admitted that zoologists have too often overlooked the history of man, *as if he was not a link in the great chain of animated nature.* We are aware that the idea of a chain of beings has been ridiculed as a philosophical reverie, but the more this question is examined with the light afforded by modern observations, the firmer will this opinion be established. . . .

Every day brings with it the discovery of some extinct animal whose structure varies more or less from those of any living being. We are insensibly led to admit that the idea of a chain of beings is neither visionary nor unphilosophical."

Rafinesque, too, in the field of botany had seen the new truth clearly and was not afraid to express it. This was in the year 1833. In 1844 Samuel Haldeman, who later became professor of natural history at the University of Pennsylvania, published a memoir in the *Boston Journal of Natural History* on recent *Fresh Water Univalve Mollusca of the United States*. He declared, "It would be a hasty inference to suppose that a physical agent, acting gradually for ages, could not carry a variation step by step, so that instead of the original, we will say, four varieties, they might amount to six, the sixth being sufficiently unlike the earlier ones to induce a naturalist to consider it distinct." By 1847 Joseph Leidy, the American paleontologist, had accumulated a vast amount of data bearing on this subject. He went so far as to sketch reasons for the survival of a species of animal, emphasizing the importance of environment in changing species gradually.

The foremost field botanist in the United States at this time was Asa Gray. Botany in the United States was still largely concerned with nomenclature and classification. Gray, however, had made many studies of the nature and distribution of plants and was thinking along the lines of evolution among plant species. In 1836 he published his *Elements of Botany*, which, together with his *Manual*, dominated botanical education here for almost two generations. He had met Charles Darwin for the first time in 1838 in London, when he was only twenty-eight and Darwin a year older. On his return from Europe in 1842 Gray was appointed professor of natural history at Harvard. Nine years later, when he was again abroad, he lunched with Darwin and his close friend, Joseph D. Hooker. In 1854 Gray wrote some philosophic conclusions about species to Hooker, noting that "Scientific systematic botany rests upon species created with almost infinitely various degrees of resemblance among each other." Hooker sent this letter to Darwin for what it was worth.

For a long time Darwin's eyes had been turned to American scientists. He scrutinized American publications very carefully and many American scientists sent him all kinds of specimens for which he was searching the four corners of the earth. Some of these Americans were coming dangerously near the conclusion which he, himself, was still afraid to announce. In March, 1854, Darwin wrote to Hooker, "I have been collecting facts for these dozen years. How awfully flat I shall feel, if when I get my notes together on species, etc., the whole thing explodes like an empty puff-ball."

Two years later Charles Lyell wrote to Darwin urging him to make up his mind, and write out his views regarding the origin of species. Darwin still hesitated. He turned to America again. He wrote to Asa Gray in July, 1856, to sound him out. "Nineteen years ago," wrote the Englishman, "it occurred to me that whilst otherwise employed on Natural History I might perhaps do good if I noted any sort of facts bearing on the question of the origin of species, and this I have since been doing. Either species have been independently created, or they have descended from other species, like varieties from one species. As an honest man I must tell you that I have come to the heterodox conclusion that there are no such things as independently created species—that species are only strongly defined varieties."

Asa Gray, who saw Agassiz almost daily during these years, kept this correspondence a secret. Darwin wrote to Agassiz on many matters, for he respected his opinions, but did not confide his ideas on evolution to him. Some months later, as the Saturday Club was celebrating the fiftieth birthday of Agassiz, Gray received another letter from Darwin asking him to be careful to keep his doctrine a secret. He had a reason. Robert Chambers, an Edinburgh publisher, had written and published a book in 1844 called *Vestiges of the Natural History of Creation*, in which he declared that there is an unbroken succession of animal life from the beginning. The work was published anonymously, for Chambers was afraid that his heterodox ideas would hurt his publishing business. It was well written (some thought by Charles Lyell) and enjoyed a long popularity. It was, however, generally attacked. Darwin was afraid that "if anyone like the author of this book were to hear of them [his ideas] he might easily work them in, and then I should have to quote from a work perhaps despised by naturalists, and this would greatly injure any chance of my views being received by those alone whose opinions I value."

This letter to Asa Gray of September 5, 1857, contained a fairly detailed account of Darwin's theory of evolution, the first to reach America. This was two years before the *Origin of Species* was published in England. It was literary dynamite. Seldom has a book on science found a public more eager to read it. Wrote Darwin to Gray: "The first edition of 1250 copies were sold on the first day, and now my publisher is printing off as rapidly as possible 3000 more copies. I mention this solely because it renders probable a remunerative sale in America. I should be infinitely obliged to you if you could aid an American imprint, and could make any arrangement for any profit."

Gray immediately got in touch with the publishing house of Appleton; early in 1860 the first American edition of the *Origin of Species* appeared. The United States repeated England's welcome to the book, gobbling up 5000 copies before the end of January. Another 500 copies were printed in February and an equal number in March. A revised edition of the book appeared in the summer of that same year.

In spite of the dark clouds which were gathering above the country over the problem of slavery, the interest evoked by Darwin's book was widespread and intense. *The New York Times* and the *North American Review* published striking reviews of the work. The public reaction was divided chiefly on religious grounds. Here was a book which could be interpreted as a challenge to the truth of many beliefs which people had accepted regarding the place of man in nature. Most religious leaders show-ered denunciations on this heathen tome, yet there were some clergymen who could see in Darwin's assertions no assault on the godliness of man's origin. They insisted that Darwin's theory "did not make God less a creator." Henry Ward Beecher, the best-known preacher of his day, accepted evolution as the key to many of the mysteries of the biological world.

American scientists were also divided in their reactions. Edward Hitchcock, geologist and one of the earliest students of the glacial theory in this country, was a strict creationist and publicly opposed the theory of Darwin. He was joined by Arnold Guyot of Princeton University and by the Quaker conchologist and botanist of the University of Pennsylvania, Timothy A. Conrad. Matthew Maury, too, would have none of the speculations of the English biologist. He followed the Bible, and to those who pointed out that the Bible was not written by scientists, Maury replied in 1860, "The Bible, they say, was not written for scientific purposes, and is therefore no authority in matters of science. I beg pardon. The Bible is authority for everything it touches. The agents concerned in the physical economy of our planet are ministers of Him who made it and the Bible." John Torrey, too, believed in the constancy of species.

But other American scientists saw Darwin's explanations as a great advance. Asa Gray was among these. Although he did not accept all the features of Darwin's theory of natural selection, he became the expounder of Darwinism because he believed that as a provisional theory it had great merit and also because he felt that freedom of scientific thinking was at stake. Jeffries Wyman, another Harvard professor, although a very religious man, accepted the conclusions of Darwin and was not afraid to defend them in his classroom and on the lecture platform. Joseph Henry of the Smithsonian, another pious man, as early as 1860 considered the theory of evolution "the first elevation of natural history to the really scientific stage." He furthermore believed that it constituted a good "working hypothesis" for further investigation by botanists and zoologists and that "It is not necessary that an hypothesis be absolutely true, in order that it may be adopted for the purpose of explaining and predicting phenomena; it is only necessary that it should be well conditioned in accordance with known principles."

It is one of the most curious incidents in the history of science that in this momentous battle Louis Agassiz placed himself squarely on the side of the anti-Darwinians. At first he called the theory "mischievous." Later his opposition took on a stronger tone. "My recent studies," he wrote in 1867, "have made me more adverse to the new scientific doctrines which are flourishing now in England. This sensational zeal reminds me of what I experienced as a young man in Germany, when the physio-philosophy of Oken had invaded every center of scientific activity; and yet what is there left of it? *I trust to outlive this mania also.*"

Agassiz' colleague at Harvard, James Russell Lowell, sided with the scientist. "Such a mush [evolution] seems to me a poor substitute for the Rock of Ages," was his remark. He added, "I am a conservative—with God as against evolution." It was not difficult to understand Lowell's outburst. The Cambridge Brahmin hated science. "I hate it as a savage hates writing," he once said, "because I fear it will hurt me somehow." But for Agassiz to stick to his guns to the last with the assertion, "There is no evidence of a direct descent of later from earlier species"—that was something else again. The great Agassiz, who could with one broad sweep see a glacial icecap crawl over the face of the earth and produce the widespread effects of the glacial era, was as blind as a bat to the hypothesis of Darwin. The brilliant Agassiz, who for many years had studied the striking changes wrought by nature in the fossils from ancient seas, could see no passage of one fish into another among the 1500 species of extinct fish. He would not admit that his work had actually illuminated the whole evolutionary process among the fishes, nor would he admit its connection with the new story which Darwin had unfolded in its entirety for the first time.

Agassiz actually saw a marked parallelism between the stages in the development of the fish embryo and the successive forms of fish life in the successive layers of rock in which they were found. This formed the basis for the law that the embryonic development of an individual organism shows in brief the evolutionary development of the species. When reminded about this Agassiz replied, "I have shown that there is a correspondence between the succession of fishes in geological times and the different stages of their growth in the egg. That is all." He refused to accept the implications of an evolutionary development, insisting that living things were created independently and did not evolve one from the other. Wrote Jeffries Wyman in 1871: "He [Agassiz] *was just the man* who ought to have taken up the evolutionary theory and worked it into a good shape, which his knowledge of embryology and paleontology would have enabled him to do."

It could not have been scientific conservatism which prevented Agassiz from taking kindly to the new idea. His whole life was a denial of such an explanation. More than once he had broken from traditional explanations and hypotheses, as in the case of the theory of an Ice Age and the new estimate of the age of the earth in the light of geology and paleontology. Perhaps it was something in the philosophy of those six generations of ministers from whom he had drawn his first mental stimulation. His father was the sixth clergyman descended in a direct line from a Huguenot who had fled from France to Switzerland. These men saw in every flower, every beast, and every stone some design of the Creator. They would have rebelled against attributing life in all of its complex forms to some willy-nilly chance act, or to the vicissitudes of haphazard environmental changes. The idea of the fixity of species fitted in beautifully with their conception of an orderly world, every part of which was personally brought into being by God's command. Agassiz could not accept any theory which belittled *design* and enthroned chance. "All the facts proclaim aloud," he exclaimed, "the one God whom we know, adore and love, and Natural History must in good time become the analysis of the *thoughts of the Creator of the Universe.*"

Agassiz was no religious bigot. He upheld the geologist Dana in his new picture of how the present surface of the earth evolved. He fought against any attempt on the part of theologians to hamstring scientific investigation, and he actively championed freedom of thought and inquiry. He once wrote to Dana, "I, and we all, are greatly indebted to you for fighting so earnestly the cause of our independence versus clerical arrogance. No one can do it as effectively as you; from me or anyone else who does not profess to be a member of a church it would have no weight with church people at large. I am sorry to find that this clerical spirit is still alive, as bitter, vehement, and overbearing as in the worst times of religious bigotry. It confirms me in my determination not to have anything to do with church matters and church organizations. I do not see but it must come to this, that each and every one must settle religious affairs for himself, without any regard to others; for, after all, religion is a personal relation to God."

Agassiz was annoyed by the back-patting of his ecclesiastical friends for his anti-Darwinism stand, as well as by the vigorous agitation of the followers of evolution, some of whom out-Darwined Darwin himself in those early days of the great controversy. He taught and molded most of the great zoologists of the generation which followed him. It is to the credit of the personality of Agassiz and to the wholesomeness of American scientific thought that practically every one of these outstanding American zoologists followed the lead of Charles Darwin, without losing his admiration for Louis Agassiz.

The impact of the revolutionary theory of evolution upon the Negro problem was very interesting. American scientists took opposing views. In 1847, the year of his appointment to the Lawrence Scientific School, Jeffries Wyman had given the first scientific account of the gorilla as a separate species of ape, distinct from the gibbon, the orangutan, and the chimpanzee. "It cannot be denied," wrote this Harvard professor of anatomy, "that the Negro and the orang do afford the points where man and the brute, when the totality of their organization is considered, most nearly approach each other." This statement was taken up by proponents of slavery as proof that the black man was below the white man in the scale of life and hence a fit slave for the superior white man.

On the other hand, John Bachman, a Lutheran clergyman of Rhinebeck, New York, who had become pastor in 1815 of a church in Charleston, South Carolina, came to the defense of the Negro. Bachman was no anatomist or experimental physiologist. He was an amateur naturalist who had studied plants and animals for many years and had helped Audubon with his *Ornithological Biography*. He wrote three books in defense of his thesis that mankind, both white and black, was descended from a single original stock. His most effective broadside, *The Doctrine of the Unity of the Human Race Examined on the Principles of Science*, was published in 1850. He pointed out that Negroes and whites had intermarried and produced fertile offspring, and hence belonged to the same species. Bachman pointed out, too, that differences in the skin color and hair texture of white and black men could easily be attributed to environmental differences.

The accumulated evidence of the century which has since elapsed points to the correctness of this thought. Both Franz Boas, distinguished American social anthropologist, and Aleš Hrdlička, eminent American physical anthropologist, agreed that the three or four basic races of mankind originated from the same stem. While the American Negro may be less evolved in certain physical characteristics, such as the massiveness of his head, he is higher in the scale of evolution in the matter of the bodily distribution and character of his hair.

As a leader among American scientists Agassiz was called upon to express his views regarding the mental level of the various races. He believed in the inferiority of the Negro, who he thought had been derived from a separate stock. The proslavery elements delighted in repeating Agassiz' words: "The Negro race for thousands of years have shown in natural propensities and mental abilities pretty much what we find them at the present day—indolent, playful, sensual, imitative, subservient, good-natured, versatile, unsteady in their purpose, devoted and affectionate. While others were developing the highest culture of antiquity, the Negro race groped in barbarism and never originated a regular organization among themselves." Agassiz would have changed his mind had he lived to see today a more emancipated race of Negroes contributing to music, art, literature, and science. An estimated one hundred thousand Negroes annually attend American colleges. The achievements of Tuskegee's George Washington Carver in chemurgy, of Ernest E. Just in experimental embryology, of Charles R. Drew in blood preservation, and of other American Negroes would have shown him the effects of environment in shaping the lives of men. So important were the contributions of Carver in the partial solution of the agricultural problems of the South that Congress in 1943, by an unprecedented Act, established the region around Diamond Grove, Missouri, the birthplace of this Negro scientist, as a national monument.

If the proslavery champions found comfort in some of his racial opinions, the abolitionists in their turn could point out that Agassiz was passionately opposed to slavery. "Negroes," said Agassiz, "are entitled to their freedom, to the regulation of their own destiny, to the enjoyment of their life, of their earnings, of their family circle. They should be equal to other men before the law. . . . How to prevent the whites from securing the lion's share of the labor of the blacks? This is a question which my want of familiarity with the operations of the laboring classes prevents me from answering in a manner satisfactory to myself."

For decades after the appearance of the *Origin of Species*, religious leaders among the fundamentalists fought the theory of evolution all over the world. The battle between the strict creationists and the believers in organic evolution was long and bitter. Even today it cannot be said that the last skirmish has been fought. Out from the mountains of ignorance still come bigots to attack the theory from time to time. Tennessee passed a law "forbidding the teaching in state-supported schools that man has descended from a lower order of animals," and the schoolteacher John

Thomas Scopes was prosecuted, found guilty, and fined for this crime only three decades ago. Tennessee, Mississippi, and Arkansas still retain their antievolution laws but they are largely dead letters today. The informed and unprejudiced world accepts organic evolution as a well-established doctrine, even though the complete mechanism of the evolutionary process still remains a matter of opinion. "Evolution cannot be proved, but like wisdom, it is justified of its children," wrote the late Sir J. Arthur Thomson, the English scientist. Yet a survey made twenty years ago reported, "Between one half and one third of our high-school teachers today are afraid to express acceptance of the theory of evolution even if they make no effort to persuade their pupils. The theory is often taught after it has been diluted."

Agassiz did not give up his independent investigations. Near the close of the Civil War he went to Maine to continue his study of the phenomena of glacial drift. Soon afterward he left for Brazil for similar work and also to take up again the study of the fishes of that country, the first scientific project which had engaged him some forty years before in Switzerland. The Emperor of Brazil gave him a military escort during his explorations among the Brazilian rivers. When Agassiz left the South American country he took back with him 1800 new fish from the Amazon and its tributaries as well as the good will of a nation whose friendship was vital to the United States at that time. Charles Sumner, chairman of the Senate Committee on Foreign Relations during Lincoln's administration, had written to Agassiz, "You will see the Emperor of Brazil. You are a naturalist, but you are a patriot also. Plead for our country to the end that its rights may be understood." Agassiz succeeded in this mission.

The importance of Agassiz in the history of American culture is based upon his influence on the progress of science in the United States rather than upon his work as a fundamental researcher or generalizer. It was as an educator and disseminator of scientific knowledge that he gained renown in this country. Practically all of the basic scientific discoveries which he made were accomplished before he set foot on American soil. But his appearance on the American cultural scene gave us a great zoologist and an outstanding teacher of science who initiated a number of educational reforms and introduced new approaches to the teaching of biology.

Agassiz reminded America that science could not be learned from musty textbooks. "If you study nature from books, when you go outdoors you cannot find her," he told his pupils. He emphasized the importance of field trips in the study of science and laid stress also on laboratory work in the study of biology. "In 1847 I gave an address at Newton, Massachusetts," he wrote, "before a Teacher's Institute conducted by Horace Mann. My subject was grasshoppers. I passed around a large jar of the insects and made every teacher take one and hold it while I was speaking. If any one dropped the insect I stopped until he picked it up. This was at that time a great innovation, and excited much laughter and derision. There can be no true progress in the teaching of natural science until such methods become general." He called upon the fisherman and the farmer to co-operate with him in some of his work, and from all parts of America came specimens and data which proved of great help to his investigations. "Agassiz was a sort of Johnny Appleseed of science," wrote Van Wyck Brooks, "sowing seeds of learning wherever he went."

Scientific collections, said Agassiz, in properly supervised and generously supported museums, were essential to teachers and research men if they were to do their best work here and not be dependent upon European museums. With this thought in mind, he worked hard and against many obstacles to create the Museum of Comparative Zoology at Harvard University, which was completed near the close of 1860 with the help of a legislative appropriation of $100,000 and an equal sum raised by private subscription. He was convinced also that research could be improved tremendously by having the work done in laboratories on the spot, where, for example, the live specimens to be studied could be picked right out of the sea.

Soon after his return from a year's dredging expedition down the eastern coast of South America, around Cape Horn and up to San Francisco, made at the invitation of Benjamin Peirce, superintendent of the United States Coast Survey, Agassiz turned his attention to another important project. He initiated the first marine biological laboratory, which became the forerunner of many similar laboratories in various parts of the United States. This project was a science research summer school at Penikese in Buzzards Bay, eighteen miles off New Bedford, Massachusetts—the precursor of all American summer schools. From this descended also the well-known marine biological laboratories at Woods Hole, Massachusetts; the Scripps Institution of Oceanography founded by W. E. Ritter, near La Jolla, California; the Kerckhoff Marine Laboratory at Corona del Mar, in California, and the marine laboratory of the Carnegie Institution at Tortugas, Florida.

The summer-school project at Penikese was the last large undertaking of Agassiz. He had thought about this scheme of gathering promising students of biology together during the summer months at a place where they could spend a healthful vacation busy with research in marine growth. He laid the scheme before the Massachusetts legislators. John Anderson, a merchant of New York, gave $50,000 for such a project, and turned over Penikese, one of the Elizabeth Islands, for the laboratory site. A group of fifty students came to the island early in July, 1873, to listen to lectures by Agassiz, Guyot, and several other eminent biologists. On the second day of the school's opening, the great teacher closed with a prayer which was the inspiration of Whittier's poem, *The Prayer of Agassiz*.

When the summer months were over, Agassiz returned to Harvard. He was a powerfully built man, six feet tall and sturdy, who crammed a tremendous amount of work into one lifetime. Again and again, however, overwork brought on physical breakdowns which forced him to take to his bed or to suspend work. In January, 1852, during the second of these attacks, Agassiz wrote to his friend Dana, "I find my nervous system so overexcited that any continuous exertion makes me feverish. I go around much as the weather allows, and gather material for better times." That last project to get the summer school at Penikese going as quickly as possible was the final blow. On December 2 of that year Agassiz went to Fitchburg to fill a lecture engagement on *The Structural Growth of Domesticated Animals*. He came back tired out and feeling "strangely asleep." Ten days later he was dead. The school at Penikese never reopened, but one of his most brilliant pupils who attended the summer session there, William K. Brooks of Johns Hopkins University, carried on the idea by starting the Chesapeake Zoological Laboratory in Virginia five years later.

Agassiz was buried in Mt. Auburn at Cambridge, Massachusetts. Over his grave was placed a large boulder from the glacier at Aar in Switzerland where he had made his classic investigations. Of money he left none, for, as he had once remarked, "I cannot spend my time in making money." His son, Alexander, followed in the footsteps of his father, and, as a member of the United States Coast Survey, became a specialist in marine ichthyology. Later, however, he branched off into the sphere of mining. From the Calumet and Hecla copper mines near Lake Superior, he managed to accumulate profits which enabled him to give to Harvard and other centers of biological research upward of a million dollars to be used for biological research in honor of his great father.

CHAPTER ELEVEN

JAMES DWIGHT DANA
(1813-1895)

FEDERAL AND STATE SURVEYS AID THE ADVANCES
OF SCIENCE

A TRAGIC ERA followed the assassination of Lincoln. The South was ruined. Four million slaves had gained their freedom but they were left without land, farming implements, or education. Southern leaders did not help matters. They passed the Black Codes which virtually sent the Negro back to serfdom. A hostile Congress passed a Reconstruction Act which placed the South under military rule. Northern industrialists saw their chance of further weakening their economic rivals by making sure that Southern agrarianism would never rise again to challenge their control. The development of the South was retarded for at least a generation.

Western farmers, however, gained strength. They had helped to assure the passage of the Homestead Act in 1862, a measure which had been stymied for many years by the South in its fear of a growing free West. The disbanded armies of both the North and South and other disgruntled elements took up their 160 acres each of free, fertile land in the Middle West. Many Europeans, particularly Scandinavians, learning of the Homestead Act, came over in droves to add to the strength of America.

These Westerners wanted railroads. In 1849 Senator Thomas Hart Benton of Missouri, inspired by the glowing reports of the Far West by his son-in-law, John C. Frémont, had introduced a bill for the construction with Federal funds of a railroad from the Mississippi River to the Pacific Ocean. The discovery of gold and our increasing trade with the Orient were other factors in this development. In 1862, with the South out of the Union, the lawmakers at Washington passed a bill authorizing the building of a railroad from Omaha westward by the Union Pacific Railroad Company. The merchants of Sacramento, California, saw their opportunity and organized the Central Pacific Railroad Company, which was to start from the Pacific Coast and build a line eastward to meet the Union Pacific rails.

The Federal government, in the midst of a costly war, saw fit to hand out liberal subsidies to both of these companies. It paid them $16,000 for every mile of road that was built on level land and as much as $48,000 per mile for rails laid over mountains. Large sections of land were also granted the railroad builders. Railroad companies and steamship lines vied with each other in recruiting foreign labor for this huge engineering program. Europe and Asia, dazzled by fantastic promises, sent streams of immigrants to help forge the first iron link across the United States. Chinese laborers worked feverishly for the Central Pacific to push the iron ribbons eastward, battling against disease, fatigue, heat, and hostile Indians. Irish and other European workers struggled to bring the Union Pacific Railroad nearer to the Pacific.

Twenty-five thousand workers finally came to a halt on May 10, 1869, at Promontory Point, Utah. The last spike, of shining gold from the mines of California, was hammered into place by Leland Stanford. Telegraph wires picked up the hammer blows and sent their sounds throughout the nation. The first transcontinental railroad was completed. Other lines kept knitting the country more closely together. The Northern Pacific Railroad was completed in 1883; and the Atchison, Topeka, and Santa Fe road reached the Pacific the following year. Between 1868 and 1873 there were as many miles of rail laid (about 28,000) as in all the years prior to 1860.

Among the many factors that made this mighty record possible was the invention of a cheap method of making steel. Both wrought iron and steel had been made for centuries. They were manufactured in small batches by a slow and expensive process by a handful of skilled workers. The demands for steel were not very heavy until the invention of the rifled cannon, the locomotive, and other machines stimulated intensive work in metallurgy to meet an unprecedented demand for huge quantities of cheap steel. William Kelly, a Pittsburgh drygoods merchant, found quantities of rich iron ore near Eddyville, Kentucky. Steel was selling at $300 a ton at this time, and he got the notion that a blast of air could be used to make good steel from cast iron quickly and inexpensively. He reasoned that the air, instead of chilling the molten cast iron, would actually increase its temperature by oxidation of its impurities. The idea seemed preposterous, and he was scoffed at by the experts. His father-in-law questioned his sanity and had him examined by his physician.

Kelly went right ahead, however, and in 1851 gave a public demonstration, in Johnstown, Pennsylvania, of his new process. An eyewitness reported this trial as follows: "We saw a vessel that had a mouth open on one side and near the top. The whole was shaped something like an egg. We saw molten cast iron poured into the vessel. Then Kelly turned on a blast of cold air. The vessel set up a roaring noise, and fire belched furiously from its mouth, making many colors. But only for a few minutes. The noise and fire died down. We then saw a blacksmith take a small part of the iron which had cooled, and contrived and threw at the feet of the amazed spectators a perfect horseshoe. No one laughed at Kelly now." This was a momentous event. It ushered in the age of steel and made possible the iron horse. Kelly's invention lacked the drama of Sutter's find, but consequences, though unheralded by the public press, were far greater than those which followed the discovery of the yellow metal.

While Kelly worked to improve his process, Henry Bessemer was discovering the same method independently in England. During the Crimean War, he had invented a new type of cannon, but he could not find steel strong enough to withstand the high pressures of the expanding gases released by the explosion of the powder. This led him to researches in steel; in 1856 he solved the problem and obtained a patent. Kelly then quickly obtained a patent on his own method in the United States. Bessemer built a more efficient furnace and bought out Kelly's patent. The world was waiting for inexpensive steel, and almost overnight the iron industry was revolutionized. The first Bessemer converter used in this country was set up at Troy, New York, in 1864. The new process accomplished in ten minutes what it took the old a whole month to perform. Soon steel took the place of wrought iron produced in the old puddling furnaces now rapidly disappearing. In production figures, pounds were replaced by tons. By 1870 steel production had forged ahead so rapidly that it was equal in bulk to that of wrought iron. Today production of the latter represents only about one per cent of the total output of steel in the United States.

The building of the railroads also gave a sharp impetus to the study of the mineralogical wealth and the geological structure of the country. This led directly to important advances in both of these sciences. These studies had really started with Harriot's first visit to America, when among his scientific labors he included the collection of rocks. Later came hundreds of rock and mineral collectors who continued to chip the crust of the United States; this scientific pursuit became one of the earliest and liveliest activities of amateur scientists. Even before the eighteenth century, the chemist Thomas Cooper had studied the blue-earth deposits of New Jersey. Samuel L. Mitchill made a detailed report of the geological and mineral resources of the banks of the Hudson River, and published the first book of its kind in the United States. In 1806, when Benjamin Silliman became head of the geological and chemical departments of Yale College, the first such department in America, "geology was still hardly known by name in this country. The whole rock cabinet of Yale was hardly a half bushel of unlabeled stones." In 1810 Dr. Archibald Bruce of New York City published the first journal devoted to this subject, *The American Mineralogical Journal*. This appeared in but one volume

(1810-14) and was succeeded in 1818 by Silliman's *American Journal of Science*, which published an enormous quantity of geological information. Of the 92,000 pages of scientific matter published in this journal during the first century of its existence, at least 20,000 were devoted to geology and mineralogy. Many of the earliest chemical investigations in the United States dealt with the chemistry of minerals. One of the earliest of these investigators was Dr. Adam Seybert, whose large mineral collection in the early 1800's was of great help to Silliman.

The first serious study of American geology may be said to have begun with the pioneer work of William Maclure of Philadelphia. In 1809 his paper *Observations of the Geology of the United States, Explanatory of a Geological Map* was published in the *Transactions* of the American Philosophical Society. This first geologic map of a portion of the United States was the result of very careful study of the rock structure of the eastern part of the country, including the Appalachian Mountains, which Maclure crossed and recrossed half a hundred times in this investigation. This map was followed eight years later by a more complete treatment of the geology of the country. In 1819 a number of the country's leading students of geology gathered at Yale to organize the American Geological Society. This association was an important factor in the establishment of geological surveys in connection with the building of canals and highways and later with the construction of our railroads.

Some of our leading scientists were actively engaged in the many state surveys which operated for half a century. One of the first of these was Amos Eaton, lawyer, land agent at Catskill, New York, botanist, and geologist. As early as 1818 Eaton made a survey for New York State for the proposed Erie Canal. He recognized that sedimentation in rocks occurred in cycles and wrote a textbook, *Index to the Geology of the Northern States*. He persuaded his friend De Witt Clinton, Governor of New York, to initiate a study by the state of the natural history of New York, which was finally completed in 1842. Another New York State

Geological Survey got under way in 1836, continuing until 1843.

Ebenezer Emmons, who was graduated from both the Rensselaer Polytechnic Institute and the Berkshire Medical School, threw away his medical kit for the geologist's hammer and worked on this project. He discovered a whole system of stratified rocks consisting of a series of schists, quartzites, and limestones all the way from Canada to southeastern New York, which he called the Taconic system. The conchologist, botanist, and mineralogist, Timothy A. Conrad, was another member of the New York State Geological Survey. He had a salon in Philadelphia where poets and geologists vied with one another for the exaltation of nature or in the naming of new rocks. It is said to have rivaled that of Wistar.

Lardner Vanuxem, son of a well-to-do shipping merchant of Philadelphia, gave up business for geology and went to Paris to study under René Haüy, father of the new branch of mineralogy known as crystallography. Upon his return, Vanuxem was appointed by New York State to study the geology of Ohio, Tennessee, Kentucky, and Virginia. This excursion into other states was made in connection with a more extensive study of the rock formations of New York, for rock layers often extend to regions hundreds of miles distant.

Denison Olmsted, first of Silliman's students to take up geology as a profession, investigated the rock formations of North Carolina and wrote a two-volume report on its geology—one of the earliest state geological reports ever completed. Elisha Mitchell of Connecticut, minister and professor of mathematics at the University of North Carolina, worked in the area around Black Mountain, North Carolina, only to lose his life in 1857 during one of his expeditions to the crest of the Appalachians. Mount Mitchell, the highest peak east of the Rockies, was named after him.

Vermont chose as its state geologist Zadoc Thompson, who had worked his way through the University of Vermont as an almanac seller. An almost incredibly accurate forecast of snow in July in this region, which he made by accepting certain erroneous data, boosted the sales of his almanac that year sky-high. In addition to his geological work he found time to preach in the Protestant Episcopal church and to teach school as well.

David Dale Owen, son of the social reformer, Robert Owen, made his home at New Harmony and was appointed first geologist of Indiana. Later, at the request of the United States Land Office, he extended his investigations into part of the Northwest Territory now known as Wisconsin and Illinois. Kentucky and Arkansas, too, saw the labors of this man completely "married to his geological laboratory" until he died of malaria just before the outbreak of the Civil War. His brother, Richard, succeeded him as state geologist of Indiana. Ohio, too, conducted a geological survey under the direction of William Mather, graduate of West Point and descendant of the witch-hunting Cotton Mather of Massachusetts.

Virginia had a state geologist in the person of William B. Rogers, the second of four brothers who all made contributions in this field of science. This same Rogers became the first president of the newly established Massachusetts Institute of Technology. Edward Hitchcock, minister and first president (1840) of the Association of American Geologists and Naturalists, studied the rock formation of the Connecticut Valley, of Vermont, and of Martha's Vineyard, off the coast of Massachusetts. Practically every state, with the exception of Louisiana and Oregon, had its own official geologists who undertook surveys to study the geological and mineralogical resources within its boundaries. Among these early geologists were many chemists, and some chemical progress also resulted from this country-wide investigation.

Federal surveys for the purpose of finding the best routes for canals and railroads, and also to determine the location and extent of valuable mineral deposits, were of further help in the progress of American geological investigation. In 1817-18 Henry R. Schoolcraft, graduate of Union College, where he had specialized in chemistry and mineralogy, made a significant contribution in this field. He explored part of the Middle West and brought back

valuable information about the lead mines of Missouri and the resources and physical geography of other sections of this region.
Two years later John C. Calhoun, in Washington, invited this
broad scientist to join a party led by General Lewis Cass to study
the metallic wealth of the Lake Superior region, especially its copper mines. Schoolcraft published a book on this survey, in 1821,
which created quite a bit of public excitement. He became Indian
agent at Mackinac, married a Chippewa girl, and wrote a book on
the Indians which was published by the government.

Such surveys became more frequent because of the agitation
started by the illegal entry of miners and smelters into publicly
owned lands in the Mississippi Valley. Many of these men refused
to pay royalties to the government for the lead and copper which
they took out of land which did not belong to them. These illegal
mining ventures, which culminated in the copper fever of 1844-
46, hastened action by the Federal government in the survey of
the area around Lake Superior prior to the sale of these public
lands to private mining companies. David Dale Owen was in
charge of this survey, and issued his final report in 1851 as United
States Geologist for Wisconsin. Dr. Charles T. Jackson, of the
Ether Controversy, was also connected with this project for a time
in 1847-48, after serving as state geologist for Maine, New York,
and Rhode Island.

In 1853, despite some differences, Congress appropriated
$150,000 for a series of surveys to examine four possible routes for
a railroad to the Pacific. The party which was finally selected for
the job included botanists, zoologists, and a number of geologists.
Under the auspices of the Smithsonian Institution, detailed and
elaborate instructions were prepared to make possible the gathering of the maximum amount of important scientific data in regions
which, in many cases, were virgin ground for our scientists.

For almost four years this party of engineers and naturalists
roamed the wild West, mapping, surveying, collecting, painting,
and noting a mass of data. Their observations filled thirteen large
volumes of *Reports of Exploration and Surveys to Ascertain the*

Most Practical and Economical Route for a Pacific Railroad from the Mississippi to the Pacific. This great project was carried out under the direction of the War Department. The Department of the Interior, too, sent out topographical engineers to the new Southwest, the Black Hills of Dakota, the Yellowstone Valley, and other parts of the country. Private surveys were organized by railroads and mining companies. Hundreds of scientists brought back valuable data from a field so rich and broad that even today the complete story has not yet been told.

Among the group of men who struggled to piece together the story of the rock formations of the New World none stood out more prominently than James Dwight Dana, who lived through more than eight decades of this stirring episode in the scientific conquest of a new country. This distinguished American scientist came of a long line of intellectual men. The original members of the Dana family came over to Massachusetts as early as 1640 and were partly of Italian origin. A chief justice of Massachusetts, a United States Senator from Connecticut, an author, Richard Henry Dana, who wrote *Two Years Before the Mast*, a governor of Maine, a professor of chemistry at Dartmouth College, and Charles A. Dana, the distinguished editor of the *New York Tribune* and the New York *Sun*, belonged to this unusual family.

James Dwight Dana, the first of twelve children of James and Harriet Dana, was born in 1813 at Utica, New York, when this city had a population of only 1700. He was an average lad, very curious and full of fun. He attended the local high school, where his science teacher took him on field trips and started him collecting minerals. At Yale Benjamin Silliman stimulated his interest with the new geological knowledge and reports of the controversies which were raging in Europe. Silliman had just returned from abroad, bringing an excellent collection of minerals, which captivated young Dana.

After three years at New Haven, an opportunity came to Dana in 1833 to become tutor in mathematics to the midshipmen on the United States sloop *Delaware*, which was ready to sail for the

Mediterranean. At this time the United States had no naval academy and the young midshipmen obtained their education on board ship in this way. Dana seized the chance, for he wanted to have a look at some of the earth features about which Silliman had lectured. He cruised through the Mediterranean, stopping at Gibraltar, Minorca, Athens, and Smyrna. Dana's duties were light, and he had the leisure to study geology and crystallography, as well as the guitar. He collected many rocks and minerals. In a wheat field in Minorca he caught some perfect specimens of the Hessian fly, writing home to his brother John that "this then is no longer to be considered an American insect," as some had believed.

When the sloop returned to New York in December, 1834, after a voyage of sixteen months, Dana left the Navy and wondered what to do next. He was twenty-one. Work in his father's store in Utica did not appeal to him. His father would have been happy to see him through a law or medical school, although he frowned upon the idea of a career as a professional scientist. James was not interested in the law. "Medicine, however, is not so much opposed to my taste," he wrote, "yet I hardly think I should like the practice, it is so laborious, and in many instances so disgusting."

What he really wanted to do was to work in a college atmosphere among scientists and books. "There is much advantage," he told his father, "in being with those who are attending to the same studies with yourself. You seem to be carried easily by the current." He was thinking of a small group of men who that year, while he was sailing the Mediterranean, had organized the Yale Natural History Society. Silliman had taken a liking to Dana, not because he was a brilliant student but rather because he was attractive and had a very likable personality. When the Yale scientist offered him an assistantship, Dana did not hesitate a moment about accepting it. His duties were routine. He carried out some simple chemical analyses of rocks, set out specimens of minerals and fossils for the professor, and prepared a few geological charts.

Dana found plenty of time to study the new branch of mineralogy known as crystallography. Its outlines had been given to the world in 1801 in Haüy's famous four-volume *Traité de Min-éralogie*. Mineralogy, a broader science than crystallography, describes, classifies, and correlates the different kinds of minerals according to many characteristics. Part of this study involves the investigation of the shape and angles between the surfaces of a pure mineral crystal. This is crystallography. Dana measured thousands of angles found in hundreds of minerals which passed through Yale and which he himself had collected. He worked out the mathematical relationship between the various angles and axes of crystals. He even constructed his own hollow glass crystal models, among the earliest made in this country. He developed his own system of naming these crystals, after reading Berzelius' system of chemical nomenclature and the so-called natural system of classification of Haüy, based on such physical properties as hardness, luster, and specific gravity. Dana later abandoned this earlier classification, explaining that "To change is always seeming fickleness. But not to change with the advance of science is worse, it is persistence in error." His new classification of 1850, the first accurate one introduced, was based entirely upon chemical composition and the crystal structure of minerals.

In 1837, when he was only twenty-four years old, Dana published his *System of Mineralogy*, which became a classic among American textbooks. Revised in 1944, it still continues in general use—more than a century after its publication. This book described the locations, crystal shape, physical and chemical properties, and formulas of thousands of different minerals. It sent America out mineral collecting. Thousands of men, women, and children went into the mountains, the fields, the valleys, the caves, mines, and dried-up river beds in search of new specimens and new data. Geological exploration became one of the most popular outdoor pastimes of America for decades.

This achievement launched Dana's reputation as a geological authority. It was immensely enhanced the following year when a new opportunity rushed him into another adventure which was to prove for him what the trip on the *Beagle* just a few years before had done for Darwin. Dana's association with the United States Naval Exploring Expedition gave him a four years' trip around the world and made it possible for him to develop the breadth of scientific vision which turned geology from the study of isolated rocks, minerals, and crystals into a planetary problem embracing whole mountain ranges and chains of mountain barriers. It made possible his synthesis of the geological story of America. This expedition to the South Seas (1838-42), under the command of Lieutenant Charles Wilkes, gave him the leisure, the intellectual companionships, and the whole globe to study at close range. As in the case of Maury, the United States Navy became the great university for Dana.

Wilkes was interested in the scientific aspects of the expedition, for which several scientists had been selected to study birds, insects, arachnids, and Crustacea. Dana, who was recommended by Asa Gray, was the mineralogist and geologist. Nathaniel Hawthorne wanted to accompany the party as historiographer, but the plan never materialized. The main purpose of the expedition, however, was not scientific. It was launched primarily for a strictly utilitarian purpose, "that commerce might be benefited by surveying the coasts frequented by our hardy fishermen . . . and that new channels might be opened for commercial pursuits, especially in animal fur." American interests were afraid that Britain might extend its control of the whaling industry in the Pacific. Furthermore, "Congress [which authorized the expedition in 1836] was satisfied that, in the seas which it was proposed to explore, the whale fishing alone gave employment to more than ten per cent of all our tonnage, and that the annual loss of property upon the islands and reefs not laid down upon any chart was equal to the expense of the expedition and surveys requested." Out of this utilitarian venture came fruit of the ripest sort in theoretical science.

Dana wrote home about his geological expeditions on the island of Madeira, of the survey work in the harbor of Pago Pago, where the United States was establishing a coaling station, and of his visit to the Samoan island of Apia, where Robert Louis Stevenson was to spend his last years. He had a long stay in Sydney, Australia, then a city of 24,000 inhabitants, including about 5000 convicts. From here, Wilkes proceeded to the icy barriers surrounding the South Pole and discovered a vast antarctic continent on the morning of January 19, 1840, only ten hours before a French expedition, suffering terribly from scurvy, reached the same spot. Dana and the other members of the scientific corps had been left behind in Australia, since they were regarded as "worse than a useless appendage" on so hazardous a voyage to such a frigid waste.

Dana, a very religious man, wrote to his mother and to Benjamin Silliman, his future father-in-law, about the possibilities of establishing missionary stations in various parts of the heathen world he had visited. He had found that several missions which had previously been established were thriving; others, however, were having a great deal of trouble and seemed hopeless. Two of the Wilkes party were captured by Fiji Island cannibals and murdered. Dana wrote home, "The Feejee Islanders prefer a roasted Feejee to a fatted hog (a white man, they say, tastes better), and sometimes kill a slave when no enemy has been taken prisoner."

Upon the return of the expedition, Dana's boat was wrecked on a bar in the mouth of the Columbia River and he narrowly escaped death. When he got back to Washington by way of the Cape of Good Hope, after an absence of almost four years, he went to work on the mass of scientific material he had collected both in geology and zoology. He had no university connection at this time. He lived on the savings he was able to accumulate during his connection with the expedition, augmented by the money which came to him as a silent partner in his father's store in Utica. Congress was very niggardly in granting funds for the publication of the scientific material collected during the expedition. "It is most shameful," wrote Dana, "that I have not received from the government even one single copy of my own work." Most of the copies had been sent to foreign sovereigns and libraries all over the world.

Washington society was not to Dana's liking, either. He made frequent visits to New Haven, where, in the summer of 1844, he married the daughter of Professor Silliman. He built a house on Hillhouse Avenue, and New Haven became his permanent residence. In 1848 he published his *Manual of Mineralogy*, which has been revised and reprinted to this day. Asa Gray tried several times to get him to come to Cambridge and join the Harvard faculty. But Yale decided to hold on to Dana through the founding, after the resignation of Silliman, of the Silliman professorship of natural history and geology. In 1849 Dana was named the first occupant of this chair, which he filled for almost half a century.

With Dana the science of geology took on new meanings. In 1862 he published his *Manual of Geology*, which gave to the new science greater clarity and more definite direction than it had ever enjoyed before. "Geology," he said, "is not simply the science of rocks, for rocks are but incidents in the earth's history." He looked upon geology as a historical science. For the first time in America, geology was treated not as a collection of facts about rocks and crystals or even as a study of isolated geological formations, but rather as the dynamic story of the great changes which had occurred upon the earth during its long history. Dana viewed geology in its grand relation to the various strata found in mountains, plateaus, plains, and valleys, shaped by the cosmic forces of heat, pressure, water, atmosphere, and organic evolution—the same forces which are still active on the globe.

He ascribed time periods to the geological structure of the earth, starting with the *Archeozoic* epoch, which began perhaps one and a half billion years ago, through the *Pleistocene* or glacial period of about 40,000 years ago. This time division was used by Dana in the study of the intricate geological complexion of the North American continent. He looked upon the whole of the United States as one great mass of different layers of rocks formed under varying conditions. Some of these layers stretched for thousands of miles, distorted and thrown out of order by local conditions, making the relative positions of rock layers often confusing and almost impossible to explain. This was the fascinating puzzle which Dana attempted to decipher with the newer knowledge of historical geology. "Historical geology," he wrote, "finds strata of sandstone, clayey rocks and limestone lying above one another in many successions, belonging to successive periods in the earth's past. The rocks are regarded as records of successive events in the history—indeed as actual historical records. Every new fact ascertained by a close study of their structure, be it but the occurrence of a pebble, or a seam of coal, or a bed of ore, or a crack or any marking whatever, is an addition to the records to be interpreted by careful study."

Out of his earliest observations during his field trips as a Navy schoolmaster; out of his experiences during his four-year voyage around the world and his many years of watching hundreds of railroad cuts, excavations, and rock boring in many areas of the country; from the numerous reports of the many state geological surveys, the written records of railroad engineers, and especially from the almost endless stream of geological papers which came pouring into the office of the *American Journal of Science* (of which he became joint editor with Silliman in 1846)—out of all these came the basis for a splendid synthesis of the geology of the United States. Dana skillfully fitted into his final canvas the contributions of many American geologists. The earliest historical geological papers of William Maclure, the writings of the paleontologist and geologist, James Hall of New York, on the eruption of volcanoes (vulcanism) as a geologic force, and W. B. Rogers' theory of the formation by great heat and strong pressure of metamorphic rocks from sedimentary deposits (such as the change of mud into slate); the papers on stratigraphy (relative position of the layers of the crust of the earth) by Ebenezer Emmons; the nature of sedimentary rocks formed by water, glacier, or wind, such as stratified sandstone, as explained by H. D. Rogers; the process of diastrophism or the deformation of the earth's crust, as seen by Henry D. and W. B. Rogers—all were added to Dana's own studies of the rock system of western New England and the very hard, igneous trap rocks of Connecticut.

It was a titanic job—to piece together bits of isolated information and mountains of seemingly unrelated data, to sift out from hundreds of theories regarding the origin of local rock formations those which were well founded, to keep abreast of the wealth of new discoveries which were being made all over the country, might have made many another man a strictly armchair scientist. But not so with Dana. He made numerous field trips to check the data which he clarified and from which he elaborated on the events leading up to the formation of the mountains of the United States. In his paper *On the Origin of Continents* he explained the formation of some mountains as a result of the contractive forces liberated as the hot earth cooled. This caused a wrinkling of the earth's surface, with a consequent rising above it of large hot masses of rock. This explanation was not entirely new with Dana, but he used this approach to explain the formation of the Appalachian Mountains. Dana enjoyed such a tremendous reputation that Bailey Willis, who later became professor of geology at Stanford University, remarked, "As a college student in the late 1870's had I been asked why the earth was cooling and contracting I might have answered: 'Because Dana says so.' "

To the thrilling story of the dynamic geological past Dana made other substantial contributions and clarifications. Charles Lyell and other geologists had thought that the continents and the oceans repeatedly changed places during the long history of our solid planet. Dana produced evidence to shed doubt on this theory, and offered other data which seemed to show that the positions of the continents and the oceans were, broadly speaking, permanent.

He also made a contribution to our understanding of the formation of coral regions. In 1872 he published his *Corals and Coral Islands*. During the Wilkes expedition he had studied the long coral barrier reefs which fringe the coast of Australia, as well as several other coral reefs and atolls in the South Seas. Dana saw these coral lands formed by the growth and piling up of the limestone secretion of the coral, a small animal living in colonies attached to the ocean floor. Coral polyps grow in warm, shallow water around the equator. They are responsible for three kinds of land formations—fringing reefs, barrier reefs, and atolls. Fringing reefs lie close to the coast of the Hawaiian Islands and other places. Barrier reefs enclose a lagoon between them and the coast. These reefs extend for 1200 miles along the northeast coast of Australia. An atoll, a ring of coral around a central lagoon, is frequently formed where the coral has grown on the top of a shoal within about a hundred feet of the surface of the ocean. Dana explained the formation of barrier reefs and atolls as due to the slow sinking of the ocean floor, with the concurrent piling up of coral growth upon it.

At Sydney, Australia, Dana had read in a brief newspaper account Darwin's recent ideas regarding atolls and barrier reefs. This was the first time he had learned that Darwin had studied these formations. He was so pleased that the English scientist agreed with his own conclusions of 1839 that he made further studies and collected even more data than Darwin himself obtained in support of his theory. Twelve years later Agassiz found the coral reefs of Florida somewhat different from those described by both Darwin and Dana. His observations led him to believe that a good portion of southern Florida consisted of successions of concentric reefs separated by deep channels which had filled up (the Everglades).

Vulcanism was another problem in geology to which Dana made some modest contributions. His first scientific paper, published when he was twenty-two, dealt with some observations and studies he had made *On the Conditions of Vesuvius* while he was engaged as teacher to midshipmen on the *Delaware*. Five years later, during his service with the Wilkes expedition, he climbed other volcanoes on Hawaii and in 1860 made further investigations on the nature of volcanic eruptions when he revisited Vesuvius. When he was seventy-four years old, Dana took his wife and daughter to Hawaii and showed them the volcanoes he had studied more than a third of a century before. The natives there called him *Kahuna wawaki pohaku*, or "the rock-breaking medicine man." In 1890 he published his *Characteristics of Volcanoes*, and in that same year he finally relinquished his college duties. Only a few weeks before he died in New Haven in 1895, Dana made his final appearance in the *American Journal of Science* with an original contribution on part of the rock structure of Nebraska. This completed his literary output of 215 papers and books, and rounded out threescore years of scientific writings.

Geology and mineralogy were not the only scientific fields which occupied Dana's attention. For fourteen years after his return from the Wilkes expedition, he was busy preparing for publication all of the notes and collections he had made not only in geology but in zoology as well. His report on *Zoophytes* (coral-like animals) appeared in 1846, and the one on *Crustacea* (lobster- and shrimplike animals) in 1854. Aside from the less important fact that he described no less than 200 new species of coral animals (almost doubling the number then known), and about 500 new species of Crustacea, his broad view of natural history enabled him to make sound classifications of the material he had collected.

Dana took little part in the social and political life of the troublous times in which he lived. He lived the life of a modest, busy professor wrapped up in his work, his immediate family, and a small social circle including the Sillimans, who lived next door. In spite of the fact that he was a striking figure with a full head of white hair and an almost poetic face, and was a recognized authority in a field in which the public was extremely interested, the public-lecture platform never took hold of him as it did Agassiz. Unlike his fellow scientist from Harvard, Dana disliked lecturing and his dependence on written notes made him a poor speaker. "I am no public speaker," he told his friend Asa Gray, "and I have a dread of public life." Although at one time he filled a commitment for a series of lectures for the Young Men's Institute, he preferred to stay home and read scientific papers, or to play the flute and guitar. He seldom even attended a concert or the theater.

Yet Dana was not altogether indifferent to the critical problems which he and his fellow countrymen had to face. He felt that the cause of the North was a just one, and wanted to see slavery abolished all over the land. In the dissemination of knowledge, he championed the spread of the truth as science saw it. Only once did he enter the arena of public conflict. When fundamentalists fought against the new geology which they thought denied the truth of the Bible, spread infidelity, and undermined the faith of school children and college students, both Dana and Agassiz, two men of virile religious faith, supported the findings of science. When scientific truth and freedom of inquiry were in danger, Dana came to their defense. "Truth," he wrote in 1857, "though so glorious in itself, how it is feared and fought against by self-deluded men! Give the trilobites a chance to speak and they would correct many a false dogma in theological systems."

In spite of his dread of public life, his reputation as the incontestable leader of geologists in the United States propelled him into the highest scientific offices of the land. He was elected president of the Connecticut Academy of Sciences, and later headed the American Association for the Advancement of Science, as well as the National Academy of Sciences.

Dana was regarded with equal esteem abroad. Humboldt considered his work among the most splendid contributions to the scientific advance of his day. Darwin had a great deal of respect both for his scientific knowledge and for his philosophical opinions. As early as August, 1849, he wrote asking Dana to lend him some of the many species he had collected during the Wilkes expedition. He consulted the American about the craters of the Hawaiian Islands and continued to correspond with him for almost a quarter of a century. Dana tried to persuade Darwin to come here to lecture, but he begged off, complaining of his "poor health which allows me to work but an hour or two daily." Three years later, Dana repeated his invitation. This time Darwin replied, "No tour could be half so interesting to me, but with my large family, I do not suppose I shall ever leave home."

Dana's reaction to the *Origin of Species* was less positive than that of Agassiz. In 1855 Dana was a catastrophist and did not regard the facts of paleontology as proof of organic evolution. He was at this time a strict creationist, holding that "No senseless development principle evolved the beasts of the field out of monads and men out of monkeys, but all can claim parentage in the Infinite Author."

When Darwin's book appeared a few years later, Dana was suffering from the first of his recurring attacks of nervous exhaustion. He had gone to Europe for relief, and upon his return wrote Darwin that he had not as yet opened his book. It was not until March of 1863 that he was able to finish reading Darwin's biological bombshell. Even then he was not convinced. He wrote to the English biologist that in his own field of geology there were still not enough facts to convince him that life had evolved through a method of development from species to species. Darwin wrote back, "Do not suppose that I think that, with your strong convictions and immense knowledge, you could have been converted. The utmost that I could have hoped would have been that you might have been here or there staggered." Added Darwin, "I remember well how many years I fought against my present self."

While Dana's first reaction to Darwin's theory was not too sympathetic, his closer study of the doctrine during the next few years helped to overcome his original coolness. He finally accepted the theory of evolution with one reservation. This change was clearly expressed in the final revised edition of his *Manual of Geology*, prepared only a few weeks before his death. "Whatever the results of further research, we may feel assured in accord with Wallace who shares with Darwin in the authorship of the theory of Natural Selection that the intervention of a Power above Nature was at the basis of Man's development. Believing that Nature exists through the will and ever-acting power of the Divine Being and that all its great truths are manifestations of his Wisdom and

Power, Nature with Man as its culminating species, is no longer a mystery." He accepted the evolutionary process under the direct and intimate control of God, the Creator.

Dana's books, which brought together the newer knowledge of the nature and evolution of the earth, were read by millions of Americans. They helped in the intellectual revolution ushered in by Darwin's *Origin of Species* and *Descent of Man* (published in 1871). This was Dana's greatest contribution to the intellectual development of the United States. Far more important than his prodigious work in opening and deciphering the stony pages of a continent was his achievement in helping to liberate the human mind.

CHAPTER TWELVE

OTHNIEL CHARLES MARSH

(1831-1899)

DINOSAURS AND OTHER FOSSILS OF OUR GILDED AGE

FEW SCIENTISTS have reflected the period in which they lived more faithfully than did the American paleontologist, Othniel Charles Marsh. He worked during the decades which followed the close of the Civil War. The period of his activity covered the second phase of the industrial revolution, which saw the rise of big business, the development of mass production methods, and the installation of new machinery requiring large-scale financing. Northern merchants had made handsome profits from the sale of blankets, food, and clothing for the million soldiers of the Union Army, and from the huge shipments of our crops to Europe, where the harvests were below normal. The railroads were showing a phenomenal growth. The infant packing industry had got under way in earnest under the leadership of Philip Armour. Munitions of war and new machinery from cheap steel stimulated the development of the metal industry. A building boom was under way in many new industrial areas. In 1870 the Standard Oil Company of Ohio came into being through the pooling of seven important refineries in Ohio for the purpose of getting better freight rates and stifling competition. The establishment of the oil, steel, beef, lead, and power trusts soon followed, stimulated by the corporate form of ownership, which was developed primarily in order to get sufficient capital for these huge enterprises.

Corruption was rampant not only in the cutthroat competition of our railroad, steel, oil, and meat-packing barons but also in government. General Grant had been elected President of the United States in 1868 because he was a popular military hero. But he was a poor choice, for, although honest, he was politically incompetent and a poor judge of men, his appointees being guilty of the most corrupt Federal practices the country had ever known. A wild scramble for material aggrandizement spread fraud and corruption into state, county, and city governments.

In spite of this grasping for material conquest and its accompanying corruption, a new America was rising—an America which grew more nationalistic and less dependent upon Europe. The individualism of the frontier, with its love of independence, also nurtured a more active democratic spirit. Reform was in the air. After fifteen years of agitation, a national Civil Service Act was finally passed in 1883, an example gradually followed by the individual states.

Out of the orgy of business battles, wild speculation, and political corruption of this time emerged a handful of millionaires. Thousands of less wealthy men who reached their comfortable status by more honest means also appeared during this period of new growth. To this latter group belonged George Peabody, who had risen from poverty to wealth by way of clerking in a grocery store, peddling, storekeeping, exporting raw cotton and drygoods, heading a railroad, and finally as an investment banker and foreign-exchange operator. Since 1837, Peabody had made his residence in England and most of his investment banking and foreign-exchange business was carried out between the United States and England. In 1863 he retired from business, and George Peabody and Company became the firm of Junius S. Morgan and Company, parent of the J. P. Morgan and Company of today.

Peabody became a close friend of the humanitarian and philanthropist, Robert Owen, and followed in his footsteps. He distributed most of his fortune of about $8,000,000 to educational and civic causes. He gave $2,500,000 for model homes for the London poor, and $3,500,000 for the education of the Negro of the South after the Civil War. He never married, and directed his care and affection to his many relatives, including his nephew, Othniel C. Marsh. This boy's father, Caleb Marsh, was a descendant of English folk who came to this country in 1634. He was a farmer near Lockport, New York, a rather stern man who had to cope with a rebellious son who preferred roaming to farm work. Othniel's mother was a sister of George Peabody. She died of cholera when the child was hardly more than a year old, and Peabody took a special interest in her son. When the boy became interested in astronomy and then in geology—the trilobites and brachiopods in the debris of the newly built Erie Canal only a mile away from his home fascinated him—and expressed a desire to go to college, it was not difficult to get the money from Uncle Peabody.

Marsh attended Phillips Academy at Andover, where he wrote for the school paper, became president of the debating club by a bit of shrewd electioneering, and was graduated in 1856 at the head of his class. That year he saw his wealthy relative for the first time, and he whispered that perhaps his uncle might be pleased to see him through Yale College. The necessary arrangements were soon made. Marsh spent his uncle's money rather freely, indulging in expensive pranks.

At his graduation from Yale in 1860, Marsh was elected to Phi Beta Kappa and received a Berkeley scholarship for his performance in an examination in Greek and Latin. What was of greater importance, however, was the fact that this award carried with it the stipulation that its recipient spend from one to three years at Yale in graduate studies. At this time the Sheffield Scientific School was being established at Yale College with large funds donated by Joseph E. Sheffield, and some additional money allocated to agricultural and engineering schools by the Morrill Act. Here advanced work in the sciences was to be offered for the first time at Yale. James Dana had watched Marsh at college and had tried to persuade him to continue his boyhood interest in rocks and fossils.

Marsh finally made up his mind. He was going to specialize in vertebrate paleontology.

Marsh now planned his career with great shrewdness. He carried it through with all the perseverance, the single-mindedness, the stubbornness, the acquisitiveness, and even, at times, with the ruthlessness of an industrial magnate of his day. His goal was to serve science on as colossal a scale as Peabody's money would permit. His uncle was giving away his wealth for philanthropic purposes: why, then, could not a modest slice of it be wheedled out of him for the glory of paleontology, of Yale, and of Othniel C. Marsh?

In July of 1860 Marsh wrote to his uncle about his ambition to devote his life to science. Peabody, who was then sixty-five, answered his nephew from his castle in Scotland, "It has always been my intention to consult the wishes and act liberally towards all those who are in a pecuniary point of view comparatively dependent upon me, and who show by their character and exertions that they are worthy of my confidence. From my own observation and from the report of others I place you on that list." With this letter came $2200 to finance two years of postgraduate work at the Sheffield Scientific School.

Marsh made sure to satisfy the old man. Within about a year he presented a paper to the Geological Society of London on the newly discovered gold fields of Nova Scotia, which he had explored that summer. Nova Scotia was not entirely a new region for him. In his student days at Phillips Academy he had made a find of two vertebrae in its upper carboniferous coal deposits. At that time he thought these bones came from "the backbone of a halibut." But now, in the opening month of 1862 Louis Agassiz, who had been shown the bones, sent a new analysis of their origin to the *American Journal of Science*. They were actually the fossils of a fifteen-foot aquatic animal which Marsh named *Eosaurus acadianus*, a creature which Agassiz declared to be "undoubtedly a nearer approximation of a synthesis between fish and reptile than has yet been seen."

Upon his graduation from the Sheffield Scientific School that year, Marsh declined a major's commission in the Union Army because of poor eyesight. He also turned down a professorship at Yale and was now free to embark upon a long period of further study in vertebrate paleontology in Europe. He planned to prepare himself thoroughly at Berlin, Paris, London, and in Switzerland. Part of the time spent in Europe was taken up with various meetings and correspondence concerning the matter of obtaining financial aid from his uncle for Yale University. Benjamin Silliman, the elder, had already approached Peabody in 1857 in an effort to get some funds for the contemplated Sheffield Scientific School. Nothing came of this attempt. Most of Peabody's family had gone to Harvard, and it was only natural that the Cambridge university would be his beneficiary. But when Marsh broke the family tradition and matriculated at Yale, the outlook for getting some of Peabody's philanthropies for his alma mater was much brighter. Word came to Benjamin Silliman, Jr., through Marsh, who had seen his uncle in 1862, that Peabody was on the point of presenting Harvard with $150,000 for a new school of design. The Yale professor wrote at once to Marsh, advising him to get in touch with his uncle and try, as he suggested, to get an equal amount for a science building or museum of natural history for Yale College.

Apparently Peabody still favored Harvard, for Marsh reported back to Silliman that his uncle contemplated a legacy of only $100,000 for natural science at Yale, to be made available at his death. Silliman was not satisfied and reminded Marsh that the codicil in his uncle's will would be insufficient to complete the large museum he had planned for Yale. He explained further that construction must be started at once in order to be ready for Marsh in time "so that Peabody may enjoy the pleasure of seeing you installed in his lifetime in a manner so honorable to both."

Silliman closed his letter on an optimistic note. "I have faith to believe that your noble relative will rise to the level of the occasion if the subject is properly presented, as I am sure you know how to present it." He was right. Marsh presented the whole situation with such adroitness that Peabody's money came to Yale earlier than he had at first proposed. Furthermore, Peabody visited Yale in 1866 and changed the original $100,000 legacy to an immediate gift of $150,000 for the construction and upkeep of a museum of natural history, which was finally completed in 1876. In addition, while he was in Europe in 1863, Marsh obtained from his uncle $2000 in cash for the purchase of a library and a cabinet which he told his benefactor "are to a professor of science exactly what capital is to a man of business, with the advantage that in the former case no risk of loss is incurred." A diplomat as clever as Marsh was bound to go places.

Through these successful maneuvers Yale obtained the first professor of paleontology in the United States, as well as the Peabody Museum of Natural History, which was to be filled by this most prolific collector of new and startling fossils. In Marsh, Yale had acquired a man of independent means, a professor who did not want to teach in the classroom but preferred to devote the rest of his life to the spending of the considerable fortune he inherited for the enrichment of Yale and the world of science. They had a man, too, who had the daring, the initiative, and the ruthlessness of a buccaneer setting out to pre-empt a territory which he had marked for his own. No cost, no effort, no man or set of men were to be permitted to stand in the way of making the department of vertebrate paleontology of Yale University the greatest in the world. Othniel Charles Marsh was to become the most celebrated collector of a paleontological pile the world had ever gazed upon.

Before sailing for home in the summer of 1865 Marsh had spent more than two years of work in paleontology in Europe. He met the leaders in this field wherever he went. Charles Lyell, whom he visited in England, proposed his name as a Fellow of the Geological Society of London. He traveled to the country home of Darwin to talk to him about the great turmoil his evolutionary theory had evoked all over the world. Marsh was already an avowed evolutionist, and his special study among the fossils made him an outspoken champion of the new doctrine. "To doubt evolution," he declared, "is to doubt science, and science is only another name for truth." Marsh also visited his uncle at his castle in Scotland. Then, loaded down with two and a half tons of fossils and $5000 worth of books, mainly on biology, he sailed for home. The following year, at the age of thirty-five, he was installed as professor of paleontology at Yale—a position he was to hold to the end of his life.

Dana's *Manual of Geology* had appeared four years before. In it Marsh's new colleague at Yale had ascribed time periods to the geological structure of the earth. He had divided geological time into a number of main epochs, or eras, revised as shown in the table on page 286.

According to this time scale, life appeared first on earth about 1,500,000,000 years ago. Vertebrates came upon the scene in their simplest forms during late Paleozoic time and developed into the highest forms of life late in the Cenozoic era. It was mainly upon the fossil life of these two later eras that Marsh had decided to concentrate his attention.

Only the topmost thin layer of this deep mine had so far been scratched. For example, George Croghan, who had migrated to Pennsylvania from Dublin in 1741, made a collection of fossils from the Big Bone Lick section of Kentucky. He sent his specimens to Europe for study since there were no paleontologists on this side of the Atlantic. Some of his fossils went to Lord Shelburne, who was in charge of the American colonies, and others were addressed to Benjamin Franklin, who was also in London at the time. Peter Collinson read an account of them to the Royal Society in 1767. Franklin, after comparing the tusks and grinders of a mastodon with those of the Siberian elephant, took the bones to be the fossils of an ancient elephant. His reasoning was sound, but his conclusion that they were the remains of a different but not necessarily an extinct animal was incorrect.

Fifteen years later Jefferson expressed the need for collecting more fossils and soon after obtained the fossil bones of a sloth,

Megalonyx, dug out of a cave in Virginia. He also sent Clark, one of the leaders of the Lewis and Clark Expedition, to search the Big

Eras and Periods	Began About ---------- Years Ago	Forms of Existing Life
Archeozoic Era	1,500,000,000	Unicellular forms of animal and plant life appear.
Proterozoic Era	1,000,000,000	Primitive, multicellular forms of life dominate. Shell-less invertebrates appear.
Paleozoic Era (*a*) Cambrian period (*b*) Ordovician (*c*) Silurian (*d*) Devonian (*e*) Carboniferous (*f*) Permian	500,000,000	Invertebrates dominate—sponges, coral, trilobites. Rise of land plants. Fishes dominate. Amphibians appear. Rise of primitive reptiles and insects.
Mesozoic Era (*a*) Triassic period (*b*) Jurassic (*c*) Cretaceous	150,000,000	Rise of cold-blooded, egg-laying dinosaurs (some only a few inches long). Rise of birds and giant dinosaurs. Great reptiles gradually become extinct.

Cenozoic Era
 	
(*a*) Tertiary period
  1. Paleocene
  2. Eocene
  3. Oligocene
  4. Miocene
  5. Pliocene
(*b*) Quaternary period
  1. Pleistocene, or glacial
  2. Most recent, or postglacial
	60,000,000
	
	40,000
		Rise of archaic mammals.
		
		Rise of higher mammals.
		
		Manlike apes, cats, dogs.
		
		Neanderthal man appears.
		
		Modern man appears.

Bone Lick region for more fossils in the summer of 1807. Clark, at Jefferson's expense, was able to bring back three hundred mastodon bones, which were placed in the White House. Caspar

Wistar of Philadelphia was called to Washington to study them and by 1809 identified them as belonging to mastodons, bisons, and other large animals.

Another Philadelphia physician and member of the American Philosophical Society, Richard Harlan, contributed a paper on mammoth teeth in 1823, and continued to write on American fossils, to which he gave Linnaean names and which he viewed for the first time in the light of the new paleontological principles laid down by Cuvier, the French pioneer. He also described a specimen which he thought was a fossil fish but which was actually a mosasaur from Missouri.

For a considerable time the Big Bone Lick fossils dominated American paleontology, which was descriptive and taxonomic. Soon, however, other areas began to be searched, and American paleontology approached the subject from a wider and evolutionary point of view. Vertebrate paleontology continued to make little progress. Dana, in his *Manual* published in 1868, devoted only two pages of more than seven hundred on the geology of North America to vertebrate fossils of the United States. He mentioned the remains of elephants, mastodons, sloths, horses, and other fossil mammals dug out of the sand and rocks of Arkansas, Connecticut, Georgia, Kentucky, Mississippi, Missouri, New Jersey, New York, Texas, and Virginia.

Joseph Leidy, physician and professor of anatomy at the University of Pennsylvania, and a few others had already hinted that the West would turn out to be a paradise for the vertebrate paleontologist. Lewis and Clark in 1806 and Dr. Hiram Prout of St. Louis, who had found a titanotherid tooth in the Bad Lands of South Dakota in 1846, had made a very halting beginning. In the summer of 1868, Marsh was convinced of Leidy's assumption. He had just attended the meeting of the American Association for the Advancement of Science, in Chicago, and had been elected general secretary of the association. After the meetings he joined a holiday party which rode westward the entire length of the Union Pacific Railroad to a point sixty miles beyond Benton,

Wyoming. The last mile of road over which they had come was finished with the rails which their own train had brought forward two hours before. Marsh saw visions of hidden fossil wealth in "this bottom of an ancient sea, and I was not long in deciding that its past history and all connected with it would form a new study in geology, worthy of a student's best work even if it required the labors of a lifetime."

Soon after his return to New Haven he completed plans for an expedition into this huge boneyard of the distant past. His outline called for a complete and systematic study of the whole region of Kansas, Nebraska, the Dakotas, Colorado, Utah, Wyoming, and Montana. For such an undertaking he needed young, adventurous men who would welcome the excitement of life in the new lands of wild buffalo and hostile Indians. Men, too, who could pay their own expenses would be ideal. It was not difficult to find such men at Yale. Marsh had many friends among the young sporting blood of the college. He was known as a crack rider, an excellent shot, a good fisherman, and a pleasant story-telling companion around a campfire. He was also considered the sort of leader who could organize an undertaking of this kind with all the care and practical knowledge of a business executive. He was influential enough to get the United States Army to provide escorts if necessary through unusually hostile areas and to persuade the officials of the Union Pacific Railroad to extend to his party every help at their command. The completion of the first transcontinental railroad in 1869 made the success of the whole project possible at this time.

His plans for the first expedition were delayed by Indian wars which had broken out with great intensity. While waiting, Marsh went to Syracuse, New York, to inspect the Cardiff Giant, a ten-and-a-half-foot fossil of a man purported to have been dug out of the ground and now exhibited to thousands who were paying fifty cents a person to view it. Marsh exposed the racket. The giant had been carved from gypsum, buried, and then dug up as a bona fide fossil.

That year, too, his uncle, George Peabody, died, leaving his nephew a legacy of $100,000. Then for four successive summers, beginning in 1870, Marsh led parties of from four to twelve Yale students and graduates on four exciting bone hunts into the West. Henry B. Sargent, of the hardware firm of Sargent and Company; James W. Wadsworth, who later became a Congressman from New York; Eli Whitney, grandson of the inventor; William C. Beecher, son of Henry Ward Beecher; and Henry G. Cheney, of the Cheney Silk Mills of Connecticut, were among those who participated in Marsh's paleontological parties.

Out in the Western prairies and on the high plains of the Rocky Mountain country, guided by Buffalo Bill and other Army and Pawnee Indian scouts, the adventurous blades from the East hunted ancient fossils. They led their pack horses under the torrid heat of a burning sun into the hills and canyons and among the mesas of a stifling basin often seven thousand feet above sea level. They found grass growing in the deep ruts of the California emigrant-wagon trails. The prairie schooner had been ruthlessly replaced by the railway car. When fossil finds were too infrequent or when the business of wrapping and packing fossils began to pall, they would mount their Indian ponies and, armed with muskets and hunting knives, go out to hunt the buffalo. Brave to the point of recklessness, Marsh rushed into a herd of buffaloes and almost ended his paleontological career under the hoofs of a stampeding herd. In 1865 there were fifteen million buffaloes in the United States. Between 1866 and 1868 Buffalo Bill himself killed nearly five thousand to help feed the army of railroad workers. Between 1871 and 1874 nearly a million more were killed each year to supply the hide market and to satisfy the hunting desires of sportsmen. Marsh and his men helped to supply some of the innumerable bison heads which marked the offices of the Western Union Telegraph Company in those early days, before the well-known blue-bell identification was adopted.

Out of these semiscientific, semiadventurous student campaigns came a number of finds which began to place the name of Marsh in the foreground of paleontological history. In that mountain of rock brought back from the West were parts of the fossil remains of strange animals long extinct. Some supplied the links which were missing in the chain of evidence being forged to support the accuracy of Darwin's theory of organic evolution. Much newspaper publicity advertised these finds. Of the many valuable discoveries three especially stirred the attention of the world.

In the soft chalk that formed a dried-up riverbank in western Kansas, Marsh stumbled over a small hollow fossil bone about six inches long and one inch in diameter. "A peculiar joint that I had never seen before challenged me," he wrote. "It looked so much like the tibia of a gigantic bird, but such a joint no known bird possessed, as it indicated a freedom of motion in one direction that no well-constructed bird could use on land or water." The Yale scientist had studied enough anatomy and seen enough fossils at universities and museums during his three years in Europe to warn him that here was something really important. He therefore very carefully chipped out the bone, wrapped it securely, and took it back with him to New Haven. After a painstaking study of the bone he concluded, "The only joint much like it that I could find in any animal, living or extinct, was in the wing finger of the *Pterodactyl* or flying dragon."

With only a single bone to guide him, Marsh reconstructed the entire extinct animal in his mind and then made as bold a prediction as any cautious scientist would dare. He announced the discovery of the *pteranodon*, the first American flying dragon. It must have had a wingspread of about twenty feet. This toothless pterodactyl with fish-eating habits appeared to be a reptile at least twenty times the size of any reptile known, and perhaps the greatest flying creature of all. "Truly," wrote Marsh, "a gigantic dragon even in this country of big things." Three years after his discovery of this flying dragon, word reached the United States that the complete fossil of another long-tailed pterodactyl had been unearthed near Eichstätt, in Germany. Agassiz tried to buy it for Harvard, but Marsh outbid him and secured the fossil for Yale for about $1000.

Marsh's discovery of the fossils of the earliest birds was his first great triumph. In 1861 the fossil of what was perhaps the first true bird to appear on the earth was dug up at Solnhofen, Germany. Structurally, the creature looked like a reptile, but outwardly it was a bird. *Archaeopteryx*, as it was named, had wings, a long lizardlike tail, claws, and feathers, and probably glided from tree to tree during Mesozoic time. Unlike true birds, it possessed teeth in both jaws, and seemed to be the missing link between reptile and true bird. This evidence, which Marsh had seen in Germany in 1865, was, however, not conclusive. The many fossils which he was later able to get together out of the cretaceous rock of Kansas left no further doubt about the toothed birds. Among these were *Ichthyornis dispar*, discovered in 1872, a bird which could fly and was about a foot high. Others were *Hesperornis regalis Marsh*, found in 1870, a diving bird four and a half feet high, resembling the thirty-inch loon of today, and the flightless diver, *Hesperornis Crassipes Marsh*, a man-sized loon with ninety-four sharp teeth.

These discoveries of the extinct toothed birds of the Cretaceous period of a hundred million years ago were put together in *A Monograph on the Extinct Toothed Birds of North America* and published in 1880. This was Marsh's first great monograph. Its contents bridged the gap between the reptiles and the birds which followed them in the evolutionary process. Thomas Huxley, who had foreshadowed this discovery, gave credit to Marsh. "The discovery of the toothed birds by Marsh completed the series of transitional forms between birds and reptiles and removed Mr. Darwin's proposition that 'many animal forms have been utterly lost' from the region of hypothesis to that of demonstrable fact." Darwin himself wrote to Marsh to tell him that "your old birds have offered the best support to the theory of evolution" since the publication of his *Origin of Species*.

The second major find during this early period embraced a

whole series of fossils which enabled science for the first time to trace the evolutionary changes which occurred during the emergence of the modern horse. Prior to these discoveries it had been supposed that the horse originated in the Old World and that none appeared in the Americas until they were brought here by the Spanish explorers. Marsh completely exploded this theory. Joseph Leidy of Philadelphia had already done some preliminary work in this field, discovering a number of remains of some prehistoric horses. By 1874 Marsh knew of at least thirty more species of fossil horses, the first of which he had casually picked up in the excavation of an old well dug in an ancient lake bed in Nebraska. This find was made during his first trip to the West in 1868, at Antelope Station, just east of the Wyoming border. The bones of this creature, *Protohippus*, which lived during the Tertiary period, indicated a horse hardly three feet high and having thin legs terminated by three toes. In 1872 Marsh found the earlier horse, *Orohippus* of Eocene time, a little animal about the size of a fox, with its forefeet bearing four distinct digits. Two years later he unearthed *Miohippus* of the Miocene period, also with three toes but as large as a sheep. The rocks of the Pliocene period surrendered their fossils of *Pliohippus*. The modern one-toed horse, *Equus*, finally emerged from the rocks of Pleistocene time.

When Huxley, the fighting champion of Darwinism, came to the United States in 1876 to lecture, he went to examine the horse fossils of Marsh. He became so excited about them that he remained two days with the American to make a complete study of them. As Marsh brought out box after box of fossil-horse material, Huxley, who had predicted their existence, exclaimed, "I believe you are a magician. Whatever I want, you conjure it up." Huxley changed his mind about the European origin of the horse and told his American audiences that Marsh had ample proof to show that the horse was indigenous to America.

After the fourth student expedition to the West in 1873, Marsh changed his method of fossil collection. Now that the railroads had opened up this region it was less difficult to reach. The influx of large numbers of people into the area made available a number of trained local collectors, many of whom would send him their finds so that he could remain at New Haven and have more time to study the fossils and complete the Peabody Museum. In 1874 he received word of a rich fossil area in the Big Bad Lands of South Dakota. He was advised to come out at once or the fossil riches would fall into other hands. Rushing out West, he was confronted with a serious situation which threatened his plans for further explorations in this area as well as the future of the Indians in this region.

In 1824 the Bureau of Indian Affairs had been organized, and a quarter of a century later was transferred from the War Department to the Department of the Interior. In 1851 Lewis H. Morgan, a Rochester lawyer who became America's outstanding comparative sociologist, wrote the first complete scientific account of an Indian tribe under the title, *League of the Ho-de-no-sau-ne or Iroquois.* In spite of the promises of Presidents Monroe and Adams, Indians were removed from their lands against their consent. These forced migrations, together with the ravages of tuberculosis and smallpox which the white man had brought them, gradually cut down their numbers to about 300,000 by 1860.

As the railroads thrust their way through the new regions, the Indians were forced farther away from the rail lines. Their lands were confiscated and their buffalo food supply was slaughtered. There was much bloodshed, too, during the incessant Indian wars. In 1869 President Grant appointed a Board of Indian Commissioners to try to improve the situation. Indians were placed on reservations, treated as a subject people, fed, clothed, and given some money, with the government acting as their guardian. Their land was communally owned and administered by Indian Bureaus, which were empowered to lease timber and mineral lands for the benefit of the Indians.

Grant's policy was no solution, and the shortcomings were aggravated by the corruption of the Indian Bureau. The Indians became indolent and many were killed off by drink. They were fleeced of their timber and mineral wealth, their rations were meager and often inferior in quality. To make matters worse, General Custer, who had been ordered into this region to find a suitable site for a fort, reported finding gold, and something of a gold fever struck the area. This still further complicated the situation, and the mood of the Indians became increasingly ugly. When Marsh, on his way to the fossil fields, reached the Indian Red Cloud Agency near the Black Hills of South Dakota, he had a talk with Red Cloud. The Indian chief complained about the shabby way in which his tribe was being treated by government officials. He showed the scientist samples of inferior beef, beans, pork, tobacco, and other articles which had been supplied to his people.

Marsh took the story back to the United States Commissioner for Indian Affairs at Washington. Getting nowhere, the following day he called on President Grant and demanded an investigation. The *New York Tribune*, getting wind of a scandal, seized the opportunity to attack its enemies in the Grant administration. It published lurid stories of the iniquities of Columbus Delano, Grant's Secretary of the Interior. "I do not believe that anything but a radical change will prevent the demoralization of the Indian service. You alone," Marsh told the President, "have the will and the power to destroy the combination of bad men, known as the Indian Ring, who are debasing this service." The outcome of this episode was the resignation of Delano and the dismissal of several other officials. Reforms were instituted, and the *Boston Transcript* publicly praised Marsh for his patriotic part in this reform. It brought the Yale scientist into national prominence. In 1879 the Bureau of American Ethnology was organized by Congress under the supervision of the Smithsonian Institution, which selected Major John W. Powell director.

The greatest excitement which Marsh was to provoke was yet to come. It was to show him in another role, that of an intellectual buccaneer fighting ruthlessly to pre-empt the whole of a new field of dinosaur research. Up to 1869 fragmentary bones of a few of the smaller dinosaurs were known. Wistar in 1787 had written a paper on a thigh bone found in Gloucester County, N. J. This was the first dinosaur bone recorded. The *Journal* of the Lewis and Clark Expedition recorded the finding in 1804 of the "backbone of a fish 45 feet long all petrified." This was doubtless a fossil dinosaur from Montana. Edward Drinker Cope of Philadelphia had found some of the remains of an eighteen-foot dinosaur in the same state. Dana's *Manual* mentioned only a few bones and a tooth which belonged to a few dinosaurs, and Lyell's *Elements of Geology* of 1871 did not even mention the word dinosaur. Marsh was to make the word *dinosaur* (from the Greek *deinos*, huge and terrible, and *sauros*, lizard) a household word in every hamlet in the country. He was to describe eighty new forms and thirty-four new genera of dinosaurs and to reconstruct and restore many of them before his death.

His interest in this field started in the spring of 1877 while he was busy with the newly opened Peabody Museum of Yale. Out in the hard cretaceous sandstones of Colorado, Arthur Lakes, an English clergyman and schoolteacher, had been hunting for fossil plants. One day near Morrison he stumbled across a huge verte-bra, six feet long, which his scientific training at Oxford whis-pered might be unusual. It might be of special interest to that Yale professor who, everybody around these parts knew, was avid for fossils. Lakes made a sketch of the bone and sent it to New Haven. He then gathered together a ton or more of other fossils in the vicinity of this find and shipped them all to Professor Marsh. Lakes thought that Marsh would rush out to the West to make a deal with him. When this did not happen soon enough, the amateur paleontologist sent some of his new fossil finds to another collector, Edward D. Cope.

Then things began to pop. Marsh, hearing of this, rushed a tele-gram to Lakes to keep the news of the fossil mine secret. He wired to one of his paid collectors in Kansas to hurry to Morrison, Colorado, to purchase the fossils and try to retrieve the bones which had been dispatched to Cope. Then he hastily wrote a very brief description of *A New and Gigantic Dinosaur*, which was printed on July 1, 1877. The description of this largest of all land animals then known was based on some of the bones, including a huge femur about eight feet long, which Lakes had sent him. The monster was from sixty to seventy feet long, and twenty feet high. Marsh named the creature *Titanosaurus montanus*. Nineteen days later Cope, who planned to pay for the bones which Lakes had sent him, made some preliminary remarks about them before the American Philosophical Society. Just as he was about to publish an article describing the dinosaur whose bones he had studied, he received an order from Lakes to turn the fossils over to Marsh. The Yale man had manipulated their purchase before Cope had time to pay for them himself.

This incident began one of the most unmannerly conflicts in the history of American science. Even before Marsh and Cope had fought for possession of the vast fossil graveyard of the West, Joseph Leidy had dipped into its riches. Leidy was an unusually broad scientist who had written a classic book on the amoeba, added to parasitology by discovering a parasite in hogs, and made some first-class contributions in the field of American vertebrate paleontology. A considerable amount of fossil bones had been sent to him for study from the West as early as 1849, and he dominated the field until the appearance of Marsh and Cope. Leidy had obtained his fossils from friends without cost, but when Marsh and Cope arrived on the scene he could not compete with them and silently withdrew from the arena.

Cope, on the other hand, was not to be removed so easily from these happy fossil-hunting grounds. Like Marsh, he was a man of considerable wealth, knowledge, and possessiveness. His English ancestors had settled in Delaware in 1687, and his grandfather was an importer who owned the first line of packets that ran between Philadelphia and Liverpool. This business, upon his death, was taken over by the Cope brothers—Alfred, the father of the scientist, and Henry. Edward Cope studied anatomy for a year under Leidy. Instead of receiving a regular college education, he joined the Smithsonian Institution and became the greatest comparative anatomist of the United States. Cope had met Marsh even before they visited museums in Europe together during the Civil War years. Marsh had found his rival clever, strong-willed, and not averse to a stiff fight. Although he knew Cope would be no pushover, Marsh was egotistical enough to believe that he could defeat even so worthy an antagonist.

For years these two scientists locked horns in a personal fight over the dead bones of terrifying creatures which had fought each other to utter extinction millions of years ago. The two paleontologists would frequently find bones of the same creature within a few days of each other and a struggle over priority would result. They often named the same animal within a few hours of each other. Cope used the telegraph to get his papers to the Secretary of the American Philosophical Society in time for quick publication. In 1872 he tried to transmit a description of a new genus, *Loxolophodon,* by telegram, "a document probably unique in paleontological history." The telegraph operator got the strange name wrong, but the creature was described in quick time. Marsh accused Cope of predating some of his publications, and the fight was on.

Almost on the same day that Lakes had uncovered the fossils at Morrison, another schoolteacher, O. W. Lucas, made a similar discovery about one hundred miles away, near Canon City, Colorado. When Marsh learned that Lucas was sending his finds to Cope, he dispatched one of his men to the spot with instructions to offer the teacher more for his fossils than he was to get from the Philadelphian. Lucas hesitated, but a telegram from Marsh telling him that Cope was breaking all agreements and that he himself was ready to purchase everything he could dig up brought a prompt decision. Marsh triumphed and Cope was left in the cold.

Other rich fossils were falling into Marsh's hands. A letter from Laramie Station, in Wyoming, reached him in the summer of 1877. "We are desirous," it read, "of disposing of what fossils we have, and also the secret of the others. We are working men and not able to present them as a gift, and if we can sell the secret of the fossil bed and procure work in excavating others we would like to do so. We would be pleased to hear from you, as you are well known as an enthusiastic geologist and a man of means, both of which we are desirous of finding, more especially the latter." Well said and to the point, thought Marsh. He liked their blunt approach. He sent the money at once. One of his professional fossil collectors was dispatched to the scene. It was the exact location where almost ten years before he had been shown a dinosaur bone by the local station agent of the Union Pacific Railroad.

Out of this greatest dinosaur boneyard of the world came some big discoveries for Marsh. Fabled monsters were dug out of their rocky hiding places. Frightening, nightmarish, gigantic animals set men, women, and children all over America gaping, and made the world of the strange dinosaurs the table talk of millions. Out of the thousands of bones which came pouring into the Peabody Museum of Natural History, Marsh and his aides reconstructed some of the giants of Mesozoic and Cenozoic times. One of these was the colossal *Brontosaurus* (thunder lizard), whose stupendous bulk of perhaps forty tons stood sixteen feet high and stretched to a length of about sixty-seven feet. This harmless, cold-blooded dinosaur lived during Jurassic times in swamps, browsed on aquatic vegetation, and came ashore to lay its eggs. Its tribe finally died out completely before the Cenozoic era. Marsh, at a cost of $30,000, finally set up its six-and-a-half-ton skeleton in the Great Hall of Yale University, for the public to gaze upon. He was not interested in reconstructing his monsters in plaster. After viewing one of these dinosaur reconstruction jobs on the grounds of the Crystal Palace, he remarked, "The dinosaurs seem to have suffered much from both their enemies and their friends. Many of them were destroyed and dismembered long ago by their natural enemies, but more recently, their friends have done them further injustice in putting together their scattering remains."

The horrible-looking monster, *Triceratops*, with its more than six-foot-long skull armed with three-yard-long horns, was another restoration of Marsh. This Cretaceous beast, which once roamed Wyoming, was twenty or twenty-five feet long, was herbivorous, and possessed a brain which weighed less than half a pound.

The terror of Jurassic time, the powerful twenty-five-foot-long *Stegosaurus* (roofed lizard) also came to bony life under Marsh's direction. A hundred million years ago this dull brute, which shuffled over Colorado, defied the mightiest with its thick outward armor reinforced by huge bony plates which stood up vertically above its back and four pairs of massive spikes above the lower part of its powerful tail. So long and massive was its tail that a separate nervous center controlled its movements, according to evidences found by Marsh. This herbivorous animal apparently had two nervous centers, a brain in the head weighing perhaps three ounces and a very simple nervous system in its tail. When this choice bit of news reached the public, Bert Leston Taylor was moved to chirp merrily:

> *Behold the mighty dinosaur*
> *Famous in prehistoric lore,*
> *Not only for his weight and length*
> *But for his intellectual strength.*
> *You will observe by these remains*
> *The creature had two sets of brains—*
> *One on his head (the usual place),*
> *The other at his spinal base.*
> *Thus he could reason "a priori"*
> *As well as "a posteriori."*
> *No problem bothered him a bit:*
> *He made both head and tail of it.*

So wise he was, so wise and solemn
Each thought filled just a spinal column.
If one brain found the pressure strong
It passed a few ideas along;
If something slipped his forward mind
'Twas rescued by the one behind.
And if in error he was caught
He had a saving afterthought,
As he thought twice before he spoke
He had no judgments to revoke;
For he could think without congestion,
Upon both sides of every question.

Marsh's fame spread widely, and he became one of the most talked-about men in the United States. He built himself a three-story, eighteen-room house in New Haven, Connecticut, at a cost of $30,000, and spent an equal amount in furnishing it. The main room, a huge octagonal reception room, was done in the elaborate baroque style typical of the Gilded Age. It was filled with all kinds of mementos—a bison head, the peace pipe given to Marsh by Red Cloud, skins of animals he had killed in the West, an array of pistols, Chinese and Japanese art pieces, a miscellaneous assortment of bric-a-brac, the personal Bible of Brigham Young, whom he had visited at Salt Lake City in 1873, gaudy trinkets, and a number of art objects from Mexico about which Marsh delighted to talk. The great Barnum was one day engaged in conversation on a train by Marsh, whom the famous showman did not recognize. They got to talking about objects of art and curious decorations, and Barnum told the paleontologist how through his agent he had made a clever deal with "some little cuss up in New Haven" who had bought some Mexican trinkets from him. Marsh gulped, then smilingly informed Barnum that he was that "little cuss" from New Haven.

In this museum of a home Marsh entertained lavishly. He was greatly impressed by wealth and loved to be invited to the homes of the rich. He enjoyed, too, putting on a show for members of the National Academy of Sciences and other visitors. He did pretty well for a bachelor who had to handle all the details of entertainment. Marsh never married, not because he was opposed to marriage—he had proposed to the daughter of a United States Senator and also to the heiress of a railroad magnate—but rather because his egotism and lack of tact with the ladies were stumblingblocks. He was well built, had blue eyes, sandy hair and an almost red beard, but he was stiff, rather pompous, and somewhat stern in appearance as he grew older. One of his friends suggested that Marsh, the paleontological collector, had not married because he never would have been satisfied with anything less than "a collection" of wives.

Marsh was one of fourteen members of a Round Table Club which met once a month at a hotel for good eating and light talk. Yet he made no close friends. He was a difficult man to get along with, autocratic, and a hard bargainer. He was suspicious of strangers and jealous of others in his field. In his later years some of the fire and joviality of his early days died away and he was a rather lonely man. To make matters worse, his old rival, Cope, kept popping up every now and then to plague him. In 1890, when Marsh was almost sixty, the feud between them became a national scandal.

The United States Geological Survey had been established by Congress in 1879 to eliminate waste and to co-ordinate all the various surveys then under way. Clarence King, a capable and energetic leader, was made head, but two years later he went into the mining business and was succeeded by Major John W. Powell. Soon afterward Marsh became officially connected with this new department as Vertebrate Paleontologist, and he was asked to collect fossils from the West both for the National Museum and the Smithsonian Institution. He was still busy collecting for the Peabody Museum at Yale University.

Major Powell, as head of the United States Geological Survey, had sent an order to Professor Cope, of the University of Pennsylvania, to turn over his collection of fossils to the National Museum of Washington, where Marsh had been appointed honorary curator of the department of paleontology. Cope hit the ceiling. It was true that he had been chief paleontologist for both the Hayden and the Wheeler Surveys, and that these surveys were government projects. But it was also true that he had discovered and named more than a third of all the fossils of the 3200 vertebrates of North America known at this time and had spent more than $80,000 of a legacy left him by his father in this work. He had been forced to sell his home to keep his fossils, most of which were his personal property. He was ready to pour out all of his long-nursed anger upon both Marsh and Powell.

The Sunday supplement of Bennett's *New York Herald* of January 12, 1890, ran the screaming headline, "Scientists Wage Bitter Battle." Cope brought charges against Marsh not only for plagiarism, scientific ignorance, and the unlawful appropriation of government-owned fossils for his museum at Yale, but also of ruthless obstruction in the collection of paleontological material of others. He charged that Marsh had instructed his field men to break all fossil specimens which could not be brought East, lest they fall into the hands of other collectors, and that when the Princeton College Expedition went out into the Western fossil fields in 1882 Marsh "hired the guides to obstruct the work."

Furthermore, Cope attacked Powell for holding up the printing of his work after it was authorized by Congress. He called the United States Geological Survey under Powell "a gigantic politico-scientific monopoly run on machine methods like Tammany Hall." He charged that it was filled with the sons of Congressmen who were thus influenced to pass upon appropriations for the Survey, and that the National Academy of Sciences, of which Marsh was president, was packed with members who could be relied upon to support Powell. The *Herald*'s headlines continued to describe the battle round by round for two whole weeks, and also commented editorially. The public was treated to as crude an attack as had ever appeared in the history of American science on the integrity and motives of Marsh.

If this attack had come from a man who was an innocent victim of unscrupulous scoundrels, it might have made some sense. But Cope was no paragon of virtue. He did not always fight fairly. In 1889 he bitterly fought the re-election of Marsh to the presidency of the National Academy. His slanderous attacks and whispering campaign made even those who preferred the warm and likable Cope to the rather cold and stolid Marsh recoil from this method of electioneering. Enough of them supported Marsh so that his re-election was assured.

To add to the public washing of paleontological linen, a Congressional quarrel followed. Powell was accused of working with the Appropriations Committee of the Senate in the hope of cashing in on profits from the sale of public lands irrigated as the result of a project which he had supported. This charge was groundless, for Powell was motivated by only one thought—to improve the public domain. The matter of unnecessary appropriations for other projects was injected into the debate. Some Senators objected to the unnecessary use of public money for the collection of useless fossils and the publication of paleontological literature. "Birds with Teeth" became a catchword in this battle. This fight ended in a sectional struggle between those who wanted land surveys but not land reclamation and opposed Powell and Marsh, and the Western Senators who were championing the irrigation and reclamation of Western lands. (Eighteen million dollars were to be spent on such projects during the two decades which followed 1882.)

During the newspaper publicity on the Marsh-Cope-Powell controversy, Albert Edmund Lancaster was moved to compose the following set of stanzas of Paleozoic poetry. It was printed on January 19, 1890, under the title: *The Unfortunate Pterodactyl Wings Its Flight Through Prosody*.

I

PROFESSOR COPE TO PROFESSOR MARSH:

Your ignorance of saurians is something very strange;
The mammals of the Laramie are far beyond your range.
You fail to see that certain birds enjoyed the use of teeth,
That pterodactyls perched on trees, nor feared the ground
*   beneath.*
You stole your evoluted horse from Owalevsky's brain.
And previous people's fossils smashed, from Mexico to Maine.
To Permian reptiles you are blind—in short, I do insist
You are—hinc illae lachrymae—you are a plagiarist!

II

PROFESSOR MARSH TO PROFESSOR COPE:

'Tis strange that you, who always get the cart before the horse,
Should dare to state my equine screed I filched without remorse.
'Tis strange that you, who helped to kill a moribund magazine,
Should hint that I have fossils smashed of prettiest Pliocene.
Your reference to a horn cone on an ischium sends a chill,
Professor Huxley is my friend, and likewise Buffalo Bill.
Though paleontologic facts you've studied since your youth,
You shun the streptasauria as if they were the truth!

III

MAJOR POWELL TO PROFESSOR COPE:

A scandal and a shame you are to stab me in the back;
If I but answered all I could you'd be upon the rack.
Geology you do not love, you furnish copy slowly;
You like to see your name in print and are not meek and lowly.
You don't respect biology; your rules of life are gleaned
From planes so far beneath contempt that you're a "species
*   fiend."*
Through natural selection's laws you are, as I'm alive,
Of all survivals ever found the least fit to survive.

MORAL

So science walks, with gait serene, her crown an olive sprig,
Intent alone on holy truth and otium cum dig.

The upshot of the affair was the refusal of the Appropriations Committee to make available more funds for paleontological research, on the ground that the United States Geological Survey was already too costly. On July 20, 1892, Marsh was asked to resign from his position as Paleontologist of the United States Geological Survey. This was a severe blow to his pride and prestige. Coming at a time when the income from his investments had reached a new low, it did much to put the rest of his life under a cloud. He was compelled to mortgage his sumptuous home to Yale, and to accept a salary for the first time in the twenty-five years since he had joined the faculty of Yale University.

Marsh spent the remainder of his life putting into final shape and publishing the mass of material he had collected. Between 1896 and 1898 his two large monographs, *Dinosaurs of North America* and *Vertebrate Fossils of the Denver Basin*, appeared in print. He was the author of three hundred other publications. Death cut short the completion of the description of the 500 new species, 225 new genera, sixty-four new families, and nineteen new orders of vertebrate fossils which he had given for the first time to science. One day in February, 1899, after visiting Carl Schurz at a dinner in New York City, he walked from the New Haven railroad station to his home in a rainstorm. He became sick but refused to remain in bed and insisted on going to his laboratory. He was soon down with pneumonia, from which he died several weeks later at the age of sixty-eight. Except for this final illness, he had enjoyed vigorous health throughout his life.

His will contained no family bequests. His residence was left to Yale, the National Academy of Sciences received $10,000 for scientific research, and $30,000 was set aside to complete the publication of the results of his Western explorations. He turned over his complete private collection of fossils, estimated to be worth about a million dollars, to the Peabody Museum of Yale University. Dr. George G. Simpson, of the American Museum of Natural History, believes that "Vertebrate paleontology has been the most important single factor in the rise and popularization of natural history museums. This is perhaps its greatest contribution to the social history of America."

To the United States National Museum went those other fossils which Marsh had gathered with government funds while he was vertebrate paleontologist attached to this museum. Marsh spent altogether more than a quarter of a million dollars for science, and died with less than $200 in cash assets—a rare example of a man of wealth who spent a fortune in the active participation of researches in pure science.

Even today the task of preparing the rest of Marsh's data for publication has not been completed. The work of finishing the paleontological story of vertebrate North America also still goes on. In 1915 the Dinosaur National Monument was established by presidential proclamation. It comprises an area of 200,000 acres in northeastern Utah and northwestern Colorado, where the precious store of dinosaur bones is now guarded against unnecessary destruction. From the tar pits of Rancho La Brea, close to Los Angeles' Wilshire Boulevard, have come the remains of many animals now extinct in the United States. Here, through the efforts of J. C. Merriam and others, have been found hundreds of fossils of camel, sloth, elephant, lion, and the saber-toothed cat. Out in the Bad Lands of Dakota, the South Dakota State School of Mines is still digging for fossil treasure. The American Museum of Natural History of New York City is still hunting in the Big Bend region of southern Texas for dinosaurs even larger than Brontosaurus. In 1941 footprints a yard wide and four and a half feet long were discovered there. How they would have excited Othniel Marsh, namesake of the book of Joshua's "powerful man of God"!

CHAPTER THIRTEEN

J. WILLARD GIBBS
(1839-1903)

AMERICA IN THE NEW WORLD OF CHEMISTRY

THE PHENOMENON of the rich Marsh devoting his life to vertebrate paleontology was a curious episode in American science. But it was no stranger than the career of his contemporary, Willard Gibbs, who walked the same halls and breathed the same air of Yale College.

A bitter war had been fought over human freedom and a great intellectual revolution in human thought was stirring in and outside New Haven, yet Gibbs walked through it all undisturbed. Yale's president, Noah Porter, fought against Herbert Spencer's *Synthetic Philosophy*, based upon evolution as a key to both political and natural history. "Rank materialism," Porter called it, and banned the textbook. Gibbs remained silent. John Fiske strove to indoctrinate America with the ideas of Spencer and gained the support of the newly elected president of Harvard, Charles W. Eliot, a young teacher of chemistry. Lowell Institute banned Fiske's lectures. Gibbs continued to remain silent. His head was full of thoughts about another problem which to him was much more important.

Near the close of the eighteenth century Benjamin Thompson had proved that heat was a form of energy and had attempted to determine the exact relationship between the energy expended in boring a cannon and the amount of heat generated. This is known as the mechanical equivalent of heat. About forty years later, in 1842, the German scientist Julius Robert Mayer, using a different experiment, also determined the mechanical equivalent of heat. Furthermore, he clearly stated for the first time the new principle of the conservation of energy. With the establishment of this grand principle, one of the most important milestones in the whole history of science was reached. According to this principle, energy can be neither created nor destroyed, but it may be changed from one form into another. All the various forms of energy, such as electricity, light, heat, chemical and mechanical energy, may be converted one into another. The energy of rushing water may be changed into electricity. An electric current thus generated, passing through a metal wire, produces both the heat for the electric toaster and the light of the incandescent lamp. The chemical energy of coal is converted into heat and light energy by burning.

Thermodynamics is the branch of science which deals with the laws of one of the forms of energy, namely *heat*. The *first law* of thermodynamics was expressed very succinctly by Rudolf Clausius: *Die Energie der Welt ist konstant*. When, in 1850, Clausius published his first memoir on this subject, "the science of thermodynamics was secure." The *second law* of thermodynamics was stated just as simply as the first by the same master theoretical physicist. *Die Entropie der Welt strebt einem Maximum zu* was the way Clausius put it. By entropy is meant a final state in which all the energy of the whole universe is uniformly distributed. Just as water travels downhill from a higher to a lower level, so energy always moves from a higher to a lower level. A warm object gives off heat energy which may be picked up by a colder object, but, said Clausius, "It is impossible (for a self-acting machine, unaided by any external agency) to carry heat from a *colder* body to another at a *higher* temperature." Now, as the energy of the universe distributes itself in this way, the entropy of the universe increases, and finally approaches a maximum. When this maximum situation is reached, no further exchange of energy will be possible. The universe will then be completely run down to a dead level of intense cold after eons of time, and the so-called *heat-death* of the universe will bring a final doom to all life.

The new developing industrialism had compelled the re-examination of the entire subject of heat and power. Out of this practical necessity grew the further development of thermodynamics as applied to the steam engine, which is a heat engine. Sadi Carnot, a young French physicist, had formulated the first law which attempted to improve the steam engine. Others entered the field, and thermodynamics was developed and hammered into shape as a tool for bringing the steam engine to its highest possible point of efficiency. Clausius brought thermodynamics to its greatest usefulness in the improvement of the steam engine by banishing much of the guesswork and empiricism from the construction of this machine.

Willard Gibbs, too, had been very interested in this field of science. It required a deep knowledge of mathematics as well as a thorough grounding in physical principles. What seemed to him a beautiful problem for solution was the extension of the second law of thermodynamics. This had already been applied to simple, homogeneous substances such as steam. He wanted to use it in the realm of the more complex and heterogeneous mixtures handled in chemistry and the numerous metal mixtures or alloys used in metallurgy.

For several years Gibbs spoke little and published nothing about these new developments. He kept thinking about them, mulling them over in his mind, and, on rare occasions, jotting down a few mathematical formulas. Mathematics was a language, he had said, and with it he could express the new thoughts that were welling up in his mind. The term "entropy" had already been introduced as a mathematical necessity in the formulation of the second law of thermodynamics. Gibbs was playing with the idea of using that term, for it represented what he termed the *mixed-up-ness* of heterogeneous mixtures, a concept which could be made into a very useful mathematical tool in the solution of several chemical problems.

To this Yale professor of mathematical physics there seemed no point in discussing his thoughts with other scientists. They probably would not be able to follow him easily. His closest friend, the astronomer Hubert A. Newton, was lost in Gibbs' mathematical wilderness. As for his graduate students, they would listen with outward attention, but inwardly they gaped. Even though Gibbs prepared his lectures carefully and used no notes, he seemed to speak in baffling numbers. He is said to have remarked in 1902, after thirty years of teaching, that not many of his graduate students were really getting anything valuable out of his courses. Among this small group were Lee de Forest, inventor of the radio tube and pioneer in television and the sound film; Irving Fisher, eminent economist, who applied Gibbs' contributions to the problems of the exchange of money and goods, and Henry A. Bumstead, who helped to edit Gibbs' papers after his death. As a teacher of undergraduates in his earlier years Gibbs turned out to be a worse than mediocre pedagogue. There was gossip at one time that he might be replaced or dismissed from Yale because most of his unruly students were getting nowhere in either Latin or Natural Philosophy.

Finally, after his long silence, Gibbs sat down in his study and wrote out a whole series of mathematical formulas embracing a vast system of physical and chemical phenomena. In 1875, when he was thirty-six, he was ready to publish his conclusions. As a member of the Connecticut Academy of Arts and Sciences he submitted his 140-page paper, *On the Equilibrium of Heterogeneous Substances*, to this body. No one on the editorial board of the *Transactions* of the Academy really understood what Gibbs had composed. But Gibbs was a professor of mathematical physics at a distinguished college, and H. A. Newton and a few others knew that he was an able fellow. It was therefore decided, after a long discussion, to publish the material if enough money could be raised to meet the high cost of printing such a large and difficult communication. The money was finally collected from friends, and between October, 1875, and May of the following year the first part of his work appeared. This was followed between May, 1877, and July, 1878, by a second paper which ran to 181 pages and covered further explanations in the same field.

It is impossible to estimate how many read these papers through from the first sentence, which began, "The comprehension of the laws which govern any material system is greatly facilitated by considering the energy and entropy of the system in the various states of which it is capable," to the last line, which ended with the 700th mathematical equation: $(V''-V')\ de \leqq -\ d\flat$. It is certain, however, that no one in the United States made any fuss about it at the time, even though the American Chemical Society had just been organized in the lecture room of the College of Pharmacy of New York University, in April, 1876. True, in the following year the National Academy of Sciences did elect Gibbs a member when he was only forty years old, and two years later he was awarded the Rumford Medal of the American Academy of Arts and Sciences. But American science saw no genius in his highly abstract contributions and turned no intellectual handsprings over them.

Europe's reaction was somewhat different. James Clerk Maxwell, perhaps the greatest theoretical physicist of his day, was then director of the Cavendish Laboratory of Experimental Physics, in London. He had been following the work of American physicists and had already raised one of them from obscurity to scientific recognition. The physicist was Henry A. Rowland, who had written a paper in 1873 on the magnetic properties of iron, steel, and nickel. The editor of the *American Journal of Science* to whom it was submitted saw nothing unusual in the paper and rejected it. When Clerk Maxwell saw it he submitted it immediately for publication in the *Philosophical Magazine*. Daniel C. Gilman, president of Johns Hopkins University, was so impressed by Maxwell's opinion of the scrappy experimentalist, "Rowland of Troy, that Doughty Knight," as the Englishman dubbed him, that he selected him to become the first professor of physics at Johns Hopkins.

Clerk Maxwell had also been watching the work of that Connecticut Yankee, Gibbs, since the publication of his two papers in 1873: *Graphical Methods in the Thermodynamics of Fluids* and *A Method of Geometrical Representation of the Thermodynamic Properties of Substances by Means of Surfaces*. These two contributions contained no world-shaking ideas but they did show to the keen mind of Maxwell a brilliant preliminary attack on several problems which were being tackled by a number of other men. Maxwell was so impressed by the work of the American that he explained it to English chemists at a meeting of the Chemical Society of London, saying that by means of it "problems which have long resisted the efforts of myself and others may be solved at once." He incorporated Gibbs' material in a chapter of the new edition of his textbook, *Theory of Heat*. He also, with his own hands, constructed casts of models representing the thermodynamic surfaces so completely pictured by Gibbs. Then he sent to Gibbs one of the three solid plaster models he had made—a tremendous tribute from one genius to another.

But Maxwell died very soon after, stricken in 1879, at the age of forty-seven, by a very painful illness. The only voice that would have spoken out loudly and with authority was stilled, and for thirteen years the gem that was buried away in the *Transactions* of the Connecticut Academy remained unknown. Then in 1891 Wilhelm Ostwald, the crusading chemist of Germany who had championed the heterodox theory of ionization first expounded by Arrhenius in 1883, picked it up, recognized its great value, and with Gibbs' lukewarm permission translated it into German and had it printed. Ostwald labeled Gibbs "the founder of chemical energetics." Finally, in the last year of the century, Le Chatelier, another great scientist, translated Gibbs' paper into French. It was not until 1906 that it was reprinted for the first time in English.

America continued to ignore the Yale professor. So completely had he failed to impress his contemporaries in the United States that even his name was unknown to many in high scientific places.

Sir J. J. Thomson, formulator of the modern electron theory, recorded that "When a great university was founded in 1887, the newly elected President came over to Europe to find professors." (This was a common procedure even at this late date, for it was believed that the really great minds were to be found only in Europe.) "He came to Cambridge," continued Thomson, "and asked me if I could tell him of anyone who would make a good professor of Molecular Physics. I said, 'You need not come to Europe for that; the best man you could get is an American, Willard Gibbs.' 'Oh,' he said, 'you mean Wolcott Gibbs,' mentioning a prominent chemist. 'No, I don't,' I said, 'I mean Willard Gibbs,' and I told him something of Gibbs' work. He sat thinking for a minute or two and then said, 'I'd like you to give me another name. Willard Gibbs can't be a man of much personal magnetism or I should have heard of him.'" As the American college president sat talking to Thomson, there must have passed through his mind the names of Agassiz and Marsh. These men had blazed across the scientific skies like brilliant comets, arresting the attention of all America with cosmic theories of creeping glaciers and spectacular finds of colossal dinosaurs.

Gibbs, to be sure, was no publicity-seeking Marsh nor a vivacious lecturer like Agassiz. He was a modest, retiring teacher who kept a good deal to himself and made no effort at all to spread his work or found a new school of physical or chemical thought. In fact, his failure to take other people into his confidence, especially his graduate students, concerning the great problems with which he was wrestling, was in some measure responsible for his early neglect. Even in 1899, when Edwin Bidwell Wilson, after graduating from Harvard, sought advice about taking advanced work in mathematics, only one man at Harvard suggested Gibbs. Professor Benjamin O. Peirce, himself an eminent mathematician, casually suggested that Wilson might try some of the courses offered by Gibbs, "whom some of us here think a rather able fellow." At that, Wilson took Gibbs' course in vector analysis only because he had *to fill in a fourth course*. It was not that Gibbs, the scholar, considered himself too profound for the little men around him, nor was he a man who was in the least suspicious or jealous and so feared to divulge his ideas. Rather he was indifferent to fame and glory.

There were other reasons why science failed to recognize Gibbs immediately and to seize the new tools fashioned out of his mind. His papers were not easy reading and were very difficult to understand. He gave only the barest outlines of treatment and left the embellishments and applications to others. He described no specific experiments which others could easily follow, although the principles which he laid down in mathematical language could have been verified by experiments. But more important than all these reasons, there was no science of physical chemistry to speak of in the United States at this time. Nor had the American chemical industry yet reached a point where it was ready to make good use of the epochal work of Willard Gibbs. Gibbs' papers dealt with problems in physical chemistry, metallurgy, and electro-chemistry, as yet scarcely exploited by the industrial world.

American industry had not yet realized the importance of research in pure science as an indispensable aid to the success of their manufacturing processes. New scientific discoveries in chemistry were only just beginning to show their devastating effects upon old and firmly established business organizations. The first synthesis of indigo by Adolf von Baeyer, in 1880, was followed by its extensive commercial production, and the death knell of the natural indigo industry was soon sounded. But the wider revolutionary effects of synthetic chemistry did not shake the world to its foundations until after Gibbs had passed away from the scene. American industrialists were to slumber through another two decades of unconcern about the imperative need of keeping abreast of research in order to prevent their discomfiture by more farsighted rivals. They had not as yet learned the lesson that the magic of chemistry might produce a new method or a new product which would almost overnight replace the old. As a result of this lethargy there were no men in the United States who were searching for just such new approaches to chemical problems as Gibbs' papers had presented, and his contributions were permitted to gather dust on quiet library shelves.

The time was not altogether ripe. When, a generation later, industry finally came to the realization that research in pure science was the very lifeblood of its continued existence, trained research men were called in to study theoretical papers in science and to attempt to apply the new discoveries to better methods of production.

Gibbs' paper on the equilibrium of heterogeneous substances was full of fresh approaches and brilliant guides to the many problems involved in the manufacture of chemicals. It was a top-flight achievement. "Having greatly extended and developed the method of theormodynamic potentials," wrote Paul S. Epstein, professor of physics at the California Institute of Technology, "Gibbs was the first to realize what a powerful tool it was in the treatment of chemical problems. Once started on this road, he went to the end; we see here a phenomenon almost unparalleled in the history of science. A young investigator, having discovered an entirely new branch of science, gave in a single contribution an exhaustive treatment of it which foreshadowed the development of theoretical chemistry for a quarter of a century."

For example, in order to clear up the intricate problem of the equilibrium of mixtures such as chemical solutions and metal alloys, early in his paper Gibbs introduced five pages of mathematical equations which are now known as the *phase rule*. The mathematical formulas of the phase rule made it possible to determine in advance the exact concentrations of the various substances that were to be used in making the mixture required. They gave the temperatures and pressures best suited to produce a final mixture whose components would remain in equilibrium with each other, and thus not separate out and destroy the mixture. The phase rule also enabled an experimenter to calculate in advance the conditions necessary for making physical separations of one or more of the substances found in a complex mixture of salts or metals. Thus the scientist could be spared the expensive and time-consuming business of undertaking thousands of experiments before the final conditions for a successful process could be found. The phase rule was, therefore, an efficient timesaver, and frequently also the only practical key to the solution of hitherto insoluble problems.

According to the phase law, a physical system made up of ice, water, and water vapor is in equilibrium—that is, no more ice will melt to water and no more water vapor will condense to liquid when $F = C + 2 - P$, where:

F (degrees of freedom)	= the number of physical conditions such as temperature, pressure, and concentration, which must be fixed before there can be equilibrium of the mixture.
P (phases)	= the number of parts of any system of substances which can be separated mechanically, such as ice, water, and water vapor.
C (components)	= the number of integral parts of which a system is composed. In the case of the ice, water, and water-vapor system, $C = 1$, since water is the only component.

In such a system of ice, water, and water vapor, $F = C + 2 - P$
$$F = 1 + 2 - 3$$
$$F = 0$$

Hence no physical condition such as temperature, pressure, or concentration can be varied in such a system without destroying a phase, since it has no degree of freedom. The system can, therefore, be in equilibrium only at one fixed temperature, and with a fixed value for its water-vapor pressure. None of these variables can be arbitrarily changed without causing the disappearance of one of the phases.

John D. Van der Waals, an eminent Dutch physicist who was working at the University of Amsterdam on the equilibrium of

gases, read Gibbs' paper, saw its value at once, and incorporated it
into his own work. Furthermore, he was so impressed with the
importance of the contribution of the American professor that he
brought it to the attention of his graduate students. One of these
was Bakhuis Roozeboom, a Dutch chemist who was investigating
the very complicated and practical problem of the nature of steel,
an alloy of iron and carbon. Roozeboom seized the key prepared
by Gibbs and used it with success in the clearer understanding of
the composition of steel alloys.

Another application of the phase rule involved the industrial
synthesis of ammonia gas from its two elements, nitrogen and hydrogen, according to the equation:

$$\text{nitrogen} + \text{hydrogen} \rightleftarrows \text{ammonia gas}$$
$$N_2 \quad + 3H_2 \quad \rightleftarrows \quad 2NH_3$$

This chemical reaction is reversible, that is, it can proceed in
either direction. In trying to make ammonia on a commercial
scale according to this equation, it was soon realized that something had to be done to prevent the ammonia, NH_3, from decom-
posing and returning to its original elements, nitrogen and hydrogen. Otherwise a very small yield would be obtained and the
method would be impractical. In 1913 Professor Fritz Haber was
called in by the German High Command to solve this problem.
Its success meant an unlimited amount of ammonia which could
be converted into nitric acid and finally into nitroglycerin for
high explosives, and also for the making of the nitrates so necessary in fertilizers.

Haber finally worked out the method successfully, partly with
the aid of the principles of the phase rule. More explosives and
more fertilizer enabled the Germans to fight hunger and stave off
defeat much longer than the Allies had expected. Gibbs' papers
and Haber's experiments helped forge for Germany the I. G.
(Interessen Gemeinschaft) chemical company. With this establishment it hoped to erect a super world monopoly of chemicals
by means of which it might eventually capture and subdue the

whole world. As a reward, "After Hitler's rise to power, a grateful government forced Haber to resign his professorship and research posts, for which he was deemed unfitted by his non-Aryan ante-cedents." Fritz Haber died an exile in Switzerland, a victim of the Nazi principle of racial superiority which contradicts every find-ing of anthropology and biology.

The British, too, made use of this work of the American. During the First World War they were enabled to manufacture sufficient ammonium nitrate because of the more efficient methods made possible by Gibbs' theory. Exploitation of the rich deposits of potash and other salts in Searles Lake, California, since World War I was made possible by the mathematical equations of this scientist. Many an industrial problem in the manufacture of steel and other alloys was solved by applying the formulas of Gibbs, whose contributions were also utilized in the manufacture of hun-dreds of plastics, drugs, dyes, and organic solvents. Biology and physiology were similarly enriched. Medical advances resulted from investigations in such fields as the equilibrium of the various salts in the blood and other tissues, made by the Americans, Law-rence Henderson and Donald D. Van Slyke, who borrowed freely from Gibbs' papers dealing with surface tension, semipermeable membranes, and osmotic pressure. The purification of serums and the preparation of blood plasma are also tangent to the same prin-ciples which Gibbs was the first to express with such mathematical accuracy and simplicity. The *phase rule* was even picked up by Henry Adams in 1909 to explain the pulse of world events in his distorted *Tendency of History* first published in 1920.

The great chemical age which came after the death of Gibbs, and many other advances in the field of human health and safety, may be said to have been ushered in sooner by the genius of this man. The difficult and important fields of catalysis, adsorption, and research in extremely low temperatures were also clarified in the blueprints of Gibbs' papers of 1875 to 1878. Even today, more than eighty years after the appearance of the great paper, *On the Equilibrium of Heterogeneous Substances,* men in research laboratories all over the world still scan its pages and study it minutely for timesaving formulas and new starting points.

Willard Gibbs may be ranked among the ten most influential physical scientists of the eighteenth and nineteenth centuries. He was the greatest mathematical physicist America has produced. Yet, during his lifetime and for many years after his death in 1903, he was a shadowy figure in the world of science. Even as late as 1945, Gibbs failed to be elected to New York University's Hall of Fame, which had already honored Robert Fulton, Samuel Morse, and Eli Whitney. Thanks to Muriel Rukeyser's stimulating biography, which appeared in 1942, Gibbs is now less of an unknown figure.

Willard Gibbs' first American ancestor, Robert Gibbs, came over from Warwickshire, England, and settled in Boston in 1658. His posterity were sent to Yale and Harvard for six unbroken generations. Willard's father, Josiah Gibbs, had a license to preach but seldom did. He preferred to devote his time to his duties as professor of theology and sacred literature at the Yale Divinity School, and was known as a scholar of high attainments and as an authority on comparative grammar. He also distinguished himself in the successful defense of a number of African slaves in the Amistad mutiny case, which John Quincy Adams finally won in the Supreme Court in 1840.

Willard's mother was Mary Ann Van Cleve, daughter of a graduate and trustee of Princeton University. Her fourth child and only son was born in New Haven in 1839. He was named Josiah Willard, the middle name going back to Samuel Willard, who was acting president of Harvard College in 1701, and a man of considerable executive and administrative ability. The boy inherited the scholarly qualities of his forebears but, apparently in the shuffling of the genes through the generations, had lost all the attributes of the administrator and executive. After four years at the Hopkins Grammar School in New Haven, the second oldest grammar school in America, he entered Yale College. He was graduated in 1858 at the age of nineteen, and gave the salutatory address in Latin. He was an all-around scholar, winning prizes not only in mathematics but also in Greek and Latin. Since one of these awards carried with it the stipulation that its winner continue his graduate studies at Yale, Gibbs continued his studies under Benjamin Silliman, Jr., and Hubert A. Newton, with whom he would often stay up late in the night at the Connecticut Academy, observing meteors.

Two weeks before the outbreak of the Civil War, Willard Gibbs' father died, leaving an estate of $38,000. This enabled the young man to continue his studies, to obtain his doctorate in 1863, and to accept a tutorship at Yale in Latin and later in natural philosophy. While thus engaged, he began to have much trouble with his eyes. Gibbs set to work to find by experiment the best formula for glasses which would correct his astigmatism. So well did he work out the mathematical details of the experiment and so skillfully did he handle the physical apparatus which he had set up that he quickly found the answer. He had the proper eyeglasses made, and his eyes never again seriously troubled him. This was one of the very few cases in which Gibbs resorted to actual physical experimentation. All his life he depended almost exclusively upon purely mathematical treatment of scientific problems.

In 1866 Gibbs followed the stream of American students to the scientific centers of Europe for further study and stimulation. America still had no university devoted wholly to graduate work and especially to scientific research. It was to take another decade before Johns Hopkins University was organized (1876) and dedicated to advance studies in the sciences. True, Yale University had in 1863 established the Sheffield Scientific School, with its reshaped curriculum and elective system, to meet the requirements and affect the future careers of the sons of the growing industrial world. But graduate work in Europe was still the normal course for young scientific luminaries. Asa Gray, Eben H. Horsford, James Dana, Othniel Marsh, Edward Cope, Wolcott Gibbs, and others had made the same pilgrimage. Previous to 1840, American students of chemistry went to Paris to study under Dumas,

Gay-Lussac, and Thénard. When, later, Liebig opened his laboratory, they went to Giessen, and still later the tide turned to Woehler at Göttingen. Ira Remsen, who received an M.D. from the medical school of Columbia University in 1867, spent five years in Germany for advanced work in chemistry. When in 1879 he prepared saccharin for the first time in history he published the account in the Berlin *Berichte*.

For nearly three years Gibbs attended the lectures of the great figures in the world of mathematics and physics at Paris, Berlin, and Heidelberg. He watched and absorbed the new developments in light, heat, electricity, thermodynamics, and pure mathematics with keen, scholarly devotion, quietly laying the foundations of the new structure which he himself was to erect in New Haven. Willard Gibbs was perfectly happy and very busy. His younger sister Emily had died in 1864, and with him now were his two other sisters, Anna and Julia. Addison Van Name, his classmate and Yale librarian, had come to Berlin to marry Julia in 1867. William James was in Berlin, too, at this time. He was not so happy. He had just come back from a trip through the Amazon with Agassiz, and was trying desperately to prepare himself for the new science of psychology, which he thought was perhaps now ready "to begin to be a science." But the study of physics and mathematics, both of which he felt he needed for this new science, were very difficult for him, and he was finally obliged to give them up.

Without going to England, where great activity was also under way in the physical sciences, Gibbs left Europe and reached New Haven in June, 1869. Things had happened since he had left for Europe. A liberal movement in education was under way. Harvard had broken an old tradition and put a young chemist at its head. (It had already in 1847 established the Lawrence Scientific School.) The trustees of Yale College also decided to consider changes to meet the demands of the new industrialism. No tremendous revolution was accomplished, but a committee which included Hubert Newton, Addison Van Name, and James Dana recommended the further stressing of science education and the formation of a chair in mathematical physics, in view of the importance of this branch of science to the new America.

This recommendation was accepted by the Yale Corporation, and in 1871 Willard Gibbs was named to occupy the first chair of mathematical physics in America. That same year young Clerk Maxwell was appointed to a somewhat similar chair, that of experimental physics, at Cambridge University, in England. The establishment of these two chairs of mathematical physics in the same year was no mere coincidence. It marked the recognition of the urgent need for more complete information and training in the sciences of heat and electricity by the new industrialists and manufacturers who were replacing the merchants and the ministers on the boards of trustees of our colleges. It mirrored the pull of the times, just as the increase in professorships in astronomy more than two centuries before had reflected the need for an accelerated study of navigation.

For thirty-two years Gibbs held this professorship and "was absorbed in systems in all the senses of that word." During these years he made his immortal contributions. He taught the wave theory of light, sound, capillarity, heat, magnetism, and electricity, in addition to mathematics and later thermodynamics. His life continued to be that of the scholar. While he was alert to the many events taking place about him, he kept his thoughts to himself, and attended occasional class reunions, faculty meetings, conferences of the trustees of the Hopkins Grammar School, of which he was a member, and scientific meetings at which, on rare occasions, he lectured. He organized the Yale Mathematical Club and once read a paper before its members on *The Paces of a Horse*. Gibbs was an excellent horseman and did considerable riding during his summer vacations. He and his sister Anna lived with his sister Julia and her husband in their father's house on High Street, almost across from the Sloane Physics Laboratory, where Gibbs had a small office. He would arrive there in the morning, lecture to a small group of perhaps half a dozen graduate students for a little more than an hour a day, walk home for lunch, return at about one in the afternoon, and retire to his office to prepare for the next day's lecture. At about five he would return home after taking a turn or two around the block for some fresh air.

Gibbs helped his sisters in their household duties, always insisting on mixing the salads on the ground that he was a greater authority than any other member of the household on the equilibrium of heterogeneous substances. He attended church regularly on Sundays, had very simple tastes, was broad and tolerant, and showed none of the usual eccentricities expected of a genius.

Late in 1879, after the appearance of his famous papers, Gibbs accepted an invitation to deliver a series of lectures on theoretical mechanics at the newly opened Johns Hopkins University. The following year its president asked Gibbs to join the faculty. It was a tempting and flattering offer. The progress of mathematics in this country had been very slow. We had produced a few bright mathematical luminaries—Nathaniel Bowditch (1773-1838), Robert Adrian (1775-1843), and Benjamin Peirce, who became professor of mathematics at Harvard in 1833, at the age of twenty-four. Peirce, who for some years was in charge of the *Nautical Almanac* and was superintendent of the United States Coast Survey, was one of the creators of linear associative algebra. Among his students at the Lawrence Scientific School was Simon Newcomb, the well-known astronomer, who later became professor of mathematics at Johns Hopkins and proved mathematically that one could turn a tennis ball inside out without bursting it. George W. Hill (1838-1916) and Emory McClintock (1840-1916) were also doing good work in mathematics at this time.

There was, however, a serious paucity of first-rate mathematicians in America until about 1870, because our best mathematical minds had been drained off into practical projects such as Federal surveys and engineering. Gilman, president of Johns Hopkins, had recognized this weakness and had brought to Baltimore one of the world's most distinguished mathematicians, James J. Sylvester. He was born in London of Jewish parents in 1814, and joined the mathematics department of Johns Hopkins at the age of sixty-two.

Soon afterward he founded and edited the *American Journal of Mathematics*. This event, according to Eric T. Bell, professor of mathematics at the California Institute of Technology, "gave mathematics in the United States a tremendous urge in the right direction—research." The new algebra was almost unknown in this continent, and Gibbs was working in this field. Sylvester realized the importance of having with him in Baltimore a man who was not only a master mathematical physicist, but also the equal of almost any mathematician of his day both here and abroad. After much thought, however, Gibbs turned down the invitation to join the staff of Johns Hopkins University because "a very unexpected opposition to my departure has been manifested among my colleagues."

In 1843 William R. Hamilton, the greatest Irish mathematician of all time, had invented his system of quaternions, which made quite a stir in mathematical circles all over the world. He thought it would be the key to the physical universe. Gibbs, too, had studied the system but had not found it suitable for use in his own researches on the physical sciences. He had worked out his own *Elements of Vector Analysis*, which was privately printed for his students between 1881 and 1884. Benjamin Peirce had also worked in this field, but it was Gibbs who brought it to completion and perfection. Gibbs' "theory of dyadics as developed in the vector analysis of 1884 must be regarded," according to one of his students, Henry A. Bumstead, "as the most important published contribution of Gibbs to pure mathematics." The vector analysis of Gibbs gradually displaced quaternions as a practical applied algebra.

The most active champion of Hamilton's system of quaternions was P. G. Tait. In 1890, in the preface to the third edition of *Quaternions*, Tait called Gibbs' vector analysis a hermaphrodite monster. When this was brought to the attention of Gibbs, the American professor was called upon for the first time in his whole career to answer a critic. He entered this mathematical controversy in no spirit of rancor nor with any idea of claiming priority or to defend a superior method. Gibbs was certain of the accuracy of his work and wanted only to make the record clear. He sent a letter to the journal *Nature*, giving a logical explanation of his position. It contained not a single word of anger or of censure. The fire was still sizzling two years later, and Gibbs sent another letter to *Nature* in March, 1893. "There are two ways in which we measure the progress of any reform," he wrote. "The one consists in counting those who have adopted the shibboleth of the reformers; the other measure is the degree in which the community is imbued with the essential principles of the reformer. I should apply the broader measure.

"Now," continued Gibbs, who hated authoritarianism deeply, "I appreciate and admire the generous loyalty toward one whom he regards as his master which has always led Professor Tait to write as if everything was contained in the ideas which flashed into the mind of Hamilton at the classic Brougham Bridge. But not to speak of the claims of historical justice, we owe duties to our scholars as well as to our teachers, and the world is too large, and the current of modern thought is too broad, to be confined to the *ipse dixit* even of a Hamilton."

Eric T. Bell has described this quaternion-versus-vector-analysis war in his usual keen manner: "The *casus belli* was a purely mathematical difference of opinion: were quaternions a good medicine for applied mathematics, or was some one of several diluted substitutes a better? The language of the disputants even bordered on quite un-Victorian indelicacy at times, as when Tait called the vector analysis of Gibbs 'a sort of hermaphrodite monster, compounded of the notations of Hamilton and Grassmann.' That was Scotch and Irish against American. Gibbs, being a New Englander to the marrow and a confirmed bachelor cherished only by his sister, was but slightly acquainted with the inexhaustible resources of the American language. Tait got away with his abnormal physiology, but Gibbs got the better of the mathematical argument."

In his own quiet way, with the grace and refinement of a distinguished scholar, Gibbs tumbled stubborn authorities to the ground even as, at the same time, he acknowledged his own "tangles." Where principles and fundamentals were concerned he was no meek, timid professor who feared the power of established leaders. He fought, but always with the disarming charm of one whose sole motive was the defense of truth and freedom to differ. The most severe words he ever used were uttered against a letter of criticism and ridicule written in 1893 by Professor Knott. Gibbs was shocked by "the incredible rashness" of his critics.

For fourteen years after the publication of his last paper on thermodynamics as applied to chemical equilibrium, Gibbs did not concentrate in this field and did not even lecture on thermodynamics. The problem of the nature and speed of light had long been boiling in the scientific pot, and a number of first-rate men were again giving it their attention. Gibbs, keeping a weather eye on every new development in physics, also became interested. Between 1882 and 1889 he published a number of papers in the *American Journal of Science* on the electromagnetic nature of light. Then for ten long years he published nothing at all. However, he must have been doing a great deal of thinking, along many lines.

Momentous events were happening during this decade in the realms of radiation and the nature of matter. William Conrad Roentgen had discovered X rays, Henri Becquerel had stumbled upon the phenomenon of radioactivity, which was cleared up by the Curies in their epochal investigations and discoveries. Pieter Zeeman discovered the magneto-optic effect, and J. J. Thomson was passing electric discharges through highly evacuated tubes. This culminated in 1897 in the discovery of the electron and the enunciation of the electron theory of matter. Planck, at the turn of the century, was advancing his revolutionary theory of the nature of energy as composed of discontinuous particles or quanta of energy. Yet Gibbs published nothing during this stirring period. He would not publish unless he was certain he had an original contribution of real importance to communicate to the world of science. Referring to several books on his shelves sent him by their authors and with their pages still uncut, he told E. B. Wilson, "a person who writes so much must spread his message rather thin."

In 1901, just about the time when the Royal Society of London was honoring Gibbs with the Copley Medal for being "the first to apply the second law of thermodynamics to the exhaustive discussion of the relation between chemical, electrical and thermal energy and capacity for external work," Gibbs was busy on his last great work. E. B. Wilson, who was a student of Gibbs at this time, says that the Yale mathematician wrote *The Elementary Principles of Statistical Mechanics* in something like nine months. During this time he was also occupied with his regular teaching duties. "All through the winter and spring of 1900-1901 he worked not only by day—the light in his study on the second floor of the old Sloane Laboratory could be seen burning at night. The manuscript was finished in the summer at Intervale, New Hampshire, where he spent his vacations; Gibbs worked to the limit of his strength to get the volume finished on time for Scribner's."

Arthur Haas has called this book "a monument in the history of physics which marks the separation between the nineteenth and twentieth centuries." A huge volume of research has flowed under the bridge of science since 1901. Yet the older statistical mechanics of Gibbs, revamped and dressed in the newer raiment of quantum statistics and quantum mechanics, is still a powerful tool in the elucidation of many problems concerning the nature of matter and radiation.

Willard Gibbs was never very strong. An attack of scarlet fever during childhood had left its mark on his health and he remained frail. A quiet, well-regulated life had enabled him to carry on without serious illness up to within a very short period before his death at the age of sixty-four. The end came after a year or more of minor ailments. The direct cause of death was a sudden and acute attack due to an intestinal obstruction which his physicians could not relieve.

Gibbs was a great scientist who strove to bring order out of the heterogeneous mixtures of metals and salts in solution. He was also a symbol of America struggling to bring system and law out of the chaos of an expanding industrialism. He may have seemed to stand apart from the forces that were changing the United States, but actually he was the unconscious instrument of those forces. To continue to believe in the legendary indifference of Gibbs to the possibilities of practical applications of his classic work would come too near, wrote his friend Charles S. Peirce, son of Benjamin Peirce and founder of pragmatism, "to making Gibbs a gifted idiot, rooting up his mathematical truffles like a Perigord pig, and as oblivious of being deprived of them."

Even in his student days Gibbs was thinking of the machine age into which America was passing. It is of more than passing interest that the first important manuscript written by him in 1863 as a doctorate dissertation had the very modern title, *On the Form of the Teeth of Wheels in Spur Gearing*. He was definitely interested in wheels and gears and teeth of steel which in time would transform America. Before the close of the Civil War he was actually busy with plans and drawings for a railroad brake "to dispense with the brakeman for railroad cars and to secure prompt action of the brakes." He pursued this practical invention until he received from the United States Department of Interior Patent Office Patent No. 53,971 on March 24, 1866. This was six years before George Westinghouse patented his famous automatic airbrake. Gibbs also played around with two other inventions; one of these was a new governor which was constructed for him in the shops of the Sheffield Scientific School at Yale. He also took an active part in another very immediate and practical problem—that of securing for the United States the best system of weights and measures. He actively participated in the fight for the acceptance of the metric system by this country, which was led by his friend and neighbor, Hubert A. Newton. Three days before Gibbs received his first patent, he addressed the Connecticut Academy of Science urging the acceptance of the metric system.

Twenty years later, in 1886, speaking on *Multiple Algebra* before the American Association for the Advancement of Science, of which he was vice-president, Gibbs expressed his awareness of the gradual enthronement of the machine, in his remarks, "The human mind has never invented a labor-saving machine equal to algebra. It is but natural and proper that an age like our own, characterized by the multiplication of labor-saving machinery, should be distinguished by an unexampled development of this most refined and most beautiful of machines." These were not the words of a detached philosopher spinning impractical theories in an ivory tower of scientific abstraction.

According to Professor Paul Epstein, Gibbs, before he wrote his classic papers on chemical equilibrium, gave thought to the future possibilities of industrial chemistry and the age of alloys. He looked upon thermodynamics as the practical tool with which to bring the new world of science into being. He may have been the unconscious servant of society faced with a vital problem which had to be solved before the new world of industry could finally appear with its huge smokestacks belching smoke from thousands of factories. In a sense Gibbs was the symbol of the new universe which, to quote Parrington, "unfolded itself to chemistry and physics as vaster and colder than biological evolution ever imagined—a vibrating mechanism, shot through with energy, that revealed itself in action and reaction, impersonal, amoral. The clouds drew over the brilliant Victorian skies. With the substitution of physics for biology came a more somber mood that was to substitute a mechanistic conception for the earlier teleological progress of biology."

But this symbol, in the life and work of Gibbs, was not wholly materialistic. The glowing figure of Walt Whitman was shining in the land. The author of *Leaves of Grass* had a tremendous faith in the common man and in the democracy which was America. New Haven and perhaps Gibbs, too, may have shown no warm feeling toward this paradoxical being. But Gibbs was ready to accept the age in the spirit of Whitman, as the poet had expressed it in his song of himself, *Walt Whitman*:

> *I accept reality, and dare not question it;*
> *Materialism first and last imbuing.*
>
> *Hurrah for positive science! long live exact demonstration!*
> *Fetch stonecrop, mixt with cedar and branches of lilac;*
> *This is the lexicographer—this the chemist—this made a grammar of the old cartouches;*
> *These mariners put the ship through dangerous unknown seas;*
> *This is the geologist—this works with the scalpel—and this is a mathematician.*
>
> *Gentlemen! to you the first honors always:*
> *Your facts are useful and real—and yet they are not my dwelling;*
> *(I but enter by them to an area of my dwelling.)*

CHAPTER FOURTEEN

SAMUEL PIERPONT LANGLEY

(1834-1906)

AMERICAN SCIENCE GIVES MEN WINGS

THE SIXTY-FOUR YEARS which embraced the full life span of Willard Gibbs was a period of great inventions in this country. The year of his birth, 1839, witnessed Charles Goodyear's introduction of the method of vulcanizing rubber. Seven years later came the sewing machine of Elias Howe and the rotary printing press of Richard M. Hoe. In 1852 Elisha G. Otis gave us the elevator, and before the end of that decade the production of cheap steel by the Kelly-Bessemer process was announced. In 1866 Cyrus W. Field developed the submarine cable; the first successful typewriter was placed on the market two years later by Christopher Sholes and Carlos Glidden. That same year John W. Hyatt made celluloid for the first time. The 1870's saw the introduction of George Westinghouse's automatic airbrake, the telephone of Alexander Graham Bell, Edison's phonograph and incandescent electric-light bulb. In 1880 Lester A. Pelton, an Ohio mechanic who had driven an ox team to the mines of Nevada during the gold-rush days, devised the Pelton wheel, to generate power. Four years later Ottmar Mergenthaler invented the linotype machine. The Hall process for the commercial electrolytic extraction of aluminum from bauxite was patented in 1886, and the Burroughs adding machine became a reality two years later.

In the final decade of the nineteenth century the first automobile was driven on the road by two young mechanics, the Duryea brothers. In the same decade the alternating-current motor was developed by Nikola Tesla, who had come here from the Balkans in 1884. Edison brought a number of variously authored inventions to fruition in the first practical moving-picture machine. Charles P. Steinmetz, who fled from Germany in 1889, was employed by the General Electric Company at Schenectady, New York, and began to pour out the first of his more than two hundred patents in motors and other electrical equipment. The year of Gibbs' death, 1903, marked mankind's conquest of the air by a heavier-than-air, motor-driven flying machine devised by the mind and hand of Americans.

Most of the basic inventions were the products of individual men, many of them mechanics who lacked advanced scientific or engineering education but whose practical experience and unusual skills solved the many problems which confronted them. Thomas Alva Edison stood high among these men. When in 1869 he resigned his position with Western Union and announced his intention of devoting all of his energies to commercial inventions, science turned a new corner. When he hung out his shingle as a professional inventor, he was telling the world that invention need no longer be the fortuitous career of the lone tinker, praying for guidance, light, and luck to bring him fame and fortune. Scientific invention could now be planned, organized, and executed by men gifted with mechanical skill and fertile, imaginative minds. New inventions could be made to order at the request of society.

In 1876 Edison opened his research laboratory at Menlo Park, New Jersey, and began to hire men to help in the completion of several new inventions. By 1880 he had surrounded himself with half a hundred expert assistants, and planned invention was under way. While Edison and his assistants still depended to a great extent upon the methods of trial and error, his workshop was the forerunner of the many huge industrial laboratories of today where research in theoretical science is carried on in the justifiable belief that practical inventions will eventually flow from new discoveries in abstract science.

Both the method of Edison and that of the abstract scientist played their parts in the invention of the airplane. The story of the final conquest of the air is the story of two skillful mechanics and practical Americans, Wilbur and Orville Wright. Their success came almost at the moment when the American theoretical scientist, Samuel P. Langley, failed to reach the same goal. The problem of human flight had occupied Langley's thoughts a full decade before the Wright brothers had switched their interest from bicycles to gliders. A paper on bird flight which Langley heard read at the annual meeting of the American Association for the Advancement of Science, at Buffalo in 1886, suddenly rekindled his old interest in the mysteries of flight. He remembered as a boy lazily lying in a field for hours watching hawks and buzzards soaring on wings which appeared perfectly motionless. He wondered how a bird with a body hundreds of times denser than the air around it could apparently float in that ethereal ocean. Many had observed this phenomenon before Langley, and many, too, had wondered about the explanation. Darwin, for example, in his voyage on the *Beagle* had noted, "When the condors are wheeling in a flock round and round any spot, their flight is beautiful. Except when rising from the ground, I do not remember ever having seen one of these birds flap its wings."

It had been believed for centuries that the flapping of a bird's wings was responsible for its flight. In the myths and legends of many peoples are stories of men who took unto themselves wings and flew. In Greek mythology, the sculptor Daedalus and his son Icarus tied a row of quills to their bodies, flapped their wings by their own power, and flew, Icarus to disaster. The earliest attempts to construct flying machines were based upon this principle. Roger Bacon, who lived during the thirteenth century, was convinced that this was the proper approach to the problem of human flight. "Flying machines," he wrote, "are possible so that a man may sit in the middle turning some device by which artificial wings may beat the air in the manner of a flying bird." Leonardo da Vinci's *Treatise on the Flight of Birds*, published in 1505, contained drawings of a bird in flight, an airplane wing which closely resembled the bird's wing, and an illustrated description of a flapping machine set in aerial motion by the muscle power of the flier transmitted to the wings by a system of pulleys and cords. It was not until centuries later, in 1809, that Sir George Cayley, an English engineer, finally showed the scientific difficulties involved in the ornithopter, or flapping flying machine, and turned to other principles for the basis of a successful flying machine. He discovered an important principle of flight; namely, that the forward motion of a surface through air produces lift.

In 1887 Langley embarked upon a series of experiments to determine the laws underlying the flight of a heavier-than-air machine through the atmosphere. He was well equipped for such a project. Behind him were more than thirty years of engineering research and experience. Born in Roxbury, near Boston, in 1834, he attended the Boston Latin School and, after completing high school, continued to study by himself the two subjects he liked best—mathematics and mechanical drawing. He became a successful architect and civil engineer in Chicago. Like his father, a wholesale merchant and banker, he had been an amateur astronomer for years. In 1864, when he was thirty years old, Langley returned to New England, decided to give up his business career and prepare himself for the life of a professional astronomer. He sailed for Europe with his younger brother, John, a graduate of Harvard's Lawrence Scientific School, and spent a year visiting scientific societies, astronomical observatories, and centers of research in physics.

When Langley returned to this country, immediately after the close of the Civil War, he obtained an assistantship in the Harvard Observatory, where he proved to be an excellent observer. During the short time he remained there he discovered two faint stars in the great nebula in Sagittarius. Two years later he was called to Annapolis to teach mathematics at the Naval Academy, and to become director of its astronomical observatory. He remained at this post for about a year, and then joined his brother on the staff of the University of Pittsburgh as teacher of astronomy and physics and as director of its Allegheny Observatory. At the observatory Langley inherited an old equatorial telescope but no transit instrument or other up-to-date astronomical apparatus. Funds had to be raised for new and better equipment. If no philanthropist could be induced to make such a gift, then some other means of obtaining funds had to be found.

Langley looked about him and saw a great network of railroads spreading across the face of America. There was no standard method of fixing railway time for the numerous lines which radiated from Pittsburgh. This situation brought errors, complaints, and confusion. Langley worked out a system of furnishing automatically and simultaneously, twice each day, the correct time based on astronomical measurements. His proposal for *Regulating the Clocks of Railroads* was contained in an eight-page pamphlet printed on December 1, 1869, just a few months after the first transcontinental railroad had spanned the continent. The Pennsylvania Railroad purchased his service, and for many years every one of its railway stations was furnished with this uniform and correct time. This system of Langley's was the parent of the present system, introduced in 1885 to do away with the half hundred varieties of time then in use in this country.

Langley had undertaken to solve this practical problem in order to raise money for his astronomical research. For the next seventeen years he busied himself with problems in pure science and made a number of first-rate contributions in the field of solar research. Langley was interested not so much in the traditional astronomy of position of the heavenly bodies but rather in the newer physics of their structure and properties. He tackled first the question of the nature of sunspots.

These dark spots on the surface of the sun had fascinated observers since the Chinese had noticed very large solar areas with the naked eye in A.D. 301. Galileo, thirteen centuries later, had observed and made numerous drawings of similar spots which freckled the face of the sun. He watched the motion and the changing sizes of these spots across the surface of the great rotating ball of fire, but could not satisfactorily explain them. Some scientists believed the spots to be solid, opaque objects revolving around the sun near its surface and blotting out its brightness wherever they happened to be. Others thought they were composed of vast volumes of smoke issuing from colossal solar volcanoes. Clouds in the solar atmosphere offered another possible explanation, while to still other astronomers the spots were clearly the summits of colossal mountains first uncovered and then submerged by the ebb and flow of gigantic rivers of fiery molten metals and rocks. It is almost incredible that Sir William Herschel, one of the world's greatest astronomers, saw the sunspots as the cold, opaque body of the sun visible through breaks in the solar atmosphere. Believing the sun to be a cold sphere like our own planet, but hidden behind hot gases, Herschel wrote, "I think myself authorized, upon *astronomical principles*, to propose the sun as an inhabitable world."

Langley could not accept any of these theories. Over a period of many months he studied the structure of the sunspots with his unaided eyes. Out of these studies in 1873 came a pen sketch of a sunspot which for fidelity and beauty of drawing has never been surpassed. He saw the sunspot, with his limited means (solar photography had not yet been introduced), as an inflowing whirlpool of titanic dimensions on the surface of the sun. To Langley, sunspots appeared to be round openings or great whirls *down* the vortices of which the chromospheric vapors were being sucked by mechanical action. Nineteen years later the American astronomer, George Ellery Hale, equipped with an instrument of his own invention (the spectroheliograph), made his classic investigations on sunspots which proved that Langley had been absolutely right. Sunspots *were* regions "where clearly defined whirls point to the existence of cyclonic electric and magnetic storms or vortices," with the vapors traveling down into the vortex rather than up and out of the region of disturbance.

The next problem which absorbed Langley was the question of

the distribution of heat in the spectrum produced by the sun. The elder Herschel had attempted to solve this question but left it unfinished. Science still possessed no instrument delicate enough to measure quantities of radiant heat so minute. Therefore, in 1879, Langley decided to try "to invent something more sensitive than the thermopile," which until then had been the most sensitive heat measurer devised by scientists. The Rumford Committee persuaded the National Academy of Sciences to appropriate funds for this project.

After a year of steady work Langley produced a new instrument which he named the *bolometer*. His paper on *The Bolometer and Radiant Energy*, published in 1881, remains one of the classics of science. The heart of the bolometer is a thin blackened thread of platinum which, on being exposed to the sun, absorbs its radiant heat. This heat produces tiny electrical currents which are proportional to the amount of heat falling upon it. The new device would not only detect but actually measure differences in temperature as small as one millionth of one degree. The presence of a cow a quarter of a mile away could be detected by the heat of its body. With the bolometer Langley examined the full spectrum of the sun, and brought to light a portion of the infrared spectrum never before studied. Later, during the last five years of the nineteenth century, he succeeded in mapping out 740 different narrow areas (absorption lines) in the solar spectrum, which he recorded photographically.

Langley was interested in solar radiation measurements primarily for the purpose of learning more about the complete spectrum of the sun. By 1884, however, after a series of observations made on Mount Whitney, California, he found another motive for this research. "If the observation," he wrote, "of the amount of heat the sun sends the earth is among the most difficult in astronomical physics it may also be termed the fundamental problem of meteorology or the science of the weather." Langley saw the practical and immediate need in a country as vast as ours for a more exact system of weather prediction. He recognized the value of a system of accurate long-range weather forecasting which would arm and protect the man who tilled the soil, shipped its products by land and sea, or engaged in a multitude of other activities.

Nearly all of the phenomena of the weather would become more easily predictable, thought Langley, if we could learn both the original quantity and kind of this solar radiation or heat, how it affects the constituents of the atmosphere on its passage earthward, how much of it actually reaches our soil, how through the medium of the atmosphere which acts as a blanket over the earth it controls the surface temperature of our planet, and how, in diminishing intensity, it is finally radiated out and returned to the same blanketing atmosphere. Langley attempted to determine the *total amount* of solar heat just before it enters the earth's atmosphere, a quantity which is termed the *solar constant* of radiation. From measurements which he took both at a valley station and from an observatory on Mount Whitney, several thousand feet above the earth's surface, Langley made several new determinations of this solar constant.

These preliminary researches were continued by Charles Greeley Abbot. In June, 1904, Langley and Abbot announced that they had found evidence that the sun is a variable star—in other words, that the sun's radiation is subject to important variations of intensity. Furthermore, they were bold enough to suggest that changes in terrestrial temperatures, hence the weather, are definitely related to this fluctuating solar radiation. Langley and Abbot were too solemn a pair of scientists to get hastily or unduly excited and raise high hopes. "While we are far," wrote Langley in 1900, in the *Annals of the Astrophysical Observatory of the Smithsonian Institution*, "from looking forward to foretelling by such means the remoter changes of weather which affect the harvests, still it is hardly too much to say that *we appear to begin to move in that direction*." Abbot continued with new instruments of his own invention to track down the behavior of the sun. For fifty years, in solar observatories on high mountains and in deserts of both hemispheres, Abbot continued to make new contributions in this field.

These many and important contributions to theoretical science gave Langley not only a national reputation as a first-rate scientist but an international fame as well. In 1878 he was called to become assistant secretary of the Smithsonian Institution; in 1887, on the death of Spencer F. Baird, he became its Secretary. Baird was the eminent zoologist who had organized the United States National Museum and been responsible for the establishment of the United States Commission of Fish and Fisheries, which later became known as the United States Bureau of Fisheries. Through his efforts the Federal government had finally recognized the great need to conserve our animal life and the economic value of such a Federal project. Baird was encouraged to establish fish-hatching stations in many parts of the country, and to arrange for the introduction of fish from one section of the United States to another and to prevent the disappearance of such fish as striped bass on the Atlantic Coast. This fish he introduced into the Sacramento River, where it became of tremendous economic importance.

During the nineteen years which followed his appointment as Secretary of the Smithsonian Institution, Langley directed his major efforts to an entirely new field for him, that of aeronautics. Listening, in 1886, to that paper on bird flight had stimulated him to a reconsideration of the theories then accepted regarding the principles of bird flight. He began his work that same year while at the Allegheny Observatory, with the help of an appropriation from the Bache Fund of the National Academy of Sciences. Four years later he wrote a brief letter about these studies to the Academy of Sciences of the French Institute.

In 1891 Langley published his *Experiments in Aerodynamics.* "Schemes for mechanical flight," he wrote, "have been so generally associated in the past with other methods than those of science, that it is commonly supposed the long record of failures has left such practical demonstration of the futility of all such hopes for the future that no one of scientific training will be found to give them countenance." While recognizing that this view was natural, he refused to accept it, and embarked on an inquiry regarding the lifting power of surfaces by artificial winds. He constructed a large whirling table composed essentially of two symmetrical wooden arms each thirty feet long, revolving in a horizontal plane eight feet above the level of the ground. This table was driven first by a gasoline engine of one and one-half horsepower; later a ten-horsepower steam engine was utilized to give the arms a maximum speed of about seventy miles an hour.

Langley collected a mass of data on inclined surfaces of different weights moving through air of different velocities. Automatic recording devices registered the lifting power. By applying the known laws of physics, he came to the conclusion that "it was possible to construct machines that would give such velocities to inclined surfaces that bodies definitely heavier than air could be sustained upon it and moved through it with great velocity, and capable of carrying other than their own weight." Furthermore, he found that the wind was not a uniformly moving mass of air, as was then supposed, but actually consisted of a succession of very brief pulsations of varying amplitudes. In a book which he published in 1893, *The Internal Work of the Wind*, Langley insisted that this potential *internal work* is sufficient to support a motorless heavier-than-air flying machine traveling in the air for hours at a time. This was an accurate conclusion, as later long-soaring flights with gliders showed clearly.

Langley obtained further data disproving some of the flight theories of past experimenters, and unearthed new evidence of the principles governing the lifting power of plane surfaces moving through air. Then he took the next logical step, that of constructing and testing the behavior of small models of airplanes. These were propelled through the atmosphere by means of small gasoline engines on a circular track about forty feet in diameter. Between 1891 and 1895 Langley repeated the pioneer experiments of several other European and American inventors. Sir Hiram Maxim, for example, built much larger experimental airplanes weighing

8000 pounds and costing as much as $100,000. William Henson and John Stringfellow of England had also built model airplanes which actually flew.

The newer knowledge gained by Langley enabled him in 1896 to make more and more changes on a new airplane model having a wingspread of twelve feet and a length of fifteen feet. After a trial of compressed carbon dioxide gas as the motive power, it was powered by a steam engine. From a houseboat anchored in the Potomac River and in the presence of several friends, including Alexander Graham Bell, he catapulted his twenty-six-pound machine into the air and watched it fly half a mile to land safely when the engine stopped. Within six months he had constructed a still larger model which he called *Aerodrome No. 6* (Langley coined the word *aerodrome* from the Greek words meaning *air runner*). On November 28, 1896, this machine flew three quarters of a mile, attaining a speed of thirty miles per hour. It was then that Langley wrote his memorable words: "I have brought to a close the portion of the work which seemed specially mine—the demonstration of the practicability of mechanical flight—and for the next stage, which is the commercial and practical development of the idea, it is probable that the world may look to others. The world indeed will be supine if it does not realize that a new possibility has come to it, and the great universal highway overhead is now soon to be opened." Langley was thinking, perhaps, of the prophecy which Tennyson had expressed in 1842, in his *Locksley Hall*:

Saw the heavens fill with commerce, argosies of magic sails,
Pilots of the purple twilight, dropping down with costly bales.

For a while Langley "looked to others" for the further development of aeronautics. At that time, military men in the United States, hearing of the interest which foreign governments were taking in flying machines as a possible new weapon of warfare, became mildly excited. This was not the first time that Americans had been interested in human flight; several had already made aerial history with balloons. Only two years after Benjamin Franklin had watched the first successful aerial voyage in history, made in a hydrogen-filled balloon by Dr. Charles in Paris in 1783, Dr. John Jeffries, a Boston physician, not only financed the first balloon crossing of the English Channel from Dover to Calais, but accompanied the aeronaut, the Frenchman Jean P. Blanchard. Blanchard, on the advice of Franklin, came to the United States and, partially financed by George Washington, who was one of the spectators, made the first aerial voyage in American history on January 9, 1793. He took off from Philadelphia, then the capital of the United States, and traveled fifteen miles in a hydrogen-filled balloon south across the Delaware River to Woodbury, New Jersey. During the Civil War Professor Thaddeus Sobieski Constantine Lowe, with the help of Lincoln, organized and commanded the first United States Aeronautic Corps. From his hydrogen-filled balloon he made observations for the Army of the Potomac, took photographs, and sent the first aerial telegraph message to Lincoln in Washington. In 1873 John Wise of Philadelphia, backed by the *Daily Illustrated Graphic* of New York, attempted the first crossing of the Atlantic in a balloon, but failed. The balloon crashed at New Canaan, Connecticut.

In the early part of 1898, the year of the outbreak of the Spanish-American War, a board of Army and Navy officers investigated the work of Langley and reported favorably on the possibility of building a heavier-than-air flying machine which might be used in aerial reconnaisance. The Board of Ordnance and Fortifications of the War Department made an allotment of $50,000 for further research and for the construction and testing of such a machine. Langley was asked to undertake the project, and he agreed to take on the task without compensation. The Smithsonian Institution added another $20,000 to help in the experiment.

Langley started at once the planning and construction of a machine of dimensions large enough to carry a pilot. What he needed most of all, he thought, was a motor light and powerful enough to sustain the machine in flight once it had been hurtled into the air by some mechanical catapulting device. After a long search, he contracted with the best motor manufacturer in the United States for such an engine. A second motor was ordered, but "in the spring of 1900 it was found that both contract engines were failures for the purpose for which they were intended, as neither one developed half of the power required for the allotted weight."

Finally, taking his engineer, Charles M. Manly, with him, he went to Europe in search of the engine he wanted. Europe had been busily engaged in developing the internal-combustion engine, which Gottlieb Daimler, Karl Benz, and others had invented. Already a number of manufacturers were turning out engines for the automobile which had just made its appearance as a new vehicle of travel. Wherever Langley went he was told that it was impossible to build a motor as light as he planned; that is, one weighing less than ten pounds per horsepower (without fuel and water). His flying machine had, in the meantime, been practically completed.

There was only one thing left to be done. Manly was given the order to design and build an engine in the Smithsonian shops. In a short time he produced a water-cooled gasoline engine of fifty-two horsepower which weighed less than five pounds per horsepower (including water for cooling). While a special houseboat was being constructed from the top of which the plane was to be launched, experiments were undertaken to fit the new engine into the flying machine. When the necessary changes and adjustments had been completed, the fifty-five-foot-long, forty-eight-foot-wide machine, with a wingspread of 1040 square feet, was lifted to the upper deck of the houseboat. Boat and plane were then towed to a point in the Potomac River directly opposite Widewater, Virginia, about forty miles from Washington.

The first trial was made on October 7, 1903, with Manly at the controls of the plane. It almost ended in complete disaster when the front portion of the machine was caught in the launching car, and man and machine fell into the Potomac. Two members of the United States Ordnance Department and many spectators, including several newspaper reporters, witnessed the accident. There was general disappointment and a little grumbling by the newspapermen, but many decided to stay around for a second trial. They were still confident that the Secretary of the Smithsonian Institution was no crackpot inventor, and that the United States War Department was not throwing away money on an impossible project.

Two months later, on December 8, 1903, the second test flight was made. When the crowd saw the repaired machine again plummet into the water, pilot and all, it lost patience. Newspaper reports told the country of the complete failure of Langley's Folly, and the inventor was criticized in no sugar-coated words. The conquest of the ether by a heavier-than-air flying machine, they said, was just a madman's dream. Langley, who was now almost seventy, recalled philosophically how the public had laughed at the first steamboat, gas light, electric light, and other improvements, and even resisted their introduction. Nevertheless, he felt the blow keenly. He went back to the Smithsonian Institution to resume his earlier researches in solar radiation. No more funds were to be had from the War Department to continue his seventeen years' work with flying machines.

Exactly nine days after the disastrous episode on the Potomac, a young American mechanic made the first successful flight in a heavier-than-air flying machine among the sand dunes of Kitty Hawk, North Carolina, only one hundred air miles away. In spite of his own disappointment, Langley felt a deep thrill of joy at this momentous triumph won by a fellow American. There was no bitterness in his heart. His own personal failure mattered little; after all, fate had selected another American to play the final act in the great drama of man's attempt to fly like a bird. Only the sting of the fickle press remained to cloud his last years.

The successful conquerors of the air were two brothers, Wilbur and Orville Wright, sons of Milton Wright, bishop of the Church of the United Brethren in Christ and editor of *The Religious Telescope*. Bishop Wright was descended from English and Dutch ancestors who had been among the early settlers of Massachusetts. The mother of the inventors was of Swiss-German extraction. Wilbur was born at Newcastle, Indiana, in 1867, and Orville at Dayton, Ohio, four years later. As owners of the Wright Cycle Company, which they had established in 1888, and as makers of the Van Cleve bicycle, the brothers had considerable experience with all sorts of mechanical devices. Their attention was turned from the affairs of their little bicycle shop in Dayton to the problem of human flight by a newspaper account of the death on August 11, 1896, of Otto Lilienthal in Germany during the last of his more than two thousand gliding and soaring flights. Lilienthal was the first man actually to soar in a glider—that is, to utilize the air currents to make his machine rise in the air. Gliding is *coasting* down the air. The Wrights approached the daring problem of human flight in a self-propelled heavier-than-air machine from the same vantage point of actual gliding and soaring experiments.

Lilienthal was only one of the many pioneers in this field. Clement Ader, a French engineer, after studying the flight of bats and vultures in Africa, had developed a glider, which unfortunately was wrecked in 1897 when he tried to fly the machine equipped with a twenty-horsepower steam engine. Octave Chanute, a retired American engineer who had learned of the gliding experiments of Lilienthal, had established a gliding school among the sand dunes of Lake Michigan and gave instruction to numerous young American enthusiasts in 1896. Professor John J. Montgomery, professor of physics at Santa Clara College in California, after studying bird flight had built and operated gliders, starting in 1884. He gave many public exhibitions in California until he met his death in one of his gliders in 1911.

Undaunted by the tragic fate of Otto Lilienthal and Percy Pilcher, an Englishman who was killed in a glider experiment in October, 1899, the Wrights continued their dangerous experiments. Their hopes were sustained by the achievements of Langley and the prestige of the Smithsonian Institution. In 1906, before their names became famous throughout the civilized world, Wilbur wrote to Octave Chanute, "The knowledge that the head of the most prominent scientific institute of America believed in the possibility of human flight was one of the influences that led us to undertake the preliminary investigations that preceded our active work. He recommended to us the books which enabled us to form some ideas at the outset. It was a helping hand at a critical time, and we shall always be grateful."

The mechanics from Dayton, Ohio, also read the reports of Chanute and Mouillard and kept in touch with the new data and theories which were being printed in various journals. Then they embarked upon a comprehensive and systematic program of experimentation and measurements of their own. They decided upon a combination of bridge-building method, such as Langley had used, and actual glider experiments from which they would make continuous changes as necessity demanded. In 1899 they experimented with kites.

To obtain the best possible site for their gliding experiments the Wrights wrote to the United States Weather Bureau. From bulletins sent them they concluded that an ideal location would be the narrow strip of sandbar which runs along the coast of North Carolina at Kitty Hawk. Here strong and steady winds would supply the atmospheric conditions most suitable for their efforts. They traveled to the Carolina coast, and in 1900 they flew their first biplane glider as a kite. In 1901 their second machine was used as a glider. On their return to Dayton, Orville built a small wind tunnel sixteen inches square and eight feet long, which was supplied with air by a fan run by gas. With this wind tunnel they experimented with various surfaces of different curvatures (using more than a hundred different airfoils), to determine lift, drag, pressure center, and other data.

These experiments confirmed the fact that while any inclined surface projected through the air (or a body past which air is blown) will experience a lift, a curved surface will receive a greater lift than a flat one. The Englishman, Francis Wenham, showed in 1871 that this lift could overcome the force of gravity and keep a model airplane aloft. The principle of the lifting power of a curved plane wing was discovered in 1738 by a Swiss scientist, Daniel Bernoulli. He noticed that an object at the side of a swiftly moving stream would be pulled *into* the stream rather than be pushed away from it as one might expect. He found the explanation for this phenomenon in the fact that water, passing from a wider path to a narrower or constricted area, increases its velocity. The constricted region through which the water is moving more swiftly exerts a lower pressure than the wider region where the speed of the water is less. The same principle holds true also of moving gases such as the air. Bernoulli's principle is illustrated in Fig. 6.

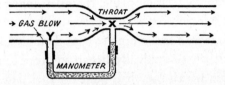

Fig. 6. Greater pressure at Y, where the velocity is lower. When a gas flows over a surface that causes its speed to increase, the pressure at that point, X, is decreased.

When air flows over the curved front (leading) edge of an airfoil (plane wing, rudder, or aileron), the direction of the air is changed and new pressure areas are set up, as shown in Figure 7.

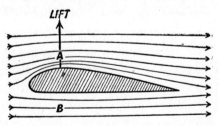

Fig. 7. Constriction at A increases the velocity of air and produces a lower pressure at A than at B.

The effect is the same as that of air going through a constriction. The region directly over the airfoil becomes an area of low pressure, while the region below the airfoil remains one of relatively higher pressure. Hence the airfoil is forced upward against the force of gravity, and the plane rises. In many cases as much as seventy-five per cent of the lift of a plane is due to this upward rush of the airfoil.

With the knowledge gained from the wind-tunnel experiments, the Wrights built another glider, incorporating the necessary changes. Returning to Kitty Hawk in September, 1902, they made more than a thousand flights.

All this time the brothers were also studying the important problem of keeping their machine in equilibrium while in flight, a problem which in the beginning was solved largely by the pilot shifting his own position as he soared through the air. To obtain better lateral control of their plane, they developed a wing bending or warping device for which they sought a patent on May 23, 1903. They were also learning to land their glider more safely, and their accident rate gradually began to drop. Finally they installed an engine which they had built for their last machine and decided to launch their plane from the ground rather than to rely upon the catapulting from a houseboat, which Langley had thought essential.

A twenty-one-mile wind was blowing on the cold morning of December 17, 1903. At 10:30 in the morning, Orville Wright crawled into the biplane glider equipped with a four-cylinder, twelve-horsepower gasoline motor. The motor was started, the twin pusher-type propellers of their own design connected with bicycle chains were set in motion in opposite directions. A wire which held the airplane was unfastened, the plane shot forward into the wind, ran along a track, and finally, at Orville's control, leaped into the air. It flew perfectly for twelve seconds and covered about 120 feet before it alighted safely. The first human flight in a powered heavier-than-air machine had been achieved, and history was made once again by an American. Three more flights were made that day. Wilbur Wright, tall, gaunt, and hawk-eyed, was at the controls on the last one, and flew for a second short of a full minute, covering 852 feet in the air. The Wrights were tremendously excited. Orville wired home to his father in

Dayton: "Success, four flights Thursday morning all against twenty-one-mile wind, starting from level with engine power alone, average speed through air thirty-one miles, largest fifty-nine seconds, inform press, home Christmas."

Bishop Wright, too, was excited. He sent his other son, Lorin, to the office of the *Dayton Journal* with the news. The editor was not impressed. In fact, only three newspapers in the whole country printed some account of this historic flight the next morning. Furthermore, the accounts were fantastically inaccurate. The following day the *Dayton Journal*, however, printed Orville's telegram, but the public at that moment attached no great significance to the event. There were no newspapermen and no scientific correspondents present at the dunes of Kitty Hawk on that morning when a new means of travel was born. In spite of the fact that a general invitation had been extended to the people living within six miles of the flying field, only five persons were actually present at that historic moment to witness the first flight of the Wright brothers.

After that fourth flight, when Wilbur Wright had crawled out of his plane safely, a sudden gust of wind caught the machine and damaged it seriously. In the spring of the following year the Wrights moved to a field near Dayton and built a new machine equipped with a seventeen-horsepower motor and weighing, with the pilot, about 900 pounds. This machine was flown repeatedly, and in less than two years a circular flight covering twenty-four miles was made near Dayton. So thoroughly had the press ignored the public's interest in the Wrights' experiments that they were able to fly their machines near a public road and trolley line, within full view of thousands of people, without arousing any undue excitement about this great achievement. *Gleanings in Bee Culture*, A. I. Root's publication printed in Ohio, contained the first magazine story of these pioneer flights.

On May 22, 1906, Patent No. 821,393 was issued to the Wright brothers for a flying machine. Many inventors jumped into the field. Alexander Graham Bell invited a young New York bicycle mechanic, Glenn H. Curtiss, who had introduced the motorcycle and became a champion motorcyclist, to come to Nova Scotia in the summer of the following year. Here Curtiss, with F. W. Baldwin and J. A. D. McCurdy, two engineers from the University of Toronto, and Thomas E. Selfridge, started the Aerial Experiment Association of America. With Bell's funds they built a man-carrying plane of their own design based on the Wright plane.

In the meantime, the Wrights looked around for customers for their full-blown invention. American capital was not tempted, and the United States Army was still unconvinced of the importance of this extraordinary machine. European governments, however, showed a greater interest in it. In 1906 Albert Santos-Dumont, son of a wealthy Brazilian coffee planter, had built a huge box-kite plane which flew him 175 feet at Bagatelle, France. Captain Ferber, who had also experimented with gliders, heard of the Wright plane through Chanute. Through his efforts the French War Department sent over a commission to talk to the Wrights. As a result the French government was urged to purchase a Wright plane for possible military use.

Near the close of 1907 the chief signal officer of the United States Army, General James Allen, had a talk with Wilbur Wright. The Army was again interested in planes. After their talk, Allen invited bids from the public for a heavier-than-air flying machine which would successfully carry two men with fuel sufficient for a flight of 125 miles. The machine must fly at a speed of thirty-six miles per hour over a five-mile course with and against the wind. The Wright brothers built a machine and Orville started the Army tests in this plane in the late summer of 1908. Wilbur, in the meantime, took another plane to Europe and exhibited its flying abilities at Le Mans, France. On September 9 of that year Orville managed to stay aloft for one hour and two minutes. On the seventeenth of the same month he took up Lieutenant Thomas E. Selfridge as a passenger. During this flight one of the plane's wires was struck by the propellor. The plane crashed, Orville was severely injured, and the Army officer was killed, the first victim of a powered heavier-than-air machine. The tests stipulated by General Allen were finally completed before Army officials at Fort Myer, Virginia, in June of 1909. The plane was turned over to the United States War Department in August. This was the first plane ever purchased by the Army. It marked the beginning of a long period of tremendously important developments in both commercial and military airplanes. One of the very early American Army pilots was Lieutenant H. H. Arnold, who in 1942 became our first four-star air general in command of our huge air forces.

Less than three months before the Wrights received their airplane patent, Langley passed away at Aiken, South Carolina, at the age of seventy-two, after an attack of paralysis. Octave Chanute and some of his friends at the Smithsonian believed that Langley had constructed the first airplane that was capable of flying with a man aboard. Only an unfortunate accident caused by a faulty launching device, they felt, had prevented a successful flight. This repaired ship had been placed on exhibition in the place of honor at the Smithsonian Institution. The Wrights felt slighted. When, therefore, the Science Museum at South Kensington, London, invited Wright to ship his plane, in which he had made the first flight in history, to England for temporary exhibition, he regretfully agreed to send it out of the United States in 1928.

On the twenty-fifth anniversary of the flight at Kitty Hawk a great celebration was planned to honor the Wright brothers. Congress had authorized the erection of a national monument on Kill Devil Hill near which the historic flight had been made. A huge white shaft of North Carolina granite was mounted on top of the principal migrating dune which had been anchored by the National Park Service by planting hardy grasses. A ten-ton boulder bearing a bronze tablet was placed there by the National Aeronautics Association of the United States to mark the spot from which the first flight was made. Delegates and guests of the International Civil Aeronautics Conference held at Washington were taken on a pilgrimage to this site situated only a few miles from that hallowed spot on Roanoke Island where Thomas Harriot had landed 340 years before, to write on the flora and fauna of what was to become the United States of America. Captain William J. Tate, the original host of the Wright brothers when they first arrived at Kitty Hawk, was there. Three of the original five men who had witnessed the first flight were also present. Dwight F. Davis, Secretary of War, Senator Bingham, and other distinguished guests paid homage to the memory of Wilbur Wright, who had died of typhoid fever in 1912 at the age of forty-five, and to his surviving brother, Orville. It was a great tribute to two great American inventors.

The original Kitty Hawk machine was in the Science Museum of South Kensington, London. Attempts were made to get it back. Orville Wright made no move in that direction. In spite of the action of the Smithsonian in awarding the Wrights the first Langley Medal in 1909 "for specially meritorious investigations in connection with the science of aerodynamics," and in exhibiting their Fort Myer machine later in the National Museum, the surviving brother could not forget the part the Smithsonian Institution had appeared to play during the years of litigation between the Wrights and another plane manufacturer. He was ready to overlook the original slight, but an incident of 1914 still rankled. In that year the Smithsonian Institution, after establishing the Langley Aerodynamical Laboratory, decided to determine whether the original Langley aerodrome, which had come to grief on the Potomac in 1903, really could fly with a man aboard. Dr. Charles D. Walcott, then Secretary of the Smithsonian, employed Glenn H. Curtiss for the test. Curtiss in 1911 had received the first American pilot's license ever issued by the Aero Club of America. In 1913 he had received the Langley Medal, and was now manufacturing his own planes at Hammondsport, New York. Manly, Langley's original pilot, had also asked for permission to make the crucial test. Orville Wright had felt that some disinterested person should have been selected for this important trial.

Curtiss made many extensive repairs and alterations on the Langley machine, modified Langley's 52 H.P. engine, fitted the plane with pontoons, and on May 28, 1914, raised it from the waters of Lake Keuka at Hammondsport, New York. It flew about 150 feet, according to A. F. Zahm, who later directed the aerodynamical laboratory of the U. S. Navy. The press hailed this achievement as proof positive that the original Langley machine was the first heavier-than-air machine ever built which would fly with a man at its controls. The public was led to believe that Langley and not the Wright brothers had actually built the first successful machine. The aerodrome was returned to Washington, overhauled, and set up in the Museum with the legend:

THE FIRST MAN-CARRYING AEROPLANE IN THE HISTORY OF THE
WORLD CAPABLE OF SUSTAINED FREE FLIGHT

Orville Wright was hurt, for at this very moment Glenn Curtiss was an unsuccessful defendant in a patent suit brought by the Wright Company. The alleged flight of the original machine might have weakened the position of the Wrights in court.

In 1928 the newly elected Secretary of the Smithsonian Institution, Charles G. Abbot, in an effort to smooth over the disagreeable situation, directed that the label under the Langley machine be changed to read simply:

LANGLEY AERODROME. THE ORIGINAL SAMUEL P. LANGLEY
FLYING MACHINE OF 1903, RESTORED

He renewed the invitation to Orville Wright to turn over his original Kitty Hawk plane for perpetual preservation in the United States National Museum. Wright answered that "a correction of history" by the Smithsonian was essential first. This finally came after a painstaking investigation of the entire matter by a number of experts. The Smithsonian Institution, speaking in 1942 through its Secretary, publicly acknowledged without reservation that "Wilbur and Orville Wright made the first sustained flights in a heavier-than-air machine in 1903, and the 1914 flights of Langley's machine, as reconditioned and altered, did not prove that it could have flown in 1903 before them." Dr. Abbot also offered "sincere apologies to Orville Wright for misleading statements by former Smithsonian officials." Mr. Wright accepted the apologies, and agreed to bring the plane back to America.

In the meantime this new weapon, which had grown so quickly to undreamed-of potency, had been used by the Nazis in an attempt to bomb Britain into submission. The ruins of London and Coventry stood as frightful evidence of the power of the new machine which America had given to the world. During this *Blitz* the first innocent and fragile bird of the new brood of destruction was tenderly moved from the South Kensington Museum in London and tucked safely away in a protected shelter deep in the earth. Mankind was not to lose this symbol of the power of science. It was later returned to the United States and since 1948 has been exhibited at the Smithsonian Institution. The genius of man, the scientist, had made possible a new machine which could bring peoples closer together for clearer understanding and better living. But science had been frightfully abused when the power of the plane was turned into the bomber of destruction.

During the many years of controversy over priority of airplane invention, the friends of Langley tried to enhance his fame. It is certain that Langley himself, a scrupulously honest man, would never have engaged in this battle had he lived. He shunned arguments and stood aloof from most of his contemporaries, surrounded by an armor of cold dignity. Shy and reserved, he made friends with difficulty, never married, had no close family ties, and lived a somewhat secluded life. Yet he worked hard to disseminate and add to scientific knowledge. He was president of the American Association for the Advancement of Science, vice-president of the American Philosophical Society, a member of the Council of the National Academy of Sciences, and for nineteen years the active Secretary of the Smithsonian Institution. The spirit of this institution was nurtured by him in more than one way. He undertook several courses of science lectures for the general public and wrote *The New Astronomy*, a book dealing with the physics of the heavens for the layman. The National

Zoological Park in Washington was founded by him for public use, and he obtained substantial appropriations from a reluctant Congress for the creation of the National Gallery of Art and of the Astrophysical Observatory in Washington.

Langley was a careful writer, taking pains to submit for publication only that which he had very carefully worked over. More than once from his pen would come delightful bits of writing which bear rereading especially in the light of recent events. "I have read somewhere," he wrote, "about a race of ephemeral insects who lived but an hour. To those who are born in the early morning the sunrise is the time of youth. They die of old age while its beams are yet gathering force, and only their descendants live on to midday; while it is another race which sees the sun decline, from that which saw it rise. Imagine the sun about to set, and the whole nation of mites gathered under the shadow of some mushroom to hear what this wisest philosopher has to say of the gloomy prospect. If I remember aright, he first told them that, incredible as it might seem, there was not only a time in the world's youth when the mushroom itself was young, but that the sun in those early ages was in the eastern, not in the western, sky. Since then, he explained, the eyes of scientific ephemera had followed it, and established by induction from vast experience the great 'Law of Nature' that it moved only westward; and he showed that since it was now nearing the western horizon it was about to disappear forever, together with the great race of ephemera for whom it was created. What his hearers thought of this discourse I do not remember, but I have heard that the sun rose again the next morning."

The vital role played by Langley in the development of the airplane has been commemorated by the naming after him of the first United States airplane carrier, launched in 1922. Langley Field near Norfolk, Virginia, was also named in honor of this great American scientist whose theoretical research helped pay the way for the great air fleets of today and tomorrow.

CHAPTER FIFTEEN

ALBERT ABRAHAM MICHELSON

(1852-1931)

AMERICA PARTICIPATES IN THE REVOLUTION OF
MODERN PHYSICS

WHEN IN THE WINTER of 1872-73 the eminent English physicist, John Tyndall, came to America to deliver a series of lectures on light, he had an opportunity, as an outsider, to survey science in the United States. "I have been unable to see anything in the constitution of society," he observed, "to prevent a student from bestowing the most steadfast devotion on pure science. If great scientific results are not achieved in America it is not to the small agitations of society that I should be disposed to ascribe the defect, but to the fact that the men among you who possess the endowments necessary for profound scientific inquiry, are laden with duties of administration, of tuition so heavy as to be utterly incompatible with the continuous and tranquil meditation which original investigation demands."

He added a word of advice. "You have scientific genius amongst you. Take all unnecessary impediments out of its way. Keep your sympathetic eye upon the originator of knowledge. Give him the freedom necessary for his researches, not demanding from him so-called practical results—above all things avoiding that question which ignorance so often addresses to genius, 'what is the use of your work?'"

In spite of a fairly rapid industrialization, and in the face of a mounting emphasis upon practical science, America was already

356

producing men of science whose eyes were turned toward investigations of a broad, theoretical nature. But, let it be added, these men were serving pure science under difficulties. In the last quarter of the nineteenth century, Gibbs, Langley, Newcomb, Young, and Rowland, among others, were working in the field of pure science. Henry A. Rowland, son of a Pennsylvania clergyman, had written when he was twenty, "I intend to devote myself to science. If she gives me wealth, I will receive it as coming from a friend, but if not, I shall not murmur." In 1870 he was graduated from the Rensselaer Polytechnic Institute. Later, while serving as the first professor of physics at Johns Hopkins University, he ruled between fourteen and twenty thousand thin parallel grooves very close together on concave glass and speculum surfaces. With these superb gratings which split light into its components, he mapped the solar spectrum more thoroughly than anyone before him in any part of the world had done. This work started a new era in spectroscopy, for it made possible the direct photography and higher resolution of spectra of the heavenly bodies. When in 1881 Rowland went to London and Paris to explain his new technique, he had his foreign audiences, which included Lord Kelvin, gaping at his skill and applauding his brilliance.

Europe considered Rowland one of the truly great scientists of his day. He established the law for magnetic flux similar to Ohm's law for electricity. While Rowland was pursuing his researches at Baltimore, Simon Newcomb, who had married the great-granddaughter of the colonial scientist, David Rittenhouse, was busy in the office of the Nautical Almanac at Washington. He, too, was doing first-rate work in celestial physics. He was also studying the motions of the moon and other heavenly bodies, and finding more accurate figures for the constants of astronomy. At Princeton University at this time another scientific investigator, Charles Young, was making contributions of more than passing interest in physics and astronomy.

It was among these theoretical scientists that America was at last to find one whose achievements were of such a basic character

that he was to become the first American recipient of the Nobel
Prize in science. The story of Albert A. Michelson is the story of
a segment of America transported from the soil of revolutionary
Europe. The political upheavals in Europe in 1848, and the after-
math of the temporarily unsuccessful battle for liberty, led to
much persecution. Hundreds fled, and many of these political
refugees came to America. Abraham Jacobi, the great physician,
Henry Flad, the engineer-inventor, and Charles T. Mohr, the
botanist, were among the German scientists who sought refuge
in America soon after 1848. Others, too, caught in the economic
backwash of these difficult years, abandoned the Old World to
try their luck in the United States.

Michelson's Jewish parents took part in this exodus. In 1854
they left Prussia, bringing with them their two-year-old infant,
Albert, who had been born in Strelno, a little town near the
border of Poland. In New York City Samuel Michelson, the
father, found employment as a jeweler, but before long decided
to join his sister, who had gone to California during the gold-rush
days. The Michelsons made the journey to the West by boat via
Panama. In San Francisco, Albert attended grammar school until
his parents moved again, this time to the center of the thriving
mining industry. The Civil War was on, and millions of dollars'
worth of silver were being dug out of the rich Western mines to
help win the war for the North.

Young Albert for a while mingled with the noisy, colorful
miners of Murphy's Camp in Calaveras County, California. He
was later sent back to San Francisco to complete his high-school
education. There he lived in the home of the principal of the
school, who was quick to see the unusual mechanical abilities of
the youngster and encouraged him in his studies. Even while a student he was put in charge of the school's scientific instruments.
When at sixteen his secondary education was completed, young
Michelson returned to the home of his parents, which was then in
Virginia City, Nevada, center of the Comstock Lode silver-
mining ventures. The following year his brother, Charles, was

born, and in 1870 his sister, Miriam, was born in Calaveras. Charles Michelson was later to become director of publicity for the Democratic National Party, a position he held until 1942, and Miriam grew up to write several novels.

The men of the mines fascinated the impressionable boy. The variegated and many-colored ores dug out of the hills and smelted in huge furnaces became the subject of one of his collecting hobbies. Beyond this, mining as a profession held no interest for him. He had shown unusual ability in mathematics, and friends who came into his father's store in Virginia City often talked of the boy's great future. His mother, Rosalie Przlubska, daughter of a German physician, would have liked to see Albert enter the medical profession, but his father thought that the Navy suited his son's bent and talents better. Albert finally decided on the Navy.

He passed the examination for cadet in the United States Naval Academy creditably, but did not receive an appointment. It went to another lad who was tied with him in the examination. Albert decided to appeal through his Congressman to the President of the United States for another possible opening at Annapolis. Virginia City was a long way from Washington and the overland trip was neither rapid nor comfortable. The chances of getting favorable action from the President were not too rosy. But Albert Michelson thought it worth the effort. When he arrived in Washington, President Grant saw the seventeen-year-old boy and explained that the last of the special ten appointments at large had already been made. But he did advise him, nevertheless, to see the Commandant of the Naval Academy. To Albert's great surprise and delight an additional opening was made for him, and he received the "eleventh appointment." This incident prompted Professor Michelson, many years later, to remark that his whole career as a scientist had started with an "illegal act."

The four years at Annapolis passed quickly and without dramatic incident. Michelson stuck fairly close to his studies, and in 1873 was graduated as a midshipman in the Navy. He had made a good scholastic record as a student, and was given an appointment as instructor of physics and chemistry at the Naval Academy. He held this position between 1875 and 1879. Then for a short time he served with the office of the Nautical Almanac in Washington.

While teaching physics at the Naval Academy, Michelson undertook his first piece of research in science. It was in the field of optics, an area of science which from that moment on held his attention almost without interruption for more than half a century. The speed of light had long been recognized as one of the most important constants of nature. It was of pivotal importance to the solution of some of the most compelling problems in the entire field of physical science. Ever since Olaus Römer, a young Danish scientist, had made in 1675 the first experimental determination of the speed of light, the need of a more accurate determination was paramount. Römer obtained his figure for the speed of light (180,000 miles per second) by measuring the time lag (sixteen minutes and thirty-six seconds) of the reappearance of a satellite behind the planet Jupiter. The observer on earth made two measurements, one when the earth was nearest Jupiter and the other six months later. Römer's experiment destroyed the belief that the speed of light was instantaneous. He showed that it was tremendously great but, nevertheless, finite and measurable.

The method used by Römer depended upon astronomical determinations. A purely laboratory method which could be performed without resorting to such measurements was desirable to obtain a more accurate figure. The speed of light remained a tantalizing problem for scientists for nearly two centuries. By 1877 three purely terrestrial methods for its determination had been developed. These included one devised by Armand Fizeau in 1849, a second worked out by Jean Foucault thirteen years later, and in 1872 a third by another Frenchman, Marie Alfred Cornu.

Fizeau made the first terrestrial determination of the speed of light in history. He used a source of light at *S*, which struck a mirror *B*, which reflected the light back and forth between two stations, *A* and *B*, five miles apart as shown in Fig. 8, page 361.

Fizeau's calculations showed the velocity of light to be 195,344 miles a second. The world rubbed its eyes and wondered whether this colossal figure, a speed which took light around the earth in one eighth of a second, was really reliable. It seemed impossible that such a tremendous speed could be measured by man with his puny instruments. Light had to travel across those five miles of his setup in less than 1/18,000 of a second. Incredible, many said.

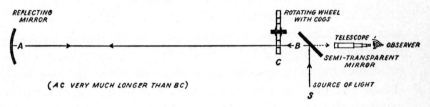

Fig. 8. Fizeau's method for determining the speed of light.

While scientists were reeling from the effects of this fantastic figure, Foucault made another measurement of this constant by a different means. His method depended upon the time required to displace the image of a fine wire by the angular change in the position of a small mirror making about five hundred rotations per minute. This device shortened the distance of the beam of light required by Fizeau from five miles to a few feet. Foucault obtained the figure of 185,150 miles per second for the speed of light.

Michelson, as a young man, was attracted to this problem. "The fact that the velocity of light is so far beyond the conception of the human intellect, coupled with the extraordinary accuracy with which it may be measured, makes this determination one of the most fascinating problems that fall to the lot of the investigator," he wrote. In November, 1877—he was then twenty-five years old—Michelson hit upon a slight but vital modification of the method used by Foucault. He dispensed with the Frenchman's concave reflector, enabling him to use practically any distance through which his beam of light would pass. He planned to use two plane mirrors, one fixed and one revolving at the rate of about 130 turns per second. The distance between the mirrors was to be 500 feet. See Fig. 9, page 362.

In May of the following year Michelson submitted his first scientific communication to the *American Journal of Science* for publication. It consisted of half a page of explanation of his new method but gave no experimental data. Just prior to this, Ensign Michelson had married Miss Margaret McLean Hemingway, whose father became extremely interested in this work on light and gave his son-in-law $2000 with which to try out his new technique. Within a few months Michelson went to St. Louis and submitted before the American Association for the Advancement of Science a new figure for the speed of light—186,508 miles a second. This result was, he estimated, correct to within one part in 10,000. The news was printed in the April, 1879, issue of the

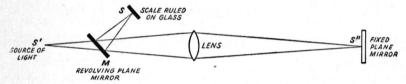
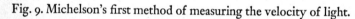

Fig. 9. Michelson's first method of measuring the velocity of light.

American Journal of Science and even found its way to Virginia City, where the local newspaper printed the event: "Ensign A. A. Michelson, a son of S. Michelson, the drygoods merchant of this city, has aroused the attention of the country by his remarkable discoveries in measuring the velocity of light." In the mining community this bit of news may not have aroused much discussion, but to the world of science it was historic.

Michelson determined to continue this branch of research until he had given science as accurate a figure as human ingenuity could obtain. With a view toward learning at first hand what the European theorists and experimenters were doing with this problem, he sailed for Europe in 1880. With him went his wife, their daughter, and their infant son, Truman, who later became an ethnologist and authority on the American Indian. For the next two years Michelson hovered about the universities of France and Germany, absorbing all the information he could find.

A fundamental question in physics had to be answered. Christian Huygens, a Dutch mathematician and astronomer, had advanced in 1678 the wave theory of light. According to this theory, luminous bodies such as a lighted match or the sun set up vibrations which travel as light waves until they strike the eye of the observer. But that was not the whole story, nor did Huygens himself believe it to be as simple as all that. Light could travel even through a vacuum, where nothing material was present to carry his hypothetical light waves. Then what did carry the light waves? To answer this tantalizing question Huygens, who came very close to choosing the law as a career, did what pseudo-scientists before him had done, and what abstract scientists after him have continued to do. He coined a new word, the *ether*, to explain his wave or *undulatory theory of light*.

This ether was some mysterious entity which filled all space; it was even present in solid matter. The vibrations set up in this jellylike ether transmitted light even in a perfect vacuum. Ether was invoked on numerous other occasions where it offered a plausible way out of some scientific morass. This ghost of the world of physics remains today, aged and tottering, a challenge to some who are still trying to prove its existence. The behavior of light seemed to demand some form of medium capable of carrying wavelike radiations through millions of miles without weakening or diluting their initial energy. Was there really such a thing as the ether? Could science prove or disprove the existence of this theoretical ghost?

It was a basic question, which a bold approach might answer unconditionally. A crucial experiment was needed. The young science teacher from America thought he might find the answer over which the older scientists of Europe still pondered. His idea was a simple one. A modification of his method of determining the speed of light might give up the secret. Michelson reasoned that if the stationary ether was something material and surrounded the earth as an ocean, then this ether sea would offer an obstacle to the passage of light. Since it takes longer to row upstream a mile and then back to the starting point than to row the same distance

across water and back, light would be held back by the ether to
a lesser extent if it passed through space at right angles to the direction of the earth's motion. If, on the other hand, there was no
ether, then it would make no difference in what direction the light
moved.

Michelson therefore planned the following experiment. He
would send one beam of light a definite distance and another beam
an equal distance but at right angles to the direction of the first
beam. Both beams would be returned to their common starting
point. If the ether was a reality, the two pencils of light would return to their starting point at slightly different times and produce
an *interference effect*. That is, their light waves would cross each
other and produce alternate bands of darkness and light. If, on
the other hand, the two light rays returned at the same instant because there was no ether, then no interference effect would be
observed.

Since light is the fastest thing in the universe, Michelson had to
be able to make extremely accurate observations. Even the slight-
est defect of his apparatus or the smallest error of manipulation
would give inconclusive results. The work demanded a boldness
and a manipulative skill of the highest order. These difficulties did
not deter him. He drew plans for a machine, which was constructed by a Berlin manufacturer. Alexander Graham Bell appeared as a patron of science to provide the necessary funds for
this investigation.

With his new instrument (the *interferometer*), Michelson split
a ray of light A in two by causing it to fall on a plane glass plate
B, the surface of which was covered with a thin film of silver.
This film of metal was so thin that part of the light was reflected
to D and part of it was transmitted through the plate to C, both
rays of light emerging with approximately equal intensities. One
half of the original beam of light moved in a direction at right
angles to the other but covered an equal distance. At the end of
their journeys the two halves of the original light beam were reunited. See Fig. 10, page 365.

The first experiment was tried in Helmholtz's laboratory in the Physical Institute of Berlin. The instrument was set up on a stone pier, but the vibrations caused by the city's traffic at night interfered. Michelson went, therefore, to the Astrophysical Observatory in Potsdam in April, 1881, to make another attempt. Here the extremely sensitive instrument finally gave results, even though footsteps on the pavement a block away from the observatory cellar made the observations very difficult.

Michelson's experiments produced a zero result. He found no drag on the transmission of light in either direction—no interference phenomenon. Both rays of light returned at the same instant. He reported his findings in the August, 1881, issue of the *American Journal of Science* under the title, *The Relative Motion of the Earth and the Luminiferous Ether.* "The hypothesis of a stationary ether is erroneous," he wrote.

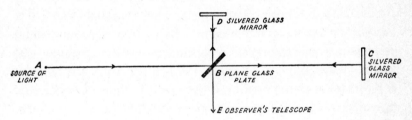

Fig. 10. Simplified diagram of Michelson's apparatus of 1881.

Lord Kelvin, the eminent English scientific authority who always insisted on some mechanical model to explain any theory of nature, continued, however, to believe in the ether. Sir Oliver Lodge, another bigwig in English scientific circles, who was the stanchest supporter of the ether theory, refused to accept the experimental conclusion of Michelson. He still defined the ether as "one continuous substance filling all space; which can vibrate light; which can be sheared into positive and negative electricity; which in whirls constitutes matter, and which transmits by continuity and not by impact every action and reaction of which matter is capable." In spite of this skepticism of many leading scientists, Michelson's experiment was destined to play a vital part in the great upheaval which was to shake the world of science with the opening of the twentieth century.

When Michelson returned to the United States, having in the meantime resigned from the Navy, he accepted a professorship in physics at the Case School of Applied Science in Cleveland, Ohio. He began teaching here in September, 1882, and at the same time continued his researches on the ether and the speed of light in air, water, and carbon bisulfide. Through the influence of Simon Newcomb, who was working in the same field, Michelson received a small government grant to continue these investigations.

In 1884 he had the good fortune to meet Professor Edward W. Morley of Western Reserve College, and together they planned another series of experiments at the Case School to determine the reality of the ether. This investigation, which became widely known as the Michelson-Morley ether-drift experiment, made use of Michelson's improved interferometer. In 1887 the whole massive apparatus was mounted on a heavy stone slab and floated in liquid mercury to prevent errors due to vibration, stresses, and strains. Observations were made and then the device was rotated at right angles to the motion of the earth through space for further data. When all the measurements had been completed, Michelson and Morley found no interference pattern of the light beams, no matter in what direction the apparatus was turned. There was no stationary ether observable.

Michelson reported, however, that while there was no stationary ether, the results of his experiments could still "be accounted for by the assumption that the earth drags the ether along nearly at its full speed, so that the relative velocity between the ether and the earth at the surface is zero or very small." Forty years later, while addressing a distinguished audience of scientists at the Mount Wilson Observatory in California, he remarked, "This assumption is a very dubious one because it contradicts some other important theoretical considerations." Michelson was referring to another phase of the same problem, the interpretation of which eventually brought forth the work of a young scientist, Albert Einstein, who was destined to revolutionize physics as radically as did Copernicus or even Newton.

The whole problem of the nature of light, of the reality of the ether, and of the meaning of *absolute motion* was still very much a matter of opinion. Could light be used to find out whether there was such a thing as absolute motion? If there was an ether, was it at rest? There were contradictions and anomalies in all of these concepts. Even if there were an ether, the zero result obtained by Michelson and Morley might still be explained. In fact, in 1895, two mathematical theorists of great eminence independently suggested a way out of the difficulty of accepting the zero conclusion and the reality of the ether at the same time. George F. Fitzgerald of Trinity College, Dublin, and Hendrik A. Lorentz of Leyden offered a very unusual explanation. What their involved mathematical reasoning boiled down to was this: the length of an object actually changes when the motion of that object is increased tremendously. In other words, a stick which is measuring the distance between two fixed points actually shrinks in size if that stick is moving through space at a very great velocity along the line of its length. The actual shrinkage—that is, the difference in length of the stick when at rest and when at high speed—depends upon the rate of motion of the stick. It was a sort of Mad Hatter's deduction to anyone accustomed to thinking in terms of the recognized truths of physics. But these two men had arrived at the same theory from certain mathematical considerations based on the electromagnetic properties of light first proposed by Clerk Maxwell.

The traditional physicist was disturbed by this unorthodox explanation. He argued that no one had ever seen a solid rod actually shrink, no matter how fast it was traveling in the direction of its length. That is true. But Fitzgerald and Lorentz were not talking about the ordinary speeds with which practical engineers dealt. They were not even talking of speeds such as those of bullets. Their mathematics showed them that a speed of 300 miles per hour would cause a shrinkage of only one million mil-lionth of one per cent, a shrinkage which, of course, our instru-ments could not detect. When, however, they used a theoretical speed of *90,000 miles per second*, the theoretical shrinkage amounted to thirteen per cent. As this speed was stepped up fur-ther, this percentage also rose, until finally, according to their calculations, when the speed reached 186,000 miles per second (the speed of light) the percentage of shrinkage reached a theo-retical one hundred per cent. In other words, at this speed the material stick disappeared as a result of total shrinkage, and was completely converted into its equivalent amount of energy.

Now Michelson's conclusions had completely ignored such a phenomenon as expressed in the Lorentz-Fitzgerald contraction theory. This new idea could explain with a fair degree of plausi-bility the apparent negative result of the Michelson-Morley ex-periments because the Americans had not taken into account the shrinkage of the interferometer arm during the measurements. The effect of this shrinkage was just enough to counterbalance the slowing down of light by the ether. The average physicist, not to mention the man in the street, thought the Lorentz-Fitz-gerald idea thoroughly fantastic. Some of them were reminded of Gibbs' remark, "A mathematician may say anything he pleases, but a physicist must be at least partially sane." But more serious students of mathematical physics began to examine this weird explanation more carefully.

The Lorentz-Fitzgerald explanation, bold as it was and effec-tive as it seemed in answering the apparent negative results of the ether-drift experiments of Michelson, was still based on the laws of the old classical physics. It still dealt with absolute motion of particles and possible variations in the speed of light. It shook men of science, but did not cause them to collapse altogether. Newton's classic laws of motion still stood enthroned. But a much deeper shock was in store for them, a blow which came directly out of the experiment which Michelson had thought up back in 1881 and the mass of data which had been piling up from the fields of the electron, X rays, and radioactivity. J. J. Thomson in 1897 had discovered the electron and had proved that matter is electrical in nature. Studies in the field of radium, discovered by the Curies, had shown that electrons shot out of radioactive elements traveled at speeds far greater than ever before thought possible. For example, Kaufmann in 1901 had demonstrated experimentally that electrons shot out of radium at speeds approaching that of light suffered a change of mass and that this change of mass depended upon the speed with which the electron was moving. In other words, mass was not constant, as Newton had believed. Max Planck's enunciation in 1900 of his concept of energy as being granular and made up of photons or bundles of energy also helped shatter the older physics. The Michelson-Morley experiment had produced an impasse in the world of physics. If there was no ether, then how was light carried? The ordinary laws of physics were incapable of explaining their result.

The whole complicated problem of ether drift, velocity of light, absolute motion, invariability of mass, and relationship between energy and matter had attracted Albert Einstein while he was working as a patent examiner in Berne, Switzerland. Einstein, born of Jewish parents in Ulm, Germany, in 1879, had been graduated from the University of Zurich as a promising student of mathematics and physics. He set out to re-examine the problem of the electrodynamics of moving bodies in terms of Maxwell's electromagnetic theory of light and the new information regarding the electron. Lorentz and his brother physicists had made the natural assumption that there *was* such a thing as *absolute motion*. This so-called absolute motion was constant regardless of the position of the observer or of the body, such as the earth, to which it referred. Einstein saw no reason for accepting this idea, although it was in harmony with the physics of his day. Refusing to accept this axiom, he worked out his own mathematical explanation, and in 1905 issued the paper now known as the *Special Theory of Relativity*. In this paper Einstein, at twenty-six, overthrew classical physics and revolutionized our whole conception of space and even time. Einstein's theory of relativity banished forever the whole concept of absolute motion. There was no absolute motion and no absolute rest. Motions had to be referred to some definite object or framework, such as the earth or the sun or some other body in the universe. Motion was a relative, not an absolute phenomenon.

The great English scientist-philosopher and mathematician, Sir Arthur Eddington, once gave an interesting analogy to explain the meaning of absolute and relative motion. Suppose, he said, we consider a man in a sealed elevator dropping through space with the accelerated motion of gravity. He is not aware of the earth or of gravitational attraction. He takes an apple out of his pocket and extends his hand. He lets go of the apple. The apple remains suspended in space because, as we know, the apple is falling as rapidly as the elevator, and can drop no faster. It therefore appears to remain motionless to the man in the moving elevator. He takes another apple out of his pocket and extends his hand out again at the same level but nearer his body. The second apple also remains at apparent rest but separated from the first by, let us say, a distance of one foot. After some time he notices that the apples seem to be *closer* together although at the same height. He comes to the conclusion that the apples attract and hence approach each other.

To an outside observer, however, there is an entirely different explanation. The apples are dropping through space attracted by the gravitational pull of the earth. As can be seen in Fig. 11, page 371, both apples are moving downward to the center of the earth. Their paths therefore approach each other and the distance between them shortens. The distance between their first position at *A* is greater than that at their second position, *B*. Gravitation has been the cause of this shortening of their distance rather than some unknown attraction between them as conceived by the man in the elevator. What is motion then? Is motion *absolute*, that is, the same for all observers regardless of their position or motion, as was believed, or is motion *relative*, depending upon the observer's position and motion? Einstein showed that there was no such thing as absolute motion—all motion was relative motion.

Einstein also pointed out that while there is really little that can be called absolute, this term can be applied to the speed of light. He showed that the speed of light, regardless of any previous notion, is one of the few basic, unchanging constants of na-

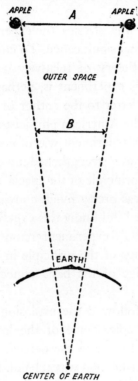

Fig. 11. Illustrating *relative* motion. The two apples, falling toward the earth's center, get closer together. Distance B is smaller than A.

ture. It is the same for all observers, and independent of the position of the source of the light. This conclusion fitted in with the results of Michelson's experiments. Several other assumptions of Einstein's theory of relativity were later verified by experiments. For example, in 1919 two solar-eclipse expeditions, one in Africa and the other in Brazil, found that light does not travel in straight lines, as was supposed, but that great masses such as the sun and other stars attract light and bend its path. The bending of the light from a distant star as it passed close to the sun actually agreed with the prediction of Einstein. In that year Einstein published his *General Theory of Relativity* in Berlin, where he had returned, after having been forced to leave his post during World War I because of his refusal to sign a public protest defending Germany's entry into the war.

In this great upheaval in physics, the experiment of Michelson had been of fundamental significance. To contend, as some have done, that Einstein's theory of relativity could not have been arrived at without this experiment is, perhaps, to overstate the case. But in a private letter to the author of this book, Einstein expressed his debt to the American physicist as follows: "It is no doubt that Michelson's experiment was of considerable influence upon my work insofar as it strengthened my conviction concerning the validity of the principle of the special theory of relativity. On the other side, I was pretty much convinced of the validity of the principle before I did know this experiment and its result. In any case, Michelson's experiment removed practically any doubt about the validity of the principle in optics, and showed that a profound change of the basic concepts of physics was inevitable."

The battle which followed the explosion of Einstein's relativity bombshell was epic. Some of the leading mathematical physicists of the world came to the defense of the theory even before experimental verification was at hand. Einstein's treatment was so logical and his mathematics so flawless that they were compelled to accept the new interpretation. Michelson watched the conflict with the detachment of a cautious scientist who insists upon waiting until all the evidence is in and all sides have been heard from. He agreed that the mathematical equations were correct but that the reasoning was not altogether clear. Michelson was not a first-rate mathematician. He thought in terms of physical models rather than mathematically. He had the knack, however, of eliminating individual terms or symbols from an involved equation until it was shorn of its complications and reduced to some simple formula. He spoke little about the relativity theory and wrote even less on its merits or demerits. Michelson, said Dr. Paul W. Merrill of the Mount Wilson Observatory, had a very low "p/f," or *publication factor*. A man who published all he knew had a p/f of 1. If he published ten times as much as he really knew his p/f was 10. "Michelson's p/f was less than 0.1," was the way Merrill expressed Michelson's aversion to publishing scientific papers. The newer physics was outside his active interest. Thermodynamics, radioactivity, electronics, and quanta were not investigated by him, even though he did some work on X rays and on the Zeeman effect (spread of spectral lines under the influence of a magnet). He once asked John Anderson of the Mount Wilson Observatory, "What is the Eddington star theory?" "Matter can be condensed to about 30,000 times the density of water," Anderson started to explain. "You mean," interjected Michelson, "to a density greater than lead?" And when Anderson nodded assent, Michelson replied, "Then there must be something wrong with his theory."

At the time of the publication of Einstein's paper, Michelson was head of the department of physics of the University of Chicago. He had been called there by President W. R. Harper in 1892 from Clark University, where he had held a professorship of physics for three years. At the University of Chicago he engaged in some teaching. His teaching schedule was, however, very light. Robert A. Millikan, who later also became a Nobel laureate in physics, first met Michelson in 1894 at the dedication of the Ryerson Laboratory. He took a summer course under him. Michelson would lecture twice a week and would quiz once a week on the two previous lectures. He was quite an arresting figure, of medium height, with jet-black hair, dark, piercing eyes, a military bearing, and meticulous dress. His graduate students thought him somewhat unapproachable and too demanding, especially in the early years of his professorship.

Michelson continued to engage in research while at the University of Chicago. He was much more interested in experimentation than in teaching. He took no part in the general administration of the university and seldom attended faculty meetings. His research projects were undertaken without help from his graduate students, but he always kept an expert designer and instrument maker attached to his personal staff. He would slowly work out an idea in his head. As soon as he had made up his mind that his plans were good, he would make a very rough sketch of his plans and call in his instrument maker. He was very positive and clear in his requests and expected a perfect piece of apparatus to be turned over to him without being consulted about it after that first meeting for instructions. Julius Pearson, who worked for him as technician for twenty-five years, made three unusual diffraction grating machines for Michelson. The largest of these was fourteen inches as compared with Rowland's largest machine of six inches. Pearson recalls that Michelson appears not to have been a very hard worker. He seldom "trembled on the verge of discovery." When, however, something pressing demanded his energies, he would work like a demon for a spell and afterward settle back to a rather slow tempo of activity.

Michelson had something of the aesthete in him. He dabbled in water-color painting, played the violin, and approached the subject of physics as a poet took to verse. In a lecture before the Lowell Institute he remarked, "If a poet could at the same time be a physicist, he might convey to others the pleasure, the satisfaction, almost the reverence, which the subject of light inspires. The aesthetic side of the subject is, I confess, by no means the least attractive to me." During the many years which he spent developing his echelon spectroscopes he came to regard these machines "as having a personality—I had almost said a feminine personality—requiring humoring, coaxing, cajoling, even threatening. But finally one realized," he added, "that the personality is that of an alert and skillful player in an intricate but fascinating game, who will take immediate advantage of the mistakes of his opponent, who 'springs' the most disconcerting surprises, who never leaves any result to chance, but who nevertheless plays fair, in strict accordance with the rules he knows, and makes no allowance if you do not. When *you* learn them and play accordingly, the game progresses as it should."

It was this aesthetic element in his nature, coupled with an experimental alertness of the highest order, which made Michelson a top-flight scientist. It was his insistence on perfection and his singleness of goal which made him one of the most outstanding experimenters of America. Glorifying the machine, he pushed it to its finest precision. He saw the future development of physics only as one of further precision and newer instruments which would bring the accuracy of scientific measurements to the sixth decimal place. He saw in the later physics only the refinement of the old. In this he was a mistaken prophet, for his own work only helped to touch off a new revolution in physics. His belief in the advance of physics through more refined measurements was replaced in part by a mathematical and theoretical approach which brought new definitions to motion, time, space, energy, and matter.

Outside of his own preoccupation with the ether-drift experiments, Michelson took no active part in this great upheaval. Neither did social or political events stir him. The organization of the American Federation of Labor in 1886 and the struggle between big business and government were events for which he appeared to feel no deep concern. The military safety of the United States was something else again. He was all for declaring war upon Spain just as soon as the news of the sinking of the *Maine* reached the University of Chicago campus. While others were counseling caution, and when some of his colleagues reminded him that the true scientific man suspended judgment until all the facts were in and had been carefully weighed, Albert Michelson, the former Navy man, brushed them aside. He demanded an immediate declaration of war to uphold the honor of his country. Later, during World War I, he rejoined the service and was called to Washington with the rank of lieutenant commander in the United States Navy. He worked during this period on several government projects, especially in connection with the perfection of range finders for guns. He was able to develop one which became standard equipment in the American Navy.

This work was done in connection with the newly organized National Research Council. The establishment of this body resulted from a vote taken by the National Academy of Sciences to offer its services to the government in the interest of national preparedness. The move was made on April 16, 1916, soon after the attack on the *Sussex*. President Woodrow Wilson accepted the offer and an organizing committee was formed, headed by George Ellery Hale. The committee recommended "that there be formed a National Research Council to bring into co-operation all existing organizations with the object of encouraging the investigation of natural phenomena, the increased use of scientific research in the development of American industries, the employment of scientific methods in strengthening the national defense, and such other applications of science as will promote the national security and welfare."

The National Research Council was finally organized on September 20, 1916, more than half a year before America actually entered the war against Germany. It was composed of leading American investigators and engineers representing the Army, Navy, Smithsonian Institution, and various scientific bureaus of the government; educational institutions and research endowments; and the research divisions of industrial and manufacturing establishments. Arthur A. Noyes was put in charge of research in nitric acid and other important chemicals used in warfare. Robert A. Millikan was set to work on problems of physics. Michelson, in addition to his development of a range finder, made an intensive study of the problem of more effective submarine detection.

During the war the American Federation of Labor called upon Congress "to foster a broad program of scientific and technical research in order to increase the productivity of industry and advance the health and well-being of the whole population."

Before the armistice was declared, Hale, in order to save this newly created branch of the National Academy of Sciences for peacetime work, prevailed upon the President of the United States to issue an executive order on May 11, 1918, perpetuating the Council. Its modified aims were to stimulate research in the mathematical, physical, and biological sciences and in the applications of the sciences to engineering, agriculture, and other activities. Other objectives were to survey the larger possibilities of science, to formulate comprehensive projects of research, to promote co-operation in research at home and abroad, and to gather and collate scientific and technical information from all parts of the world. Among the methods that were to be employed to implement these progressive and laudable objectives was the establishment of the National Research Fellowships in physics and chemistry. Gifts for this purpose were acceptable from such organizations as the Rockefeller Foundation and the General Education Board.

At the termination of hostilities, Michelson returned to Chicago and undertook a project which had first tempted him thirty years before. In 1890, in describing the interferometer which he had developed for determining the reality of the ether, he mentioned another possible use of such an instrument. With it he hoped someday to measure "the apparent size of telescopic objects such as planetoids, satellites, and *possibly stars*." The telescope could not measure the diameters of stars because of their tremendous distances from the earth. Until Michelson undertook this difficult task it seemed almost impossible of achievement. At the invitation of George Ellery Hale, director of the Mount Wilson Observatory, and with the aid of Francis G. Pease, he set about trying to determine the distance across a number of stars. The work was started by Michelson in the summer of 1920; the first conclusive measurements were made by Pease in December of that year. They employed a specially constructed twenty-foot interferometer which was attached to the largest telescope in the world at that time, the 100-inch telescope located at the top of Mount Wilson, overlooking the city of Pasadena, California.

Michelson was the first scientist in history to measure the diameter of a distant star. When he flashed the news that the giant star Betelgeuse was approximately 240,000,000 miles in diameter, the world was electrified. Here was a star which was actually about 250 times bigger in diameter than our own sun, which has a diameter of only 864,000 miles, or less than a mere million miles. In fact, the sun was a dwarf star in comparison. Twenty-seven millions of our suns could fit into the body of Betelgeuse. The experiment made a tremendous impression all over the world.

Hale extended another invitation to Michelson to return to Mount Wilson for more experiments on the speed of light and the reality of the ether drift. Dayton C. Miller, of the Case School of Applied Science, had done a number of experiments on the ether question over a period of about twenty-five years, starting in 1902. He insisted that he obtained positive results of varying degree. Another determination was therefore necessary to settle the problem. Michelson came back to California several years later and set up his new instruments on the peak of Mount Wilson. He flashed beams of light across the twenty-two miles to Mount San Antonio (Old Baldy), 10,080 feet high, where another mirror had been fixed to reflect the light back to Mount Wilson. He used five revolving mirrors, three of which were made of glass, with eight, twelve, and sixteen faces, and the other two of steel, one octagonal and the other with twelve facets. Five independent series of measurements were taken; the average speed of light obtained was 299,796 kilometers per second. These ether-drift experiments again gave zero results. Michelson, in his 1927 report printed in the *Astrophysical Journal*, wrote, "The ready success of the measurements at the distance of twenty-two miles, the majority of which were made under conditions not the most favorable (due to smoke and haze from forest fires) would seem to indicate the feasibility of a measurement at a considerably greater distance." He picked another mountain peak for such an experiment, Mount San Jacinto, eighty-two miles distant from Mount Wilson, and he actually made a preliminary trial. But the light which returned was so enfeebled by smoke and haze that further attempts were given up.

Michelson's final experiment still dealt with the speed of light. He had made up his mind to catch the velocity of light without the obstruction of haze or smoke or even the atmosphere itself. He wanted to do the experiment with light galloping through empty space, through a perfect vacuum, if possible. Michelson was invited back to Pasadena. "Hale said I could have Mount Wilson and Caltech," remarked Michelson later. "The temptation was too great. So I came." He was now seventy-seven years old but still eager for experimentation. The Rockefeller Foundation, the Carnegie Corporation, the University of Chicago, and again the Mount Wilson Observatory all co-operated to supply the necessary funds and facilities. Michelson planned all the details of the campaign and left them to be worked out by his assistants, Francis G. Pease and Fred Pearson, brother of Julius Pearson.

A site was selected on the Irvine Ranch near Santa Ana. The United States Coast and Geodetic Survey was called upon to determine the exact length of the base line over which the experiment was to be performed. A huge tube was constructed at the cost of $50,000. It was made of fourteen-gauge galvanized Armco steel sheets rolled and corrugated. The sixty-foot sections, three feet in diameter, were brought together, their seams riveted and soldered to make a mile-long tube. Four manholes gave access to the interior, one at each end and two others in the main section of the pipe. A mirror made of well-annealed optical glass with thirty-two facets was rotated on its axis by means of a compressed-air turbine. The whole tube was evacuated by special vacuum pumps until the air pressure in the sealed tube was at times only half a millimeter of mercury as compared with the normal 760 mm. of air pressure outside the tube.

This tube was a sealed pipe in which light was to be shot back and forth between rotating mirrors in an almost perfect vacuum.

The speed of light through the nearly pure so-called ether was to be captured and recorded for the first time in the adventure of science. Every time something went wrong with the experiment "we had to let air in so we could go in and fix it," reported Michelson. "We had to wait forty-eight hours to evacuate the tube again with our vacuum pumps. Heat waves distorted the light image. So most of the work was done at night."

Michelson's health was not good during the last year or more of this project. He was not well enough to make the actual measurements himself. So Pearson took them instead, while Pease correlated the data. Michelson directed from his sickbed. Through all of 1930 and part of the next year hundreds of observations were taken. Two days before losing consciousness, Michelson refused to admit his condition. "My health continues to improve," he wrote. But on May 9, 1931, death came to him after a cerebral hemorrhage. He was in his seventy-ninth year. The work continued, however. More measurements were taken through March, 1933. In all, a total of 2885 determinations were made. The average figure for the velocity of light in a vacuum was found to be 299,774 kilometers (186,264 miles) per second. This figure will probably stand for many years to come as one of the soundest constants in physical science. Michelson wrote the introduction to the final report less than two weeks before he died. It bore exactly the same title as that of his first paper when he was Ensign Michelson of the United States Navy more than fifty years before. His work was completed.

While Michelson had spent the greatest part of his life on the determination of the speed of light, several others of his pieces of research may be noted. His determination of the sizes of stars was classic. Another was his work on a standard unit of length. By means of his spectroscope equipped with gratings of his own design he was able to analyze to perfection the lines of the spectrum of many elements. He found the red spectrum line of the element cadmium extraordinarily pure or monochromatic. With his interferometer he proceeded to measure the exact wave length of this cadmium light. He suggested to the International Committee on Weights and Measures that this length might be used as a standard unit to replace the standard meter stick which was deposited in Paris under careful watch. Now, for the first time, it would not matter if this world standard unit of length was injured or suffered change of length due to outside conditions. A new meter bar could now easily be reproduced at any place and time from the known measurements which Michelson's work had supplied science. His new standard of length was adopted throughout the world in 1925.

Michelson also came to the aid of geologists. One of the questions which still remained unsettled was the nature of the interior of the earth. Was it rigid as steel or molten as liquid iron? The geologist Thomas C. Chamberlin, his colleague at the University of Chicago, had asked Michelson to devise an experiment to answer this question. With the help of Professor Henry G. Gale of the same university, Michelson undertook the investigation by means of a carefully worked-out plan. He buried two pipes, each five hundred feet long and six inches in diameter, ten feet underground. One ran east and west and the other north and south, with an observation chamber at their junction point. Each had been half filled with water before burial. As the moon and the sun pull the waters of the earth, producing tides, Michelson reasoned that they ought to attract the water in these pipes, also. The strength of this pull would be affected by the nature of the interior of the earth, that is, depending on whether it was solid or molten. Using an optical fringe device of his own construction, he determined the extremely minute variations in the levels of the water in the pipes due to the pull of the moon and sun. His results led him to the conclusion that the interior of the earth is not rigid but molten.

Michelson received many honors from all parts of the world and was chosen to head three great scientific societies of the United States, the American Physical Society, the American Association for the Advancement of Science, and the National

Academy of Sciences. He was the first American to be honored with the Nobel Prize. The Copley Medal of the Royal Society of London was also given him in the same year, 1907. He lived long enough to see the United States definitely take leadership not only in the sphere of physics but also in other areas of scientific research. He witnessed other Americans receiving the same distinguished award that had honored not only him personally but also the nation in which he worked. He saw Alexis Carrel receive the Nobel Prize in medicine in 1912, Theodore W. Richards in chemistry two years later, Robert A. Millikan in physics in 1923, Arthur H. Compton in 1927 for his work on radiations, and Karl Landsteiner in medicine the year before Michelson died. Had he lived another twenty-five years he would have seen the names of forty other American scientists added to this inspiring list.

During the long years of Michelson's great work, America had turned more than one scientific corner. It had definitely set itself on a new road. It began to take the leadership in theoretical science. Michelson, with his work in light, belongs to that small group of pioneer American physicists which includes Benjamin Franklin in electricity, Benjamin Thompson in heat, and Willard Gibbs in physical chemistry.

CHAPTER SIXTEEN

THOMAS HUNT MORGAN
(1866-1945)

AMERICAN SCIENCE COMES OF AGE

WITH THE OPENING of the twentieth century, America finally broke free from the intellectual fetters of Europe. Our scientists were finding their own powers. The new democracy, at last realizing its own strength, was ready, as Michelson had shown, to tackle wide-sweeping problems that required daring, and had the courage to break with tradition and the past. Free public education and the widening of the educative base were supplying fresh blood which could be channeled into outmoded circulatory systems to bring new vigor and new achievements.

Two outstanding biological problems were being discussed at the close of the nineteenth century. One had to do with the manner in which the adult living organism developed from the fertilized egg, a basic and tremendously important problem. The other centered around the subject of evolution and the mechanism of inheritance. Science, like all intellectual pursuits, has its changing philosophies, theories, and even vogues. During the nineteenth century, embryology, under Haeckel's exaggerations, was captured by the spell of the doctrine "ontogeny repeats phylogeny"; that is, the life history of the development of an individual repeats the race history of the species. The numerous studies of the forms of the developing embryos of different species seemed to point to the truth of this theory. The developing embryo of a pig, for example, appears to pass through various stages indicating features of lower organisms such as reptiles and fishes.

Was this approach, kept alive so long by European influence, a realistic one? Was it to persist or was an audacious attempt necessary to liberate this problem from what seemed to some a blind alley? America was learning to face the new and the difficult without regard to authoritarianism, which did not have the same hold in the United States as in the older centers of research. A realistic approach was imperative, and American science supplied it in the person of Thomas Hunt Morgan, author of the theory of the gene.

Morgan was descended on both sides from English Cavalier stock. His father was at various times American consul at Catania, Sicily; captain in the Confederate Army under his uncle, General John Morgan, the famous raider of the South; a hemp manufacturer in Lexington, Kentucky; and secretary to the Senator from that state. When the time came for Thomas to enter college, he chose the State College of Kentucky in his native town. Having formulated no idea of a career at college, and not being interested in business, he drifted into natural history for no better reason than that he liked it. Later at Johns Hopkins University he divided his time between morphology and physiology.

At this period a school of biologists in Europe known as the *vitalists* was teaching that any attempt to explain or understand the mechanism of development from purely scientific laws would prove sterile, for, they maintained, such life processes were under the control of creative forces outside the knowledge of science. When, however, there arose a school which looked for a strictly chemico-physical explanation of the development of the embryo, the bent of Morgan's mind took kindly to the new "developmental mechanics." An experiment of the anatomist Wilhelm Roux had impressed him deeply. Roux had succeeded in killing one of the first two cells of the developing egg of a frog, and had shown how this half embryo, instead of dying, had actually developed into part of a frog. Man had actually changed the predestined course of the development of an egg not only by physical but by chemical changes as well. Jacques Loeb also startled the scientific world with the first complete demonstration of the artificial fertilization (parthenogenesis) of the eggs of a sea urchin by chemical and other mechanical agents. He and other members of the school of *mechanists* pointed to all sorts of alluring possibilities of changing the course of life. The older school of *vitalists* fought back.

The classic struggle was renewed with greater vigor. Physicochemical changes, the vitalists insisted, could not explain altogether the marvelous development of the fertilized egg to the fully adult organism. The vitalists accepted the physical and chemical changes which took place, for example, when the sperm entered the ovum during fertilization. They insisted, however, that behind and beyond these relatively inconsequential changes were forces that guided the process and brought it to a successful and purposeful completion. The mechanists, on the other hand, believed that every phenomenon of nature was the result of physical and chemical changes completely divorced from the control of any mystic or vitalistic force. They were ready to believe that eventually perhaps every one of the complex biological phenomena would be duplicated by scientists in the laboratory.

In 1895, five years after receiving his doctor's degree for a piece of research on the embryology and phylogeny of "sea spiders," Morgan went first to Germany and then to the famous zoological station at Naples, where in a room next to his own worked Hans Driesch. The long battle between the mechanists and the vitalists was still waging. The shouts of the mechanists, certain that all of life could be explained by the ordinary laws of physics and chemistry, were becoming louder. The vitalists held their ground against the new phalanx of younger zoologists. Hans Driesch, the philosopher, joined the vitalists. "One day entelechy [an agent which, according to the vitalists, directs and regulates all life to a purposive end] appeared to him as a dream. From that time he believed, very soon he ceased to work." Morgan, however, fought for neither side. Vitalism, and the terms invoked by it, such as entelechy, *élan vital*, and holism, were but words to him, for just as he insisted more than once that ex cathedra statements are not arguments, so also did he believe that any appeal to mysticism is outside of science. At the same time he declared that mechanism in its current state was still frankly a naïve philosophy. But this admission, he wrote in the preface to his *Scientific Basis of Evolution* in 1932, "may not altogether be a drawback, if progress along scientific lines is looked upon as more worth while than a stultification of the whole field of investigation by arbitrary metaphysical subtleties."

There have been many attempts to find the laws of inheritance; to discover in what arithmetical order, if any, hemophilia, eye color, albinism, and the characteristic Hapsburg lip were transmitted from generation to generation. There have been many theories to explain the appearance of new species of living things, such as the one-toed horse, the Ancon breed of short-legged sheep, and the Lombardy poplar. Darwin, after spending a lifetime on the problem, admitted that "our ignorance of the laws of heredity and the origin of new species is profound," and he died without finding an answer satisfactory even to himself.

Up to the opening of the twentieth century it was generally accepted that environment alone was the cause of those slow changes in organisms which eventually resulted in definitely new species. But this explanation was not altogether convincing. For centuries the Chinese had bound the tender feet of female children to make them small. Yet since this custom has been officially abolished, the infant feet, left free to grow, develop as normally as though foot-binding had never existed. Man-made environment has evidently had no effect on the transmission to coming generations of this new characteristic, small feet. Is there, then, another process at work to explain the appearance of new characteristics which *are* inheritable?

By chance, as frequently happens in the haphazard advance of science, a Dutch biologist, Hugo de Vries, came across a new type of evening primrose growing wild in a field near Amsterdam. This was eighteen years after the death of Darwin, when the appearance of new types of living things was still only partially explained. The whole story was still an enigma. De Vries, in an effort to find whether the new type of plant was really a new species—that is, would breed true—planted fifty thousand of its seeds. Before long he found that this variation did breed true, and he was further rewarded by the appearance of several entirely new types of the same plant, such as dwarf primroses that gave rise only to dwarf offspring. This evidently was incontestable proof that one species could suddenly give rise to another which could maintain itself. *Mutation* was the name De Vries gave to this process whereby a new character spontaneously appeared from a pure ancestral stock and bred true. A few cases of this sudden appearance of a new character or variation had previously been vaguely reported, but De Vries actually showed the process at work and emphasized its importance.

Here was the key to further research—to breed living things and watch for mutations. For the first time science had at its disposal a tool which could place evolution and heredity upon the experimental table. In 1909 Morgan, then forty-three, took hold of this tool, feeling that it was more significant than most biologists suspected. "Mutation," Morgan was convinced, "plays a role in the evolution of living forms, and the old speculative method of treating evolution as a problem of pre-history is ready to fade." He had no patience with those who cried out *Ignorabimus*—"We shall not know."

Science often does not have to wait for natural phenomena to take place before studying them. It prides itself upon its ability to set the stage for controlled experimentation, thus saving time and effort. Investigations concerning the many problems connected with evolution could now be brought into the laboratory. The evening primrose did not satisfy Morgan. He wanted a short-lived organism and one that could be easily bred in the laboratory under changing conditions. He tried the mouse, the rat, the pigeon, and even undertook some painstaking experiments on the intricate life cycle of a plant louse, until one day he heard of another insect, which W. E. Castle of Harvard had been using in connection with certain investigations in inbreeding.

Drosophila melanogaster, the vinegar fly, is a tiny organism about a quarter of an inch long. It is commonly seen feeding on decaying fruits. In one day its eggs change to slender white larvae which after two or three days more change into pupae, and five days later emerge as winged adult flies. Completing its life cycle from egg to fly in about ten days, this insect supplies as many as thirty generations a year, an enormous advantage compared to the relative slowness of the usual laboratory animals. Drosophila is an ideal organism—easily bred, fertile, amenable to laboratory conditions, adapted to careful microscopic analysis, and with a life span which may reach ninety days. Thousands can be handled in a few milk bottles, while the cost of feeding and keeping them healthy is negligible. Morgan obtained a few of these flies, scarcely suspecting that within a few years this Cinderella of the biological kitchen was to become, in the queenly robe of genetics, the most famous experimental organism in the world. Drosophila, said one wit, must have been created by God especially for Morgan.

During the fall and winter of that first year, 1909, Morgan subjected his flies to all sorts of abnormal conditions, hoping that this treatment would produce new species or mutants. He exposed eggs, larvae, pupae, and adult flies to such drastic changes as unusually high and low temperatures; he immersed them in acid and alkali solutions, fed them on strange and varied diets, and even tortured them with radioactivity. But nothing of striking scientific interest resulted. Then one day in April, 1910, "in a pedigreed culture of Drosophila which had been running for nearly a year through a considerable number of generations, a male appeared with white eyes." This was an exciting development; the eyes of the normal wild fruit fly are red. Here was a sharply defined mutant which could be used in experiments in heredity. Morgan planned to cross this precious white-eyed fly to the red-eyed species, just as young Gregor Mendel fifty years before him had crossed a yellow edible pea to a green one in the garden of an Augustinian monastery in Brünn, Moravia, now the city of Brno in Czechoslovakia.

Mendel had entered the church to find time for reflection and experimentation. He continued his interest in the problem of heredity, aided by a considerable amount of empirical knowledge which had accumulated as a result of the work of practical breeders. This knowledge indicated that like did not always beget like, rather it only *tended* to do so. Thus the crossing of two black animals did not always result in dark-haired offspring. Mendel wondered if any mathematical laws could be discovered which governed the inheritance of characters. It was of course more than a mathematical question, for it perhaps involved an answer to the enigma of the origin of new species. He set himself the task of making a statistical study of the inheritance of one pair of contrasting characters at a time.

In the year Morgan was born, Mendel published the results of seven years of his plant-breeding experiments. He found that when he crossed the tall strain of a pea with a dwarf strain of the same species, all of the progeny of the first generation were tall. When the members of this first tall generation, called F_1, were self-fertilized, they gave birth to three times as many tall plants as dwarf, instead of producing tall offspring only. This Mendelian ratio of three to one held good only when a single character was involved. It was an average result when large numbers of plants were used. Since the dwarf variety had apparently disappeared in the first generation of offspring, but reappeared in the next, he called this dwarf character *recessive*, while the tall character was called *dominant* (law of dominance). He also found that the dwarf progeny of the second generation, called F_2, when self-fertilized, bred true, giving all dwarf offspring. When the tall progeny of F_2 were self-fertilized, the result was different. Only one third of the tall plants of this F_2 bred true, that is, gave tall progeny. The other two thirds behaved like the first tall F_1, giving three tall and one dwarf plant.

None of the offspring were intermediate in size, nor did one character merge with another. Mendel had discovered not only the laws of dominance and single unit characters, but also the fundamental law of segregation: "The units [individual characters] contributed by each parent separate in an exact ratio in the germ cells of the offspring without having had any influence on each other." The black and white characters, the tall and dwarf, do not interfere with each other, but carry on as individual characters or units.

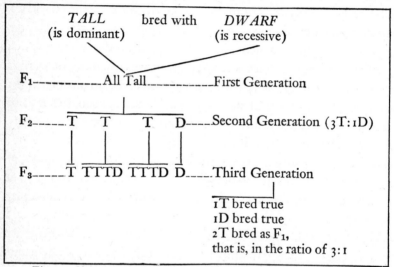

Fig. 12. Showing the Mendelian ratio of 3:1 for Mendel's peas.

For thirty-five years Mendel's work lay hidden in the pages of the *Transactions of the Brünn Society for the Study of Natural Science*. In 1900 three men, working independently, came across the paper, and a great deal of statistical investigation and experimentation was started to test the validity of Mendel's findings. William Bateson of Cambridge took up the cudgels for Mendel. Inheritance of the shape of comb and the color of plumage in fowls, the coat color of guinea pigs, the eye color of man, the color of horses, the waltzing habit of mice, and similar unit characters were reported by various observers. The conclusions of the genial abbot of Brünn seemed confirmed.

But Mendel's deductions were by no means universally accepted. Karl Pearson, a distinguished English professor who had founded a school of biometry, which concerns itself with the application of the statistical study of biological phenomena, stood out as the arch-opponent of Mendel's law. As late as the end of 1908 Pearson shouted, "There is no definite proof of Mendelism applying to any living form at present," and in rebuttal he offered the figures from his crossbreeding experiments. Morgan himself was skeptical of "this sort of Mendelian ritual which explains the extraordinary facts of inheritance." Was Mendel really right? Morgan wondered. Perhaps his flies could help settle the problem. Drosophila was to be drafted for an answer.

Morgan mated the white-eyed male fly (the mutant he had discovered early in 1910) to a virgin red-eyed female in a half-pint milk bottle containing some banana. He plugged the bottle with cotton. The union was a prolific one, for nine days later out of that bottle came a swarm of flies which, after careful etherization and examination under a lens, showed 1237 red-eyed offspring (F_1). That was as expected, for red eye was a dominant character. Some of these 1237 hybrids were then inbred, and in another ten days the second generation (F_2) appeared. Every one of these four thousand-odd offspring was as carefully guarded and scrutinized as so many diamonds. What did Morgan find? There were 2459 red-eyed females, 1011 red-eyed males, and 782 white-eyed males. Mendel's law, which called for a ratio of three red-eyed to one white-eyed fly, had worked out approximately.

The white-eyed Drosophila was not the only mutant that Morgan had detected. In March of the same year he had noticed the appearance of a fly with a definitely different wing which he called *speck*. Even before this, in January, he had picked out among the thousands of flies he was rearing one with a much darker trident pattern on its thorax than the normal fly. This mutant was named *with* to distinguish it from another, designated *without*, in which the pigmentation was so faint that all traces of the trident pattern had disappeared. Morgan kept breeding more and more of these flies; his desk and shelves became overcrowded with milk bottles and vials of all shapes. There seemed to be more activity in his multiplying colony of insects than in a three-ring circus. Mutants continued to turn up spontaneously. In May he had discovered a fly with an *olive* body instead of the usual brown, as well as another mutant which differed in that the marginal vein of its wing was *beaded*. Before the month of June had passed, another mutant with a small *rudimentary* wing was identified, together with a new variety of Drosophila with *pink* eyes. August saw the emergence of both a *miniature*-wing mutant and a *truncated*-wing variety, October a *black* fly, November a fly with vermilion eyes, one with a *balloon*-shaped wing, and another with a very deep-black pigmented thorax, *superwith*. The last month of that eventful year brought to light a fly with hardly any wings at all, the *vestigial*-wing mutant.

Morgan now had fifteen different mutants of Drosophila. Every one of the new types bred true. Rearing these mutants, inbreeding and crossbreeding them, and watching for the appearance of new ones involved a tremendous quantity of work. In addition to playing nurse to a host of flies, he had other duties. There was teaching to be done in the graduate school of Columbia University. Just at this time, moreover, a professor who gave a course in zoology was absent, and Morgan had to take his place.

In that class was Calvin Blackman Bridges, a shaggy-haired boy born in Schuyler's Falls, New York. He had had a very difficult start. His mother died when Calvin was two years old. His father, who owned a farm near Plattsburg, New York, died the following year, leaving the boy to his grandmother's care. He grew up to be a very bright lad at school, worked for a time as a printer's devil on the *Plattsburg Press*, and won a scholarship at Columbia University. Calvin was interested in all of science in a general way but was determined to be a research scientist. In Morgan's classes the comparatively new and fascinating world of genetics was unfolded to him. The professor's private talks with his students between and after classes provided an opportunity for Bridges to visit his office. Bridges suggested that someone might be needed to help with those innumerable flies breeding prolifically in the miscellaneous collection of fruit jars, milk bottles, and assorted laboratory glassware. Morgan admitted his need for help, but assured the young student that he did not intend taking on an inexperienced novice.

Day after day Bridges came back, until one morning he picked up a jar and noticed one fly with a vermilion eye color instead of the usual red. At once Morgan etherized all the flies in that jar, sprinkled them on a sorting plate, and went searching for the mutant among the hundreds of insects. Finding it under the hand lens, he was amazed. "Your eyes are so keen, you might be of help to me," he told Bridges, and added, "If you want to feed these flies and take good care of them and wash the bottles and prepare their food, you may start right now." For five years, starting in 1910, Bridges served as part-time assistant while he continued his studies at Columbia, earning his doctorate in 1916.

Hardly had 1911 begun when a single male fly with a *yellow* wing was discovered in a batch from a typical stock characterized by gray wing color. This mutant was found by Miss Edith M. Wallace, one of Morgan's research assistants and artists. Then Morgan came across another fly with an *abnormal* abdomen, and on November 16 of that year Bridges, who by this time was permitted to make fly counts, distinguished a new mutant which he called *blistered*. He added two more mutants with wings (*jaunty* and *curved*) quite different from the normal, soon after Morgan had announced the appearance of a fly with a *bifid* wing and Miss Mildred Hoge had thrilled the laboratory with a mutant showing *reduplicated* legs.

The fly squad on Morningside Heights was now well under way, and new recruits had to be added to catch up with the work. "Mutations," said Morgan, "have appeared in such rapid succession that my time has been almost entirely consumed in producing pure strains of the new forms which can be utilized later for a thorough study of the inheritance of the new types." The mutating speed of Drosophila completely eclipsed the snail-like pace of the evening primrose. Three times in both February and March of 1912 new mutants were added. Miss Elizabeth Rawls found that certain females from a wild stock were giving birth to only half as many males as was expected. These mutants contained a very harmful characteristic which prevented the normal development and birth of some of their offspring. It affected only some, since it is a recessive character, called *lethal*. All yellow-colored mice carry a similar lethal factor, and many embryos which die *in utero* have been found in such pregnant mice. Because they possess this lethal factor, yellow mice are rare.

The Drosophila workers had been gaining momentum, and before the year ended, twenty-five new mutants had been discovered, making a total of forty. In less than three years Morgan's original wild-stock Drosophila had produced more new varieties than science had ever dreamed could actually be so quickly produced in nature. The gates of discovery, it seemed, had been thrown wide open. Mutation must undoubtedly be a factor in the origin of new types. With this wealth of easily controlled and variegated mutants, Morgan made ready to elevate genetics to the rank of an exact mathematical science.

All through these busy days another problem had puzzled him. In the crossing in 1910 of one of his first fly mutants, a white-eyed female, with a red-eyed male, Morgan had noticed that in the second generation *not a single white-eyed female* appeared, although both white-eyed and red-eyed males were born. The failure of white-eyed female offspring to appear could not be explained, since as a rule male and female progeny are born in almost equal numbers. "Nature is sometimes as oracular as the priestess of Delphi," mused Morgan. In seeking the solution to one problem he had stumbled upon another puzzle. Evidently this character, white eye, was transmitted to only one of the sexes, just as in humans hemophilia is transmitted by the female only. Such characters are said to be *sex-linked*, in the sense that they tend to associate themselves with only one of the two sexes. Other characters, such as rudimentary wing and yellow wing, were also proved by appropriate breeding experiments to be sex-linked.

Morgan noticed another strange phenomenon in connection with these sex-linked characters. If, for example, a white-eyed female also possessed a yellow wing and this fly was crossed with a red-eyed, gray-winged fly, the white-eyed progeny that appeared always had yellow wings and not gray wings. Yet, according to Mendel's law of independent assortment of unit characters, such characters are inherited as units and separate independently during crossbreeding. It looked here as though certain characters were not only sex-linked but also tended to appear together.

Morgan now offered an ingenious theory for this adherence or linkage of certain characters in crossbreeding experiments. He explained that all of these sex-linked characters tended to be inherited together because they were associated as a unit or block in the nucleus of the original cell. This tendency of certain characters to appear together in groups Morgan called *linkage*. Sex linkage was not the only kind he observed. In 1911 he found that black body and vestigial wing, although linked together, were not coupled with any sex-linked characters; that is, they could be transmitted to both male and female, and always together. Black body could also appear with curved wing, balloon wing, or speck wing, but never with a sex-linked character such as yellow wing. The sex-linked group was called Linkage Group No. 1. Another, called Linkage Group No. 2, contained black body, vestigial wing, and other characters. Two years later it was discovered that pink-eyed flies were never seen with either yellow or vestigial wings, nor ebony-bodied flies with white eyes; while pink-eyed flies having ebony bodies had been bred and found fertile. Ebony body and pink eye seemed to be linked to each other, but not to the other two linkage groups. Hence this was a third Linkage Group.

By the summer of 1914 the many mutant characters that had been discovered and accurately studied for hereditary relationships seemed to fall into three distinct groups. There was a large group whose members were all sex-linked, such as white eye and bifid wing. Another still larger group had numerous characters located on many organs of the body, such as vestigial wing and black body, which were not sex-linked at all, but were all linked to one another. Finally, there was a third equally large group of bodily characters which were neither sex-linked nor linked with those in the second group, yet were joined to each other. Morgan theorized that since there were three groups of characters, there must be three separate bodies in the germ cell, each responsible for a whole series of characters linked to one another but not linked to other characters found in the other two cell bodies. Morgan thus added another law to those of Mendel, for the corpulent cleric of Brünn had never even dreamed of such a linkage phenomenon.

But what evidence had Morgan besides the results of his cross-breeding experiments? He had the testimony of high-powered microscopes. One hundred and fifty years after the discovery of the male germ cell in 1677, it was found to contain an even smaller body called the nucleus. By 1885 the fact that this nucleus of the germ cell was the "vehicle of heredity" had been independently and almost simultaneously announced by at least three eminent biologists. Later the nucleus, too, was found to contain still smaller bodies, which Waldeyer in 1888 named the *chromosomes* because they stained more easily than the rest of the cell. In 1902, a young American, William Sutton, clearly pointed out that the known behavior of the chromosome at the time of maturation of the germ cell furnishes us with a mechanism that accounts for the kind of separation of the hereditary units postulated in Mendel's theory. Thus by means of the microscope the hieroglyphics of the germ cell had been gradually deciphered.

It had also been shown that the number of chromosomes in the germ cells of *different* organisms varied greatly. Morgan, who had spent almost a quarter of a century in the study of the cell, looked carefully into the nucleus of the cells of Drosophila. It was known that it contained four distinct chromosomes, three large ones and one very small one which appeared as a mere dot. Miss Nettie Stevens, a former student of Morgan's at Bryn Mawr, had found them in 1907. The three large chromosomes could account for the three linkage groups of characters. And all the new mutant factors which popped up from time to time in Morgan's laboratory fitted into this mystic three. His theory of linkage seemed established.

But what of the tiny chromosome—the *m* chromosome, as Edmund Beecher Wilson, dean of American cell investigators, had called it? It was an enigma until one day in 1914 Hermann J. Muller, working for his doctorate under Morgan, came across a new fly with a *bent* wing. The usual routine for a new mutant was followed in an attempt to find its linkage group. After an elaborate series of selected breeding experiments, the new character refused to associate itself with any of those in the three demonstrated linkage groups of chromosomes. The obvious conclusion was that it belonged to the small fourth chromosome which all this while had been floating apparently uselessly in the nucleus, waiting for a mutant character with which to be associated. What for a moment had appeared as an obstacle to the acceptance of the validity of the linkage theory was converted into additional evidence of its plausibility. From now on it was called the *fourth* and no longer the *m* chromosome.

Once again the laboratory at Columbia was thrilled; the fly hunters redoubled their efforts in the hope of finding new mutants with characters that might be linked to the bent wing of the fourth chromosome. Again Morgan and his squad set their eyes to their microscopes. Morgan recalled the words of his friend, the English naturalist William Bateson: "Treasure your exceptions. Keep them always uncovered and in sight." He did. He searched through the thousands of flies until his head ached, looking for other mutants which might strengthen his conclusion. Before long such mutants actually appeared. Miss Hoge was the first (1914) to discover an *eyeless* fly, and Bridges five years later found one lacking bristles on its thorax, which he called the *shaven* mutant. This was linked to bent wing as well as to Miss Hoge's eyeless mutant, but not to a single other character from any of the three large chromosome groups. The evidence was most impressive. Even more amazing was the fact that the number of mutants found for each of the four groups was closely proportional to the size of the chromosome. Thus, very few mutants were discovered for this dot chromosome, while more than a hundred different characters were found for each of the other three chromosomes.

Not only was Morgan a great master, but fate, too, was kind to

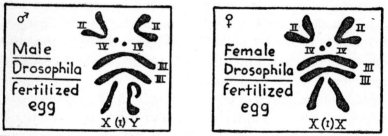

Fig. 13. I, II, III and IV are the four chromosomes representing the four Linkage Groups, as seen under the microscope. Note the X and Y chromosomes of the male egg.

him. He was fortunate in having gathered under his wing a trio of workers in genetics whose equal it would be difficult to find in any branch of scientific investigation. There were Bridges, Muller, and the other brilliant biologist, Alfred Henry Sturtevant, who more than once stepped in and helped to cross a treacherous chasm. Sturtevant, born in Jacksonville, Illinois, and brought up on a farm in Alabama, became interested in genetics at a very early age. His father and brother bred race horses, and the boy made a beautiful study of the genealogy of a line of these animals. He showed this *Study of the Pedigrees of Blooded Trotters* to Morgan, who thought so highly of the work that he helped the author, who was still an undergraduate, to publish it. Later Morgan set him to work on a more careful study of sex-linked factors in Drosophila, which in 1912, when Sturtevant was only twenty-one, resulted in his enunciation of a very fruitful theory. Two years later he earned his Ph.D. degree under Morgan. He soon joined the staff of the Carnegie Institution of Washington and continued his work with Drosophila.

It had been believed by some biologists that each chromosome contained still smaller units, *genes*, each of which represented a particular character. For example, the characters white eye, yellow wing, and rudimentary wing were thought of as existing in the first chromosome. Likewise black body and vestigial wing were believed to be present in the second chromosome. It was not unnatural to look at the chromosome in this way. In fact, De Vries and others had this notion, but could find no experimental evi-

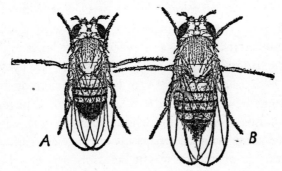

Fig. 14. Male (A) and female (B) vinegar flies (Drosophila melanogaster). Note that the male fruit fly is somewhat smaller than the female.

dence in support of the idea. The word *gene* was derived from a Greek word meaning race and was equivalent to *gen*, the word that Wilhelm Johannsen had introduced. Johannsen, a Danish physiologist, had come to Columbia University in 1909 to lecture about his now classic work on the inheritance within pure lines of beans, and Morgan then used the word *gene* to represent each unit character or "factor," as the English called it, such as red eye, bent wing, black body, and forked bristles.

The exact position of these genes in the chromosomes was of course not known, but they were believed to be arranged in a straight line in each chromosome thread. Sturtevant now postulated for the first time that the genes, instead of being present in the chromosome in any haphazard positions, were present in a linear arrangement, one gene below another. The idea of a necklace of genetic beads, each in a fixed position and threaded on a transparent ribbon, was more than a colorful picture. It formed the basis of another theory which actually located the relative position of each gene in each chromosome.

This was only the beginning of the "modern fairy tale," as one writer has called the conception of the four groups and their genes. There were more hurdles ahead. Hardly had Morgan jumped one when another and more formidable obstacle appeared. The white-eyed factor and the yellow-wing factor, believed to be linked in the sex chromosome, were found to have separated from each other in a very small percentage of cases. For instance, when a red-eyed, gray-winged female was mated with a white-eyed, yellow-winged male, one out of every hundred flies in the second generation had red eyes and yellow wings, or white eyes and gray wings. Obviously something was wrong—something more than linkage must be involved—otherwise there would never be born two new kinds of flies having white eyes with gray wings or red eyes and yellow wings. Perhaps his critics were right, after all, and the theory of linkage was at best only a poor substitute for one of nature's still hidden laws.

Again Morgan went after an explanation for this apparent exception. Once more his search ended at the eyepiece of a microscope focused on the germ cell of a fly. It had been shown that just before the female egg cell and the male sperm of an organism were ready for fertilization, both of these cells, called the gametes or marrying cells, go through a unique and peculiar process of separation known as a *reduction-division*. Each cell of most organisms contains two full sets of chromosomes. The germ cells of Drosophila, for example, contain eight chromosomes or two full sets of four chromosomes each. Before fertilization the members of each pair of chromosomes in each cell come together, twist around each other, and then separate, one member of each pair going to one end of the cell, the other member to the other end.

After the process is complete there are two rows of four chromosomes facing each other. Soon after, this cell divides into two cells, one of which, still unfertilized, contains four chromosomes. This is the reduction-division process, without which the number of chromosomes would multiply *ad infinitum* when the egg and sperm unite. When a mature sperm now burrows its head into a mature ovum, leaving its tail outside, the nuclei of the sperm and ovum fuse, and once more the fertilized egg contains eight, or two sets of four, chromosomes—one set from the father and one set from the mother. The new organism therefore begins life with a set of characters from each parent.

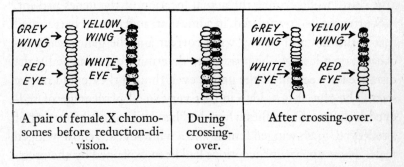

A pair of female X chromosomes before reduction-division.	During crossing-over.	After crossing-over.

Fig. 15. The crossing-over phenomenon of chromosomes.

Preceding this reduction-division process, strange things might happen, for, as we know, the two sets of chromosomes of the immature egg and sperm lie side by side twisting around each other just before fertilization. Morgan believed that during this twisting process they might be so intertwined that, on separating, part of one chromosome would separate with part of the other member of the set, resulting in a new chromosome made up of sections of both. Janssen, a priest of Louvain, without knowing anything about linkage had vaguely hinted at this before. This "chromosomal embrace" was responsible for new combinations of characters and, according to Morgan, for the break in the usual linkage groups, since sometimes the two members of the same (homologous) chromosomes, although usually similar in almost all respects, might differ in a few. It explained the one and one-half per cent of flies with yellow wing and red eye or white eye and grey wing as due to an interchange or *crossing-over* between the two original sex or X chromosomes of the female, as shown in Fig. 15, page 401.

Actual photographic evidence from microscopical investigations has since confirmed this amazing process of crossing-over, and the quantitative data from breeding experiments make it extremely unlikely that Morgan's explanation of the exceptions noted is incorrect.

On the basis of this crossing-over phenomenon, Morgan now saw a way to determine the actual location of the genes present, as Sturtevant had postulated, in a linear arrangement. He reasoned that if this fanciful theory were correct and the genes really localized, then it might be possible to determine experimentally the distance between all of the genes, even though they could not be seen. The clue was hidden in that very small percentage of red-eyed, yellow-winged flies which had hatched out of the mating of a red-eyed, gray-winged female and a white-eyed, yellow-winged male. These apparent exceptions had been explained by the cross-ing-over phenomenon which took place while homologous chromosomes were twisting around each other prior to a final separation. Where would the breaks in the chromosomal thread be more apt to occur? Morgan asked himself. Obviously, the distance between genes would determine the frequency of their separation during crossing-over phenomena. "During crossing-over," he said, "it is those genes that are farthest apart that become separated more freely, since there is between them a longer distance in any part of which the chromosome may break." Hence if certain factors rarely become separated by crossing-over, then these genes must be very close together, while, on the other hand, if certain other factors are easily separated during crossing-over, then they must be far apart in the chromosome.

No time was wasted in following up this idea. Sturtevant reduced the number of cross-overs to percentages and thus laid the basis for an orderly comparison of the gene distances. Gradually everybody in the laboratory joined in the adventure of mapping the unexplored lands of the chromosomes of Drosophila. There began one of the most exacting and amazing pieces of research in the history of biology. Tens of thousands of elaborate and carefully controlled cross-over experiments, involving millions of flies and scores of different mutants of the fruit fly, had to be skillfully executed, and the numerical results tabulated and analyzed. Numerous obstacles had to be overcome. In the cold nights of winter many of the fly cultures failed to start on time. To prevent this delay, Bridges built special incubators for these tiny insects which were to bring man closer to solving the riddle of inheritance. Never was such a huge colony of insects so zealously guarded. Thousands of glass containers had to be used, and so their size and shape were standardized. Before long, every other detail in this colossal task of creating a fly map was cunningly worked out, and the architecture of the chromosome began to emerge.

When the first numerical results came in, Morgan began to apply his theory. Crossing-over, he reasoned, between yellow wing and white eye occurs in 1.5% of cases, and we find 5.4% of crossing-over between bifid wing and white eye. This would indicate that the gene of bifid wing is farther away from the gene of white eye than is yellow wing. Now, if bifid wing is on the opposite side of white eye in relation to yellow wing, then it would be expected to give with yellow wing a crossing-over value of 6.9% If, on the other hand, bifid wing is on the same side as yellow wing, it should give a crossing-over value of 3.9% with yellow wing, as shown in Fig. 16, page 404. The number 6.9 was the one actually determined, so Morgan placed bifid wing below white in the chromosome map—a map which had to be magnified forty thousand times to make it fairly visible. By similar experiments and reasoning the location of scores of other unit characters or genes were located on the chromosome map.

This gene map of Drosophila, part of which is shown on page 421 (Fig. 22), may be likened to the table of atomic numbers of the chemical elements. The map and its spacings had to be repeatedly corrected. The appearance of new mutants, the data from fresh crossing-over experiments, the discovery of temporarily unexplained and seemingly anomalous results, all demanded frequent revamping of these chromosome blueprints. The inevitable changes evoked fierce criticism, and added fuel to the fire of those who would destroy this monstrous theory of heredity. Morgan was never seriously perturbed by this opposition; he never lost faith in the plausibility of the theory of the gene. Now and then, when the doubters shouted too loudly, he spoke out to

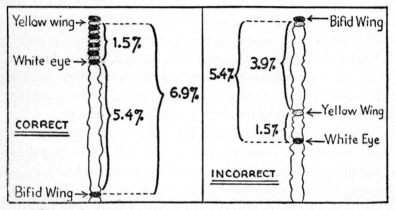

Fig. 16. Determining the positions of genes in a chromosome.

defend the tireless work of his school. "It has been said," he reminded them, "that the changes made from time to time in the genetic map of the Drosophila chromosomes discredit the method by which the localization is determined. It might as well be said that the method by which the atomic weights in chemistry were gradually improved discredited the procedure of the chemist."

Equally startling proof had in the meantime come from another direction. In May, 1922, appeared a paper from Morgan's laboratory which was to add further luster to its name. It was written by Lillian V. Morgan, whom the scientist had married eighteen years before while she was his student at Bryn Mawr, where early in his career he was professor of biology. Mrs. Morgan had left the laboratory to raise a son and three daughters. Thirteen years later, when the discoveries from her husband's laboratory began to crowd one another with overwhelming rapidity, she came back to assist the small band wrestling with Drosophila. Working independently, Mrs. Morgan had discovered a female fly with male characters. That mosaic fly was baffling. On one side of the body there was a complete reversal of certain recessive sex-linked characters. Its head, thorax, legs, color, eyes, wings, balancers, and shape of abdomen were those of neither a full normal male nor

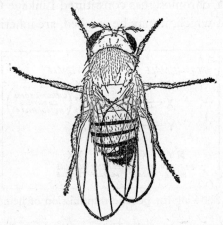

Fig. 17. A gynandromorph (hermaphrodite) of Drosophila. The right side shows the organs of a male throughout except for its genitalia which are female.

of a full normal female. Some of its characters belonged to one sex, and others to the opposite. Mrs. Morgan bred thousands of this queer intersex race of flies, crossbred them, inbred them, studied the factors in their various chromosome maps, and pondered over the possibilities of a translocation as the explanation of this singular hermaphroditic insect.

A theoretical solution soon occurred to her. It was based on a fund of information that had been gathered together during the previous decade or two. C. E. McClung, an American, working with grasshoppers, had in 1901 advanced a theory that sex is determined by the presence of one or two chromosomes now known as the X chromosomes. Four years later it had been shown that in the female of certain insects the pair of chromosomes in the first linkage group consists of two X chromosomes and in the male only one X chromosome and another chromosome called the Y chromosome. Drosophila had been shown by Miss Stevens to belong to this type. Now, all fertilized eggs which received two X chromosomes developed into females, and those which received one X and one Y turned out to be male insects. This chromosome arrangement determined what the sex of the insect would be. These X and Y chromosomes constituted Linkage Group No. 1, all the genes of which, it may be recalled, are inherited usually as a whole.

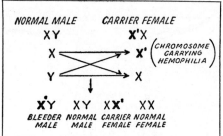

Fig. 18. Showing the genetic transmission of hemophilia.

With this knowledge of the X-Y mechanism of sex determination, Morgan had been enabled to trace those characters which were sex-linked. The crucial discovery of a difference in the pairs of sex chromosomes carried by the male and female made it a fairly simple matter to explain also such sex-linked characters in man as color blindness, night blindness, and hemophilia. This last abnormality is characterized by the failure of blood to clot, so that even a slight cut often results in death due to excessive bleeding. Hemophilia was studied in such famous bleeders as the Czarevich Alexis of old Russia and the Prince of the Asturias, son of the late Spanish king. "Bleeders" are almost always males. The mother carries hemophilia, which she transmits to her son. A male child gets his single X chromosome exclusively from his mother, and the X chromosome of the son goes only to his daughters. Since this process is continued from generation to generation, therefore if a bleeder male marries a normal female, a carrier female results, and from the union of a normal male with a carrier female, a bleeder male is born (see Fig. 18, page 406).

Mrs. Morgan reasoned that the two X chromosomes of the female fly might pass together into one ovum if accidentally united at their tips by failure of the two halves to separate at reduction-division. This would produce a fertilized egg containing the sex chromosomes of both male and female. If this were actually what had occurred, the microscope should show the evidence. Carefully she sectioned a selected female egg, and actually found the two chromosomes joined like a V, end to end. The cytological pictures fitted beautifully with her genetic deductions. The male-female fly possessed the sex chromosomes of both male and female, hence the characteristics of both sexes. This brilliant piece of work was not Mrs. Morgan's last, for almost to the day of her death in 1952, at the age of eighty-two, she continued to contribute valuable discoveries in this field.

Other chromosomal abnormalities were revealed. For example, a broken fragment of one chromosome was found attached to two normal chromosomes of the same linkage group (*duplication*), causing this individual to carry certain genes in triplicate. Such an oddity, unless the extra piece was extremely small, brought death to the fly. Bridges also deduced from genetic results that certain sections of some chromosomes disappeared altogether, lost in the chromosome shuffle. He showed that when this *deficiency* was considerable, it, too, proved fatal to the insect. Mrs. Morgan, in 1925, was the first to find cellular evidence for this phenomenon— she actually saw a sex chromosome with a large part missing. Then from breeding experiments she furnished sufficient data to account for this abnormally small chromosome.

The new testimony was overwhelmingly in favor of the gene theory. Until then Bateson had looked askance at the Drosophila work, which he considered interesting, to be sure, but "pernicious" because it went beyond the evidence. When in 1922 he

visited Morgan and under his beetling gray eyebrows watched
the Drosophila workshop in full swing, the cellular data he was
shown worked wonders. However uncongenial the evidence was
to his trend of thought, he had to admit the fruit fly was unbiased.
Overcome with excitement, he wrote back to his wife in England:
"I can see no escape from capitulation on the main point. The
chromosomes must be in some way connected with our trans-
ferable characters." And he added, "We must try to get a cytolo-
gist for our work." Until then his genetic conclusions had been
drawn wholly from statistical data. He had not made use of the
evidence of cytology; that is, the microscopic investigation of the
cell.

Bateson's published conversion made a tremendous stir all over
the world. "We have turned," he admitted, "still another bend in
the track and behind the egg and sperm cells we see the chromosomes. For the doubts—which I trust may be pardoned in one who
has never seen the marvels of cytology—cannot, as regards the
main thesis of the Drosophila workers, be any longer maintained.
The arguments of Morgan and his colleagues, and especially the
demonstration of Bridges, must allay all skepticism as to the direct
association of particular chromosomes with particular features of
the mature germ cell." The response was instant. From all over
Europe came requests for cultures of Drosophila mutants. England and Japan soon had Drosophila workers, young geneticists
from Germany came to study with the fly squad in New York,
then returned home to carry on the work. Norway, Sweden,
Portugal, China, Hungary, and France became interested in the
genetics of the fruit fly. Soviet Russia received ample fly supplies,
kept in constant touch with the American school, and her Drosophila workers rapidly increased in numbers. By February, 1935,
when the new quarters of the Institute of Genetics was opened in
Moscow, the Soviet Union ranked second in the number of researchers busy with Drosophila. The United States led with 45%,
Russia followed closely with 37%, and Germany, although third,
accounted for only 7% of the total number of research men en-

gaged in the problems connected with the hereditary make-up of the famous fly. Russia sent us some of its most brilliant workers, including Theodosius Dobzhansky of Columbia University.

The Drosophila work was not the only convincing evidence that made Morgan's theory the outstanding biological principle since Darwin's contribution. About the time the first Drosophila flies were being bred at Columbia University, Rollins A. Emerson, son of a long line of farmers including the celebrated Adams family, was teaching horticulture at the University of Nebraska. He had spent some time on the genetics of beans, which he had found extremely difficult to unravel. In an effort to supply his students with an organism from which they could more easily learn the laws of Mendel, he turned to corn. He crossed white rice popcorn with sweet corn, and distributed a bushel of the inter-pollinated grain to his classes to check the Mendelian ratios. When the laboratory results came in, he was surprised to find that the expected three-to-one ratio did not materialize. He wanted to know the reason for this. He soon found the answer.

In 1914 he had discovered the first mutant in corn, *blotched leaf*. Then he came to Cornell, where he developed a group of workers in genetics now spread over the country, and initiated a remarkable organization for co-operative work. Once a year he and his pupils met at Cornell, the clearinghouse of corn genetics in America, to exchange notes and unpublished data. The voluminous work of linkage, cross-over, and chromosome mapping was discussed, and the mass of problems which would overwhelm any single worker was parceled out for research.

The corn work, starting independently of Morgan's, took fresh impetus from the publication of the first important Drosophila papers. Emerson and his fledglings watched the Morgan group for leads and tagged along, feeling that the complete genetic architecture of their botanical Drosophila might prove a weighty ally. They had to tag along for various reasons, not the least the fact that the fruit fly would produce thirty generations before the corn plant completed one. But they had one great advantage over the fly workers. The chromosomes in corn cells are more easily studied under the microscope, and this cytological simplicity made their mapping less difficult. Corn (*Zea mays*) has ten chromosome pairs, which are all shaped differently.

Certain markers present on some of the chromosomes, such as a knob, a constriction, a nonstainable area, a satellite, and a spindle fiber attachment, have helped in the mapping of the genes. Most of this delicate cytogenetic work was done by Dr. Barbara Mc-Clintock, one of the most brilliant, skillful, and persevering of the pioneer genetic workers in America. Already more than two

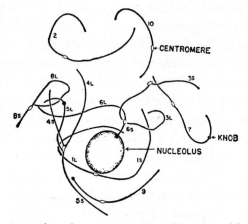

Fig. 19. The ten-maize chromosome atlas. (Courtesy M. M. Rhoades, University of Illinois, 1957)

hundred mutants have been reported. More than a hundred genes influencing color, leaves, anthers, pollen sterility, disease resistance, carbohydrate metabolism, plumule, silks, number of kernel rows, root development, and sex abnormalities have proved the existence of ten—and only ten—linkage groups. This *Zea mays* chart well merits a place beside the genetic map of Drosophila.

The inheritance of several different organisms engaged other workers in America. For example, the Jimson weed, a species of plant from which the drug belladonna is obtained, was the subject of interesting investigations, especially by Albert F. Blakeslee at the Cold Spring Harbor Station for Experimental Evolution of the Carnegie Institution of Washington. *Polyploidy*, or the increase in the normal number of chromosomes of an organism, is particularly observable in the Jimson weed. Tetraploids, for example, contain double the number of chromosomes of the fertilized egg, due, it is believed, to the failure of the cell to divide when the chromosomes divide. The offspring of such a cell continue to have this double number of chromosomes, offering for study many interesting and complex problems of heredity.

The evening primrose made famous by the pioneer observations of De Vries still presents baffling abnormalities of inheritance. A few geneticists, including George H. Shull at Princeton and Ralph E. Cleland, who had stubbornly refused to be discouraged by its difficulties, made enough headway with this plant to show that it, too, fits in perfectly with the theory of the gene. Others doing significant work were E. B. Babcock on the *crepis* plant, H. S. Jennings on the genetics of the single-celled Paramecium, A. M. Banta on water crustaceans, and Richard Goldschmidt on moths. Some progress was also made with organisms higher in the scale of evolution. During thirty years of research, starting in 1911, W. E. Castle, father of mammalian genetics, found sixteen separate genes in the chromosomes of the rabbit, of which nine affect the color and five the structure of its coat. Their actual location in any particular chromosome is still unknown. Charles R. Stockard chose the dog; Sewall Wright, a brilliant mathematical analyst of evolution, worked at the University of Chicago with the twenty-one pairs of chromosomes of the guinea pig. In this famous experimental animal, black coat, dark eyes, and short hair have been shown to be dominant over white coat, pink eyes, and long hair. Oscar Riddle used pigeons. Others handled the mouse, the rat, and the cat, while C. B. Davenport studied the genetics of man. Horse genetics, which had already demonstrated that bay color is dominant over black, was studied on the Kellogg Farm of the University of California.

The study of the genetics of man offers the most complicated picture and at the same time the most alluring hopes. Morgan believed that the complexity of the genic composition of man made it somewhat hazardous to apply only the simpler rules of Mendelian inheritance. He was of the opinion that the development of many inherited characters depends both on the presence of modifying factors and on the outside environment. No case of human linkage, for example, is definitely known. If it were really true, as some wrongly believe, that blond hair and blue eyes are linked in the chromosomes of man, then crossing-over could be offered as an explanation for the fair-haired child with brown eyes. The late H. H. Newman remarked that if red hair and a certain well-known disposition were linked, as is popularly supposed, then "crossing-over might be a saving grace."

We are a relatively long-lived species and our cells have forty-eight, or perhaps forty-six, chromosomes (see Fig. 20) containing between 10,000 and 100,000 different genes. Aside from the field of fiction and dubious speculation, very little has been accomplished in positive human genetics, largely because of the tremendous difficulty of converting *Homo sapiens* into a laboratory guinea pig or fruit fly. In no other field of science has so much rubbish been published about the potentialities of eugenics in purifying and renovating a group. At best, eugenics is still a pseudo-science, and its most optimistic champions might justly be classified with the phrenologists and astrologers of bygone ages.

While it is true that geneticists can now produce strains of plants and even animals that are free from certain hereditary defects and that they have also been successful in breeding plant populations that are resistant or immune to certain diseases, it would not be desirable to do the same for man even if we could, except that here and there a hereditary defective may be discouraged from breeding. According to Morgan, "the same end is accomplished by the discovery and removal of the external causes of the disease rather than by attempting to breed an immune race. Rather must we look to medical research to discover remedial measures to insure better health and more happiness for mankind."

The tantalizing possibilities of creative and controlled evolution were dramatically brought before the world in 1926 by the startling announcement made by one of the early workers in Morgan's laboratory to a distinguished audience at the Sixth International Congress of Genetics in Berlin. Again the fruit fly was the experimental organism used. Hermann Joseph Muller reported the results of several years of experimentation with the germ plasm of Drosophila. Muller had been interested in genetics ever

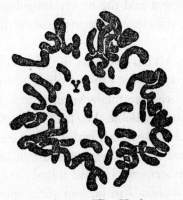

Fig. 20. The chromosomes of man. The X chromosome may be distinguished at the upper left-hand corner of the letter "Y" which has been inserted. The Y chromosome is the small round body to the left and just below the X chromosome. The cell of a woman would have a second X chromosome instead of the Y chromosome. After T. S. Painter.

since he was a small boy. His father took him when he was seven to the American Museum of Natural History in New York. Here the child saw a display of the evolution of the modern horse, which haunted him from that day on. His father had explained how the four-toed *Eohippus borealis*, the dawn horse which lived in the Bad Lands of Wyoming forty-five million years ago, had gradually evolved into a three-toed *Mesohippus*, and finally to the small, clumsy one-toed *Pliohippus*—ancestor of the modern horse.

Perhaps, thought Muller, a knowledge of the mechanism of inheritance would enable mankind to cut down this tremendous time scale needed for evolution. "It was basically," he said, "because of my belief in the future artificially controlled biological evolution of the human species that I started studying genetics by myself in the summer of 1908. This possible eventual application has been the mainspring of my interest in genetics ever since." In 1918, while at the University of Texas, he began a series of researches to determine first the normal rate of spontaneous mutation, and then the speed of mutation induced by various outside agencies, such as heat and the newly introduced X rays, which he hurled against the chromosomes of the fertilized eggs of Drosophila.

For eight years Muller lived the life of a recluse. Hours, days, seasons, meant little to him. He was obsessed by an idea and sustained by a belief that he might succeed in achieving what was then considered unattainable. He broke down from overwork, but later renewed his search. Finally, when he had checked the mass of data he had collected and was sure of his results, he made his epochal announcement. He had jolted the genes in the chromosomes of Drosophila, had broken them apart and rearranged them; he had increased the mutation rate one hundred and fifty times; he had artificially speeded up the evolutionary process. He had actually transmuted species and created new ones by exposing flies to the action of ordinary X rays! Muller had, with the aid of this radiation from an X-ray tube, stolen into that holy of holies, the germ plasm, and tampered with it. Controlled mutation was a demonstration that we might no longer have to be at the mercy of the slowness of nature. Some maintained that a critical period in human history had arrived, and that man could here and now directly participate in creative evolution by creating new species of living organisms and replacing natural selection by human selection.

Muller had placed his finger on the spring controlling inheritance; overnight, at the age of thirty-six, he became world-famous. Hearing of this monumental achievement, Morgan was proud of this man who had cut his scientific eyeteeth under him at Columbia in 1911. At about the same time Lewis J. Stadler of the University of Missouri published a paper on the speeding up of mutation in Indian corn and the barley plant, while T. H. Goodspeed of the University of California had done the same with the tobacco plant. They had both been beaten by a few weeks in their announcement of results which, although similar, were by no means as clear cut or significant, for Muller had used large numbers and accurate controls. But that is one of the gambles in the adventure of scientific research, one of the disappointments of success in the laboratory.

Others set their feet on the path Muller had opened. It led to a virgin field of great wealth and promise. The male Drosophila, the virgin and the pregnant female, and the fertilized egg were all forced to undergo this new ray treatment. Drosophila was subjected to other cunning devices and techniques. Ultraviolet light, rapid sound waves, various ionizing radiation such as gamma rays, alpha particles, neutron, proton, and electron bombardment, high temperatures, drying, aging, rapid whirling of germ cells, and other methods were used to produce translocations, deletions, and new mutants in all sorts of organisms. One Russian investigator X-rayed the germ cells of Drosophila and produced mutations in the first generation. Then he bombarded the offspring with these radiations and reversed the changes, causing the third generation of flies to become normal again, thus indicating that perhaps mutations were reversible. An American research worker experimented with X rays to produce new species of Jimson weed. This plant mutated into a form which yielded a higher percentage of belladonna. Workers at the General Electric Company used X rays on seeds and produced flowering of grapefruit in six weeks, whereas the normal period of the flowering of this tree is about six years. They also succeeded in changing the color of the sorghum plant, and in altering the sex ratio in the hemp plant.

Others subjected the tips of tomato plants to radium and X-ray bombardment, and obtained a new tomato which refused to cross-breed with the ordinary variety. In Moscow genetic workers exposed seeds in closed bottles for twenty days to a temperature of 131° F., and found new mutants with chromosomes which were badly damaged. These and hundreds of other later experimental results may be but the beginning of similar accomplishments in higher organisms. It is, however, risky to forecast the future of this line of attack, for scientific advance in this field is unpredictable.

As we survey the half-century which has elapsed since that lucky moment in 1909 when Morgan turned to the problem of inheritance, we find the new genetics applied in many branches of scientific advance. In laboratories spread over the civilized world, geneticists have proclaimed the truth of the theory of the gene. The gene is a definite, conclusively proved entity whose existence is as accurately established as that of the atom, the electron, and many of the virus units of medicine, which "although still unisolated and unseen are nevertheless by no means unreal." The gene is no longer to be ranked with the theoretical "gemmules" of Darwin, the "plastidules" of Haeckel, the "micellae" of Nägeli, or the "pangenes" of De Vries. These were the names for the hypothetical forerunners of the experimentally proved genes. The genes are the beads strung by nature on the nebulous threads of the chromosomes, which seal the fate of all life, including that of mankind. If the fates are weaving our destinies, it is with the gene-filled chromosome threads that they spin.

Morgan, in moments of relaxation when the buzz of Drosophila had set his mind to pondering ultimate sizes and shapes of the genes, had tried to picture them. He saw a definite structural unit with perhaps slight differences of form and about the size of a large protein molecule. A single gene was about 0.1 micron or about 1/250,000-inch in diameter. Some idea of the actual size of a gene may be obtained by imagining a hen's egg raised to the size of the earth, and a gene increased in volume on the same scale. The individual gene would then, says J. B. S. Haldane, the eminent geneticist of England, be large enough to place on a table, while the electron would just be visible to the naked eye.

Sturtevant first demonstrated in 1925 that the developmental effects of genes are influenced by their neighbors. While each gene is considered to be a separate unit and, in general, if it is changed or displaced, affects a definite character of the individual, still it is also true that in a sense *each character is the product of all the genes*. Bridges paid a great deal of attention to this phenomenon of *genic balance*, and was led to the conclusion that each character or feature of the adult is produced by the joint action of all the genes of the entire complement of chromosomes. For example, it has been shown that at least fifty genes work together to produce the red color of Drosophila eyes. The presence of one particular gene will not result in red eye unless at least forty-nine other genes are functioning. Hundreds are needed to produce a normal straight wing. Just how these genes work together is not as yet understood, but we do know that each gene is the center of diffusion of active products. In like manner "there is demonstrable evidence today that there is not a single gene for femaleness and another for maleness, but several, perhaps many, genes distributed through the chromosomes."

Professor Morgan came to the California Institute of Technology in 1928 to become chairman of its new Division of Biology. Sturtevant was brought along to become professor of genetics. Two other geneticists, Ernest G. Anderson and Sterling H. Emerson, were brought from Michigan. Morgan's work was supported in part by grants from the Carnegie Institution of Washington from 1915 on. These grants also took care of two full-time investigators, Calvin Bridges and Jack Schultz. At the end of the first year, the first Ph.D. degree was given to Albert Tyler, who was then appointed to the staff. Work on Drosophila proceeded at full blast.

The structural details of the chromosomes continued to be pretty much a matter of conjecture until the publication of a paper on December 22, 1933, on *A New Method for the Study of Chromosome Rearrangements and the Plotting of Chromosome Maps,* by Theophilus S. Painter of the University of Texas. It was a brilliant piece of research, which Morgan regarded as one of the classics of genetics. For the first time, undeniable evidence was furnished of a definite chromosomal structure which made the Drosophila map a stereometric reality.

Until then practically all of the work on Drosophila had been done with the chromosomes of the egg cells. For some time, however, it had been known that the giant salivary gland chromosome of some of the Diptera insects showed a banded structure. This had been pointed out by Edward Balbiani as early as 1881. It was also established that the chromosomes of the salivary gland cells

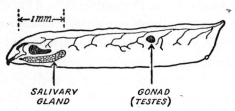

SALIVARY   GONAD
GLAND   (TESTES)

Fig. 21. A Drosophila larva, highly magnified, showing location of the salivary gland cells and gonad.
From Smithsonian Report. Publication No. 3365.

of the mature Drosophila larva were about seventy times larger than the chromosomes of the egg cells of this fruit fly.

Painter worked out a technique for bringing out some of the details of the structure of these larger chromosomes by staining them with an acetocarmine dye. By means of this treatment he succeeded in identifying about one thousand bands of rings on these giant chromosomes, and showed a close correspondence between the sequence of the banding and the sequence of the genes on Bridges' maps. As soon as Painter had opened the pages of this new and exciting chapter, Calvin Bridges joined the investigation for further refinement of technique and fuller and more salient details. He stretched the chromosomes of the salivary gland cells until they were more than 150 times longer than those of the egg cells. He made preparations from larvae which had been raised to their maximum size by supplying them with an extra diet of yeast. Under the outside wrappings of the chromosomes he made out three times as many segments as Painter had photographed, for he found that some of the bands were really doublets. He was also able to distinguish greater detail in these banded affairs. He considered the bands as representing the edges of solid disks that run clear through the chromosomes, the spaces between the disks representing the homes of the individual genes. The old idea of beads on a string was replaced by a conception of eight or sixteen slender strands twisted to form a cable. Each cross band consisted of sixteen dots, and each dot was possibly a duplicate gene.

Bridges kept working on these large salivary glands, studying deficiencies and duplications in an effort to revamp his chromosome maps. The work was getting harder and more and more alluring and the mass of experimentation was mounting sky-high. In addition, he was carrying 900 separate stocks of Drosophila largely built up by his own hands. Aided by Millislav Demerec, he continued to issue bulletins of the Drosophila Information Service (D.I.S.) containing unpublished material for the use of hundreds of researchers in genetics. In the summer of 1936 his son, Philip N. Bridges, came to his help. The younger Bridges had turned from his studies in physics and mathematics at Columbia University to genetics at Cold Spring Harbor Laboratory. He began analyzing salivary-gland chromosome slides prepared by his father, and before the year was over he had studied and remapped with his father the normal banding in the neighborhood of break points at 89C and 96A in the chromosome. Two years later the elder Bridges published his *Revised Map of the Salivary Gland X Chromosome*, a drawn-to-scale map which showed 1024 bands instead of the original 537. In the summer of 1938 the two Bridges worked on the chromosome map of the right limb of the *second* chromosome. But Calvin Bridges, a brilliant, simple, and unaffected worker, never finished this study. He had driven himself so hard during this work that he died of a heart attack at Los Angeles on December 27, 1938, in his forty-ninth year.

The work which Bridges had failed to complete was too important to be left undone. In 1938 the Carnegie Institution sent the
younger Bridges as a fellow to Morgan's laboratory at the California Institute of Technology to continue his father's work.
That year the new map of the right limb of the *second* chromosome was completed from the data left by Calvin Bridges. It
showed 1136 lines instead of the previous 600. Then in 1941
Philip N. Bridges published a new map of the left limb of the
third chromosome map, showing 884 lines instead of 542, while
the right limb of the same chromosome showed an increase to
1178 from the original 725 lines. Soon after the attack on Pearl
Harbor, Bridges, while completing the left limb of the *second*
chromosome map, applied for a commission in the Naval Reserve. Genetics was to be abandoned, temporarily, he hoped, for
communications work in the Navy.

This veritable spectrum of the hereditary unit of the cell is the
tool *par excellence* for locating the position of each gene and for
tracing inversions, duplications, translocations, deficiencies, and
other abnormalities in the chromosomes of Drosophila. The positions of genes, said Bridges, "can now be located as easily as the
houses on Main Street in the old home town." This new development is further testimony to the accuracy both of Morgan's geog-
raphers of Drosophila and of the whole theory of the gene. An
amazing climax to half a century of research!

Morgan did not hesitate to tell us that we are visionaries when
we pretend to solve the ultimate problems of nature. He himself
came perilously close to solving one, not with intricate apparatus, but with skilled hands, an imaginative mind, broad and
deeply planted in the literature of science, and his persistence in
probing phenomena which seemed to offer solutions to large
problems. Morgan's contributions have brought us nearer to the
solution of more than one important riddle.

He supplemented and clarified the theory of evolution. Darwin
stressed the mechanism of evolution resulting from slight variations produced by changes in environment, variations eventually

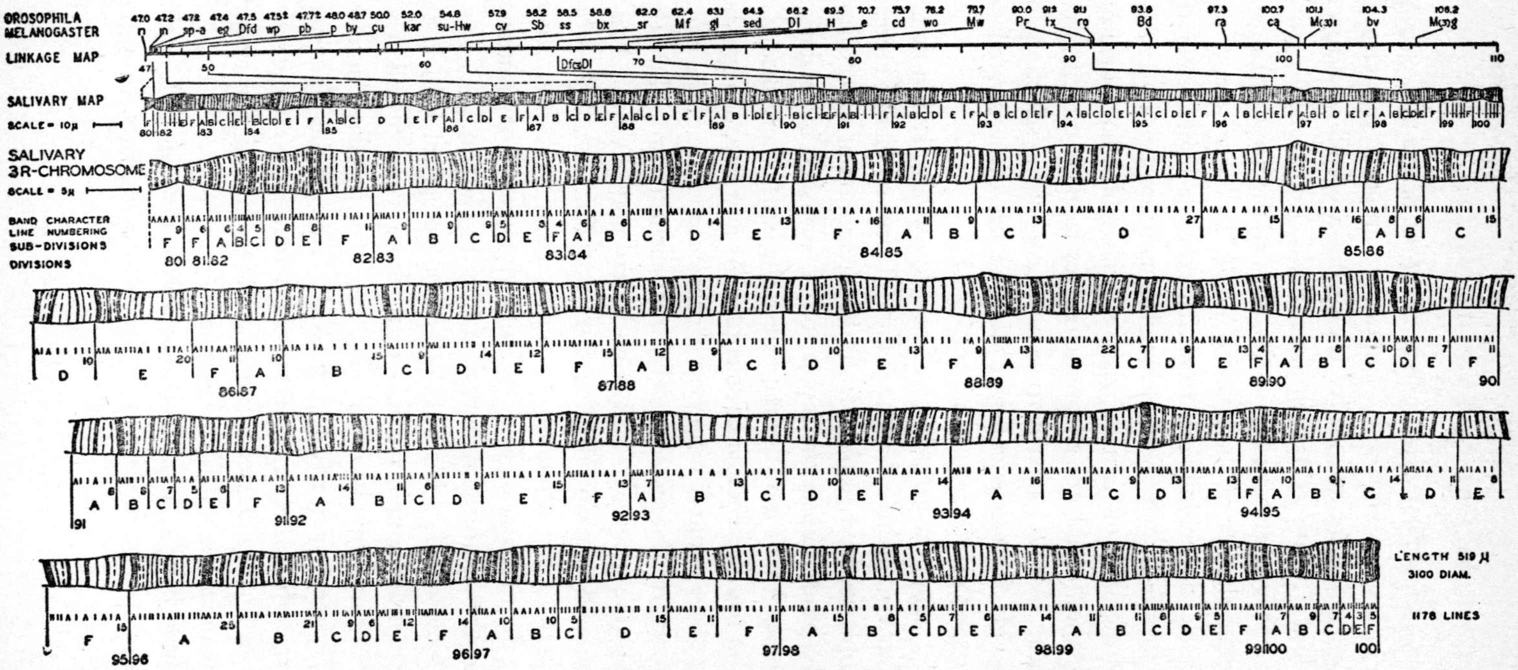

Fig. 22. Revised reference gene map of the Salivary Gland of Drosophila Melanogaster. Note the typical accordionlike structure of the chromosome showing the positions of the gene loci. (From the *Journal of Heredity*, Copyright by the American Genetic Association.)

inherited and sifted out during nature's great drama of the struggle for existence. Harmful changes were nipped, but changes advantageous to the survival of the species were allowed to develop. Unfortunately, Darwin knew nothing of Mendel's work, although they were contemporaries, nor had the name of Darwin ever passed the lips of the obscure monk. Today we know that natural selection, while a matter of inexorable logic, is not the creative force in evolution, although it may explain in part the absence of many of nature's trials—species which have died out because they could not adapt themselves to their merciless environment. We no longer harp so much on natural selection and the struggle for existence, since Morgan has demonstrated the creative part played by mutation.

Today, from the great body of new knowledge still in flux, it seems fair to conclude that the many different species of increasing complexity have resulted from the interaction of some sort of selective process upon the raw material furnished by mutation. The mechanism of heredity must be at the basis of any theory of evolution that pretends to be scientific. At any rate, Morgan believed that we could rest our case for the acceptance of the mutation theory on the same experimental scientific procedure that has led to the great advances of chemistry and physics. "And it may be," said Lancelot Hogben, the British scientist, "that when the history of the evolutionary hypothesis is written two centuries hence the name of Thomas Hunt Morgan will be mentioned in its pages more often than that of Charles Darwin."

The new genetics has already been of practical help in the breeding of better animal stock—cattle that give more and better beef, cows that supply more milk, and hens that lay triple the number of eggs formerly laid. F. A. E. Crew of the University of Edinburgh was able to decrease the number of monstrosity calves born to the Dexter breed of cattle from as high as twenty per cent to less than half this number.

Attempts have been made to alter the sex ratio of cattle so that larger numbers of females might be born than males. Cows are more valuable to breeders than bulls, and hens more wanted than roosters. Nicolai Koltzoff of the Institute of Experimental Biology at Moscow reported success in separating the sperm cells of the male rabbit whose chromosomes showed characteristics that would lead to the birth of female rabbits. He then injected them into female rabbits, thus making them artificially pregnant. Of the first 200 trials, Koltzoff reported 108 successful; that is, female rabbits were born. The results of experimental work of this sort are quickly disseminated among livestock breeders of the Soviet Union. The Russian said the method was probably applicable to man, too.

In 1957 Manuel Gordon of the University of California reported the separation of male sperm cells from female sperm cells by electrophoresis. The female-producing sperm traveled to the positive pole of the machine and the male-producing sperm migrated to the cathode. He then injected rabbits with the sperm cells and obtained significant though not complete success in predicting the sex of the rabbits born.

In plant breeding, too, the old empirical method of breeders like Luther Burbank has been placed on a more accurate and easily controlled basis. George H. Shull, one of four American brothers who were biologists, published some classic studies on inbreeding and crossing-over in corn. This work was done while he was a botanical investigator for the Carnegie Institution of Washington. Seven years later, in 1915, while professor of botany and genetics at Princeton University, he produced a hybrid corn which started a broad program of hybrid-corn experimentation around the country. By 1930 the average yield of corn in the United States was about 22 bushels per acre. Twenty years later this figure had risen to 33, and seventy-five per cent of our corn planted was hybrid corn. The value of the American corn crop was increased by hundreds of millions of dollars. Other valuable plants, from the extremely important rustless, cold-enduring, and even grasshopper-resistant wheats, and a new type of tobacco leaf generally constructed for cigar manufacturers, to the lowly non-odoriferous cabbage, have also been produced for the first time. In Kansas, a mutant of Turkey wheat resistant to black stem rust was found in 1906. Professor Herbert F. Roberts of the Kansas State Agricultural College experimented with this mutant, and in 1917 it was successfully introduced. It is not only rust-resistant but it withstands cold winters. In England, Sir R. Biffen, by crossing and selection, produced a "hard" grain rich in gluten, as well as a strain (*Yeoman*) which is not so easily crippled by storms. By 1927, fifteen years after they were placed on the market, these grains occupied about one third of the wheatlands of the earth.

The theory of the gene has pointed the way toward the solution of even more vital problems—social problems involving idiocy, feeble-mindedness, and a number of the insanities. Physicians are frequently called upon to give advice on the suitability of marriage where a hereditary taint is suspected. Lawyers have made use of the knowledge of the inheritance of blood groups in cases dealing with such problems as questionable paternity. We already know that various characters in humans, such as eye color, hair color, blood grouping, albinism, the appearance of extra digits (polydactyly), short and crooked little fingers or toes (brachydactyly), and lobster claw—that is, the absence of all digits except sometimes the thumb and little finger—are inherited according to the Mendelian laws. Color blindness, night blindness, sensitivity to the bitter taste of the chemical compound phenyl thiourea, Huntington's chorea, and phenyl kenonurea are also inherited in man. We know much more, of course, about the hereditary factors in plants and animals. On the basis that nature uses the same mechanism on all living things, medical science has already begun to attack such serious and possibly hereditary diseases as cancer, tuberculosis, and *diabetes insipidus*.

The award of the Nobel Prize in physiology and medicine to Morgan in 1933 was a recognition of the significance of this modern theory of heredity for physiology, as well as of the part which genetics is destined to play in the future of medicine. When the notice of the award came to Morgan at Pasadena, his whole laboratory was elated. Morgan did not want to go to Sweden that winter and so postponed the ocean voyage until the following spring, when Mrs. Morgan and their daughter, Elizabeth, accompanied him. He took advantage of this vacation to try to find some English physiologists for his laboratory. England was considered the traditional center of experts in physiology. Finding no one in England exactly suited for the work he had in mind, Morgan went to the Continent and found a man in Holland. In Demark he paid a visit to the great atomic physicist, Niels Bohr, and met a number of other old friends who had come to see him in America. He traveled to southern Sweden to inspect the experimental station where much brilliant work in wheat and rye genetics was being done. The Nobel Prize winner attended all kinds of receptions and dinners given in his honor, and, after a while, he learned not to mind them. Said Morgan, "The host welcomes you and you respond . . . you soon drop into the pattern and offer nice little compliments and everybody is happy."

To a brilliant gathering of scientists, diplomats, and other distinguished citizens, Morgan gave his Nobel address in Stockholm that spring on *The Relation of Genetics to Physiology and Medicine*. He told his audience, "The most important contribution to medicine that genetics has made is intellectual. The whole subject of human heredity in the past has been so vague and tainted by myths and superstition that a scientific understanding of the subject is an achievement of the first order." He prophesied that "the phenomenon of linkage may some day be helpful in diagnosis. It is true that there are known as yet no certain cases of linkage, but there can be little doubt that there will in time be discovered hundreds of linkages, and some of these, we may anticipate, will tie together visible and invisible hereditary characteristics." Perhaps in years to come the proper study of the ills of mankind will be the further study of the genetics of Drosophila.

For the past twenty years a vigorous effort has been made to identify, isolate, and purify genes by methods partly embryological, partly genetic, and partly physical and chemical. One of the many men who was active in this daring project was Jack Schultz. He tried several approaches. One was a study of the chemical composition of the genes by a method which he learned from Torbjorn Caspersson of the Caroline Institute of Stockholm. Here he worked for more than two years on a Rockefeller fellowship, while on leave from Morgan's laboratory. Caspersson had hit upon the idea of photographing the chromosome with ultraviolet radiation. He found different absorption of the radiation by different sections of the same band due to a difference in their chemical composition. This resulted in a photographic picture showing areas of different light intensities.

Schultz attempted to find similarities between the stuff in the chromosomes and several nucleic acids which responded to the ultraviolet treatment in the same way, as well as by quantitative data on the nucleic acids. Staining chromosomes, taking pictures in color, and then analyzing these kodaslides was another approach. Chemical treatment of the genes was still another method employed. Strictly genetic techniques on inert sections and mutants also led Schultz, head of the Department of Genetics and Cytochemistry at the Institute of Cancer Research in Philadelphia since 1943, to the belief that "We have a chain macromolecule . . . the specificities of the genes reside in the nucleoprotein portion, and the continuous structure is a protein fiber."

The fact that a single ionization in the right place can cause a gene mutation suggests that the gene might be a single protein molecule. Furthermore, the gene seems to act like an organic compound in resisting changes and responding to radiation and other physical and chemical attacks. We therefore believe at present that the gene is made up of a complex organic compound called desoxyribonucleic acid (DNA) and a protein, forming a so-called nucleoprotein. DNA is a giant molecule or high polymer composed of a long chain of alternate sugar (desoxyribose) and phosphate groups. To each sugar is attached a nitrogen-containing base. In 1953 James D. Watson of Caltech, working with

Francis H. C. Crick in the Medical Research Unit of the Cavendish Laboratory at Cambridge, attempted to outline the first complete structure of the DNA molecule. It was based on X-ray diffraction pictures taken at Kent College, London.

According to these two young investigators at the Cavendish Laboratory, the backbone of the chromosome is composed of DNA molecules, segments of which represent individual genes. The DNA molecule itself consists of two chains turned round each other in a helical structure and cross-linked by pairs of purine or pyrimidine bases—adenine and thymine, or guanine and cytosine. This compound-helix or coiled-coil idea was independently suggested also by Linus Pauling, campus neighbor of Thomas H. Morgan.

DNA, which is found nowhere else in nature, is generally regarded at present as either the whole gene or a very important part of it. The gene molecule can form exact replicas of itself and is the only self-replicating entity in the cell. It acts as a model or template. This is characteristic of living things, and so life may have begun with the gene molecule. Heredity is at last getting closer and closer to the relative simplicity of the molecule of the chemist.

Other men are thinking and talking of searching for chemicals that will dissolve out some genes and not others, destroy some genes and leave others unharmed, and of learning the secret of focusing radiation on specific parts of the chromosomes where mutations are desirable. Bolder spirits are even dreaming of isolating these crucially important genes for use in the creation of new forms of life, even as the chemist has used atoms and molecules to synthesize brand-new compounds and alloys. But the impossibility of producing philosophers such as Plato dreamed of for his Republic will not stop geneticists from trying to achieve other lesser miracles.

In June, 1941, Morgan, at the age of seventy-five, was retired as active head of his department at the California Institute of Technology. But this did not mean cessation of research for the

new "Emeritus Professor of Biology in residence at the Institute."
Now that he was relieved of all administrative duties he "could
get some work done," he remarked. He continued his daily work
on a problem which he had first approached in 1903 at Woods
Hole, Massachusetts. It was a problem not related directly to the
genetics of Drosophila, but rather to the whole question of cross-
and self-fertilization and the kind of genetic situation that will
account for individual differences. Morgan was trying to find out
why the spermatozoa of the common hermaphroditic sea squirt
almost never fertilize the eggs of the same individual, but fertilize all the eggs of all other sea squirts. This very low form of
animal life, known to biologists as the ascidian, *Ciona*, is a queer
organism in many ways. The adult is a translucent tubelike animal
about five inches long. It functions both as a male and as a female,
and is the only animal whose envelope consists of cellulose. It is
found abundantly, living attached to the bottoms of floats and
ships in sea water. Fresh water kills it. The sea squirt's life span
is eight months. It is not eaten by man or even by fish.

By treatment with mild acids and by some other simple means,
Morgan was able to fertilize an individual's eggs with its own
sperm. The resulting offspring was raised to maturity, and thus
successive generations were obtained from a single parent for
further study. Saturday mornings Morgan worked at the Kerckhoff Marine Biological Station at Corona del Mar on Newport
Beach, California, which he helped establish in 1931. He was
driven the fifty miles to this Pacific Ocean station by Albert
Tyler, who is doing brilliant work on certain proteins obtained
from the eggs and sperm of the sea urchin and the key limpet.
These protein substances seem to interact in a manner similar to
antibodies and antigens. While Tyler worked on his sea urchins
Morgan helped himself to several "cultured" sea squirts. Professor
George E. MacGinitie, director of the station and an expert on
the care and feeding of Ciona and other tunicates, raised these
from the eggs and sperm. After the day's work was done, Morgan
was driven back to Pasadena with a week's supply of Ciona to

keep him busy until the next Saturday in his laboratory at the California Institute of Technology. For many years this routine was followed, and after thousands of experiments Morgan admitted that he had not solved the problem but had reached a "state of mind, if not a solution." And the work went on without a stop until one day, late in 1945, the grand old man of genetics passed away in his eightieth year.

At a reception given in his honor on his joining the California Institute of Technology, Morgan had remarked, "Of course I expected to go to California when I died, but the call to come to the Institute arrived a few years earlier, and I took advantage of the opportunity to see what my future life would be like." If his long stay in California was a faithful picture of this future, Morgan is now surrounded by many more than five hundred mutants of that famous fly which may yet show us all its ways and make us wise. He is the guardian of thousands of living specimens of Drosophila which men have been able to see for the first time—flies with all shapes and colors of eyes, wings, thorax, legs, bristles, sex mosaics, not forgetting a four-winged fly that cannot fly, produced in 1957 by Edward B. Lewis in Morgan's old laboratory.

Thousands of bottles in air-conditioned rooms, millions of flies living (since the more expensive banana diet was abandoned) on a mixture of yellow corn meal, molasses, water, agar, and yeast, and making public their private lives. A little group of men and women watching and plodding, counting bristle for bristle and hair for hair, waiting for favorable mutants, hoping for new openings, trusting to luck and spinning hypotheses, probing into the ever present and still unsolved problem of the cytoplasm or medium in which the genes live, trying to discover the reason for the mutation process. That is still the spirit of the quiet, cloistered William C. Kerckhoff Laboratory of the California Institute of Technology where Morgan once held sparkling seminars watched by the whole scientific world.

Perhaps someday, as has already been proposed, the name of

Morgan will be lifted on the wings of the insect Pegasus to immortality like that of his fellow Americans Bell, Henry, and Langley, in the unit *morgan*, the space between the genes on the Drosophila map having a cross-over value of one per cent.

Soon after the death of Morgan another geneticist was called to Pasadena to become chairman of Caltech's Division of Biology. He was George Wells Beadle, forty-three-year-old professor at Stanford University. Beadle, born in Wahoo, Nebraska, became interested in science while still in high school and planned to become a farmer. He went to an agricultural college for that purpose. There he was attracted to genetics, was urged to go to graduate school, and was helped to get an assistantship at Cornell University, where he took his doctorate.

He was not a stranger at the Kerckhoff Laboratory. He had been a National Research Council fellow and instructor at Caltech from 1931 to 1935, had written a textbook, *An Introduction to Genetics*, with Sturtevant, and had done some experiments with him on Drosophila more than ten years before. And he had also published some papers on corn genetics.

George Beadle was already a celebrated scientist. Pioneering in a new field, biochemical genetics, he had opened up another intriguing avenue of approach to several crucial genetic problems. In 1941 he had turned away from Drosophila and Zea Mays and had thrown in his scientific lot with another experimental organism called *Neurospora crassa*. This genetic newcomer is a red bread mold, a fungus whose life cycle from one asexual-spore generation to the next is only ten days—about the same as that of Drosophila. Any strain of this plant could thus be multiplied a million times in a few days without any genetic change. This baker's mold has another decided advantage as a laboratory tool. The wild strain, sometimes found on bread and cakes as a white fluffy mass which turns pink, can be grown on a pure, chemically defined minimal medium of nitrates, phosphates, sugar, and the vitamin biotin. As it grows on the surface of an agar jelly containing these chemicals in a test tube, it can gather all the elements it needs from this simple culture medium to make all the water-soluble vitamins of the B group (except biotin), all of the twenty-odd amino acids, and its own protoplasm. Its powers of synthesis are outstanding.

Some excellent genetic work had already been done on this organism. Bernard O. Dodge, of the New York Botanic Gardens, and Carl C. Lindegren, who had taken his Ph.D. at Caltech, had indicated that this microbal organism had a definite biochemical future. In 1933 Lindegren, for the first time, showed linkage in Neurospora, and three years later he published a map showing its sex chromosome with five genes. Barbara McClintock, who had done such spectacular work with the genetics of corn, correlated their genetic investigations with cytological work on Neurospora. By 1954 three of its seven linkage groups had been established and identified.

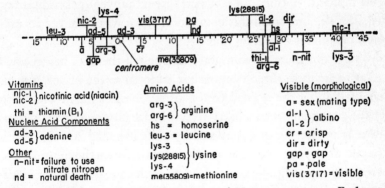

Fig. 23. Partial Map of Linkage Group I of *Neurospora crassa.* Redrawn from Barratt, *et al., Advances in Genetics,* Vol. 6. (Courtesy Academic Press, and Dr. R. W. Barratt, Dartmouth College.)

One of the many problems still nagging geneticists when Beadle began his new scientific adventure was how the individual gene functions. Beadle started with the thought that "We ought to be able to discover how genes function by making some of them defective." He went to work on this idea with his colleague Edward L. Tatum at Stanford University, and in 1941 their first paper was published in the *Proceedings of the National*

Academy of Sciences under the title "Genetic Control of Biochemical Reactions in Neurospora."

The two researchers subjected Neurospora to X-ray bombardment as Hermann Muller had first successfully done with Drosophila fifteen years before. They looked for and found several mutants which were dependent on externally supplied vitamins or amino acids. One of these mutants, for example, would not grow on the culture medium that was adequate for the normal wild type of Neurospora before radiation. But by adding different chemicals or groups of chemicals to the culture medium, they found by trial and error that the mutated bread mold would grow after the addition of only a single specific substance. In one case the mutant demanded the addition of para-amino benzoic acid. A second mutant which showed up after their irradiation had to be served the thiazole half of the B_1 vitamin to be able to grow and flourish. A third mutant had lost its power of synthesizing vitamin B_6, and when this compound alone was added to its culture medium it got along fine.

What did these three mutant strains tell them? They seemed to say that these three vitamins are essential to the life of Neurospora and that the normal wild type synthesizes them. They also made clear that "the inability to synthesize any one of the B vitamins is apparently differentiated by a single gene from the ability of the organism to elaborate this essential growth factor." The evidence seemed to be quite clear. In each case, genetic tests indicated that the mutant strain differed from the normal strain by but a single gene. And chemical tests showed that only a single specific chemical was needed to make the mutant grow normally. This was an astonishing announcement indeed.

Extensive experiments followed this discovery, and strains of nutritional mutant Neurospora were created requiring each of the vitamins necessary for growth in animal life. They seemed to establish the fact that plants evidently required the same vitamins that animals did. "It is almost embarrassing to note," wrote Beadle, "that as compared with the elementary bread mold, we humans are very defective indeed—we cannot make our own vitamins and we cannot construct amino acids. . . . An understanding of the nature and function of the gene should underlie an enlightened science of nutrition."

They could also draw the inference from these experiments that each gene controlled the production of a single enzyme which in turn regulated the synthesis of a vitamin. The gene appeared to act as a pattern or model from which the enzyme was manufactured. Without this enzyme, the essential vitamin could not be synthesized and Neurospora would die. Enzymes are proteins which act as catalysts bringing about a multitude of chemical reactions in the living organism. They are produced by bacteria, yeasts, molds such as Neurospora, and man by the hundreds. American scientists pioneered in this field. It was Professor James B. Sumner of Cornell University who, in 1926, after nine years of persistent effort, finally isolated from the jack bean the first pure, crystalline enzyme, urease. This was also the year when Hermann J. Muller announced the production of Drosophila mutants by X-ray bombardment.

Sumner's enzyme turned out to be a tiny, rectangular crystal. The isolation of about forty other enzymes followed. Among them was pepsin, obtained for the first time by John H. Northrop of the Rockefeller Institute for Medical Research. Northrop shared the 1946 Nobel Prize with Sumner and Wendell M. Stanley.

The theory that each gene controls the manufacture of a particular enzyme was an old one—half a century old. But now, for the first time, the experiments of Beadle and Tatum seemed to give it solid support. In some cases it was possible, for example, to extract the particular enzyme from the normal Neurospora but not from the mutant. Norman H. Horowitz and Herschel K. Mitchell in Beadle's department at Caltech joined in this research. At least a hundred other men in about fifteen different laboratories took the same trail. Enough evidence was gradually piled up to prompt Horowitz, whom Beadle had brought along with him from Stanford University, to spotlight the one-gene-one-enzyme hypothesis. Work on some bacteria by others seemed to point in this same direction, and although this theory is still not accepted by all biologists, it is an idea to which many other geneticists cling. If this theory turns out to be fully verified it will be a remarkable step forward in our efforts to completely decode the mystery of the function of the gene.

This pioneer work gave some confirmation, too, to certain experimental observations reported in the related field of the viruses. The outstanding figure in this fascinating area of research is the internationally known American biochemist Wendell M. Stanley. He was born in the little town of Ridgeville, Indiana, where his parents ran the local newspaper. Stanley was the first man in scientific history to isolate a virus as a pure, crystalline chemical compound. This epochal event took place at the plant-pathology laboratory of the Rockefeller Institute for Medical Research in Princeton, New Jersey, in 1935. Stanley, who was only thirty-one at the time, had come a long way since his graduation from Earlham College, Indiana, when for a while he gave serious thought to the possibility of his becoming a football coach. (He had played brilliant football for four years while at school.)

A visit to the University of Illinois, where he met the inspiring organic chemist Roger Adams, made him change his mind and enter chemical research. After getting a Ph.D. there he was called two years later, in 1931, to the newly established research laboratory in Princeton by its director, Simon Flexner. He started a study of the little-understood virus, and within three years he extracted from the juice of infected Turkish tobacco the crystalline virus of tobacco mosaic disease. For a long time "filterable viruses" were considered to be gene-containing bacteria or protozoa so very tiny as to be able to pass through even the finest filters. But the causative agent of tobacco mosaic disease which Stanley isolated turned out to be a thin, rodlike crystal about one third of a micron or 1/80,000-inch long, easily visible under the electron microscope.

This historic event opened up a whole new field of biochemical and medical investigation. Half a dozen plant viruses were found. The first virus that affects man or animal, that of polio, was crystallized in 1955 by Stanley while director of the Virus Laboratory of the University of California. That same year he and his staff reported the first reactivation of a virus (the same tobacco mosaic) from its inactive components. Viruses all have a characteristic size and shape. Like the genes, they are nucleoproteins, but whereas the gene contains DNA, plant viruses contain a different nucleic acid, namely, RNA (ribonucleic acid). RNA is found in the cytoplasm of a cell and seems to control protein synthesis under instructions from DNA. The tobacco mosaic virus is made up of ninety-four per cent protein and six per cent RNA which seems to perform a genetic function. The bacterial viruses (phages) and insect viruses contain DNA.

Viruses possess at least two characteristics shown by genes. They can mutate, and they can reproduce only within the living organism. The bacterial virus, for example, attaches itself to a living bacterium and works its way inside. In half an hour or so scores of new viruses pop out. There is much still to be learned about what Stanley called "this bridge between the molecule of the chemist and the organism of the bacteriologist."

Stanley was keenly interested in the Neurospora work from its very inception. In 1947 he remarked, "The magnificent work of Beadle and Tatum on Neurospora has served to demonstrate that definite biochemical reactions are gene-controlled. There is no reason to doubt that mutation in Neurospora which results in the gain or loss of ability to carry out a given biochemical reaction is accompanied by structural changes in the gene of the type I have described for strains of tobacco mosaic virus."

The Neurospora work illuminated other fields. Some inherited diseases result from the synthesis of enzymes of abnormal molecular structure. The first example of this phenomenon is sickle-cell anemia. There is a mutant sickle-cell gene which produces a slightly different hemoglobin molecule which is responsible for sickle-cell anemia. Only a single amino acid, glutamic acid, out of the three hundred that make up the hemoglobin molecule, has been replaced by a different one, valine, in the sickle-cell hemoglobin molecule. Linus Pauling had previously shown that the two forms of hemoglobin had different electric charges. It turned out, on further investigation, that valine had a positive charge and glutamic acid a negative one. Pauling calls this a molecular disease and looks forward to the development of a whole new field of medicine, molecular medicine.

Another molecular disease seems to be albinism, a hereditary condition characterized by the white hair, light skin, and pink eye of the albino. It is believed to be caused by the absence of the gene that controls the normal production of melanin, the pigment of hair and skin. A certain disease of Neurospora has also been cited as caused by an abnormal molecule.

Joshua Lederberg of the University of Wisconsin discovered that certain bacteria reproduce by fusing together rather than by the standard cell division. Among the individuals produced, some contain gene combinations that are not found in either parent. A new field of investigation was opened up. Later he showed that when a virus invades a bacterium, the "swiped" gene is *transducted* to another bacterium. Lederberg was awarded the Nobel Prize in 1958.

The work on Drosophila, Zea Mays, and Neurospora is still in full swing. When the complete genetics of these and other relatively simple living things have been cleared up, other, more difficult organisms will be tackled. There are still innumerable sticky biological problems to be resolved. Here is a field for the boldest and the most creative. In his address as retiring president of the American Association for the Advancement of Science in 1956, Beadle very optimistically declared that "through the understanding of heredity that man has gained within the past half-century, he has won the knowledge that makes it possible deliberately to determine the course of his own biological evolution. He is in a position to transcend the limitations of the natural selection that have for so long set his course."

CHAPTER SEVENTEEN

HERBERT McLEAN EVANS
(1882-   )

AMERICAN SCIENCE PIONEERS IN
TWO NEW RELATED FIELDS

G ENETICS WAS NOT the only field in which, at the opening of the new century, American men of science cut new paths of progress. The United States took also a leading role in the tremendously important branch of science called endocrinology (*endo*, within; *krino*, separate), the study of the internal secretions of the ductless glands. American students had gone to Europe to study bacteriology, but the world later came to us to learn about the functioning of several ductless glands—thyroid, pituitary, adrenal, pancreas, parathyroids, ovary and testis—which pass their many chemical products directly into the blood stream.

For a long time men had been slowly returning to the dictum of Theophrastus Paracelsus that the animal body is a huge and complicated chemical workshop. "In the human being," said this Martin Luther of medicine, "there is present an invisible pharmacy and an invisible physician who produces, prescribes, dispenses and administers suitable remedies as occasion demands." Paracelsus had steered chemistry away from the vain attempt to make the philosopher's stone that would transmute the baser metals into gold, and from the equally false search for the elixir of life that would delay the encroachments of old age. He had pointed out to chemistry the road that led toward its application to medicine. Now once again scientists were beginning to realize that a knowledge of the physics and chemistry of the individual cells and of the various body fluids, tissues, and organs would help to illuminate their functions.

John Jacob Abel, who was born near Cleveland of German immigrant parents, was the first to extract a hormone derivative in pure or nearly pure form. This achievement was accomplished at Johns Hopkins University in May, 1897, when an active sulfate of a monobenzyl derivative of *epinephrin* was extracted from the central core of the adrenal glands of sheep. The adrenal glands (suprarenal capsules) are two small yellow structures, shaped like a cocked hat, perched on top of each kidney. Jokichi Takamine, a Japanese chemist in Clifton, New Jersey, soon after obtained pure crystals of the same hormone, which he marketed under the name of *adrenalin*. Five years later it was synthesized. Adrenalin ($C_9H_{13}O_3N$) is a life-giving drug which can keep feeble hearts pumping and save lives during critical emergencies of shock and collapse. By constricting the blood vessels, the drug checks local hemorrhages, arrests acute hemorrhages, and checks paroxysms in bronchial asthma.

While Abel was occupied with his studies on adrenalin, the discovery of a second internal secretion was announced. This find resulted from the attempts of physiologists to unravel the mechanism by which pancreatic juice is poured into the stomach to aid in digestion. Ernest H. Starling and William Bayliss, of the University of London, showed by experiments on dogs, in 1902, that part of this mechanism was a chemical reflex. The cells lining the beginning of the small intestine produce a chemical which enters the blood stream without a duct. This chemical, *secretin*, is carried to the pancreas by the blood and excites it to supply pancreatic juice to the food canal. This *hormone*, or "chemical messenger," as Starling first called it, belongs to the same group of vital chemical compounds as adrenalin. W. B. Hardy coined the word hormone from the Greek "I excite." Hormones were now added to the other known mechanisms of the body, such as the nervous system and the blood, which co-ordinate the multitudinous activities of the living organism.

Twelve years of hard work were to pass before another of these essential hormones was extracted. On Christmas day, 1914, an American scientist, Edward C. Kendall, announced a new hormone, *thyroxin*. This Connecticut-born researcher, at twenty-eight, had stolen a march on foreign scientists working feverishly in the same field. Hardly a pinch of this crystal is present in the human body at any one time, and yet it stands between life and death, normal mentality and idiocy. In 1850 a study of a large number of cretins in Salzburg, Austria, pointed to the possibility that associated with this pitiful condition was either a badly diseased thyroid or the total absence of this gland. Cretins had been known for centuries. They are misshapen humans, fat of belly, stary-eyed, helpless and hopeless, vegetating in spite of all attempts to help them. They usually died before they reached the age of ten.

Some time later it was found by experiments with monkeys that *myxedema*, a disease appearing much later in life than cretinism, results from thyroid deficiency. Myxedema is characterized by thickening and drying of the skin, falling hair, low body temperature, low metabolism, and diminished sex function.

Many attempts were made to extract from the thyroid gland the active chemical responsible for its normal functioning. Using a number of clever techniques, Kendall finally forced thyroxin to capitulate. From three tons of the fresh thyroid glands of cattle he obtained thirty-five grams of the pure compound. The composition of thyroxin was at first inaccurately reported by Kendall, but its true formula was later determined. In 1927 it was actually prepared synthetically in the laboratory as colorless needles, $C_{15}H_{11}O_4NI_4$, containing sixty-five per cent iodine. Synthetic thyroxin placed cretins on the road to normality. "Not the magic wand of Prospero or the brave kiss of the daughter of Hippocrates ever effected such a change as that we are now enabled to make," declared Sir William Osler, the great English physician. For the first time in history cretinism, myxedema (hypothyroidism), and hyperthyroidism were brought into the province of therapeutic medicine. Hyperthyroidism is the result of too much thyroxin secretion. It manifests itself in nervousness, high basal metabolism, and a generally high-strung disposition. Its most characteristic symptom is protrusion of the eyeballs in adults. Hyperthyroidism is treated by removal of part of the thyroid by surgery, X rays, or radioactive iodine whose radiation destroys cells. More recently, the drug thiouracil is administered to slow down the production of thyroxin.

Then came Frederick G. Banting with *insulin*, and the pulse of the whole world was quickened by as spectacular an achievement as that of Pasteur or the Curies. *Diabetes mellitus*, first described two thousand years ago as "a melting of the flesh which flows away in the urine," was associated with the pancreatic gland for almost three centuries. Attempts were made to treat diabetics with extracts of this gland, but all failed. Then Banting, a young Canadian surgeon fresh from a wound at Cambrai during World War I, came back to the University of Toronto. Trying to find a cure for diabetes, he had stumbled over a fresh clue. On the night of October 30, 1920, while preparing for a lecture, he read something that Dr. Moses Barron of the University of Minnesota had reported to the effect that the tying up of the pancreatic ducts led to the death of those very cells which produced a chemical named trypsin. It was this trypsin which destroyed the excess of the active principle of the islets of Langerhans, and this accounted to a great extent for the failure of many of the early experimenters to get successful results with their pancreatic extracts. Previous to Banting's researches, the ducts were not cut off and hence the trypsin destroyed the insulin which had accumulated in the pancreas.

Banting reasoned that before the pancreas is removed, the duct leading to it should be tied to prevent trypsin from destroying the cells which produce the active antidiabetic principle. At two in the morning, he jotted down three sentences in his notebook: "Tie off pancreatic ducts of dogs. Wait 6-8 weeks for degeneration. Remove the residue and extract." He went to Professor J. R. Macleod, an authority on the pathology and physiology of diabetes. Banting told his story—he wanted laboratory facilities, an assistant for eight weeks, and ten dogs on which to experiment. His wish was granted.

Banting prepared an extract of the pancreas of dogs whose pancreatic ducts had been tied. On the morning of July 27, 1921, he shot the filtered liquid into the jugular vein of one of his dogs which he had rendered diabetic by removing its pancreas. Charles H. Best, a twenty-one-year-old medical student, borrowed money from Banting to be able to carry on research that summer. He had been assigned by Macleod to do the blood-sugar analyses. When the cry of "the blood sugar is down" reached across that hot laboratory, Banting knew he had saved a dog from a diabetic death. Six months later a still purer pancreatic extract was tried for the first time on a human being, a young lad of fourteen lying in the Toronto General Hospital in the coma that had always meant diabetic death. The magic juice brought him back from the brink of the grave. Today millions of living insulin takers bear testimony to this miracle of medicine and chemistry. For this achievement Banting was awarded the Nobel Prize in medicine, was given a life annuity of $7500 by the Canadian government, and was later elevated to knighthood. He lost his life in an airplane accident during World War II while on a government mission.

Several Americans had come very close to beating the Canadians in this insulin adventure. In 1911, for example, Ernest L. Scott, working in a Chicago laboratory, actually tied the pancreatic ducts of dogs. When success was almost in his hands, he had failed to interpret some of his findings and dropped the investigation. Then there was John R. Murlin of the University of Rochester, who rendered the urine of a pancreatomized dog sugar-free for six continuous hours, only to drop his hypodermic for a gun to go overseas. It was the old story so often repeated in the gamble of science. Priestley, discoverer of oxygen, had attributed his success to chance—chance which, to be sure, favored the mind prepared with the proper tools at the most opportune moment.

By injecting the needed insulin into the diabetic patient we relieve his condition but do not cure it. Without insulin, sugar taken into the body cannot be properly utilized. The sugar accumulates and then gradually passes off in the urine. The diabetic patient whose pancreas cannot produce any or enough insulin loses this essential source of energy and must be supplied with it artificially. Until medicine can find a way to prevent the sickening or atrophy of the pancreas, diabetics are doomed to continuous hypodermic injections of insulin, which cannot be effectively taken by mouth, as the ferments of the digestive tract split it and render it inactive.

Abel wanted to save diabetics from the dreaded prick of the needle. How much more pleasant it would be to take insulin by mouth! It was first necessary, however, to isolate the pure principle or hormone of the potent extract that Banting was using. That was Abel's first goal, which he finally reached one afternoon in November, 1925. Less than half a gram of insulin crystals appeared on the bottom of his flask. They were tested on rabbits and found to be pure. By microanalysis the chemical composition was later found to be $C_{254}H_{377}N_{65}O_{75}S_6$—a complex protein. His next job was to learn whether the whole insulin molecule was needed for its lifesaving effects. If he could break it into fragments, discover the architecture of this complex compound, he might be able to find one potent portion resistant to the juices of the alimentary canal. For years Abel worked on this problem. When death finally took him from his beaker and stirring rod, the job was taken up by the younger men he had trained in this work, and by many others in laboratories all over the world. In 1954 Frederick Sanger and his associates at Cambridge University in England, after ten years of exhaustive work, took some pure crystals of insulin, which in turn had taken years of blood and sweat by other scientists to prepare, and broke them down piece by piece and bit by bit until they had worked out the entire sequence of its amino acids and the complete structure of its molecule. Its full structural formula would fill two whole pages of this book. It is the first protein whose chemical architecture has been unraveled.

Having taken this chemical watch apart and painstakingly studied all of its many parts, the chemist was confronted with an even more difficult task—that of putting them together and synthesizing the first protein molecule in history. Could scientists really manufacture a protein that would tick as effectively as the natural insulin of the animal body? Thus far, no success. Proteins still defy synthesis. However, the world awaits such a chemical miracle with hope and a modest degree of assurance that it will be accomplished before many more years have gone by.

One of that countless number of diabetics whose lives were saved by insulin was a country surgeon in the San Joaquin Valley of the West. Dr. C. W. Evans of Modesto, California, was surgeon to the Pacific Railway in the early days, and would often be called away from his private practice to operate on victims of train wrecks. More than once he would take on these journeys of mercy his son, Herbert, whom he dreamed of making a great surgeon someday. The family already boasted several eminent physicians. Among them was Robert A. McLean, Herbert's uncle, who was the first master surgeon of California.

When Herbert grew up he entered his father's alma mater, the University of California, where scientific research began to beckon to him. The surgeon frowned upon his son's early determination to take up research as a career. He wanted the boy to study medicine and take his place beside his father in California. Herbert Evans was not deterred from his determination, however, even though it meant working his way through college as a student assistant. After graduation, he went to Johns Hopkins, where a new era in graduate education in the United States had been initiated in 1876. Here, for the first time in this country, facilities for graduate study in many fields were available. American scientists no longer had to sit at the feet of European bigwigs in science to prepare themselves for work at home. William Welch, John Abel, and many other leading men of science in this country had gone to Europe for their final training, but younger men like Herbert Evans and Elmer McCollum found the training at Johns Hopkins equally effective for a broad preparation. The tide of American students to Europe slackened, and in time European students even made their way toward our own shores.

At Johns Hopkins, Evans came under the powerful influence of Professor Franklin P. Mall, who taught physiological rather than structural anatomy. Structure to Mall was important only insofar as it threw light on function. Years later, in 1915, when Herbert Evans was made professor of anatomy at the University of California, his father, watching him fuss around with test tube, animal cages, and microscope, was flabbergasted. "Son," he said, "are you a professor of anatomy? Can you describe this bone?" holding out the sphenoid bone. His father's anatomy was the old structural anatomy; he had never used a microscope through all of his schooling. When his son's answer was in terms of knowledge not strictly structural, the old man's countenance fell. "The University of California must have fallen so low," he sighed, "as to call you a professor of anatomy." When, however, the miracle of insulin saved his life, he agreed with his son that "this monkey business of research is all right."

Evans had spoken of the possibilities of specialization to his teacher, Jacques Loeb, who had counseled him: "Don't be a classified scientist. Step out into new fields, and don't be afraid to impinge on other fields." Evans took the advice. The boundaries of science were fast falling; men were poaching on each other's territories with reckless abandon, and it was difficult to remain pent up in one's own chosen field. Evans started as anatomist, became interested in embryology, grew tired of cutting up tissues, and, wanting to see each step in the body drama, was caught up in the snare of the dynamics of biological research, including gland work.

Even as Banting was slaying dogs to save men, Evans was achieving a startling discovery in this field with another mysterious gland, *hypophysis cerebri*, commonly called the *pituitary*. This is a bit of an organ safely housed in a small pocket of bone attached to the base of the brain. Both Galen, a Greek physician of the second century, and Andreas Vesalius, the great Belgian physician who lived about four hundred years ago, knew of this gland and thought it supplied the body with spit (in Latin, *sputus*). It is one of the most inaccessible glands in the living body. For many years it had been surmised that there was some connection between body growth and the functioning of this gland. In 1783 Dr. John Hunter had bargained with an undertaker for the body of Charles O'Brien, an Irish giant of eight feet, four inches, who had died at the age of twenty-two. The physician finally bought the body for twenty-five hundred dollars, and found a pituitary almost as large as a hen's egg. That of a normal adult man weighs hardly more than half a gram. A century later, *acromegaly*, an enlargement of the hands, feet, nose, lips, and jaw, was declared to be due to a tumor of the pituitary. The pituitary glands of midgets such as Martina de la Cruz, who stood only twenty-one inches high to the day of his death at the age of seventy-four, all showed relatively small development or partial atrophy.

In the attempt to discover if the pituitary elaborated a hormone which controlled growth, Evans prepared water extracts of the pituitary glands of oxen obtained from slaughter and packing houses. In 1920 he first unsuccessfully tried oral administration of large masses of the pituitary, and then turned to injection of his extracts in baby rats. Within a few months he obtained giant rats; not just fat ones, but giants with overgrowth of bones, heart, liver, lung, kidneys, alimentary tract, and other organs. When Evans discontinued the injections soon after the weaning of the rat, the growth stopped immediately. When he injected his extract into rats dwarfed by removal of their pituitaries, the beasts regained their normal size. Lancelot Hogben in England later used a similar extract on a large aquatic salamander, and got a rapid metamorphosis. In 1922 Evans and Joseph A. Long announced the discovery of this growth-promoting hormone in the *Anatomical Record*.

If this miracle could be achieved with rats, why could it not be repeated with man? Were not the compositions and physiological actions of hormones identical regardless of the kind of animal from which they had been obtained? Was not insulin from sheep identical with insulin extracted from man, cow, pig, or even pollack or codfish? When Evans had prepared a purer and more potent extract, this experiment was actually tried on a girl, J. M., nine years old. Dr. William Engelbach of New York City treated this child, whose physical development had been dormant for almost four years, and in 1931 announced a growth of 2.7 inches obtained over a period of about eight months. Other physicians followed this treatment and more striking successes were reported. One undersized boy of fifteen gained eight and a half inches in twenty-one months.

Some saw visions of a not far distant day when midgets, giants, and dwarfs would go the way of the *Brontosaurus* and the armored dinosaur, themselves the victims of faulty glands, into oblivion. Perhaps the mushroom which Alice in Wonderland had found, one side of which will make you grow taller and the other side will make you grow shorter, was in reality the pituitary extract of Evans in California. Some pictured a race of giants springing up at the prick of a hypodermic. What would such undersized men as Croesus, King of Lydia, and Attila, the Hun, not have given to be changed to giants or even to men of normal size? But Evans himself did not break out in wild romancing. "It is said," he remarked, "that the Mikado wished to add to the stature of the Japanese soldiers. The growth-promoting hormone should be able to do it, but even the Mikado could not pay the price that it would cost at present."

The pituitary turned out to be the most complicated gland of all. It elaborates more than a dozen different hormones and appears to be the chief co-ordinator of all the other glands of the body. It has been called the "master gland," and much of its functioning still remains one of the riddles of science.

Several years even before Evans' investigation of the growth-stimulating hormone of the anterior (front part) of the pituitary, Harvey Cushing, famous surgeon of the Harvard Medical School, had removed parts of the pituitaries of two hundred dogs and had reported other changes besides arrest of growth. A sex-stimulating hormone seemed to be involved. His dogs became obese and sluggish, and their sex organs shrank. Evans, too, had found that his extract, while enabling the animal to resume growth, was powerless to restimulate the sex function of his rats. Mating in female rats deprived of their pituitaries did not result in discharge of ova, but if the gland was removed less than one hour before coitus, ova were discharged. Perhaps the anterior lobe of the pituitary gland was the seat of a second hormone—one which stimulated the production of ova.

A number of investigators undertook this research. A technique for handling the problem was available, worked out in 1917 by an American, Charles R. Stockard, and George N. Papanicolaou, one of his students who came from Greece. They had found that smears taken at various times from the vagina of the guinea pig showed under the microscope a differentiation in the kind of cells present. In animals the period of sexual activity, or oestrus, coincides with the discharge of ova. When their guinea pig was in oestrus, the cells consisted of clearly defined types and stained a bright red with the dye eosin. When it was not in heat, the cells were different. Hence, by examining vaginal smears taken at different times, the sexual activity of the animal could easily be determined. In 1922 Evans and Joseph A. Long worked out by means of this technique the regular clocklike cycle of the rat. It was found to be four days as compared with the guinea pig's oestral cycle of seventeen days and the human cycle of about thirty days.

The following year Philip E. Smith, working in Evans' laboratory at Berkeley, California, illuminated the whole field by devising a very skillful technique, including the use of a dissecting microscope, which enabled him with comparative ease to reach and remove the pituitary of the rat through incision in the throat. Deterioration of the sex function always followed removal of the pituitary. Then he also conclusively proved that it was something in the pituitary which had powers of sex stimulation, by implanting under the skin of a rat from which the pituitary had been removed the same gland obtained from another rat. This transplant led to repair of the sex damage and even to precocious sex functioning. Grafting the entire gland was not altogether necessary because injections of extracts of the gland produced the same effect.

Smith, later professor of anatomy at the College of Physicians and Surgeons in New York, was fortunate in using the rat in his transplantation experiments, for the guinea pig, rabbit, cat, and dog do not respond to this treatment. But he was also very unlucky. Four months before he could announce the results of his work, Bernhard Zondek and Selmar Aschheim, in Germany, published a report of their pituitary implants in immature young animals. They had also succeeded for the first time in obtaining fairly potent extracts of the gonadotropic hormone of the pituitary which stimulates secretions of ovaries and testes. H. L. Fevold and F. L. Hisaw of Harvard University broke this extract down further into two separate hormones. One is the luteinizing hormone (LH) which induces ovulation and gonadal hormone secretion. The other is the follicle-stimulating hormone (FSH) which stimulates the ovarian follicles and the formation of sperm by the testes.

In the course of his investigations Zondek found that injections of the urine of pregnant women had the same effect on mice as did his pituitary extract. This led Aschheim and Zondek to the discovery of the first reliable human pregnancy test. This test, much modified and improved since 1928, consists of injecting urine of the woman being tested under the skin of a nonmated female mouse, rabbit, or frog. About twenty-four hours later the animal is killed, and its sex organs upon examination show certain definite cellular changes. This method, which is ninety-nine per cent accurate, will determine human pregnancy as early as ten days after the missed period.

Hard on the heels of these developments came the announcement of the discovery of a fourth hormone of the anterior pituitary. Oscar Riddle of Cold Spring Harbor, Long Island, fed a pituitary extract to pigeons and found that their ability to secrete crop-milk was appreciably enhanced. This milk-producing hormone, which Riddle named *prolactin*, produced milk in the mammary glands of other animals, including the males: even a tomcat gave milk after being injected with this hormone. Later Riddle reported that his prolactin also stimulated the mother instinct. A hen which had refused to display any maternal instinct started to cluck two days after being injected with this hormone, and the next day it began to incubate and nest. A full-grown unmated female rat, which had been injected with the extract, instead of devouring two helpless pigeon squabs placed in its cage tenderly nursed them. Perhaps, someday, it has been humorously suggested, mother love will be bought at the corner drugstore at so many pennies a bottle.

A fifth hormone in the anterior pituitary was reported in 1933 by a French investigator who claimed thyroid stimulation as one of its effects. It is now known as thyrotropin (TSH).

In the meantime, Evans became director of the Institute of Experimental Biology of the University of California and kept plugging away at the problem of obtaining his "growth-promoting" hormone of the pituitary gland in a pure form. He used hundreds of beef pituitaries, and female rats by the score. In 1939 he announced that he had separated the growth hormone. There were still some scientists who regarded his product not as the pure growth hormone but rather as a complex. Others were not ready to accept the substance he had extracted as the *only* growth hormone. By 1941 the lactogenic or milk-stimulating hormone, as well as the thyrotropic hormone of the pituitary, seemed to have been chemically purified. These chemicals were injected into animals and growth effects were reported. The controversy was reopened. "The long fight to get my baby legitimized," wrote Evans, "gave me zest because I had plenty of opposition." Riddle asserted that while the concept of the growth hormone as an individual entity had been a very useful one, it was not necessarily true. Evans, however, saw a different picture. "It is still a fact, gentlemen," he told a group of scientists working in this area of research, "that no mammal has had administered to it the lactogenic and thyrotropic hormones in question and been seen to grow precipitously as in the case when proper concentration of the growth hormones are given, and I think you will agree with me that no mixture of these two materials has yet been made which will confer any growth effects remotely comparable to those so readily obtained when we administer what we must still provisionally designate as *the* 'growth hormone.'" According to Evans, neither thyrotropic, nor lactogenic, nor gonadotropic hormones are essential to the growth effect of the rat caused by pituitary extracts. In 1941 he showed that the presence of the thymus gland is not essential, either, to the growth of female rats. Three years later, Canton-born Choh Hao Li, who had taken his doctorate under Evans, finally succeeded in purifying the growth hormone from ox pituitaries.

The material appeared as a single protein substance in electrophoresis. All biological assays were performed with female rats whose pituitaries had been removed at the age of twenty-seven days. Intraperitoneal injections were begun about fourteen days later and were continued once daily for ten days. It did not show any lactogenic, thyrotropic, follicle-stimulating, interstitial-cell, or adrenocorticotropic-stimulating effects. It seemed to be a pure compound. Choh and Evans reported this in *Science*. Even this did not end the controversy. Charles R. Stockard believed that the disagreement and consequent confusion in this field were due to the fact that the true nature of growth was still not thoroughly understood, and that until the exact physiology of this process had been thoroughly unraveled the confusion would continue. In 1954 a three-day symposium on the growth hormone was held at the Edsel Ford Institute in Detroit. Evans, who was to be one of the main speakers, could not attend because of illness, but he was delighted at the remarkable attention given to this hormone. "This," he wrote, "is perhaps the most distinguished way in which a new baby has been baptized, i.e., to have an entire congress held on the subject."

To Evans belongs another, perhaps greater, honor. He and his associates, Choh Hao Li and Miriam E. Simpson, were the first to purify the sixth of the hormones of the anterior hypophesis. This hormone, which stimulates the outer covering or bark of the adrenal gland to produce more of its own hormone, known as cortisone, is generally referred to as ACTH, or the *adrenocorticotropic hormone*. H. D. Moon of Evans' laboratory had used rats to determine the purity of their product, and five years later, in 1942, Evans and his associates purified their sheep extract further. In 1949 its use in the treatment of rheumatoid arthritis and rheumatic fever electrified the world. Dr. Philip S. Hench, a leading authority on arthritis, and Edward C. Kendall, the biochemist who had isolated thyroxin and, later, cortisone, demonstrated that they could control both of these ailments in many cases with cortisone and ACTH. Hench and Kendall of the Mayo Clinic of Rochester, Minnesota, held out hope for millions of sufferers all over the world.

The Nobel Prize in medicine was awarded them in 1950 for the alleviation of rheumatoid arthritis by the administration of cortisone or hydrocortisone (Kendall's compounds E and F). At the Mayo Clinic and in many other places ACTH was also used and shown to exert the same effects as the adrenal-cortical hormone.

Evans' purified product was made available by Armour and Company to prominent endocrine clinicians of the United States. Extracts of cortisone were difficult to obtain. To accumulate a single gram of it (1/30-ounce) 180,000 sheep had to be slaughtered and their adrenals removed. To collect an equal amount of ACTH the pituitaries of tens of thousands of hogs had to be removed, scraped, and treated. This was too slow and costly a process. What was needed was a method of preparing them synthetically. In spite of the difficulties of creating these very complex compounds, several attempts were made, first to determine their chemical structure.

With a feeling of great urgency, chemists went to work to build the life-giving compounds. Many joined the adventure. Robert B. Woodward, who, at the age of twenty, had received his Ph.D. at the Massachusetts Institute of Technology, won the battle at least with cortisone ($C_{21}H_{28}O_5$). He not only determined its molecular structure but finally also synthesized it in 1953. The following year Woodward, who had already also synthesized morphine, added the drug strychnine to his successes. This came only after more than a century of labor by countless men and women.

But ACTH was infinitely more stubborn. It refused to yield even to the most skillful and persevering of synthetic chemists. Why? Because it is a protein, like its brother hormone, insulin. However, in 1955, two teams of research scientists working in the laboratories of the American Cyanamid Company, and another team operating under Choh Hao Li in Evans' laboratory, came up with its three-dimensional picture. They reported that it consisted of no less than fifty-nine amino-acid units linked together in the form of a long chain of atoms.

While working on ACTH, Evans, Li and associates discovered an amazing antagonism in the action of ACTH and their growth hormone. In 1944 they reported that they could defeat the growth effects of the growth hormone by administering ACTH concurrently, and "we had then in this way produced a new kind of dwarf—the ACTH dwarf."

The pituitary is, in a sense, a double gland. It consists of two lobes. The posterior part of this gland produces its own hormones. Two of these, *oxytocin* and *vasopressin*, led biochemists a merry chase for many years before they were pinned down, purified, analyzed, and finally synthesized. Among the many investigators who grappled with these endocrines was an American biochemist, Vincent du Vigneaud. Born in Chicago in 1901, he was graduated from the University of Illinois and gained his doctorate under John R. Murlin at the University of Rochester School of Medicine. Murlin was the man who, back in 1917, almost beat Banting to the discovery of insulin. Du Vigneaud began work on the posterior pituitary in 1932 while on the faculty of George Washington University in Washington, D. C. He continued it when he joined Cornell University Medical College in New York City.

Oxytocin was first recognized as a chemical entity as early as 1906 and obtained in relatively pure form in 1952. Du Vigneaud determined its chemical structure and soon after succeeded in synthesizing it. This was a historic occasion, for it was the first polypeptide hormone to be made artificially. Since it stimulates the contraction of the uterus it is sometimes injected after childbirth for that purpose. It also aids in the release of milk from the mammary glands of the mother.

Vasopressin, another polypeptide, was also studied by Du Vigneaud and also synthesized by him. It is the pressor principle of the pituitary; that is, it causes constriction of the small arteries and thus increases blood pressure. It is also an antidiuretic, since, in its absence, the individual excretes large amounts of urine. It is used in the treatment of *diabetes insipidus*, and also in the diagnosis of epilepsy. For these extended and successful researches Du Vigneaud was honored with the Nobel Prize in medicine in 1955.

Many others were busy in the hormone field. In the biochemical laboratory of the St. Louis University School of Medicine, Edward A. Doisy read Zondek's original report, which gave him a new lead in his hunt for the hormone of the ovary gland. He had already worked with the follicular liquid of pigs' ovaries with some success. To check the potency of his extract he made use of the vaginal-smear method developed by Colorado-born Edgar Allen, who later became head of the department of anatomy at the Yale School of Medicine. Allen had made a brilliant study of the sex cycle of another animal, the mouse. From lying-in hospitals, Doisy collected thousands of gallons of urine of pregnant women. By devising new condensers and novel setups of distillation apparatus, he was able to handle as much as fifty gallons of urine at a time. For six years he worked with all sorts of solvents on the problem of separating a hormone from this fluid, until he obtained an extremely potent substance present in urine only to the extent of one part in four million. In 1929 Doisy announced his isolation of a pure crystalline hormone of the ovary. Two of the most experienced biochemists of Europe, Adolf Butenandt of Göttingen and Ernst Laqueur of Amsterdam, had been beaten in the quest by but a few months.

Theelin (from the Greek *theelus*, meaning female) was the name first chosen for the new hormone by its discoverer. This was later changed to *estrone*. Its composition was found to be $C_{18}H_{22}O_2$. Seven years later, Russell E. Marker of the Pennsylvania State College synthesized this first member of the estrogens from ergosterol. Other investigators found this same chemical in the ovaries of monkey, horse, sheep, cow, pig, and fowl, and in their feces. Several other female sex hormones, such as alpha-estradiol and estriol, were found by Doisy and various other workers. *Estradiol* is the primary female sex hormone. It is responsible for the bodily changes in the female at puberty. It is manufactured by the cells lining the cavity of each follicle in the ovary and is ten times as potent as estrone.

Another ovarian hormone is *progesterone* ($C_{21}H_{30}O_2$) which is elaborated by the corpus luteum, the yellowish liquid formed from the mature (Graafian) follicles of the ovary after rupture and discharge of their ova. Progesterone was obtained as a crude extract by George W. Corner at the University of Rochester in 1930. It was prepared in pure form in Butenandt's and three other laboratories in 1934 and then synthesized. It prepares the lining of the uterus for the implantation of the egg and nourishment of the developing embryo. It inhibits contraction of the muscles and prevents expulsion of the embryo from the uterus. It is believed to be an intermediate chemical in the synthesis of both estradiol and the male sex hormone. Butenandt found it in palm-nut oil also. The richest source of female sex hormones is in the urine of pregnant animals and of stallions. They have been used with some apparent measure of success in the treatment of hemophilia, of thickening of the vagina of children, in the alleviation of abnormal menstrual conditions, in the temporary adjustment of severe menopause symptoms, in the prevention of periodic migraine and of senile affections; and in cases of functional sterility, delayed puberty, infantilism, and frigidity.

After this dramatic American scoop, a renewed attack was launched on the androgens or male sex hormones. A group of University of Chicago workers, under the direction of F. C. Koch and the guidance of the Committee for Research on Problems of Sex, had been busy on this research since 1923. Lemuel C. McGee, one of these workers, succeeded in obtaining an extract from fresh, finely chopped bull testes tissue, which proved effective in a test, based on a fact known for centuries. The removal of the testes of a cock changes it into a bird with flesh more tender than that of the normal male. The castrated fowl, called a capon, is different from the cock in other respects, also. The operation has psychic effects, changing the courageous, combative rooster into a timid, peaceful, maternal animal, which seldom crows, and in some cases even takes care of chicks like a hen. Another very noticeable change takes place on the head furnishings. The comb and wattles become less developed, and the bright, exuberant, ornamental feathering of the male less colorful.

In 1927 McGee injected his extract into a capon. Its small comb soon became large and upright, and its wattles, too, grew larger. His extract contained the male hormone which was responsible for the growth of these male characters. Then Koch and his wife began purifying the extract in the hope of obtaining the pure crystal principle. As test animals they used capons from which every vestige of the sex glands was surgically removed. While other members of the same laboratory were trying out both the guinea pig and the rat as possible test animals, word came from Europe in 1932 that a pure male hormone had been isolated in crystal form. This time Adolf Butenandt, who had previously lost out to Doisy in the isolation of a female sex hormone, was the victor. He had obtained the hormone from the kidney fluids of men rather than from their sex gland. Its formula was given as $C_{19}H_{30}O_2$, not very different from that of estrone. In fact, Butenandt theorized that it could be made from the female hormone. Late in 1934 L. Ruzicka of the Zurich Technical High School synthesized it from cholesterol obtained from the grease of sheep's wool.

This male hormone, named *androsterone,* is present in male urine and is not the hormone of the testes. It is found only in urine and is believed to be an excretory product of an adrenal cortex hormone of both man and woman. The testicular hormone, the true primary male sex hormone, was first obtained in pure crystal form by E. Laqueur of Holland in 1935. It was named *testosterone.* He isolated it from the testis tissue of bulls, in which it is present in extremely minute quantities. It is the same substance obtained from the male sex gland of boar, goat, man, and, strangely enough, the male blossoms of the pussy willow. This second male hormone has the chemical formula $C_{19}H_{28}O_2$, almost the same as that of androsterone. It is much more potent than androsterone. Within a few months Ruzicka and Butenandt reported the synthesis of this hormone also.

For the first time science had the two pure, most prominent members of the male sex hormones or androgens to evaluate the claims of the school of rejuvenation through sex-gland operations. The craze for rejuvenation by means of sex glands started in 1889. In that year Charles E. Brown-Séquard, son of an American sea captain, and at one time professor of neuropathology at

Harvard, addressed the Society of Biologists in Paris. He told his audience how he had injected himself with crude water extracts of the secretions of the testes of a dog, in an attempt at rejuvenation. This treatment, he claimed, had warded off the effects of advancing age. A large cult of gland therapeutists and rejuvenation charlatans sprang up overnight. Its members were armed to the teeth with the "evidence" of this distinguished professor, who occupied the chair left vacant by the death of Claude Bernard, the great physiologist of France—the man who had coined the term *internal secretions*.

This craze reached its height in the United States about 1919 in the widely advertised experiments of Serge Voronoff of Vienna and Eugen Steinach in Paris. Said Voronoff, after preliminary experiments with castrated rams, goats, bulls, and horses, "In 1913 I discovered a stock of spare parts for the human machine in the bodies of the higher species of monkeys. Between 1920 and 1928 I did one thousand human grafts." Newspapers gave wide publicity to these reports. Some believed tales of monkey children born of parents who had taken the monkey-gland treatment. Cartoons satirized the stories, rumors spread of men murdered to furnish surgeons with their healthy glands. Gertrude Atherton shocked many with her novel, *Black Oxen*, which told the story of a woman who, getting along in years and losing her vitality, subjected herself to gland therapy.

After the discovery of the sex hormones, Steinach replaced his famous monkey-gland technique, which required surgical operations, with simple estrogen or testosterone injections. But the problem of restoring youthful vigor to the old still remained unsolved. Said Stockard, "Steinach and Voronoff were misled into the belief that degeneration of the sex gland is itself responsible for the aging process. This is an error. It is a symptom and not a cause. The ox, the castrated horse, and the capon do not age either faster or slower than their normal prototypes, the bull, the stallion, and rooster." Voronoff performed about three thousand monkey-gland operations, while senile and other foolish people continued to pursue him, dreaming of the restored vigor of youth. One distinguished scientist summed up the majority of scientific opinion with the remark, "If the transplant be from goat or monkey, the surgeon is the monkey, the patient is the goat."

The isolation of the pure estrogens and androgens has enabled science to attempt to fathom a little deeper the many problems of sex which have bothered men for centuries. Various explanations of the mechanism of sex determination have been made. There have been theories galore to explain why certain organisms are male and others female. Aristotle thought that the male supplied the form of species, and that if the male seed was not vigorous we got an imperfect organism, or female. For centuries many believed that the contents of the right testicle produced the male while that of the left produced a female; that when an old male mated with a young female, a female was always born; that the age of the father, the diet of the mother, the temperature at the time of conception, and even the wind direction were determining factors. As late as 1933, one scientist attempted to prove that an excess of alkaline substances such as sodium bicarbonate produced male progeny, while an excess of acid compounds, like lactic acid found in sour milk, stimulated the birth of females.

The bubbling kettle of hormone research boiled over and almost engulfed the theory of sex determination based on the gene or X-Y chromosome mechanism first demonstrated by T. H. Morgan's school of geneticists. They had piled up convincing evidence of its plausibility, especially in the case of Drosophila. Today science, while still very far from one universally accepted theory of sex determination, has taken the position that both the nature of the chromosomes and the functioning of the various glands of the body are the chief determining factors. The ultimate determinant in human and most other organisms is chromosomal. Specifically, if the embryo contains two X chromosomes in each cell it will grow up to be a female. If it contains one X and one Y it will grow up to be a male. Just how the chromosomes control the development of sex is still a mystery. We do know, however, that one of the more immediate causes of sexual development lies in the sex hormones. We do know a good deal about the interaction of the various glands. There is a complex feedback system whereby each gland controls others. All keep each other in balance. We still know nothing, however, about how the chromosomes control the formation of hormones or any other aspect of sex.

Morgan, who believed that many if not all of the genes are sex-determining in the same way that many if not all affect the development of each character, said: "There is a double relation in sex-determination. Normally the presence of certain genes determines sex, but under unusual conditions their power may be partially overcome and even a reversal of sex may take place. Temperature, light, hormones, or 'age' may cause the reversal." Many examples of sex reversals have been cited to uphold this position. In cold weather, the gypsy moth produces more females. The worm *Guibea protanduca* is male in autumn and winter, female in the spring, and neuter in the summer. A starved male salamander may turn into a female. Nansen, the explorer, reported that the deepwater bagfish remains male when small, but changes to female when a foot long. The starfish *Asterina gibbosa* may be male, female, or both, according to age and circumstances. Certain old female fish develop testes and function as males.

The subject is still extremely complicated. The eminent German refugee geneticist Richard Goldschmidt, at one time professor at the University of California, believed that both the male and the female contain both male and female potentialities which are the result of genetic determinants. His conclusion was based on results obtained by crossing female European gypsy moths (*Lymantria dispar*) with male Japanese gypsy moths. He obtained normal sons but, instead of daughters, he found individuals with a mixture of female and male characteristics (*intersexes*). He defined an intersex as an individual who starts development with one sex but changes sex at a certain critical turning point during development. He believed the female sex factor is carried by the cytoplasm of the egg.

The later discovery that the sex hormones are very much alike in chemical composition and that there is evidence of their changing from one into another in the living body has brought further confusion into the problem of sex. Evans is of the opinion that "maleness or femaleness cannot be looked upon as implying the presence of one hormone and the absence of the other, but that differences in the amounts of these two may be expected to characterize each sex." There is still another explanation. Frank R. Lillie of the University of Chicago believed that each cell produced by the union of an ovum and a sperm is potentially hermaphroditic, and that glandular disturbances, environment, or other conditions might cause one sex to become stronger than the other. He also maintained that the sex of these cells and the sex in the body structure are two different things.

Herbert S. Jennings in 1932 summed up the problem of sex determination as follows: "Many of the effects of the gene in development are produced through the action of the hormones they manufacture. *What hormone is present depends again on what set of genes was present in the beginning.*"

Research men were busy with other glands besides the pituitary which produce more than one hormone. The adrenal glands give up another chemical messenger which if thwarted on its errand of life leaves dangerous consequences. In 1927 Frank A. Hartman of the University of Buffalo announced the separation of a potent extract of a hormone from the outer layers of the adrenal gland. The absence of this substance, he believed, led to Addison's disease, first described in 1855 by Dr. Thomas Addison and characterized by low blood pressure, muscular weakness, digestive upsets, and bronzing of the skin.

The life span of adrenalectomized animals was prolonged by administering this extract. Tadeus Reichstein in Switzerland and Edward C. Kendall and others in the United States found more than twenty-eight different substances with hormonal properties in these extracts. Two of the most active of them are desoxycorticosterone and aldosterone ($C_{21}H_{28}O_5$), discovered in 1953. The first is used in the treatment of Addison's disease and can almost bring the dead back to life. The second, isolated by Reichstein and others, is used for sodium salt retention. Reichstein shared the Nobel Prize in medicine with Kendall for this work.

The parathyroids, two pairs of brown bean-shaped and pea-sized bits of tissue situated on the sides of the thyroid gland, also surrendered a hormone, *parathormone*, at the hands of James B. Collip, who had worked with Banting on insulin. Adolf M. Hanson, a physician of Faribault, Minnesota, had reported a similar extract in a little-known journal and later proved priority. The patent received for this product he assigned to the Smithsonian Institution. This hormone, still unnamed and of unknown composition, is involved in the regulation of calcium and phosphate metabolism. Too much calcium results in extreme excitement and muscular rigidity associated with tetany. It is therefore used in the treatment of tetany.

The significance of still another gland, the thymus, is being investigated by American scientists. This is a soft, pinkish mass located above the heart, where it grows from about a quarter of an ounce at birth to more than a full ounce and remains so to puberty. After that, it shrinks until it becomes only a tiny remnant. In 1934 Leonard G. Rowntree, who had worked with John Abel, fed thymus extracts to rats and reported most curious results. Each successive generation of thymus-fed rats seemed to show faster growth rates and greater sexual precocity. Thymus extract catapulted rats into parenthood at an alarming speed.

Twenty years later Albert Szent-Györgyi obtained a yellow powder from the thymus of calves and found evidence of a growth hormone in it. The implications of these observations were obvious. This "precocity" hormone might revolutionize the livestock industry, for example. Cattle might be raised in a fraction of the time now required, with a corresponding decrease in cost. However, in spite of several other investigations of this alleged hormone, no clear-cut evidence of its existence has yet been found.

The last of the organs of the body to be probed is the pineal gland. This cone-shaped tissue hidden in the brain still tenaciously conceals the secret of its function. In 1957 Dr. Mark D. Altschule of the Harvard Medical School obtained some improvement in a few chronically ill mental patients injected with protein-free extracts of this gland from beef cattle, but he warned against premature enthusiasm. The following year a research team from the dermatology section of the Yale University School of Medicine headed by Dr. Aaron B. Lerner reported the isolation of 1.5 mg. of a pure hormone from the same source. This hormone, extracted from the gland which René Descartes thought was the seat of the soul, was named *melatonin*. It appeared to lighten frog skin in laboratory animals.

In addition to the large diversity of hormones elaborated in the body there seems to be an interrelation between almost all of them, making the path to their understanding a veritable labyrinth. The numerous byways and side paths often obscure the main road. For example, adrenaline seems to inhibit the action of insulin, and cortin acts as a brake on thyroxin, which, in turn, affects estrone. This has led some scientists to compare the endocrines to "a system of weights and pulleys, in stable equilibrium, in which removal of any one weight causes the whole system to hang awry."

The study of the endocrines has introduced a new medicine and a new psychiatry, which are still in their infancy. In the field of psychiatry Stockard produced some evidence to show the relation between glands and personality. Working with dogs at the Cornell University Experimental Morphology Farm, he showed that pronounced personalities are often hereditary, but that in all cases they are associated with peculiar reactions of the glands of internal secretion. He found a glandular complex responsible for a paralytic condition in some races of dogs. And he produced types of dogs which virtually parallel in growth and form certain human freaks whose abnormalities have been traced to glandular disturbances. It has also been shown that the nervous system acts on the sex glands. A bird from whose nest the eggs had been removed as fast as she laid them produced as many eggs in forty days as she might normally have laid in five years. Some are convinced that the applied physiology of the future will discover ways of modifying personality by means of hormones. Reasonable men do not talk of making robots with temperaments according to specifications—kind, even-tempered, able men instead of mean, irascible, stupid ones—but they are digging away wherever there is light, hoping to make the biological control of life a more certain achievement.

Other factors besides the hormones affect the health and personality of people. The study of the vitamins and the newer knowledge of nutrition, in general, represent another of the bright pictures of American research. As with the hormones, American contributions in this field have been basic. Evans is one of the few individuals who did pioneer work in both fields. He made classic contributions not only to the study of the hormones but also added original discoveries and achievements in the realm of the vitamins. He did his work not primarily as a chemist but rather as an anatomist and physiologist interested in all the interrelated factors affecting the life process.

"The outstanding event," wrote Elmer V. McCollum recently, "which stimulated interest and experimental inquiry into reproductive failure of dietary origin was the announcement in 1922 by Evans that rats raised on certain diets capable of inducing growth were of low fertility in the first generation and wholly sterile in the second."

Evans began his study of the vitamins while working at the Institute of Experimental Biology of the University of California on the sex cycle of the rat. He was investigating this problem in connection with his hormone studies. The diet of his animals interested him as just another factor which might affect this cycle. Vitamins A and B had already been discovered by McCollum at

the University of Wisconsin during the three years which preceded the entrance of the United States into the First World War.
McCollum had made available a number of diets rich in these
vitamins, and Evans fed his rats on these standard diets. (Fat-
soluble vitamin D was still unknown at this time.) To the surprise
of Evans and his assistant, Miss Katherine S. Bishop, animals fed
on this diet would exhibit normal sex cycles, mate, and conceive,
but could not go through a normal pregnancy. Death of the
developing embryo invariably occurred. No live progeny was
born. Neither vitamin A nor vitamin B could prevent this strange
intra-uterine death.

Then began a search for foods which might contain some element essential to normal development of the embryo. Fresh leaves
of lettuce or dried alfalfa leaves seemed to contain it, for when
these were added to the diet sterility was prevented. The wheat
germ was also potent. Even in infinitesimal amounts, Evans found,
the rich golden oil extracted from it meant all the difference between barrenness and fecundity. Evans waited until he was positive that absence of this hitherto unrecognized dietary factor led
to sterility in male rats and to destruction of the developing
embryo in females. Then in December, 1922 (the year of the discovery of vitamin D by McCollum), he announced the discovery
of vitamin X. This name was later changed to vitamin E by Bar-
nett Sure, who the following year independently confirmed the
results of the Berkeley investigator.

Evans, with a splendid technique cleverly guarded by controls,
uncovered some interesting facts in connection with this new
vitamin. He reared hundreds of mother rats on a strict ration lacking all traces of vitamin E, and then induced fertility by administering minute doses of highly concentrated vitamin E extracts.
He found that he could cure female rats of the threat of dead
embryos by giving them vitamin E extracts as late as the fifth
day of pregnancy. Evans killed normal young female rats and
fed their pancreas, spleen, or muscle tissues to sterile mother rats,
who later bore normal litters. "Therefore," he concluded, "nor-

mal young female rats begin life with initial fertility, their tissues containing vitamin E conveyed to them in intra-uterine life by their mothers." However, the supply of vitamin E must be continued in their diet, otherwise a deficiency results which causes sterility. Some of his rats were given an overabundance of his magic yellow wheat-germ oil, but this excess vitamin E had no effect on the size or the frequency of their litters.

The application of this discovery to human life occurred to Evans and many others. They thought of the thousands of women who, though otherwise normal, lose children again and again before birth. Though Evans made no claims for the vitamin E potency in humans, Dr. P. Vogt-Möller, of the County Hospital at Odense, Denmark, tried vitamin E therapy on a group of cows known to be chronic aborters, and obtained favorable results. Then in July, 1931, he reported to the English medical journal, *Lancet*, the results of his next step. Case No. 1 was that of a twenty-four-year-old woman who, after four miscarriages, was given Evans' wheat oil orally. Her next pregnancy followed a normal course and a healthy baby was born. Case No. 2 was that of a twenty-nine-year-old woman who, after the birth of her first child, miscarried four times in succession. This woman was given about two tablespoons of wheat oil each week, and responded as successfully as the first case. A small number of others, too, believe that vitamin E is necessary for the human mother, but the medical world is still very skeptical and awaits more conclusive evidence. Evans himself cautioned medical men against "the indiscriminate use of vitamin E in attempting to cure human sterility, which is most frequently due to other causes." Henry C. Sherman of Columbia University had found evidence that a lack of vitamin A also impairs the reproductive functions. Vitamin E, therefore, is definitely not *the* fertility vitamin but only one of several chemicals which are necessary for normal reproduction.

In 1935, thirteen years after the announcement of the discovery of vitamin E, Evans and Gladys A. Emerson reported that they had finally succeeded in obtaining this vitamin in pure crystalline form. During the next year Evans' laboratory reported the isolation from wheat-germ-oil concentrates of another chemical which possessed the antisterility properties of vitamin E. It is a colorless or slightly yellowish, odorless oil. Its formula was found to be $C_{29}H_{50}O_2$ and its melting point about 158° Centigrade. At the suggestion of Professor G. M. Calhoun of the University of California, this alcohol compound was named *alpha-tocopherol*—from *tokos*, meaning childbirth; *phero*, meaning to bear, and *ol*, an alcohol. When given to vitamin-E-deficient rats in single doses of three milligrams, it enabled the rats to bear normal litters. That same year Evans reported that cottonseed oil, and, later, lettuce leaves and palm oil, furnished the same alcohol.

The structure of alpha-tocopherol was found by Donald L. Fernholz in the Rahway, New Jersey, laboratories of Merck and Company in 1937. The following year its synthesis was accomplished in widely separated laboratories. Paul Karrer prepared it in Switzerland, and Alexander R. Todd did the same in England. Lee I. Smith of the University of Minnesota completed the achievement in Evans' laboratory. Then followed in quick succession the isolation of beta-tocopherol, gamma-tocopherol, and alpha-tocoquinone, all of which possess vitamin-E potency. This seemed to indicate that more than one substance appears to function as vitamin E, of which alpha-tocopherol is the most active constituent.

It is now believed that vitamin-E deficiency produces muscle deterioration and paralysis. This may be due to nerve deterioration. Certain types of paralysis in man have been treated with vitamin E with some beneficial results.

The question of the relationship between vitamin E and reproduction is still far from cleared up. According to Evans, a number of outstanding enigmas in this field include such problems as: What is the actual mode of action of the vitamin in the growth of the embryo? What is the cause of death of E-free sucklings, and how does spontaneous recovery ensue? What analogous human clinical conditions exist? To find answers to some of these questions Evans and his staff continued to wrestle with their colonies of rats on the campus of the University of California.

In the meantime, the Biochemical Institute of the University of Copenhagen released the news early in 1935 that one of its research workers, Henrik Dam, assisted by Fritz Schönheyder, had obtained undeniable evidence of the existence of another fat-soluble vitamin needed by hens. They found this vitamin in hog liver, fat, hemp seed, cereals, kale, and tomatoes. Green, leafy vegetables were rich in it, especially alfalfa. Concentrates of this antihemorrhagic vitamin when fed to young chicks stopped bleeding. It seemed to be necessary for the production of pro-thrombin in blood and thus regulated coagulation of blood. It was named vitamin K from the Scandinavian and German term, *Koagulations-Vitamin*. Dogs, guinea pigs, rats, and men need this chemical.

A search was started for the pure substance. Herman J. Alm-quist of the University of California showed that certain bacteria could synthesize it, and the following year he obtained a highly potent yellow oil. Then in 1938 Sidney A. Thayer and Edward A. Doisy isolated vitamin K_1 as colorless crystals from alfalfa at the Biochemical Department of the St. Louis University School of Medicine. Later they also isolated vitamin K_2 from putrefied fish meal. Doisy and his group synthesized the vitamin in 1939, and four years later they shared the Nobel Prize in medicine with Dam of Copenhagen. Young chicks were used in bioassaying the purity of their product. The formula of K_1 is $C_{31}H_{46}O_2$, and that of K_2 is $C_{41}H_{56}O_2$.

When Evans appeared on the vitamin scene, considerable pio-neering had already been done by other Americans. The earliest advances in this field were accomplished in connection with an attempt to find the best fodder for cattle to improve our meat and milk supply. State agricultural experiment stations were the original centers of this research. As early as 1857 Michigan had established an Agricultural College. This was followed by a gen-eral movement for state experiment stations, which culminated in the Hatch Act of 1887. By the provisions of this act the Federal government gave each state $15,000 for an agricultural experiment station. Only later was the new information revealed by these investigations applied to human nutrition.

The most important of these early investigations was undertaken at the University of Wisconsin's Agricultural Experiment Station. It was still the old question so often asked and left unanswered. Did it make any difference what foods were consumed, provided their chemical composition and energy values were the same? Perhaps the living organism was, after all, something more than a furnace to be stoked every so often with coal or oil to produce so many calories of heat. It seemed reasonable to suppose that possibly only certain components of foods present in specific diets were essential to physiological well-being, regardless of their calorific values. Was it not possible that an animal fed to satiety on some foods might yet sicken or actually starve to death for lack of certain essential ingredients?

Stephen M. Babcock planned an experiment to test the various theories then in vogue. He himself felt that calorific value was not the whole story. "Why not feed 'em coal or hot water?" he would ask. The question was more than academic. Farmers around the university were constantly asking embarrassing questions about the *kind* of feed to give their cattle. Here was a straightforward practical problem that American science was called upon to answer. So, much that followed, much that impelled the chain of events which sent American men of science on the most exciting adventure of their lives, stemmed from this imperative question raised on this Middle Western scene. It was more than an accident that made Americans the pioneers and leaders in this new chapter of human and animal nutrition.

The experiment was started early in 1907, and Edwin B. Hart was put in charge. Four groups of young heifers were fed different rations. One group received wheat, another corn, a third oats, and the fourth group was given a mixture of all three. By careful chemical analysis and accurate weighing, it was made certain that all animals received similar chemicals capable of supplying equivalent amounts of heat energy. The intake of these heifers was not the only mixture subjected to accurate testing. The feces and urine of the beasts were also quantitatively determined. The largest part of this job was left to Elmer V. McCollum, who had just reached Madison, Wisconsin. He was born among the corn fields of Kansas, of Scotch-Irish descent, and left his farm for the city to get an education. McCollum might have become a successful farmer fighting the heavy rains, the hot winds and droughts, the blistering sun that burned the corn crops year after year, the insect pests, and the fluctuating prices of farm products, with the same skill he later showed in scientific research. In high school he dreamed of becoming a country doctor. But in his second year at college he switched to organic chemistry as a career. He worked his way through the University of Kansas and earned a scholarship to Yale University, whence his teacher, Lafayette B. Mendel, later sent him on to Wisconsin for research.

Every morning the men would meet to talk over the progress of their work. Of course McCollum was interested, but somehow he looked askance at this attack on a problem that to him demanded a more easily controlled procedure. It was a well worth-while investigation, and probably would yield interesting results, but it did not reach the heart of the great problem of nutrition. "Research men who were using small animals, on the other hand, were on the right track," thought McCollum. He was going to make another change. Nothing was to enter into the diet of his animals which could not be identified as a pure chemical, the composition of which was accurately known. Chemistry had advanced far enough to place in the hands of investigators the purified chemical components of many foods. Instead of corn, a complex substance of indefinite composition, he was going to use starch $C_6H_{10}O_5$, and similarly for milk he would substitute chemically purified milk protein (casein), chemically pure milk sugar, or lactose, and so forth. The first publication which had directed his thinking in this direction was one by F. Gowland Hopkins in

1906. This Englishman was later to receive the Nobel Prize for his work on vitamins.

Late in 1907, a few months after arriving in Wisconsin, he started a rat colony for his experiments. The director of the station was a believer in the Malthusian theory and looked unsympathetically on McCollum's plan "to save the world from a shortage of food." The dean of the school was also opposed to this new attack on the problem. No state money was to go to feed rats. They were nothing but pests. Cattle—that was another story. Farmers had to feed them, and it was important to know the best and most economical ration. But Babcock came into McCollum's laboratory, perched himself on a high stool, surveyed the plan of the young man with that one good eye of his, and was for it. So McCollum kept on. He knew rats, which are excellent experimental animals, with a life span of three years and a pregnancy period of three weeks. The female produces her first litter at three months and at fourteen months has usually had six litters. It would not be very expensive to handle a large colony. McCollum's was the first rat colony in America maintained for nutrition experiments. He used wild rats at first but found them frightened under caged conditions, and ferocious. He soon abandoned them for albinos which he bought from a pet-stock dealer in Chicago.

While Babcock's heifers were frolicking, McCollum found time even with his teaching program to work with his rat colony. He regarded as superficial certain experiments at Yale undertaken to determine the relative efficiency of flesh eaters and meat abstainers. The device of determining men's endurance by means of arm-stretching and knee-bending tests to prove that flesh abstainers showed from three to six times the endurance of the others was to him not a very deep inquiry into so fundamental a problem. Even the experiments of Russell H. Chittenden, the grand old man of physiological chemistry in whose classes he had sat while at Yale, were not to his liking. Feeding professors, students, soldiers, and other volunteers on diets poor in proteins to find if there were any deterioration in well-being would never solve ultimate problems of human nutrition. McCollum was dealing with accurately controlled experiments, not with pseudo-scientific sideshows. The live rat in its cage was his unfailing test tube; his foods were pure chemicals, and his results could be accurately described and repeated by any student. That was his program from which he refused to swerve.

In 1911, while McCollum was busy with his rats, Research Bulletin No. 17 of the Wisconsin Agricultural Experiment Station appeared, giving the final results of the heifer experiment. It was a strange announcement. Every animal had received the same quantities of starch, sugar, protein, salt, and mineral matter as well as water, and yet they had reacted very differently. Only the corn-fed heifers grew sleek and vigorous and gave birth to healthy young. The wheat-fed cattle were weak, fuzzy-haired, sluggish, and never carried their calves to birth alive. The oat-fed animals, as well as the heifers fed on a mixture of wheat, corn, and oats, were not normal. Some of their young were born prematurely, and were sickly or died within a short time. Evidently the source of the food components did make a tremendous difference, but this did not explain why corn maintained the animal whereas oats did not. At this time McCollum had not heard of Christian Eijkman, who in 1897 had produced the food-deficiency disease, polyneuritis, in chickens and had then actually cured it by feeding the sick birds with the polishings of rice. Nor had Casimir Funk yet discovered that elusive substance which cured the chickens and which he called *vitamine*—the first time this word was used. The answer to the puzzle of animal nutrition seemed to be still as far off as ever.

In the meantime, Thomas B. Osborne, of the Connecticut Agricultural Experiment Station, and Lafayette B. Mendel had been working on the relative nutritive value and physiological importance of the pure proteins. Different proteins contain different amino acids. They were trying to determine which amino acids had to be present in the proteins used in foods. Their conclusions appeared in 1911 and gave McCollum's work fresh impetus.

With the help of Miss Marguerite Davis, who took care of the rat colony, McCollum continued to search for a pathway through the dietary maze. Miss Davis, a graduate of the University of California at Berkeley, remained with McCollum without pay except during the sixth and last year of their work together.

In 1914 the *Journal of Biological Chemistry* published a paper from McCollum's laboratory which opened up a new era in nutritional investigations. This paper, entitled *Isolation of the Substance in Butter Fat Which Exerts a Stimulating Influence on Growth*, contained a curve which cleared up a number of errors, and led to the discovery of a vitamin. For eighty days Rat No. 141 grew on a ration of pure casein, starch, lactose, agar-agar, salt mixture, and lard. Then a sharp decline in weight set in. An extract of butter was added to the diet in a very small amount. A definite increase in weight promptly resulted; the rat gained fifty grams in the next thirty-five days. McCollum then used the extract of egg yolk instead of butter, and the curve kept moving upward. When, however, the extract of olive oil was substituted, growth stopped. McCollum drew his conclusion. Fats and oils, differing slightly in chemical composition, were of different growth-promoting potency, because associated with their other extracts was some "yet unidentified dietary factor—fat-soluble [vitamin] A." (This use of an algebraic term to designate a vitamin gained wide acceptance, but more descriptive names were later introduced.)

Two years later, McCollum found another vitamin. He discovered it in the water from which milk sugar (lactose) had been crystallized. It proved to be a chemical which could actually cure polyneuritis in pigeons and beriberi in man, just as Christian Eijkman's rice polishings had done in 1897 in the Dutch East Indies. McCollum called this new substance *water-soluble vitamin B*. The vitamin muddle was now a little clearer. There were apparently some chemicals which were necessary in very minute amounts for well-being. McCollum had identified two of them. In 1912 A. Holst had identified a third, later named vitamin C, which prevented scurvy. It received another name, ascorbic acid, in 1933 when its structure was determined by Albert Szent-Györgyi, a Hungarian scientist who came here in 1947 and became director of the Institute of Muscle Research at Woods Hole, Massachusetts.

Other vitamin discoveries followed. In August, 1922, McCollum announced a *fat-soluble vitamin D* obtained from cod-liver oil and capable of preventing rickets. The following year, three men independently and almost simultaneously produced an amazing synthesis. Alfred F. Hess, New York pediatrician, H. Goldblatt of the Lister Institute of London, and Harry Steenbock of Madison, Wisconsin, all turned ultraviolet light upon foodstuffs poor in vitamin D and changed them into nutrients rich in this sunray chemical.

Steenbock, aided by Archie Black, used a very simple method. They raised rats in a dark room on a rickets-producing diet. The animals developed the disease. Steenbock then allowed light to shine on the hog millet and other components of the diet, and fed the irradiated food to the rats still imprisoned in a dark room. The animals recovered from the rickets. Steenbock tried his process on other foods of human consumption which lacked vitamin D and found the method effective. Then Steenbock, to protect the public from the possible exploitation of greedy business interests, patented his process of increasing the vitamin-D content of food by irradiation. This act, he felt, would enable him to control its general use by a large public. Besides, he was in a dairy state, he explained, "and there was a fight on between the oleomargarine interests and the dairy interests. I realized that the dairy industry should be supported. Since butter is not very high in vitamin-D content, I saw the possibility of making a product high in vitamin D" which could be sold at a reasonable price and increase the demand for this dairy product. Steenbock turned over his United States Patent No. 1,680,818, for which he had applied on June 20, 1924, to the University of Wisconsin, to be administered by the Wisconsin Alumni Research Foundation.

This and a subsidiary patent yielded the Foundation millions of dollars in royalties paid by numerous food companies employing the Steenbock method of food irradiation. This money is given to the university for further research. A dozen other American universities also plow back into research the royalties earned by patents granted to their research professors. In spite of these and other arrangements by other research scientists which seem socially sound and desirable, criticism has been heard from some quarters against the patenting of the fruits of research in pure science, which belong to all humanity.

Vitamin-D deficiency causes rickets in infancy or early childhood and is characterized by faulty deposition of calcium phosphate in the bones. What was considered at first to be a single vitamin D or "sunshine vitamin" turned out to be a mixture of *calciferol*, derived from irradiated ergosterol, and D_3 obtained as pure crystals by European scientists in 1932. The exact role of these and various D vitamins still remains unsettled.

Doubts had begun to arise, too, regarding the simple nature of so-called vitamin B. Reports kept coming in from many laboratories about other factors intimately associated with this supposedly pure vitamin. Vitamin B seemed to be a complex of several different vitamins. Within a period of some thirty-odd years, vitamin B was shown to be a mixture of at least eleven different and distinct factors, each of which had its own specific effects on the health of test animals and humans. All of them appeared to be universal and indispensable constituents of all living cells. By 1948 vitamin B was demonstrated to be made up of vitamin B_1 (thiamin), B_2 (riboflavin), niacin or nicotinic acid, B_6 (pyridoxine), pantothenic acid, inositol, choline, biotin (vitamin H), para-amino benzoic acid, folic acid, and B_{12}.

The isolation, chemical-structure determination, and final synthesis of many of these vitamins represent a triumph of American chemistry. In 1932 Charles G. King, then of the University of Pittsburgh and later executive director of Nutrition Foundation, obtained vitamin C in pure form for the first time from lemon juice. The following year Roger J. Williams at Oregon State College reported pantothenic acid, which he isolated in pure form in 1938. Thiamin was first prepared artificially in 1935 by his brother, Robert R. Williams, while chemical director of the Bell Telephone Laboratories. These two eminent chemist brothers were born in India of American missionary parents. In 1938 pyridoxine was isolated by John C. Keresztesy of the Merck laboratories, and four years later the complex structure of biotin was established by Vincent du Vigneaud who, like Evans and Doisy, did distinguished work in the fields of both vitamins and hormones. In 1943 para-amino benzoic acid was added to the list of synthetic vitamins by scientists working in the Merck research laboratories, and during the same year a group of researchers at the University of Texas announced the discovery of folic acid. B_{12} or *cobalamin* was isolated from liver by a five-man team of Merck and Company at Rahway, New Jersey. The absence of this compound, $C_{63}H_{90}O_{14}N_{14}PCo$, a ruby-red crystal, produces pernicious anemia. Victims of this ailment, until recently doomed to a slow death, are now easily saved by daily administration of this chemical in small doses.

In 1937 nicotinic acid, first prepared as far back as 1867 by the oxidation of nicotine, was found by Conrad A. Elvehjem, later president of the University of Wisconsin, to cure the black-tongue disease of dogs. It was actually the first pure vitamin to be isolated, but it was not recognized by Casimir Funk as such. Now, a quarter of a century later, it was identified as a vitamin. Black-tongue is similar to pellagra, which attacks man. The following year Tom D. Spies reported that he had cured human pellagra with niacin. The long drama of the search of the cause and cure of pellagra was over. Many had engaged in it, but of all who labored in this field, none was more fearless than Dr. Joseph Goldberger. He had to deal with a disease which attacked human beings but no animal so far as was then known. The only test animal available to him in the battle against this scourge was man himself. For fifteen years he had fought as a soldier of the United States Public Health Service, and in its battles he had contracted not only typhus but yellow and dengue fever. In 1914 this immigrant boy, son of a grocer in New York's East Side, was assigned to fight pellagra. Children and adults in the poor sections of the South were suffering from soreness and a burning inflammation of the tongue and mouth; from eruptions, blackening, thickening, and cracking of the skin, especially on the backs of the hands, feet, and forearms; from indigestion, diarrhea, dizziness, and nervous disorders which all too often ended in the burial service.

The medical world at that time was inclined to believe that pellagra was due to some bacterial agent. It seemed to be contagious—it was apparently epidemic in jails, orphan asylums, and the poorer sections of the corn country. Goldberger was skeptical, even though the Thompson-McFadden Pellagra Commission had just reported that pellagra was an infectious disease carried by a blood-sucking insect. The startling achievement of the Reed Yellow Fever Commission, which found an insect the carrier of yellow fever, and the dramatic discovery of Ronald Ross that malaria was transmitted by a mosquito, had a psychologic effect. Goldberger, nevertheless, had his own ideas about the probable cause of the "hard times disease" of the South.

Goldberger paid a visit to the State Hospital of South Carolina. Not a nurse, doctor, or attendant had come down with pellagra in this institution, although many of its inmates had succumbed to the disease. After experimenting there with diets, he went on to Georgia. At the State Sanitarium there he found many pellagra sufferers among its insane, and again he tried changes in diet. Then he investigated several orphanages in Mississippi, and found that most of their pellagra victims were children between the ages of six and twelve who were receiving very little milk in their daily food. His ideas about pellagra were now pretty clear. He went to the governor of Mississippi and asked for human volunteers. Twelve convicts from the Rankin Prison Farm, where pellagra had never attacked, were selected. If they survived the experiment, they were to be freed.

All of these long-termers were fed on white flour, white rice, cornmeal, pork fat, and cane sirup. If they cared to, they could gorge themselves within the limits of this menu. But they were to eat nothing else—Goldberger made sure of this. After several weeks of this strict regimen, one of that dozen began to complain of pains, a sore tongue, and sores and cracks at the corners of his mouth. More weeks went by until, at the end of the six-month experiment, one of the prisoners showed the rash of pellagra on his body. Five more of Goldberger's group came down with pellagra. Not a single case of this disease appeared among the hundreds in the Prison Farm who were not subjected to the special diet of the investigator from Washington. The volunteers were then given a diet including milk, meat, vegetables, and fruits, which are now known to contain the vitamin which prevents pellagra. They quickly recovered and won their freedom. Goldberger was certain he had produced experimental pellagra in humans, but others still insisted the disease was caused by some bacterial invasion.

There was but one step left, and Goldberger did not flinch from taking it. On April 25, 1916, he injected into his own veins the blood of a woman suffering from an acute case of pellagra. But that was not enough. The following day he swallowed the intestinal discharge of another victim. Then he and his wife ate the powdered skin rash of still another sufferer from this disease. For weeks Goldberger waited for pellagra to seize hold of him. But it did not attack him—pellagra was not of bacterial infection. In 1929 cancer of the kidneys cut short Goldberger's life.

Vitamin research attracted scores of American scientists. More and more researchers—medical, physiological, chemical, agricultural—kept turning out an ever-increasing number of papers in this field. Although in 1911 only forty-seven appeared, in 1930 there were more than fifteen hundred articles on vitamin research to be abstracted. Rats, dogs, pigeons, guinea pigs, and even roaches were sacrificed by the thousands. All sorts of new discoveries were made showing the relations of the various vitamins to each other, to hormones, to general metabolism, to susceptibility to infectious diseases, to vitamin complexes, to general bodily health and longevity. A committee appointed by the League of Nations adopted international standards for vitamin potencies, and distributed vitamin extracts gratis to dozens of laboratories engaged in new vitamin research. The whole world was buzzing with vitamin work.

Food industries became tremendously interested. Advertisements were filled with exaggerated and untested claims of vitamin potency. Every can, box, or other container of food bore a compelling announcement of vitamin contents that warded off heaven knows how many insidious diseases. Overnight the public became vitamin-conscious. The baby in its crib and the child at the dinner table were dosed with foods rich in vitamins. At first the public bowed down to the vitamin gods which lived only in fresh foods —they were wary of canned, vitaminless foodstuffs. The large companies engaged in the sale of foods quickly opened laboratories and employed chemists or subsidized university research laboratories to undertake studies of the comparative vitamin potencies of fresh and canned goods. Where the cooked or canned foods were found to be poor or altogether deficient in the various vitamins, chemists found means of enriching them with the necessary accessory factors. An amazing amount of work was done in Sherman's laboratory at Columbia University in quantitative studies of the vitamin contents of all kinds of edibles, as well as in the development of methods of controlling the vitamin contents during preserving and processing. In the great vitamin campaign, appeals were even made to patriotism. The English hailed the "unrivaled medical value of the cod-liver oils found in Scotland and Newfoundland," while Norway called the attention of the world to the fact that Norwegian fish were superior, "possessing twice the antirachitic potency of Newfoundland oil." Here was a perfect example of economic nationalism.

"Sciosophy," a word coined to denote the pseudo-scientific dicta found in the industrial advertising of vitaminized foods, held the consumer in these early days in a strong grip. The Food and Drug Administration spent thousands of dollars to run down the more flagrant of the violators. Then the public began to wonder how the human race had survived through the long centuries without this essential knowledge. Some recalled the words of George Sarton, America's greatest historian of science, "Unfortunately most men are incapable of grasping an idea unless they exaggerate it to the exclusion of all others." Slowly this vitamin mania passed. People soon realized that the average balanced diet is rich in the essential vitamins, for it contains the protective foods—milk, leafy vegetables, fruit, and eggs, with meat in moderation. (To the diets of infants, children, expectant and nursing mothers, cod-liver oil and vitamin D should be added.) Mankind has infinitely more to fear from a malnutrition problem brought on by a society that allows lands of plenty to witness millions in hunger, especially in times of economic depression. Strangely enough, the most serious medical problem in the United States today is another nutritional one, namely obesity resulting from overeating. About fifteen per cent of our population is overweight, a condition which predisposes to diabetes and to a shortened life expectancy.

The story of vitamin research is a tale not only of pure chemistry but of applied science as well. Multivitamin preparations have become standard in the diet of millions of children. Tens of millions of people are now eating bread fortified with vitamin D. Thiamin (the so-called morale vitamin), niacin, and riboflavin have been added to bread, breakfast cereals, white rice, and white flour, which is still the flour consumed by ninety per cent of our people. Tons of yeast, dried milk, oats, corn flakes, biscuits, and other foods to which vitamin D has been added are consumed daily. Cows are being fed on irradiated yeast and milk to increase the vitamin content of their milk. A number of dairies are pasteurizing milk by specially controlled electrical heating in order to preserve all of its vitamin C content. Vitamins A and D are being added to oleomargarine to equalize its vitamin content with that of pure butter. (Pro-vitamin A has even been added to cough drops and cough sirups to prevent or shorten colds. The claims of their manufacturers, however, have by no means been definitely established.) A great deal of clinical research on the vitamin needs of the human organism is still in progress.

For years special diets have been prescribed by physicians for many ailments such as asthma, rheumatism, epilepsy, and other nervous diseases, migraine, heart troubles, colds, sinus, gout, and even senility. Such dietetic therapy received fresh impetus with the vitamin publicity. Special vitamin dosing now began to be experimentally tried against various sicknesses. For example, vitamin C was tried to correct pyorrhea, certain types of hemorrhages, and even hemophilia. The same vitamin was also administered in an attempt to cure rheumatic fever and tuberculosis in guinea pigs, with the hope that, if successful, it might be applied to humans. Thiamin was tried out in the fight against the mental diseases, at the Elgin State Hospital at Elgin, Illinois.

Dentistry, too, felt the repercussions of the vitamin explosion. Tooth troubles until recently had been a matter almost wholly of therapy. Today this has become a problem of prevention and control. It is now believed by some that foods rich in calcium, phosphorus, and vitamin D will prevent tooth decay, although others are of the opinion that the vitamin theory so far as it applies to dentistry is still very much a theory.

When the complete history of the twentieth century comes to be written, it will tell how the diets of millions of people were changed by science. The old idea was to fill the belly with as much food as possible, regardless of its chemical composition. The new idea is to supply the body with only the essential factors necessary for healthy growth. A little more than a hundred years ago the Association for the Improvement of the Condition of the Poor fed its unfortunates on a diet of Indian meal, hominy, beans, peas, salt pork, and dried fish. Today the Bureau of Home Economics of the United States Department of Agriculture advises for minimum relief equally inexpensive meals comprising, however, one pint of milk, one vegetable or fruit, bread and cereals daily, with the addition of cod-liver oil for those under the age of two.

With the help of the new science of nutrition four great human scourges—beriberi, infantile scurvy, rickets, and pellagra—have been banished from the more privileged sections of the world. Science has also extended man's average life span by about fifteen years and has made him taller and stronger than ever before. No doubt more striking improvements can be expected in the future. Much of the credit for this significant advance in human history must go to many American scientists, among them Herbert McLean Evans and Elmer Vernon McCollum.

Evans is still vexing the anterior hypothesis and, with his associates, has not given up the adventure of extracting all of its mysteries. Neither has he abandoned his vitamin research. In 1957 he wrote, "Many may feel that one of the many interesting and significant things we have been able to do in this laboratory has been the production of congenital abnormalities by elimination of specific vitamins, i.e., folic acid, pantothenic acid, and riboflavin, from the mother's diet." In all of these experiments the mothers remained in good health and carried their young to term.

Most of this new and thrilling work was done with the biochemist Dr. Marjorie M. Nelson, who has been at the University of California since 1938 experimenting on vitamins, vitamin-hormone relationships, and dietary requirements in general. One of the earliest pioneers in this field is Dr. Josef Warkany, who in 1932 had come from Vienna to the Children's Hospital in Cincinnati, Ohio, to do research work in pediatrics. As early as 1940 he had shown the relation of congenital abnormalities in mammals with dietary deficiencies. Nelson and Evans were able to produce abnormalities in their experimental rats only when the vitamins were eliminated during the time when the so-called germ layers began to differentiate and form the various organs. This occurs from the eighth to the fifteenth day of pregnancy, which corresponds to about the second to eighth week in man. There evidently are precise chemical needs for the normal course of development of embryonic tissues—at least in rats. This much has definitely been established.

As for man himself, we are by no means as certain. The evidence is still sparse and unreliable, according to most of the men and women working in this field. This in spite of the fact that almost all congenital malformations such as hydrocephalus, club-foot, cleft palate, malformed hands, and eye defects in man have been experimentally produced in rats. "Since the world began," however, Evans reminds us, "every human mother has wondered in trepidation lest her unborn young might come into the world deformed. It was supposed that these unfortunate distortions were inherited, and this explanation has many adherents."

Evans adds, "With profounder questions, for example, the exact cause of the need of these dietary constituents we are still grappling." In the meantime, McCollum, loaded with honors, retired as professor of biochemistry at Johns Hopkins University in 1946. Blind in one eye and with considerable reduction of vision in the other, he took upon himself the arduous investigation and writing of a history of ideas in nutritional research. This he completed in his seventy-eighth year while new ground was still being plowed in the exciting fields of the vitamins and the hormones.

CHAPTER EIGHTEEN

EDWIN POWELL HUBBLE
(1889-1953)

GIANT INSTRUMENTS AND HUGE FOUNDATIONS FOR AMERICAN SCIENCE

ASTRONOMY WAS one of the first of the sciences to find devotees in this country. Many clergymen brought telescopes from Europe and rode their celestial hobby enthusiastically. They made use of astronomical science in sermons to show the wonders of the Lord and His firmament. Other amateur astronomers from the earliest colonial days studied this science because it was intimately tied up with navigation, so important to the life of the colonists. The American Philosophical Society commissioned one of its members, David Rittenhouse, to construct orreries—astronomical instruments with which planetary motions could be studied more accurately. In 1769 he built one of these instruments to make measurements on the transit of Venus. Six years later the same scientific body presented a plan to the Pennsylvania Assembly to erect a government observatory with Rittenhouse as "public astronomer observer." As one of the arguments for the fulfillment of this project they offered the thought that "To rescue a man from the drudgery of manual labor, and give him an occasion for indulging the best of his genius with advantage to his country, is an honor which crowned heads might glory in." The outbreak of the American Revolution put an end to the plan, but in 1779 Rittenhouse was named professor of astronomy at the College of Philadelphia, and several years later discovered a new comet.

When in 1829 Nathaniel Bowditch, at the recommendation of the great astronomer of England, John F. Herschel, became the first American to be elected to membership in the Royal Astronomical Society, astronomical ties between the two countries, already very close, became even more interdependent. Twenty years later William C. Bond, the first director of the Harvard Observatory, was made an associate of this same scientific institution. The president of the Royal Astronomical Society took this occasion to state, "The Americans of the United States, although late in the field of astronomical enterprise, have now taken up that science with their characteristic energy, and have already shown their ability to instruct their former masters."

In 1860 America gave the world one of its best builders of large astronomical telescopes, Alvan Clark. In that year he constructed an eighteen-inch telescope for the Dearborn Observatory of Evanston, Illinois, with which he discovered that Sirius was actually not a single but a double star. In 1872 Clark built for the United States Naval Observatory a twenty-six-inch telescope, through which Asaph Hall in 1877 discovered the moon of Mars. Nine years later another telescope came from Clark's shops: a thirty-six-inch instrument for the Lick Observatory, where Professor James E. Keeler discovered the composition of the rings of the planet Saturn. Other pioneer telescope makers followed Clark, who died in 1887. John A. Brashear, a steelworker, on the advice of Samuel P. Langley, gave up mirror grinding to build great telescopes not only for America but for the rest of the world as well.

American preoccupation with this field of research, which is definitely not of immediate practical importance, finally made this country the center of the astronomical progress of the world. Within the past forty years especially, the United States has assumed world leadership in this branch of science. Part of the reason for this development is the willingness of American philanthropy to pay the costs of bigger and better telescopes and more magnificent astronomical observatories. Equipped with these ultramodern and colossal instruments, our research men have been able to gather cosmological data for which no other observatories in the world had been equipped. American industrialists, fired by the slogan of bigger and better machines, became the patrons of our astronomers and made available to them the finest astronomical instruments ever devised and constructed. Among these astronomers were men of rare theoretical daring and deep intellectual acumen. These men took hold of the new instruments to enrich pure science. America took over in this field where Europe left off.

The story of this great achievement in modern astronomy has roots that go back four centuries. On May 24, 1543, modern astronomy was born. On that day a book, *On the Revolution of the Heavenly Bodies*, dedicated to Pope Paul III, was brought to the deathbed of its Polish author, Nikolaus Copernicus. The earth was indeed a globe, he declared, not stationary as Ptolemy the Egyptian had insisted, but a moving ball revolving around the sun, as Pythagoras had believed.

The universe of Copernicus was still very small, not much larger than the limits of the outermost planets. By the seventeenth century a burst of scientific accomplishment brought with it the invention of the telescope. In the hands of Galileo Galilei astronomy was at last equipped with a tool which could reach beyond the clearest eye and hold the mind in check. Half a million stars appeared, and men began to realize that "the sun is but a private in the host of heaven." Astronomy was reborn; celestial horizons continued to recede, exposing farther spaces spangled with new points of light. Then came Isaac Newton, posthumous son of an English farmer, who, while secluded outside London during the Great Plague in 1665, discovered the universal law of gravitation which explained the mysterious movements of heavenly bodies that even the genius of Galileo had failed to understand.

Then began a feverish activity to study the myriad stars that blinked beyond the orbit of the farthermost planet. Among the most prodigious workers in this virgin field was an erstwhile oboe player in a Hanover regiment, William Herschel, who had fled to England to escape the tumult of war. While teaching music to keep alive, he had, at the age of thirty-five, turned to astronomy. He might have remained an amateur star-gazer for the rest of his life had he not on the night of March 13, 1781, discovered a new planet, Uranus, a feat which brought him both the attention of the king and a wealthy wife.

Herschel built larger mirrors which he himself ground, never taking his fingers off the disks as he polished them for hours at a stretch while his sister Caroline fed him. With a nineteen-inch reflecting telescope of his own construction he swept the heavens, and hundreds of new stars revealed themselves in a great concourse of points of light. This Milky Way, he told the Royal Society in 1784, was "a most extensive stratum of stars of which our Sun and the solar system are but a part."

For a while astronomy tarried. The mantle of Galileo, Copernicus, and Herschel was waiting to fall upon the shoulders of a new explorer who could venture beyond the Milky Way. But first it was necessary to know with some degree of accuracy the distances of the stars from the earth. This was not a simple matter. Today the nearest star we know of is Proxima Centauri, which is about twenty-five trillion miles away from us as compared with the distance of the sun from the earth, a mere ninety-three million miles. Light traveling at the speed of 186,000 miles a second can cover six trillion miles in a year. Hence it takes light 4.2 years to travel the distance from Proxima Centauri to the earth. (We say that this star is 4.2 *light-years* away from us.) On the same basis light can reach us from the sun in only eight minutes. Yet this is our *nearest* star.

William Herschel had been dead only sixteen years when another milestone in astronomy was reached. His son, John, walking in the footsteps of his father, was cataloguing more stars from among the Magellanic Clouds visible in the Southern sky when in 1838 he received a letter from Frederick W. Bessel. This astronomer had determined the distance of Cygni 61 by a new method known as trigonometric parallax. The enormous distances of stars from a terrestrial observer are so great that they appear fixed in position. Constant and careful watching, however, revealed the fact that they were not fixed in space when located with reference to other stars still more remote. As the earth moves in its orbit around the sun, a near star shifts its position with respect to a farther star. The farther away the star actually is, the smaller the angle through which it appears to move. By measuring the angle between the relative positions of two stars as viewed at different times from the same place on the earth's surface, it is possible by trigonometry to compute the distance of the nearest star from us.

Bessel found Cygni 61 to be sixty trillion miles from the earth. By the same method of parallax, the German-Russian astronomer Friedrich Georg Wilhelm von Struve, great-grandfather of Otto Struve, present director of the Leuschner Observatory of the University of California at Berkeley, had found the distance of Alpha Lyrae. The method was extremely difficult, so that by 1900 the distances of only sixty out of the millions of stars had been determined. The parallax method meant "measuring the size of a pinhead two miles away."

Yet parallax measurement was assiduously pursued and improvements in technique were discovered and applied. At the Mount Wilson Observatory, Walter S. Adams devised a spectroscopic method of determining stellar parallaxes based upon peculiarities of the intensity of the light as shown in the spectral lines of certain types of stars, which by giving information about their brightness offer some clue to their distance as well. Within the five years preceding 1921, this method enabled Adams and his coworkers to determine the distances from the earth of two thousand stars. Adrian van Maanen made some brilliant contributions in this field, and Henry N. Russell and Harlow Shapley devised still another method by the study of eclipsing variable stars. But in spite of these brilliant achievements, the number of stars of which the distances were determined was nothing in the vast ocean of celestial space.

Our universe, including the sun and, of course, the earth, is the Milky Way or galactic system. Beyond our own galactic system there seemed to be other patches of light. Were they other universes? As science halted on the rim of the Milky Way she gathered new recruits, surveyed the space already conquered, and reinforced her lines for a new and deeper offensive. Then with new techniques, new devices, and new leviathans of the heavens she broke through once more in a colossal surge that carried man's vision outside the Milky Way or galactic system to within the borders of the extragalactic nebulae.

By 1782 Charles Messier, a Frenchman, had found and listed a hundred and three cloudy spots in the sky called nebulae. Some were like planetary disks and others like wispy clouds. In 1848 Lord Rosse, equipped with a telescope six feet in diameter and fifty feet long, slung in chains between two high walls of masonry, noticed for the first time the spiral form of some of them. Twenty years later Sir William Huggins was the first to use the spectroscope to learn the nature of these nebulae. Were they aggregations of stars? he wondered. "I directed the spectroscope," he wrote in 1867, "to one of these small nebulae. The reader may now be able to picture the feeling of excited suspense, mingled with a degree of awe, with which, after a few moments of hesitation, I put my eye to the spectroscope. No continuous spectrum such as is given off by the sun and other stars and such as I had expected! A single bright green line only such as is given off by a luminous gas!" But that was not the complete story of the nebulae. Later it was found that most of them give continuous spectra like the sun. These "island universes," as William Herschel had called them, were found to contain large numbers of stars, since they gave continuous spectra such as are given by star clusters. Some, however, consist not of aggregations of stars but of large masses of luminous gas.

These nebulae were evidently too remote for any method yet devised to determine their distance. Stellar parallax determinations of bodies beyond the fringe of our galactic system were out of the question. At distances greater than a hundred light-years, parallax was powerless to give any information. Some other method based on an entirely different principle was wanted. For a century astronomers kept vigil for a new technique. Its final discovery is one of the classics of science.

Among the numerous types of stars that dot the heavens, one of the strangest and least understood of all is the Cepheid variable star, so named after its prototype, Delta Cephei, located in the constellation Cepheus. Long ago it had been observed that certain fairly faint stars suddenly flare up, increase in brightness, reach a peak of light intensity, and then gradually grow faint again. Their period of fluctuation of brightness varies usually from a few days to as long as a month or even fifty days.

In 1912 Miss Henrietta S. Leavitt, a graduate of Radcliffe College working as an assistant at the Harvard College Observatory, made a capital discovery. Miss Leavitt was not the only woman who had made an important contribution to American astronomy. Before her there was Maria Mitchell, daughter of a clockmaker who corrected chronometers for New England whaling ships. Maria discovered a comet and worked out its orbit, and also added several new nebulae to our sky maps. In 1848 she became the first woman honorary member of the American Academy of Arts and Sciences. Vassar College selected her in 1865 to become the first woman professor of astronomy in America. In 1908 the Maria Mitchell Astronomical Observatory, built on Nantucket Island, Massachusetts, by a fund of $50,000 raised by American women, was dedicated to the memory of this distinguished scientist, who was born and educated there and for twenty years was librarian on that beautiful island. Other woman astronomers are Cecilia Payne-Gaposchkin of the Harvard Observatory, who is making brilliant spectroscopic studies of the atmospheres of many stars, and Henrietta H. Swope, a Radcliffe graduate, who has been doing nebular photography and spectroscopy at the Mount Wilson Observatory since 1952.

For years Henrietta Leavitt had been studying photographic plates exposed to various portions of the skies to learn more about the nature of stars and stellar aggregations. While examining some photographs of a cluster of stars out near the boundary of the Milky Way in which many Cepheids had been reported, her trained eye came across an unusual phenomenon. In these pictures taken of the Lesser Magellanic Cloud at the Harvard University Observatory at Arequipa, Peru, she discovered that the large, brighter Cepheids among its hundreds of thousands of stars fluctuated more slowly than the fainter, smaller ones. The brighter Cepheids took a longer time to reach their greatest luminosity and then die down. Other eyes had undoubtedly seen similar pictures, but had missed the story which was revealed to this woman.

In 1880 Henry Draper, who eight years before had taken the first successful photograph of the spectrum of a star, introduced the photographic study of nebulae, and large numbers of such photographs had accumulated all over the world. A number of other Americans had also made important pioneer contributions to celestial photography. Henry Draper's father, John W. Draper, was among them. As a young physician and professor of chemistry at New York University he used Daguerre's discovery to take a picture of the moon. A New York City lawyer, Lewis M. Rutherfurd, in 1864 obtained the first real photograph of the moon, and in 1868 introduced photography in star studies.

Miss Leavitt began a thorough investigation of hundreds of these photographs. From these available data she was confirmed in her belief that the period of pulsation of a Cepheid is definitely related to its brightness. She then announced her discovery of the *period-luminosity law*, which others before her had completely missed. The period of fluctuation of a Cepheid is directly proportional, she said, to its real brightness or candlepower. Now, the *apparent* brightness of a star is not always its real or *intrinsic* brightness, because the observed brightness of a star depends upon its distance from the observer—the farther away the star, the dimmer it appears. Hence if the fluctuation of one Cepheid is more rapid than that of another Cepheid star at the same distance from the earth, then its intrinsic brightness is less than that of its neighbor Cepheid.

The value of the discovery of this law was clear. If it were universally true, it could be used as a key to the problem of stellar distances. Assume the presence of two Cepheids of the same period of pulsation; that is, it takes them the same time to pass from their greatest brightness to dimness. Assume further that one of them appears a hundred times brighter than the other. Then one must be ten times farther than the other, since luminosity of a source of light, as every schoolboy knows, varies inversely as the square of its distance ($100 = 10^2$). Furthermore, if one of these Cepheids occurred in a system of a known distance from the earth, such as the Milky Way, then the other distance could be calculated. And finally the distance of this other star system would be the same as the distance of its Cepheid, of which the period of fluctuation and brightness were observable. Here, indeed, was an entirely new method for the use of stellar astronomy. Another measuring rod had been prepared, and with it another veil was to be lifted from a problem that had seemed insoluble.

The discovery of this unsought phenomenon is another example of how strangely research advances into new fields, and how avidly science grasps at any straw which appears in the surrounding whirlpool of ignorance. At about this time a former zoologist and newspaperman who had turned to astronomical research was working with the sixty-inch telescope on Mount Wilson. Harlow Shapley was studying dozens of groups, or *globular clusters*, of stars which seemed to be isolated systems, yet to belong to our own Milky Way. Some of these clusters which his telescope resolved consisted of as many as 35,000 stars. At about the same time that the importance of Cepheids was shown by Miss Leavitt's work, Shapley, too, was hunting for them among these clusters and found many of them. After a number of investigations he succeeded in 1917 in working out the period-luminosity law for several of the globular clusters, so that actual distances could be determined from Cepheids. Previously only relative distances were known. Thus he found that the cluster of Hercules with its 35,000 stars is about 36,000 light-years away, and hence within the Milky Way, the diameter of which is about 100,000 light-years. By the same method he found nearly a hundred globular clusters; the farthest, N.G.C. 7006, is about 220,000 light-years away from the earth. Shapley was now able to generalize the law that Miss Leavitt had discovered.

Shapley was hunting for universes only a quarter of a million light-years away. For 1925 this distance was altogether too close. Other universes were scattered through space—great beacons which beckoned to any explorer who was ready to leave the shores of the then known continents and venture out into the endless seas of dark interstellar space. The ship was there—a huge one-hundred-inch telescope built by the vision of a great American, George Ellery Hale, who was born in Chicago in 1868.

The year 1868 was doubly important in the realm of solar research. In that year, too, the thrilling discovery of helium in the sun's spectrum was announced by two men independently. Pierre Janssen, son of a French musician, made the discovery while watching a total solar eclipse in Hindustan. Two months later Norman Lockyer, a clerk in the British War Office in England, saw new bright lines which turned out to be those of a new element. The discovery was made by means of the spectroscope invented in 1859 by Bunsen and Kirchhoff in Germany. Actually, however, the principle of this new instrument had been described five years earlier by David Alter, a Pennsylvania physician. He described a method of determining the presence of elements by means of the colors of their flames. He even predicted that this principle would be used to discover the presence of elements in the sun and other stars.

As Hale grew up, it was expected that he would in due time take over the great hydraulic-elevator company built up by his father, and become another successful captain of industry. But his life turned out to be an all-too-rare phenomenon in a country like ours, where the commercial spirit, the profit motive, a pragmatic philosophy, and the none-too-generous adoration of the pure scientist color the prevailing atmosphere in which most of us live. The elder Hale, son of a New England Congregationalist minister, was partly responsible for his son's career. He was not blinded by the glory of the business world. To him scholarship and reverence for research in pure science were at least equally worth striving for.

Hale invented the *spectroheliograph*, and in 1891 made the first successful photograph of a solar prominence with this instrument, showing that sunspots are regions of tremendous magnetic and electrical disturbances. He had come to Pasadena to look for a site for a solar observatory. Through his efforts and a grant of the Carnegie Institution of Washington, the great observatory on the top of Mount Wilson became a reality. Hale was responsible for the forty-inch refracting telescope of the Yerkes Observatory on Lake Geneva, sixty miles from Chicago, and the sixty-inch reflecting telescope of the Mount Wilson Observatory, as well as the one-hundred-inch reflecting telescope, which had its birth in 1906.

In that year John D. Hooker, a Los Angeles businessman in the role of potentate interested in astronomy, announced his readiness to underwrite the cost of all the optical parts of a one-hundred-inch telescope, even as Charles T. Yerkes, the Chicago traction magnate, had made possible the Yerkes Observatory. Hooker wanted Southern California to become the home of the largest observatory in the world. His gift, however, did not cover the cost of mounting or housing the huge disk. Half a million dollars were needed to make that dream come true. Hale went after Andrew Carnegie. It was no easy matter to convince the wily little Scotsman that this was really sound philanthropy. Was the tele-

scope actually necessary? Would it be so much better than existing instruments? Why all this scrambling for bigger and better
fingers to reach the skies? Was it advisable to spend more millions
when the sixty-inch telescope on Mount Wilson had not as yet
been taxed to its fullest powers? Hale's answer convinced Carnegie. By a gift of ten million dollars the philanthropist doubled
the endowment of the Carnegie Institution of Washington, which
he had established in 1902. This made possible the housing of the
Hooker one-hundred-inch telescope on Mount Wilson.

The astronomical Columbus who was to lead an expedition into
the new worlds was Edwin P. Hubble. Born in Marshfield, Missouri, Hubble spent his early years in Kentucky, and frolicked
during the summers in the Ozark Mountains with his grandfather.
Later he was taken to a suburb of Chicago where his lawyer
father was engaged in the insurance business and where the boy
attended high school. Here he excelled not only in his studies but
also in all forms of athletics. Upon his graduation he was given,
through Robert A. Millikan, a scholarship to the University of
Chicago. Here he came under the vital influence of both Millikan,
his physics teacher, and Hale, his inspirational guide. Astronomy
interested him far more than any other subject; mathematics was
a second love. He might have followed an entirely different road
altogether had some of his admirers in Chicago prevailed upon
this six-foot-two amateur prize fighter who was boxing his way to
campus fame. A sports promoter who saw him in action wanted
to train him to fight Jack Johnson, then heavyweight champion
of the world. But nothing came of this offer, and at twenty-one
Hubble's keen mind took him to Oxford University as a Rhodes
scholar from Illinois. In England Hubble studied earnestly, and
he continued his interest in athletics, too, becoming a star high
jumper. For a while he gave up the idea of scientific research. He
had become interested in the common law of the land from which
his forebears had come. For it was when Cromwell came into
power in England in the early part of the seventeenth century
that several Hubbles left England in a hurry for the New World.

Some settled around New Haven, Connecticut, others went to Virginia, and still others migrated to Kentucky.

Hubble read law at Oxford and upon his return to the United States opened an office at Louisville, Kentucky. There he practiced law for about a year. Then suddenly, having had enough of jurisprudence, he turned, like Tycho Brahe, to the laws of the heavens as a research worker at the Yerkes Observatory. The old pull of astronomy had brought him back. While preparing for his doctorate in astronomy he showed his unusual powers as an observer in a paper he published in 1916 which dealt with *A Photographic Investigation of Faint Nebulae.*

When in the following year the United States found itself at war with Germany, Hubble had just received his degree of doctor of philosophy. He immediately enlisted as a private in the infantry, and telegraphed Hale, who had asked him to come to California to join the Mount Wilson Observatory staff, that he would accept the offer just as soon as he came back from the war. He kept his promise in 1919, but not before he had seen active service at the front in France, gone to Germany with the American Army of Occupation, and been mustered out as a major.

When Hubble reached the top of the mountain above Pasadena he began at once an extended study of the thousands of nebulae which were already known. In 1916 and 1917 he had made a systematic photographic study of them, and he wondered if they belonged to our system of stars. The nearest of these nebulae are visible to the naked eye as a faint cloud somewhat smaller than the moon and with a total luminosity equal to that of a fourth- or fifth-magnitude star. He concentrated his attention first on Messier 31, the great spiral nebula in the constellation Andromeda, and on Messier 33, another celestial pinwheel in Triangulum.

Messier 31 appeared many times fainter than other bodies of known distance from the earth. But that gave no clue to its intrinsic brightness. Hubble successfully searched for Cepheid variables and found a dozen of them with fluctuating periods similar to some in the Milky Way. Then with the aid of the period-luminosity law he calculated their intrinsic luminosities and found them to be four thousand times greater than that of the sun, member of our own Milky Way. From this figure he was safe in declaring that Messier 31 is about 900,000 light-years away, far from our own galaxy of stars and hence of extragalactic location. Further work resulted in an excellent analysis of the Andromeda nebula, which turned out to be similar to the Milky Way in both size and composition.

Messier 33 was also searched for Cepheids. Again the observation of these telltale bodies opened up sealed pages and told the story that this nebula, too, is beyond the celestial girdle, a remote island universe in the ocean of space, somewhat less than one million light-years from us. Hubble's ship was well on its way into the new uncharted seas. He had definitely shown that there were universes far beyond our own galaxy and pointed to the possibility of the existence of thousands of other systems inhabiting space. The theory of island universes, once contemplated and later rejected, had returned and was now an established fact.

There followed from this one of the most amazing chapters in the history of astronomical exploration. Once the way had been shown, there was a feverish rush to chart the new universes of extragalactic space beyond the Milky Way. The one-hundred-inch and the sixty-inch and other large telescopes went hunting for the new universes. Hundreds of nebulae were resolved into stars, gases, clouds of dust, and larger particles made visible by near-by stars, "primeval chaos of shining fluid," as Herschel had described them. Among them were frequently found Cepheids and even *novae*, those odd points of glaring light with a luminosity as great as 100,000 suns that suddenly rise seemingly out of nowhere, take a look at the firmament, and then die of exhaustion or despair, never to reappear.

Many of these novae were recorded by the Chinese, and tradition has it that Hipparchus made his great catalogue of stars because he once saw a nova and, inspired by it, wanted to learn if it was a rare or a frequent phenomenon. A *supernova* is the most stupendous explosion known. It may reach a luminosity equivalent to 100,000,000 suns. It is an extremely rare phenomenon. The first of these supergiant novae to arouse great interest in Europe was reported by Tycho Brahe in 1572, in Cassiopeia. It was so bright that it could be seen in broad daylight, and lasted for six months. Another supernova was discovered late in 1934 in the constellation Hercules. It expanded at the rate of ten thousand miles per minute and in one month increased in brightness a hundred thousand times. Before it disappeared from sight it was more brilliant than the North Star. In 1942 still another tremendous nova was reported by an American observer, Bernhard H. Dawson, at La Plata, Argentina. This nova in the constellation Puppis was the brightest observed in a generation, so bright that it could be easily seen in the early morning. Only about fifty of these rare stars have been reported in history since 1572; the star of Bethlehem may have been one of them. Their origin is not understood. Some think they result from the collision of a star with another hidden, dark star, or from the sudden release of pent-up energies in certain stars. Another very recent theory is that they are nuclear furnaces in which iron is built up into heavier elements such as californium. This element was created in 1952 and its half-life was found to be fifty-five days, which corresponds to the period of light from an exploding supernova. Novae also help to determine distances of nebulae, for it has been found that the maximum brightness of a nova indicates roughly the general order of its distance from the earth.

The data kept piling up. No one knew where the calculations would end. Suddenly out of these fresh researches appeared a most startling discovery—a discovery which may yet rank among the greatest in the history of science. The entire family of extragalactic universes, as far as the telescopic eye aided by the photographic plate could reach, seemed to be racing away from the speck of dust upon which mortal observers were perched. Speeding along at terrific velocities which kept accelerating with increase in distance, racing away into the farthermost limits of the heavens, zooming through space went all of the nebulae. Like a huge soap bubble the supergalaxy kept expanding, increasing in size at a rate which would double its diameter every fourteen hundred million years. This revelation came upon the world with lightning suddenness and found science unprepared to meet it with a universally accepted explanation. It was fantastic, awe-inspiring, alarming, almost ominous.

Hubble was the leader in this new development. His chief lieutenant was Milton L. Humason, who had joined the ranks of astronomers in an unusual way. He had finished grammar school at fourteen, and, although he was the son of a California banker, this completed his formal education. He disliked school. From the streets of Pasadena the top of Mount Wilson beckoned to Humason, and so he climbed the mountain to work in the hotel near the observatory. That view from the peak of the neighboring mountains, the San Gabriel Valley, Pasadena, Los Angeles, and the Pacific Ocean captivated him. The mountain fever got him, and he stayed doing odd jobs at the hotel, driving a mule team which pulled supplies and machinery up the mountain for the observatory, working in the great clockroom of the telescope, helping with the routine photographic work in the laboratory up in the clouds. Humason later married the daughter of one of the observatory staff, and soon after went at astronomy seriously. Many of the workers of the observatory began to call upon him, as a skilled stellar photographer, for aid. So valuable did he become that in 1922 he was made a member of the official staff and given a chance at the big telescopes. He had graduated from the position of "night assistant" and now, dressed in polar costume, with a woolen hood over his head and short flowing jacket to protect him from the long cold nights, he would shout his own instructions from the top of the telescope to younger "night assistants" in the darkness fifty feet below him.

Soon after Hubble first showed definitely that there existed galaxies beyond our own, he and Humason turned their attention to a problem which had been presented by another astronomer working at the Lowell Observatory at Flagstaff, Arizona. Vesto M. Slipher had been studying by means of spectroscopic analysis the motions of spiral-shaped nebulae. The method of parallax had failed to give any clear data. The analysis of the spectra of moving bodies was more promising.

The discovery of the use of this newer method goes back to a day in 1841 when Christian Doppler of Prague discovered what is now known as the "Doppler effect." After establishing the fact that the pitch of a sound rises as the source of the sound moves toward the listener (because more sound waves crowd in upon him), he proved that this same "Doppler effect" or change in frequency also applies to light. Color in light is analogous to pitch in sound. Red light has the lowest frequency (largest wave length) of visible light. Violet, at the other end of the spectrum of visible light, has the highest frequency (smallest wave length). Hence a luminous object moving toward the observer would change to a higher frequency—in other words, it would shift from the red end to the violet end of the spectrum. The amount of this shift could thus be used as a measure of the velocity of approach or recession of a light source. The first to apply this principle to a study of the movements of luminous bodies in the sky was Sir William Huggins, soon after the invention of the spectroscope.

By the use of the same method, Slipher had found that some spiral nebulae were whirling at great speeds, one end approaching the earth and the other retreating. By 1928 his data on the movements of forty-three of the brighter, closer nebulae indicated also that in general all of the spirals are rapidly moving away from the earth. He did not grasp the significance of his figures. Hubble, however, found a curious relationship between the velocities of recession of these nebulae and the distances of these moving nebulae from the earth. The California astronomer discovered that the velocity of recession as shown by the red shift of their spectral lines increased with the distance of the nebulae from the earth. The more distant nebulae were moving away faster than the nearer ones. Was this velocity-distance relationship a fundamental one? Was it applicable to regions beyond the six million light-years that had already been plumbed? Were all the nebulae rushing away from the earth?

It appeared to Hubble imperative to test this relationship at once, not only within the entire range of extragalactic nebulae which he had picked out of more and more remote space, but also to extend these observations as far into extragalactic space as his instruments would permit. First it was necessary to discover the distances of the extragalactic nebulae with the aid of new methods based on the data furnished by Cepheid variables. This was Hubble's job. Then it was necessary to determine by means of the spectrograph the shift, if any, of their spectral lines to the red. This was the work assigned to Humason. The one-hundred-inch telescope was made available to them and the project was started in 1928.

All large astronomical instruments are used as cameras rather than as visual telescopes. This is because the photographic plate is much more sensitive than the observer's eyes. Obtaining spectra of the very distant nebulae was still a tremendously difficult undertaking. Humason had to keep a nebula, little more than a point of light among thousands of others all around it, steadily fixed over the slit of a spectrograph attached to the telescope. All through the night the spot of light in the heavens had to be watched constantly for many reasons. For example, although the wheel which kept the one-hundred-inch telescope focused on that spot is approximately correct, its speed varies slightly with changes of temperature. Then just as the night ended and the first light of dawn appeared, the photographic plate had to be shielded until the following night when again it was exposed to the same spot of the same nebula. A complete exposure of one nebula often took as long as seventy-five hours, which frequently meant eight to ten whole nights. Watching points of light over a narrow slit would have broken almost any astronomer, yet after a long, lonely vigil his colleagues would often find Humason tired but still steady.

The photographic film was then carefully developed at the mountain observatory. The spectrum of the nebula was compared with that of the sun, and any shifts in the position of certain well-known spectrum lines, such as those of calcium or helium, were recorded. This was a very delicate job, for Humason was working with a picture only one tenth of an inch long and one-thirtieth of an inch wide, containing closely placed lines imprinted by light which had left its nebular source as much as a hundred million years ago. Often nothing very clear could be made out of the negative and the entire photographing process had to be repeated. At other times the lines were not quite so faint and Humason was able to record a shift of the lines toward the red end of the spectrum. The film was then brought down to the observatory office at 813 Santa Barbara Street in Pasadena, where further studies of it could be made. The time at the one-hundred-inch telescope had to be carefully divided among the various astronomers at Mount Wilson, for there were so many projects under way that Humason was forced to remain at the foot of the mountain the greater part of each month. During this time he would make additional measurements of the spectrum shift from the film, and calculate the velocity this represented. He would work very hard and concentrate his efforts like a burning glass.

Hubble would now determine the distance which this red shift indicated for the position of the nebula. Then he would study this position of the nebula from the earth with relation to the velocity with which it was moving. This was much more than routine work. It was exciting. The men waited breathlessly for the figures to shape themselves. "We never knew," said Humason, "but what we would get results that did not follow the others. There was the same excitement in the laboratory as when new planets were discovered." But each picture showed the lines were moved toward the red. The nebulae were all receding from the earth. There was no exception. Moreover, the velocity-distance relation held even way out in the deepest extragalactic space. The farther away the nebula, the faster it was receding (see Table on page 502).

As they kept piercing the heavens to more and more remote distances, Hubble and Humason placed their observational figures on graph paper. N.G.C. 385, a nebula in Pegasus, twenty-three million light-years away, was receding at a velocity of 2400 miles per second. There were other nebulae which had flown higher than Pegasus. N.G.C. 2562 in the Cancer cluster, twenty-nine million light-years distant, was racing away at a speed of 3000 miles per second. Nebulae in Perseus, thirty-six million light-years from the sun, were hurrying along at 3200 miles per second. N.G.C. 4884, a spot of light forty-five million light-years away in the Coma Bereniceo cluster of stars, was leaving us behind at the speed of 4700 miles a second. The Ursa Major Cluster No. 2, estimated to be eighty-five million light-years from the terres-

Clusters of Nebulae	Approximate Distance in Million Light-Years	Approximate Velocity in Miles per Second	Number of Nebulae Observed in Each Cluster
Virgo	6	700	23
Pegasus	23.5	2,400	4
Pisces	24	2,900	4
Cancer	29.5	3,000	2
Perseus	36	3,200	4
Coma Bereniceo	45	4,700	8
Ursa Major	85	9,500	1
Leo	105	12,000	1
Corona Borealis	120	13,500	1
Gemini	135	15,000	2
Boötes	220	24,000	1

trial observer, was dashing madly away at the even greater speed of 9500 miles per second. This cluster was discovered in 1932 by Walter Baade who had come from Germany the year before to join the staff of Mount Wilson. When the Leo cluster was discovered in 1930, one hundred and five million light-years out in space, it was found that it was ripping away from us at the stupendous speed of 12,000 miles per second. The Gemini Cluster bodies, one hundred thirty-five million light-years away, were roaring through space at 15,000 miles per second. And a nebula in a cluster in Boötes, discovered by Hubble in 1934, situated at the farthest outposts then measured (two hundred and twenty million light-years away), seemed to be moving even faster—at a superexplosive speed estimated at 24,000 miles per second (a speed equal to twice the velocity of alpha rays expelled by radium).

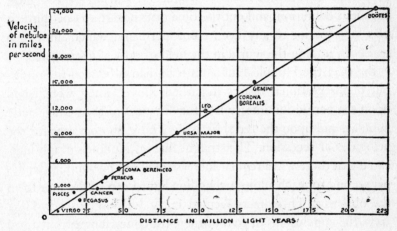

Fig. 24. Graph showing the velocity-distance relationship of some of the extragalactic nebulae as found by Hubble and Humason.

The probable error of the figures obtained was calculated and found at that time to be not more than about ten per cent—an exceedingly accurate result for this type of astronomical investigation. Both the accuracy of this method of analysis and the extreme range to which it was applicable were due in no small measure to the introduction of a new camera lens. During the course of Hubble's and Humason's amazing exploration into the heavens, they had been handicapped by the slowness of the lens they were forced to use. The nebulae which they wished to photograph were so far away and so faint that extremely long exposures often meant blurred pictures. What was therefore needed was a much faster lens, that is, one of smaller focus which would give pictures in less exposure time and hence of greater clarity.

W. B. Rayton, who had been making and improving lenses for a quarter of a century at the Bausch and Lomb Company in New York, was asked to make a short-focus spectrographic objective for the men at Mount Wilson. Before long, Humason received an eightfold enlargement of a microscopic objective with a focal length of 32 mm. and an aperture of 50 mm., or a ratio of f/0.6, which Rayton had made from his own design. Humason tried it out. It was a wonder. It had high speed, gave excellent definition, and cut the time of exposure to one third. It was far superior to any even from Germany, which until then had been leading the world in the field of optical instruments.

By 1943 the Hubble-Humason team had produced the undisputed observational results described above. They were based upon the period-luminosity law for distances of the extragalactic nebulae, and upon the red shift as shown by photographs for the velocities of recession. The straight line on Hubble's graph indicated that there was a regular increase of about one hundred miles per second for each additional million light-years of distance from the observer. These facts seemed fairly well established. They were the conclusions of two of the most competent astronomical observers of all time, equipped with the most powerful instruments in existence.

Seldom has a discovery started such a world-wide discussion. The nature and extent of the physical universe had always been one of the fundamental problems over which science had debated. Many theories had been advanced, but the lack of sufficient data had been a stumbling block to the acceptance of any one of them. Now here was a new theory—one that postulated an ever-expanding, skyrocketing universe with all the nebulae rushing away from the earth.

Sir Arthur Eddington, the bachelor Quaker astronomer of England, was moved to call it "so preposterous that I feel almost an indignation that anyone should believe in it except myself." Perhaps the red shift of the spectral lines of the nebulae did not necessarily mean that the nebulae were moving away from the earth. Fritz Zwicky, Hubble's colleague at the California Institute of Technology, seriously discussed the possibility that the red shifts might not be due to "Doppler effects." William D. MacMillan of the University of Chicago, a former teacher of Hubble, asked whether there might not be some phenomenon similar to the "Compton effect," where X rays strike a target, lose energy, and reappear with longer wave lengths. In the same way light from a distant nebula might strike particles in interstellar space, become weaker, and appear as light with a greater wave length. Such an effect would explain the observational data of Hubble without ascribing them to an expanding superuniverse. Others attempted to explain the phenomenon which the California astronomers had discovered as being due not to an actual outward moving of the nebulae but to a property of light which coming from great distances loses energy by the gravitational effects of material particles strewn through intergalactic space.

Even though Einstein himself had declared that "it is reasonable to attribute this displacement or red shift to a velocity effect," Hubble hoped to determine by further investigation whether the motion is real or apparent. He believed that red shifts are due either to actual motion or to some hitherto unrecognized principle of physics. During the Rhodes Memorial lectures which he delivered at Oxford University in 1936, he said, "The discussion ends in a dilemma, and the resolution must await improved observations or improved theory or both. We seem to face a choice between a finite, small-scale universe and a universe indefinitely large plus a new principle of nature." The cautious observer, Hubble believed, refrains from committing himself to the present interpretation and employs the colorless term *apparent velocity*.

Hubble, a skillful and enthusiastic dry-fly fisherman, would go off on one of his frequent breaks to fish and do some hard thinking. This pursuit of fishing he once described as "to follow a stream, to conform to a ritual, and, lastly, to catch a fish." He had larger and much more elusive fish to snare in the heavens above.

Another central task of astronomy, Hubble realized, was to work out a system of classification for the various types of extragalactic or external galaxies. It turned out to be almost a lifetime of work for him and his associates. Hubble divided all extragalactic nebulae into three broad groups—elliptical, spiral, and irregular. The first, such as M 32, was a spherical mass filled with stars and densest at its center. The second, such as M 31, was a spheroidal body at its center and appeared as a flat disk surrounding this central body, with spiral arms attached to the disk. The Magellanic Clouds were an example of the irregular type. Thousands of photographs were taken during this massive study.

Hubble continued to study the imprints of the light of the past on the photographic plates attached to his telescope. New and more remote nebulae revealed themselves. To gain some clearer idea of the extent and anatomy of the physical universe he followed the plan of J. C. Kapteyn of Groningen, Holland. Kapteyn a generation before had inaugurated a statistical study of the stars by concentrating research on certain selected areas and then from the data thus collected attempting to arrive at a general conclusion as to the nature of the whole heavens. Hubble made 1283 photographs of a small portion of the sky observable on Mount Wilson. Penetrating to the farthest space thus far probed, his pictures showed 44,000 separate nebulae. This number, he computed, corresponded to a total of about seventy-five million island universes within the range of the one-hundred-inch telescope sweeping but a small fraction of the sky. Since the total region observable from Mount Wilson was in turn but a fraction of one per cent of the complete universe, the probable number of universes was estimated to be about 500 trillion. This staggering number of nebulae was distributed fairly uniformly through a finite spherical space— a closed system of which he estimated the radius of curvature to be a few billion light-years.

Hubble estimated that the average distance between any two nebulae is about two million light-years. The average nebula is about 15,000 light-years in diameter and contains enough matter to make a thousand million stars. The average luminosity of each nebula is eighty-five million times that of our sun. He also found the mean density of matter in space to be about 10^{-30} grams per cubic centimeter. That is, the relation between the mass of the universe and the space it occupies is infinitesimally small—comparable, in fact, to one grain of sand inside a volume equivalent to that of the earth. According to this figure, the universe is almost wholly empty space, even though it contains billions of nebulae. The most perfect vacuum we can produce in our laboratories is still very dense in comparison with the emptiness of the entire universe.

All of the above estimates are of course highly problematical. They are based on the assumption that the portion of space which the one-hundred-inch telescope made available to the astronomer was a fair sample of the whole extragalactic system. "We must make the assumption of the observable region being a fair sample of the universe," said Hubble, "or dream." And while this structure of the superuniverse which Hubble has painted is still very vague, he reminded us that "in our generation for the first time, the structure of the universe is being investigated by direct observations."

Hubble had sculptured a new universe out of the cold, hard granite of observational data. It was, of course, a more scientifically acceptable one than theologians had furnished mankind. And now other universe-builders were busy painting pictures of the cosmos with the stuff of mathematical symbols and involved equations. Had not Pythagoras said that "God geometrizes"? Perhaps in the language of mathematics, which Galileo had declared was that in which nature's great book was written, could be found a description of the universe. Hampered by a lack of observational data, men had hunted for new mathematical symbols with which to fashion new universes.

Many years before Hubble's achievements the great Einstein himself had also incidentally tried his hand at this game of picturing the universe. He had reached a model of a *static universe*—a universe which never changed. It was a difficult picture to accept. But the days of accepting theories only when they could be converted into suitable mechanical models were gone. The universe of Einstein was indeed one which could scarcely be visualized except by a pure mathematician, and then only in terms of strange symbols picked presumably out of thin air. But then Einstein held that, in a certain sense, pure thought is competent to comprehend the real, even as the ancients believed.

Einstein's equation of a static universe appeared in 1917. Toward the close of the same year Willem de Sitter, director of the astronomical observatory at Leyden, Holland, joined the ranks of the universe-builders. De Sitter had been among the first to understand and appreciate Einstein. After a thorough study of the relativity theory he attempted to apply it to astronomy and the architecture of the universe. Like Einstein, this man went back to pure mathematics and obtained a picture of a different universe. Einstein's equation showed a universe filled with matter and at a standstill. De Sitter postulated a universe that was practically empty, but in which there might be some mutually receding particles of matter. Neither of these older models, however, agreed with the observational data collected by Hubble. De Sitter's model failed because, strictly taken, it contained no matter at all, and Einstein's because the matter in it stayed at rest and did not show the red-shift phenomenon unearthed at Mount Wilson. Einstein was ready with one terrific hammer blow to smash his static universe to smithereens in the face of the findings of the California astronomers. There was nothing sacred about his equations, admitted this greatest of all mathematical physicists. Mathematics is not a golden image that has to be worshiped, nor is the world required to serve offerings to authorities.

There was an urgent and immediate need for a revamping of cosmological models. It was only natural that some redeemer might be found in Pasadena, where Hubble, Hale, Millikan, and other luminaries in theoretical as well as experimental science had often gathered to thresh out the implications of Hubble's bewildering discovery. Among the scientists who engaged in these endless discussions was Richard Chace Tolman, professor of physical chemistry and mathematical physics, and dean of the Graduate School of the California Institute of Technology. He was a wise and kindly man, a great teacher, one of the men who "with a philosophical taste that was delightful made this place so livable."

He was born in West Newton, Massachusetts. From his mother he inherited a Quaker tradition "whose lifelong influence could be seen in his tolerant and understanding attitude toward the problems of life and antics of his fellow men."

Tolman had already had a distinguished career. After studying chemical engineering at the Massachusetts Institute of Technology, he attended technical schools in Germany, where he worked with dyes and artificial silk. His father, president of the Samson Cordage Works in Shirley, Massachusetts, was interested in the cotton industry, and this technical experience which his son was getting abroad was looked upon with great favor. But Richard was too interested in theoretical science to enter his father's business. He returned to M.I.T. to study, under the pioneer physical chemist Arthur A. Noyes, several difficult problems connected with the theory of ionization. Except for interludes in the Chemical Warfare Service during World War I, and as chairman of the division of armor and ordnance during World War II, he remained an impractical theoretical man to the end.

As early as 1907 he became enmeshed in the attractive web of Einstein's special theory of relativity, and ten years later published *The Theory of the Relativity of Motion*. He showed that he could handle highly abstract and theoretical problems like a master, and declared that "The days of adventurous discovery have not passed forever." At this time he added his testimony "to the growing conviction that the conceptual space and time of science are not God-given and should be altered whenever the discovery of new facts makes such a change pragmatic." In 1927, six years after he came to Caltech, appeared his *Statistical Mechan-*

ics, an extension of Josiah W. Gibbs' book, which was devised to investigate the laws that describe the gross behavior of systems containing many molecules if we cannot follow or predict the exact behavior of individual elements. The years that followed found him increasingly immersed in relativistic thermodynamics.

The delicacy of the astronomical discovery of Hubble and Humason on the mountain interested Tolman from the very start. The experimental discovery and measurements of small effects had always given him real aesthetic satisfaction, and he liked to discuss the details of the actual experiments which finally culminated in the discovery of the recession of the extragalactic nebulae. The implications of the discovery were equally important to him. He had faith in the value of theory as a tool of discovery. "We must admire Galileo," he said, "for insisting on observational facts as the ultimate arbiter and thus breaking away from a decadent Aristotelian tradition. But we must not let this just admiration blind us to the power and skill of those other theoretical physicists who obtain the suggestion for physical principles from the inner workings of the mind and then present their conclusions to the arbitrament of experimental test."

Tolman undertook a reinvestigation of the problem of the structure of the universe. Locked in Room 5 in the basement of the Gates Chemical Laboratory of Caltech, shrouded in the thick smoke of his ever-puffing pipe, Tolman set to work with pencil and paper. He had the difficult problem of finding the pattern of a whole universe. Tolman was not simply a pure mathematician. He was a brilliant mathematical physicist who was wrestling with the problem of getting a clear picture of a physical situation and then shaping it into a mathematical equation. His method was very much like Einstein's. He first jotted down a long equation on one of the sheets of paper that cluttered his desk. That equation represented an idealized picture of the physical universe. Partly because of the mathematical difficulties involved and partly because of the limited range of observational data available, his equation represented only a highly idealized model of the superuniverse. He kept changing his equations. When necessary he would supplement Einstein's principles of relativistic mechanics with those furnished by his own development of relativistic thermodynamics. Now he would add another symbol, remove still another, change the sign or exponent of a letter, and keep juggling the formulas as new obstacles or new interpretations reached his mind. With every stroke of his pencil a different universe appeared, with every crumpling of a whole sheet of formulas many universes were destroyed. In the morning he built; in the evening he tore down. He was like a god and a demon building and destroying worlds in his den.

Some men are guided by psychic intuitions, but most great ideas have come after long travail with numerous worthless ones. This was true of Tolman. In 1929 he finally emerged out of his self-imposed seclusion. He had witnessed the lifting of a veil. He had obtained a picture of a new nonstatic universe based on the observational data of Hubble. It was not a spectacle of myriads of stars, Cepheids, novae, comets, planets, giant clusters, vacuous expanses of interstellar space, dust, and chaos. It was a bold condensation of a single mathematical equation. This equation (or line element) did not look very different from those of either

$$ds^2 = \frac{e^{g(t)}}{\left(1 + \dfrac{r^2}{4R^2}\right)^2}(dx^2 + dy^2 + dz^2) + dt^2$$

Einstein or De Sitter. The same symbols were used. But there was in that equation enough of a variation to give a universe which could change with the time factor instead of remaining static like Einstein's, and which contained matter instead of being empty like De Sitter's.

Tolman had read a great deal on the many attempts to fashion new universes mathematically. But, as is rather common in science, he, too, had overlooked some important papers. Just a few months before his own paper was read before the National Academy of Sciences, an equation entirely equivalent to his own had been derived by Howard P. Robertson, then of Princeton University and since 1947 professor of mathematical physics at the California Institute of Technology. Seven years before, a brilliant Russian mathematician, Alexander A. Friedman, had made the first deliberate attempt to investigate line elements for a nonstatic universe. He had discovered an error in Einstein's proof for a static universe and had shown that, mathematically at least, two nonstatic models were possible. Einstein readily admitted his error—the biggest blunder of his life, he said.

To be sure, both these men had derived their equations from general geometric considerations rather than, as Tolman had done, from actual observational data furnished by Hubble. Yet, when after the publication of his own more important findings the work of these men was brought to his attention, Tolman quickly dug up the papers and acknowledged their priority. After studying them he wrote that Friedman, "in spite of the lack of attention that has been paid to his article, should receive credit as the originator of the new chapter in cosmology." Tolman was no scientific prima donna.

The first attempt to apply such mathematical equations to actual phenomena was made in 1927 by a young Belgian priest, Abbé Georges Lemaître, of the University of Louvain. This young man had at the age of nine decided to be a scientist and at the same time a priest, since his family history called for one. He took the usual seminary courses leading to the priesthood. Later, through a scholarship created by the Commission for the Relief of Belgium, he was enabled to study at Harvard University the application of the theory of relativity to astronomy. To him the search for salvation and the search for scientific truth were not incompatible, and "seeking truth was a service to God." Lemaître investigated Friedman's equation and applied his nonstatic line element to actual astronomical data. He made the important discovery that the apparent red shift of the light from the nearest galaxies could be interpreted with the help of the concept of an expanding universe. As his results were published in a rather inaccessible journal, however, they remained unknown until Arthur S. Eddington called them to the attention of the world in 1930. This was after Tolman had advanced his own cosmological model based on a mass of fresh data which was not available to Lemaître.

Einstein's mathematical model had failed to do very much, for it lacked observational evidence. With Tolman's new concept of a dynamic universe based on a fair amount of observational data, the cosmological world began to hum. Einstein was excited and declared that Tolman's work had given an original and especially illuminating mathematical equation. At the invitation of Millikan and Hale, Einstein came to Pasadena to discuss this all-absorbing question. Both in 1931 and in 1932 he sat as a schoolboy in the lecture room of the California Institute of Technology while Hubble graphically described the observational data behind his discovery of the velocity-distance relationship, while Humason showed those uncanny spectral pictures of "light howling down the spectral scale" toward the red end, and Tolman hammered out the details of his new dynamic universe built from the bricks and mortar of the new discoveries. Einstein made no secret of his amazement at the work of this American triumvirate. More than once during the course of these discussions he would rise from his seat, go to the blackboard in front of the room, and add his interpretations and suggestions, which Tolman would then translate into English to the assembled scientists.

The open season for universe-builders had arrived. It seemed that everybody capable of handling extremely involved equations took a hand. Eddington showed that Einstein's original static model would be unstable, liable to expansion or contraction if once disturbed from its original state, and hence really a special case of the then generally accepted expanding-universe model. Willem de Sitter in Holland, Laue and Heckmann in Germany, William H. McCrea and George C. McVittie in England, and many others presented their favorites. Ludwik Silberstein fashioned a universe out of nothing but radiation. Takeuchi, a Japanese, was the first Oriental to advance a mathematical model of the universe. No mechanical setups were demanded or invoked to give visual clarity to the worlds of the pure mathematicians. And Sir James Jeans was led to declare, "We can understand the universe today only if we think of it as the creation of a pure mathematician in terms of pure thought. It becomes a bewildering paradox as soon as we try to grasp it in terms of a mechanical model." Bertrand Russell was most critical, almost unkind. "It is the privilege of pure mathematicians," he said, "not to know what they are talking about."

The implications of the new discoveries which emerged from Pasadena were many and profound. For one thing, they heralded what came perilously near to being a recrudescence of those philosophical discussions reminiscent of the days of Kepler and Copernicus. Were it not for the background of scientific data which the exponents of the various schools occasionally evoked to strengthen their points of view, these discussions of the ultimate future of the universe, the teleological or purposeful aspects of creation, and the existence of a pristine power in whose hands the cosmic machine wound up billions of years ago was slowly unwinding, might have done justice to the great metaphysicians who centuries ago filled the air with pompous words trumpeting high-sounding hypotheses. Science, which centuries before had broken away from abstruse metaphysics, seemed once again to be clothing itself in the raiments of pure philosophy to such an extent that it became at times indistinguishable from philosophy. American science, strangely enough, was in the thick of it.

This eternally expanding universe was dreadful to contemplate. This ever-inflating rubber balloon might burst and end in the chaos from which it started. Why, in fact, had it not already burst? Tolman thought of this and saw the danger to science. "In studying the problem of cosmology," he said, "we are immediately aware that the future fate of man is involved in the issue, and we must hence be particularly careful to keep our judgments uninfected by the demands of religion and unswerved by human hopes and fears. The problem must be approached with the keen, balanced, critical and skeptical objectivity of the scientist."

Tolman thought of other possible cosmological equations which might keep intact the observational fact of the outer nebulae rushing away from the earth and at the same time not result in a final state of expansion. A number of such models proved possible. For example, Friedman's solution of Einstein's cosmological equation permitted a pulsating universe. These models, according to his extension of thermodynamics to relativity, could undergo a continual succession of identical expansions and contractions without ever coming to a state of rest. These postulated perpetually moving accordionlike universes; this in spite of an equilibrium demanded by the classical thermodynamics which predicted the sun and stars cold and all of creation dead and lifeless.

In addition to Hubble's and Tolman's ideas of the changing structure of the universe there was a third—much older than these. There were thus three concepts of the universe around which men rallied. The oldest was that of a universe which was constantly getting colder, with all the stars radiating their heat far into space. The universe was running down, unable to maintain its *status quo*, because of the classical form of the second law of thermodynamics. According to this law, heat and other forms of energy always pass from regions of higher intensity to regions of lower intensity. This would eventually result in a uniform distribution of heat throughout space. Extreme cold, stagnation, and death would follow, since the amount of energy would be infinitesimally small when evenly distributed throughout the colossal volume of the universe. This was the gloomy picture which until a few years ago was the orthodox model of most scientists. Jeans and Eddington were the spokesmen of this concept of the degradation of matter—modern Jeremiahs who prophesied doom and regarded the "hope of unlimited progress for human civilization to be an exploded myth." The second concept, that of Hubble, was hardly less pessimistic. The ever-expanding universe would someday have to end in the nothingness of complete expansion.

Against these two pictures the newer physics and astronomy aligned themselves with Tolman's third concept. They were armed with the weapons of a relativistic thermodynamics, equations which insisted that it was possible for a universe to expand and contract forever without coming to a state of rest (maximum entropy where free energy would cease to exist). It was now possible to believe at least in a hypothetical universe which continuously renewed its birth—a perpetually living universe which alternately expanded and shrank. Millikan, Smuts, and the mathematician Bishop C. W. Barnes stood at the head of the phalanx which saw this view strengthened by the partially demonstrated phenomenon of energy changing back again into matter just as matter is known to change into radiation. Radiation, by some mechanism not completely explained, was believed to be replenishing the lost matter of the universe. This interpretation banished completely not only the first gloomy picture of a decaying universe but also that of an expanding universe thinning out into nothingness. It held out the hope of saving mankind from an otherwise inexorable extinction.

But these concepts were, after all, based to a great extent on pure speculation. None of the adherents were dogmatists. They, too, had their deep doubts. Tolman, awed by the immensity of space and exulted by the temerity of the human spirit in attempting a solution of such a fundamental problem, reminded us that, "We do not have sufficient data so that we could assign the actual universe to any one model." His highly simplified pictures of the universe, he never failed to tell us, are analogous to the rigid, weightless levers of simple mechanics or to the spherical, rigid yet at the same time perfectly elastic molecules of the physicist. Hence we must be very careful in interpreting the actual universe in terms of conclusions that we may draw as to the behavior of our conceptual models. Yet, rather than appeal to special acts of creation as a way out of the dilemma of the structure of the universe, he was ready to skate on thin speculative ice. "The chief duty and glory of theoretical science," he believed, "is to extrapolate—as cautiously and wisely as may be—into regions yet unexplored."

Would further observational data clear up the cosmological muddle? Would they definitely answer the question of the correct interpretation of the red-shift phenomenon? If the universe is expanding would they indicate the type of expansion? Would we be able to analyze the birth and death of stars more convincingly? Would they clear up the problem of the age of the universe, the age of the earth, the birth of the chemical elements? Could we determine more accurately the mean density of the matter of the universe, or the rate of increase of red shifts in our immediate vicinity—that is, within fifty million light-years of our own solar system? What about the abundance of the various elements in the stars? If nebulae at great distances are found to differ markedly from those nearby, would that give us a clue as to the evolution of galaxies?

Hubble believed that they would, for a new instrument was now available, thanks to the vision and perseverance of George Ellery Hale. In the evening of his life Hale looked into the possibilities of more powerful telescopes. He felt it was safe to advance by a single stupendous leap from the one-hundred-inch to a two-hundred-inch telescope—a colossal instrument which might penetrate almost three times deeper into the seemingly limitless space around us, and open for investigation an unexplored sphere of about thirty times the volume of that hitherto sounded. One hundred million new nebulae should be brought into the range of astronomers. The moving parts of this celestial eye would weigh hundreds of tons, but this did not disturb Hale, who realized that "from an engineering standpoint our telescopes are small in comparison with modern battleships and bridges."

The International Education Board in 1928 made a grant of $6,000,000 to the California Institute of Technology for the construction of the two-hundred-inch mirror, mounting, buildings, and all the equipment of a new and complete astrophysical observatory. This organization was to be conducted in close co-operation with the Mount Wilson Observatory of the Carnegie Institution of Washington. Hale was chosen chairman of the observatory council and John Anderson was named executive officer in charge of the project. The Corning Glass Works of New York poured two twenty-ton pyrex pancakes, each twenty inches thick and nearly seventeen feet in diameter. The second huge glass slab proved successful, and it was carefully shipped across the continent to California, where it was to be transformed into a 14½-ton mirror in the optical shop of the California Institute of Technology in Pasadena. The work of grinding and polishing the immense piece of glass to an accuracy of one millionth of an inch to prevent image distortion continued for more than seven years.

In the meantime, on the table top of Palomar Peak, 5600 feet above sea level, about forty-five miles from San Diego and thirty miles from the Pacific Ocean, the largest astronomical observatory in the world was being completed. The inroads of civilization around the foot of Mount Wilson had ruined the ideal location of the one-hundred-inch telescope. In a third of a century the population of the valley area around this observatory site had jumped from 330,000 to 2,500,000. The lights of the valley and Los Angeles County had interfered with the observational work of the astronomers atop the mountain. Another reason for the new location, which is about 125 miles southeast of Pasadena, was the steadier air currents and the fewer storms of the region around Palomar Mountain. The housing for the new two-hundred-inch telescope is a three-story, insulated building with all modern improvements. The roof is a steel hemispherical dome covered with ⅜-inch plates and weighing 1000 tons. It is 137 feet in diameter, about the size of the Pantheon. The complete dome revolves at the simple push of a button.

Late in 1941, the huge glass eye, polished to perfection in Pasadena, was ready to be shipped to Palomar. High-gear roads had been built to the top of the mountain for the shipment. The glass disk or camera lens with a focal length of fifty-five feet was to be placed at the bottom, and at the other end of this framework of steel girders weighing 125 tons was placed the photographic plate.

For the first time, the astronomical observer would climb into a long telescope tube, ride with his instruments, and work directly at the focus of the two-hundred-inch reflector. All was in readiness for the final act when the Japanese attacked Pearl Harbor. The final completion of the observatory was halted for the duration. The glass disk was left in Pasadena. The forty or more mechanics at work on the telescope in the shops of the California Institute of Technology were rushed to more pressing work, such as making glass prisms for the Army and Navy. The new vistas ready to be thrown open to mankind remained blacked out while men went to work to make the world safe again for such things as observatories. Only the three Schmidt Reflector telescopes were left in operation in a separate building on Mount Palomar to continue their scouting work for the two-hundred-inch instrument.

Just before the completion of the two-hundred-inch telescope was stopped, Hubble remarked, "One phase of our astronomical work has come to an end. The preliminary reconnaissance has been completed at Mount Wilson. The next step is ready to be opened by the two-hundred-inch telescope. Humason has developed a better technique in his spectroscopic work and already he is getting larger and clearer spectra of the nebulae. A new chapter will soon be opened up."

When the forces of ruthless aggression began to march across three continents, Hubble saw its immediate threat to human freedom everywhere. He was no ivory-tower scientist. Science, too, would someday have to fight for its freedom. He became chairman of the Southern California Joint Fight for Freedom Committee. He worked hard to point out the great dangers that confronted us. On Armistice Day, 1941, less than a month before Pearl Harbor, in an address to the American Legion, he declared that the fight against Nazism and Fascism is our battle, and wound up by calling for an immediate declaration of war. When it finally came, Hubble stood ready to give all of his abilities to the government. His own work and that of most of his fellow scientists at Mount Palomar yielded, as did so many other projects in other fields, to the more immediate practical exigencies of the struggle to make such undertakings possible in the future.

Strangely enough, wartime conditions brought a few advantages. Baade, for the first time, got all the time he wanted at the one-hundred-inch telescope. And the blackout of the Los Angeles valley restored the ideal dark night sky of the early days at Mount Wilson for more accurate observing. Baade was able during this period to resolve the central portion of the great Andromeda nebula.

Hubble wanted to get back into the infantry. Instead he was assigned to take over External Ballistics at the Research and Development Center of the Ordnance Department at Aberdeen, Maryland. Why had he been chosen for this task? Because, he was told, ballistics has "a curious affinity with astronomy. Moreover," he recalled years later, "I was informed that as a line officer in the last war, I might appreciate the significance of some of the problems as viewed from positions in front of the guns as well as behind the guns." External ballistics, he was reminded, involved following a projectile from launching to impact or burst. At the Aberdeen Proving Grounds he was also placed in charge of the Supersonic Wind Tunnel.

Tolman had already gone to Washington in the summer of 1940 to begin a multitude of duties including those of vice-president of the National Defense Research Council, and chief scientific advisor to Bernard Baruch while the latter was United States Representative to the United Nations Atomic Energy Conferences. He contributed of his knowledge and energy to the proximity fuse and rocket projects as well.

The four long years of war dragged on, and Hubble was eager to get back to the contemplation of the heavens. At the end of December, 1945, he came home to Pasadena. He plunged into the new peacetime work with his old vigor and enthusiasm. He served on the committee for the completion of the two-hundred-inch telescope, in whose design he had greatly assisted. Ira S. Bowen, who had earned his Ph.D. degree at Caltech and had served as professor of physics in that institution, was made director of the Mount Wilson Observatory in 1946 and of the Mount Palomar Observatory two years later. Hubble was selected to act as chief of research for the Mount Wilson and Mount Palomar observatories and later became chairman of the joint Mount Wilson-Mount Palomar Research Committee in charge of selecting likely projects for the two observatories.

Hubble was waiting for the day when the new telescope would finally be ready to gather as much light as a million eyes and penetrate into space two billion light-years. This was twice as far as the one-hundred-inch could reach. With the new machine one could see a lighted candle at 10,000 miles, and one could photograph this candlelight at 30,000 miles. With it he was ready to explore a sample of the universe eight times as great as was accessible to the telescope on Mount Wilson. As a complement to the two-hundred-inch light gatherer, there was a smaller, forty-eight inch telescope invented by a German, Bernhard Schmidt, in 1931. The Schmidt reflector could not pierce the sky so deeply, but it could cover a larger area of the sky in a single photograph. This area is six thousand times as large as that covered by a single plate made with the two-hundred-inch.

Four years later the historic day dawned, and Hubble was among the first to ride its fabulous tube. Tolman, unfortunately, never lived to see it. He had returned to his home in Pasadena in 1947 and enjoyed a year of theoretical investigations in the same field he had helped to illuminate before he had rushed off to Washington. He also resumed his long and scholarly interest in the philosophy and social implications of science. He died September 5, 1948, from pneumonia following a severe stroke three weeks earlier. Thus passed a true natural philosopher and one of the most human and versatile scientists America has produced.

Regularly scheduled observations with the two-hundred-inch

were started in November, 1949, and the deep corridors of extra-galactic space were again open for inspection. There were a number of pressing problems for the new machine to tackle. High priority was given to that tantalizing riddle of the red shift. Was the red shift real? Was the universe really expanding? Would it go on expanding and for how long? Was it showing signs of tiring and slowing down?

Before and during the war, the red shifts of hundreds of nebulae had been measured in a co-operative program of nebular spectroscopy at the Mount Wilson and Lick observatories. This had begun at the latter place where Nicholas U. Mayall, as early as 1935, was in charge of observations. The total brightness of many of the galaxies was measured by Edison Pettit at Mount Wilson with special photoelectric equipment. Humason, too, was still on the job. With a new, faster, and more versatile nebular spectrograph placed at the prime focus of the two-hundred-inch telescope, new and even more exciting data were anticipated. The men at the telescope reached out farther and farther, and Humason had to go back to longer and longer exposure times. Spectra of three clusters way beyond the limit of the one-hundred-inch were obtained. They yielded velocities of recession of the order of 30,000 miles per second. Humason had boldly reached out to galaxies blazing about a billion light-years away. Here he found the Hydra cluster speeding along at the incredible velocity of 37,000 miles per second.

One especially startling fact emerged from among all the other data. The faintest clusters, about one billion light-years away, were hurrying along faster, by about 6200 miles per second, than was expected from the velocity-distance relationship established years back by Hubble and Humason. In other words, it seemed that about one billion years ago, that is, the length of time it takes light to reach the observer on earth from these very remote clusters, the universe was expanding faster than it is now. The expansion of the cosmos seems to be decelerating at the present time. Some of the nearest galaxies, in fact, seem to be almost stationary with respect to the observer perched on the earth. This was a very arresting conclusion, if true.

At just about the time that Hubble was returning home from his duties with the War Department, a fresh approach regarding the evolution of stars, the age of the solar system, and the evolution of the chemical elements was initiated at the William Kellogg Radiation Laboratory of the California Institute of Technology. Charles C. Lauritsen, its director, and Ira S. Bowen, William A. Fowler, and Jesse L. Greenstein, who came two years later, embarked on this attractive adventure. From observations and theoretical calculations involving nuclear reactions they found that the matter of the universe consists of about seventy-six per cent by weight of the element hydrogen, and twenty-three per cent of helium, the second heaviest element. All the rest of the elements put together comprised the remaining one per cent. They also found evidence that the percentage of the other elements dropped off with increasing atomic weight. In other words, there was less sodium (atomic weight 23) than helium (atomic weight 4), but more sodium than iron (atomic weight 56). Stellar-evolution studies also revealed that the most ancient stars in our solar system were about four and a half billion years old, whereas the oldest stars in our galaxy were about six and a half billion years old. Our solar system, therefore, is two billion years younger than the galaxy in which it is found. It was not even in existence at the beginning of our galaxy. "So dies the last vestige of mankind's geocentric conception of the universe," remarked William A. Fowler, who had become interested in the origin of the elements while associated with Ira S. Bowen on rocket ordnance during the last war. Here was another finding of the impractical astronomer that might have a bearing on man's present thinking about his place in the scheme of things.

In the midst of all these exciting findings, Hubble, who had played such a key role in this cosmic drama, suffered a heart attack and died in his home on September 28, 1953. He was a thoughtful, scholarly, socially aware individual. In his last years, he was troubled by the cold war and the insecurity of the whole world around him. "The problem," he said, "is that of stopping war." He believed in world federation. "War can be stopped," he felt certain, "when, and only when, we are ready to use physical sanction—when we are ready to use a police force at the price of a modicum of sovereignty. World government for the maintenance of law and order is an ultimate goal of civilization."

In his George Darwin lecture which he delivered a few months before his death, Hubble summed up his adventure into space thus: "For I can end as I began. From our home on the earth we look into the distances and strive to imagine the sort of world into which we are born. Our immediate neighborhood we know rather intimately. But with increasing distance our knowledge fades . . . until at the last dim horizon we search among ghostly errors of observation for landmarks that are scarcely more substantial. The search will continue. It is not satisfied, and it will not be suppressed."

Hubble was right. Humason and others did not stop here. They pushed forward again and attempted to measure the red shifts of two extremely faint and distant star clusters radiating more than a billion light-years away from the earth. Velocities of recession of more than 62,000 miles per second (one-third the speed of light) were predicted for them. But as yet no clear data have been picked out of this most remote and nebulous space. Other astronomers joined in the project. Among them was Allan R. Sandage, a young man who had come to the California Institute of Technology in 1951 to work for his doctorate in astronomy. During his studies he assisted Hubble, and, according to Sandage, "a bit of Hubble's enthusiasm rubbed off on me and all who knew him." The young man from Iowa City had been steered into astronomy at the age of ten, he confessed, by *Buck Rogers in the Twenty-fifth Century*. Sandage and others were using the equations of relativistic cosmology of Tolman and other universe builders to try to interpret the apparent departure of the outermost galaxies from linearity of the velocity-distance relationship.

Two somewhat new and popular conceptions of the nature of the universe had been advanced and developed during the preceding few years. A Cambridge University astronomer, Fred Hoyle, together with two other young British cosmogonists and mathematicians, Hermann Bondi and Thomas Gold, presented a picture of what is called a steady-state universe. Gold later came to Harvard University. Hoyle, a Yorkshire-born scientist who spent some time in California as visiting professor at Caltech, postulated in 1951 a strange universe that has neither beginning nor end. In this curious universe space is limitless, time is infinite, and the density of its matter never changes. As this universe expands at a steady rate new galaxies are formed to compensate for the separation of the existing galaxies. And since new hydrogen atoms are continuously being created in space, a stable universe results. According to Hoyle, the chief spokesman of this school, the universe started as a cold, dilute, and turbulent collection of hydrogen atoms. Part of this hydrogen gas condensed by gravitational attraction and eventually became stars. As these stars in turn contracted, their interiors became denser and hotter, and protons fused forming heavy hydrogen nuclei or deuterons. These then built up into the heavier elements by a step-by-step process.

The other and more popular cosmological model is the so-called evolutionary universe. It is championed by the Russian-born physicist George Gamow, who taught for a while at the University of Leningrad and came to settle in the United States in 1934. He is now professor of physics at the University of Colorado. Gamow postulated that the universe started from a very dense state of matter composed of the three elementary particles—electrons, protons, and neutrons. About five billion years ago this extremely dense core exploded. Five minutes after the cataclysm, the universe cooled while protons and neutrons joined to form larger units from deuterons by a step-by-step process, on to the heaviest of the elements. All of the fleeing matter originally present formed the stars, the planets, and the galaxies. This entire eruption took only about thirty minutes.

Abbé Georges Lemaître, a Belgian priest and cosmogonist, had compressed the creation of the universe even further some fifteen years before Gamow. Lemaître, the theoretical astronomer, pictured an instantaneous creation. He told an audience in Pasadena, "it was ten billion years ago that a lone atom, with mass equal to that of the entire universe, burst. Then the millions of island universes began to take shape for the race through space. The expanding universe started from a highly compressed and extremely hot 'primordial atom.' As this matter expanded it became thinner and cooler and reaggregated into stars, planets, and galaxies. This terrific flight is still on—a flight witnessed by the earth itself, which is part of this colossal atom."

This is the poetic picture of a priest who cannot reject the idea of an expanding universe and its implications simply because it does not coincide with the Biblical story of creation. For, at the same time, it does not exclude the belief in some divine force or creator who set the whole drama in action. Perhaps this "Universe Egg" which Lemaître laid has much in common with the vaporings of those churchmen who ordered Galileo to recite for years the seven penitential psalms for daring to teach that the earth revolved around the sun. Perhaps, on the other hand, this conception is just as meaningful as that of any of the other mathematical physicists who have attempted the ambitious task of picturing a universe for us.

The new developments in the field of cosmology revived the question of the age of the universe. As Hubble pointed out, every exploration into extragalactic space is an investigation not only of the size but also of the age of the universe. These recent discoveries have played havoc with the more or less generally accepted old ideas. For the age of the cosmos, scientists had previously spoken of tens of billions of years, based on evidences furnished by meteorites, radioactivity, saltiness of the sea, depth of rock strata, and other similar data. But as the newer horizons spread out, they synchronously crowded the years into shorter epochs. An expanding universe must have started within much more recent times, or by now it would have been scattered more widely or have completely thinned out before it could start to shrink again. This pulsating universe could not have been on its expanding journey more than just a few billion years.

Much earlier observations seemed to indicate that many of the stars were much older than a mere few billion years. Some of the double stars, for example, seemed to be at least one hundred billion years old, as indicated by the shape of their orbits. Here we had a situation in which the stars appeared much older than the universe itself. Could it really be that the offspring was older than its parent? That was a riddle until Eddington stepped in and, in his characteristic fashion, offered a solution. "Cuts are in fashion now," said Eddington, "and if the theory of an expanding universe is right, it looks as if we were in for a cut of about 99 per cent in our time scale. That naturally causes a great deal of concern to the department affected; namely, the department of stellar evolution." Perhaps, he reminded science, our ideas of the time that it took stars to pass through their many evolutionary stages from birth to the present are very inaccurate. We may have miscalculated the speed of evolution of stars which could have passed through their life cycles in much shorter time than we had supposed. They might, in fact, be very much younger than we ever dreamed—much younger, in fact, than the universe. Hubble's estimate was about two billion years.

In 1952, Walter Baade of Mount Palomar discovered that the yardstick we had been using to determine the distances between galaxies was apparently wrong. Doubts were also raised about the accepted uniformity of the Cepheids. Cepheid variables in the Milky Way *may* be different from those of other galaxies, according, for example, to Halton C. Arp of Mount Wilson and Mount Palomar observatories. His observations during 1956–1957 at Pretoria and Cape Town, South Africa, pointed to this possibility. The distances between galaxies may be greater than we formerly thought—in fact, more than twice as great. This would make the universe twice as large and change the age of the cosmos to about five or six billion years, in agreement with astrophysical and geological estimates.

From the last observational data available in 1957, Sandage concluded that the model of the universe is probably of the evolutionary type—a conventional, expanding one of finite dimension and a positive radius of curvature. This expansion, which is already slowing down, will stop in time. Contraction will then set in, and we will have a pulsating or oscillating universe and not a static one. These conclusions are still tentative, however. More data are needed. It may well be that the two most remote clusters, more than a billion light-years out in space, now under investigation by Humason may furnish the answer to this and other baffling questions of form and age.

Perhaps, too, an entirely new approach very recently undertaken may help in these great questions. Radioastronomy, born accidentally and in early obscurity, may be the tool. Radiotelescopes may take over when the limits of the two-hundred-inch have been reached. These new fingers, which can reach out to hitherto unprobed corners of the universe, were invented by a young Oklahoman fresh out of the University of Wisconsin.

Karl G. Jansky got a job on the technical staff of the Bell Telephone Laboratories at their Holmdel, New Jersey, station in 1928. He was assigned the task of studying some unidentified sources of static. It was a very practical problem. Static was interfering with transatlantic radiotelephone messages. Young Jansky built a special aerial and listened. There was definitely a distinct type of noise but a strange one. The noise was "very weak, very steady, causing a hiss in the phones." What could be the cause of this hiss? He first made sure it was not due to noisy power lines. There was also no interference from local radio transmitters. He had made certain of that, too. The disturbances did not come from the upper atmosphere. This also had been ruled out.

Jansky worked for five years with a rotatable directional antenna to track down the cause of this static. He finally came to the conclusion that its source was somewhere way out beyond the earth's atmosphere. He believed it was somewhere in the center of our own galaxy, some 26,000 light-years away. A new window to the universe was ready to be thrown open. Had the importance of pure research in this country a quarter of a century ago been more deeply recognized, Jansky might have continued with these studies, which turned out to be a new field of radio-astronomy. It would have enabled scientists to penetrate the interstellar dust and clouds which hampered the men at the two-hundred-inch telescope. Jansky worked on radio direction finders during the war and died in 1950 at the age of forty-four.

As long ago as 1925 it was postulated that the electron spins on its axis like a top. This led to the discovery that atoms transmit radio waves. How to tune in on these waves was a difficult problem. Scientists in other countries seized upon this new method of approach and began a feverish effort to pick out radiation impulses from the turbulent hydrogen clouds in outer space. This song of the hydrogen ion was not the only target of these astronomers. They were also eager to pick out other significant notes from the din of cosmic noise. American science lagged here. The President's report on basic research issued in 1957 pointed out that "most basic work on Jansky's original observation was done abroad, and the United States is still in the process of catching up."

In England, Australia, Holland, and the Soviet Union larger and more sensitive radio receivers were designed and constructed to narrow down the radio noises and pinpoint their sources. A radiotelescope collects and focuses radio waves just as an optical telescope collects and focuses light waves. One type is a parabolic reflector which focuses the radio waves received on an antenna whence the induced voltage sends a current to activate a radio receiver. The University of Manchester, England, built a 250-foot radiotelescope in 1950 at Jodrell Bank in Cheshire. It has a steerable disk. Netherlands radioastronomers worked with a 75-foot instrument, Australian scientists were also equipped with a large machine, and the Russians have reported one with a 350-foot saucer. The Cavendish Laboratory of Cambridge University will have an even more up-to-date machine capable of penetrating to six billion light-years, about three times farther out into space than our telescope atop Mount Palomar.

American activity in this field is picking up. On the night of March 25, 1951, radiations from hydrogen clouds in outer space were first recorded at Harvard by Harold I. Ewen, working for his Ph.D. under Nobel laureate Edward M. Purcell, who had suggested the research problem. Soon after, the Harvard College Observatory initiated a hydrogen-cloud research project in the Milky Way with their 24-foot radiotelescope and in 1956 acquired a new machine at its Agassiz Station. This machine has a 60-foot disk. The United States also possesses a 50-foot disk at the Naval Research Laboratory in Washington, and an 84-foot instrument at Riverside, Maryland. Two more laboratories are being planned and financed by the National Science Foundation and the Office of Naval Research. One will have an 85-foot saucer-shaped steerable instrument and the other a 140-foot device, largest in this country. They will both be constructed at the National Radio-Astronomy Observatory in Green Bank, West Virginia, and will be in operation in 1960. They will be managed by Associated Universities, Inc., of New York. Ohio State University and the University of Michigan will also soon have large radiotelescopes of their own.

A considerable amount of work has already been done in this alluring and rapidly growing field of research. In 1946 the first *radio stars* were discovered in Cygnus, Cassiopeia, and the Crab Nebula. By 1950 Cambridge sky watchers had turned up fifty radio stars in the Northern Hemisphere, and an Australian team had uncovered an equal number in the Southern heavens. Five years later two thousand of these spots had been identified, and these radio sources seemed to increase in density with distance. This would lend support to the evolutionary theory of the universe.

This is an unusually exciting field. In 1951 F. G. Smith of Cambridge reported a very strong point of radio emission in the constellation of Cygnus A. The following year Walter Baade and Rudolph Minkowski at the two-hundred-inch telescope on Mount Palomar, working closely with English and Australian investigators, found among their photographs what appeared to be a close collision of two galaxies in the region of the sky containing that Cygnus radio star. More unexpected and highly provocative phenomena will undoubtedly be observed as more sensitive devices with greater resolving power are constructed, such as the more perfect diffraction gratings produced by a new electronically controlled engraving machine recently developed at the Massachusetts Institute of Technology. In 1954 a new radio-wave amplifier was developed by Charles H. Townes of Columbia University in co-operation with scientists of the Naval Research Laboratory. It is known as MASER (microwave amplification by stimulated emission of radiation). Three years later, Nicolaas Bloembergen of Harvard University developed a new type of MASER built to operate specifically on the wave length of interstellar hydrogen—twenty-one centimeters. This is a synthetic ruby crystal device which will extend the range of radio-telescopes as much as tenfold. It will enable Thomas Gold at Harvard and other astronomers to detect signals from outer space one-one thousandth as strong as those now observable and bring us close to the "edge of the universe."

Perhaps, out of this new and boiling cosmological pot, heated and stirred by American science, will come fundamental answers to more than one perplexing question concerning the nature of the universe.

CHAPTER NINETEEN

ERNEST ORLANDO LAWRENCE (1901-1958)

THE TURN OF THE TIDE IN WORLD SCIENCE

SCIENCE HAD TO WAIT until the twentieth century before it could launch its great offensive against the heart of the atom. The attack was planned to find the answers to the mysteries of both matter and radiation. It had been delayed so long because new tools, new advances in engineering, and new techniques had to be made available for this prodigious task. Men, too, had come to the realization that only by co-operative effort on a world-wide scale could the fundamental problems of science be successfully attacked. Said one of the leaders in the vanguard of this new chapter of history, "The day when the scientist, no matter how devoted, may make significant progress alone and without material help is past. Instead of an attic with a few test tubes, bits of wire and odds and ends, the attack on the atom's nucleus has required the development and construction of great instruments on an *engineering* scale." This demanded large sums of money which were made available by new research foundations and other philanthropic institutions. Although the beginnings of this great adventure took place in Europe, American physicists and chemists soon joined the attack and finally assumed leadership in this field.

In 1897 one of the great upheavals in physical science shook the world. The bubble of the atom as the ultimate unit of matter was pricked by Joseph John Thomson, head of a brilliant group of disciples gathered in the Cavendish Laboratory of Experimental Physics in Cambridge, England. On April 30 of that year, Thomson announced that cathode rays are *particles* of negative electricity, or *electrons*, which are part of all atoms. He denied the ultimate reality of the indivisible atom. There was something simpler than the atom—the electron. Another sacred cow of science had been slaughtered.

Thomson estimated the weight of the electron at about one eighteen-hundredth of that of a single atom of hydrogen, lightest of all the chemical elements. The world was not altogether convinced by Thomson's experiments. After all, many whispered, it was only a "calculation," another piece of scientific abracadabra. Thomson himself was not satisfied. He called in one of his research students, Charles Thomson Rees Wilson, and asked, "Can you photograph the elusive electron?" There was nothing left to do but to make the attempt, even though it came perilously near to the work of a magician. Wilson worked for six years to improve and develop a supercamera that would trap a single electron, and he obtained his first rough photographs in 1911. A tangled skein of threads representing the paths of single electrons after expulsion from their atoms appeared on his plate. These *fog tracks* of electrons were as incontestable a proof of the existence of electrons as is a furrow of ruin of a cyclone's passing.

The invention of the Wilson *cloud chamber* apparatus, with its manifold improvements, has been the most valuable, if not the altogether indispensable, ally of man in his attack upon the nature of matter. Without it, nearly all of the spectacular raids on the citadel of the atom would have been impossible. Today it is as much a standard piece of equipment in the outposts of atomic physics as is the telescope in astronomy or the microscope in biology. Sixteen years after the invention was completed, Wilson was honored with the Nobel Prize for his achievement.

Thomson's figure for the mass of an electron was only an estimate. The final and unequivocal determination was accomplished in the physics laboratory of the University of Chicago by Robert Andrews Millikan. On his father's side Millikan was descended

from Scotch-English farmers who had come to this country during the Scotch-Irish migrations to buy land from the Indians and
till the stubborn, rocky soil of the Berkshire Hills around Pitts-
field, Massachusetts. With the opening of the Erie Canal in 1825
the Millikans moved westward in covered wagons, taking their
sheep, their cattle and horses, together with an intense evangelis-
tic religion. They settled on the "Western Reserve" around Freedom, Ohio, and here Robert Millikan's father was born, to become
the Reverend Silas Franklin Millikan, Congregationalist minister.
On the maternal side, Millikan's descent has been traced to English ancestors of the Puritan type who had settled in Salem, Massachusetts. His mother, Mary Jane Andrews, came of seafaring folk
from Taunton, Massachusetts.

His parents never dreamed of a career in science for Robert. If
he had any aptitude or leaning in that direction, he did not know
it until he was in his twenty-second year; he was twenty-five
before he decided to try to get the training which would permit
him to become a physicist. Science took hold of him with steel
fingers. He studied under Michael Pupin, who later lent him
money to go to Göttingen to study under Walther Nernst. From
here he was suddenly recalled by Michelson, who offered him an
assistantship in physics at the University of Chicago.

Millikan was going to weigh the electron. He devised an ingenious scheme (oil-drop method) which gave him an electrical
balance thousands of times more sensitive than the best mechanical scale. He isolated and determined the charge of a single electron and found it to be one eighteen-hundred-and-thirty-fifths
the weight of a single atom of hydrogen. This classic of physical
science helped to gain for Millikan the Nobel Prize in 1923.

The electron theory clarified many baffling questions and many
curious effects. It offered the first satisfactory explanation of a
phenomenon discovered by Thomas A. Edison in 1883. Edison
had noticed that when the carbon filament in an evacuated glass
bulb was heated by a battery, a current of electricity appeared
in the metal plate in the bulb. This happened only when the *posi-*

tive binding post of the battery was connected to the cold metal plate. No current flowed when the plate was joined to the negative side of the battery. How did the current get across the vacuum from the hot filament to the cold plate, and why did the plate have to be connected to the positive terminal of the battery? There were no answers to these questions until the electron was discovered. John A. Fleming, the great English electrical engineer and friend of Edison, then explained that this *Edison effect* was due to the stream of negative electrons shot out of the heated carbon filament and attracted to the positively charged plate in the vacuum tube the inventor was using. The glowing carbon

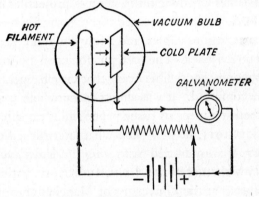

Fig. 25. The Edison Effect.

atoms of the filament threw off electrons. In 1904 Fleming made use of this tube as a valve or rectifier to change alternating current into direct current. Later he invented the thermionic valve for detecting radio waves, and when another American, Lee de Forest, added a third electrode (grid) to the Fleming valve, the invention of the modern radio tube was completed.

After the discovery of the electron J. J. Thomson reasoned that there must be present in the neutral atom of all elements some positive electricity to counteract the negative electron. But how was one to prove the presence of positively charged particles in all matter? That was the problem that Ernest Rutherford, one of Thomson's students who had come from New Zealand to Cambridge, set himself to investigate. If he was to discover the nature of the interior of the atom, he must use projectiles small enough to enter it. In 1902 he had discovered such a bullet—the *alpha particle*, which he had trapped in thin glass tubes as it was given off by radium, and had identified it as an electrified atom of helium. The alpha particle was spontaneously ejected from radium at a speed of 12,000 miles per second, and its mass was about 8000 times greater than that of an electron. It possessed the greatest individual energy of any particle then known to science—7,000,000 electron volts.

For years Rutherford, aided by his young assistants, Hans Geiger and James Chadwick, threw these projectiles against thin films of gold. Some of them passed through the films, others were turned aside at various angles, and a few could not penetrate and actually bounced back. This last phenomenon floored him. "It was quite the most incredible event that ever happened to me in my life," he confessed. "It was almost as incredible as if you fired a 15-inch shell at a piece of tissue paper and it came back and hit you." In May, 1911, he published what later turned out to be a classic paper. It was entitled *Scattering of Alpha and Beta Particles and the Structure of the Atom*. Rutherford, at this time professor of physics at the University of Manchester, reported that thousands of his fog tracks showed his alpha particles plowing through billions of gold atoms in straight lines. But there were a few alpha particles which seemed suddenly to have been thrown off their course as they crashed into something very hard. There must be, he was convinced, something very solid in the center of the atom to twist the flight of this submicroscopic projectile. Furthermore, the positively charged atom of hydrogen was ejected from every element he had bombarded. Rutherford had discovered another building block of every atom, the counterpart of the negative electron. This positive particle, which he christened the *proton*, was 1835 times heavier than the electron. The proton was the ordinary atom of hydrogen minus its single electron.

Rutherford also postulated a nuclear atom for the first time.

He gave us a new picture of the structure of matter. Matter was composed of atoms which resembled the solar system, each atom having a massive center or nucleus of positive electricity or protons, around which at a relatively great distance revolved tiny planetary electrons. In between the nucleus and the electrons was an immense void—empty space, so vacant, in fact, that the atom resembled a net of gossamer thread—nearly all holes. *All matter was made up of nothing but electrons and protons.*

The electrons around the nucleus were by no means fixed in position. They were in constant motion, zooming around at tremendous speeds in different orbits. It was this particular structure of the atom that led Rutherford to speak of the atomic universe as a miniature solar system with the nucleus representing the sun and the many electrons as the planets revolving around the sun. It was the speed of the electrons around the nucleus that prevented them from falling into the center, which was charged positively, just as the earth and the other planets in their elliptical courses around the sun are prevented from being pulled into the massive sun by gravitational attraction.

The jetlike and perpetual motion of the electrons of each atom also accounts for the solid behavior of this huge emptiness of an atom. Said Sir William Bragg, another pioneer in the field of the atom's structure, "It is strange to think of an atom as being empty as a solar system, not a hard impenetrable body but a combination of nucleus and electrons which occupies a certain space somewhat as an army occupies a country. The bodies of the soldiers do not fill the country from boundary to boundary, but enemy soldiers may not enter nevertheless."

The next crucial question was, "How many protons are present in each atom?" Rutherford ventured the guess that "The charge in the nucleus of every element ought to be proportional to the atomic weight of the element." In 1912 he had turned this problem over to twenty-six-year-old Henry G. J. Moseley, one of his most brilliant students. Before the year was over, Moseley had discovered the *law of atomic numbers*. The atomic number of an element represents its numerical position in the list of all the ninety-two chemical elements. The first element in Moseley's table was hydrogen, with an atomic number of one; uranium, with atomic number 92, was the last. This new table of the chemical elements was more fundamental than that of Dmitri Mendeléeff, the Russian who in 1869 had given the world the *periodic table of the elements*. For the first time, a scientific limit was set on the number of the building blocks of the universe. Three years later Moseley, a volunteer in the British Army, was on his way to the front at Gallipoli. Within a few months a Turkish bullet pierced his brain at Suvla Bay.

Rutherford kept hurling alpha particles at atoms of nitrogen gas trapped in a flask. The years rolled by as he performed thousands of experiments. When World War I broke out, the string-and-sealing-wax Cavendish Laboratory had ceased to be the busy hive of research students fighting a battle against the atomic world. Almost overnight its workers scattered to the various government services. Rutherford, however, found some time to continue his experiments at odd moments when he could steal time from heavy commitments he had made to the military. While he was hot on the trail of a solution, four bloody years were passing. At one time he had to disappoint a committee of scientists working on a method of detecting enemy submarines. He explained that he was going to be delayed because he was, at the moment, completely taken up with experiments which seemed to indicate that he was on the verge of splitting the nitrogen atom. "If this is true," he told the startled committee, which included Robert Millikan, "its ultimate importance will be far greater than that of the war."

The war ended, Rutherford succeeded Thomson as head of the Cavendish Laboratory and on June 19, 1919, celebrated his return by announcing the success of his crucial experiment. The evidence was minute, fleeting, difficult to observe at first, but later unmistakably captured in the emulsion of a photographic plate attached to a Wilson cloud chamber. A broken line in a fog track on this plate (see Fig. 27, page 545) told the story. An alpha particle had found its tiny target, plowed its way into the nucleus of a nitrogen atom, ejected a proton from its inner sanctum, and thereby changed the chemical element nitrogen into a different element, oxygen. This was the first successful artificial transmutation in history.

Rutherford's solar-system concept of the atom still left much to be desired, however. It failed to give a consistent explanation of the peculiar spectra or bright lines given off by gaseous elements when heated to incandescence. If this spectrum light was caused by electronic motion, then Rutherford's atom ought to radiate this light *continuously*, since the electrons were always moving about. Moreover, the electrons should be attracted and fall into the nucleus unless their stupendous speed were maintained in some way to counteract the powerful pull of the atom's kernel. What the spectroscope had revealed scientists could not explain by the known facts of classical electrodynamics. Here was a mighty impasse.

Niels Bohr, a young Dane, was to break this jam. He had come to Manchester in the spring of 1912 to work under Rutherford. Convinced of the value of the concept of the nuclear atom, Bohr published three revolutionary papers the following year at the age of twenty-eight. He bravely abandoned the classical laws of electrodynamics which, he declared, did not apply *within* the atom. He took hold of a new tool, Max Planck's conception of *energy quanta*. This conception, one of the great revolutionary theories in the history of science, had been announced near the close of 1900. Planck insisted that energy was granular, emitted not in a continuous flow, but in tiny, finite bundles called quanta, the mass of which depended upon the wave length. Bohr pictured the outer electrons of the atom as revolving in circular orbits around the nucleus unless disturbed by some outside force such as cathode rays, X rays, or even heat. When thus disturbed, electrons would jump from one orbit to another closer to the nucleus. The transfer to each different orbit represented a distinct spectrum line, every jump being accompanied by a characteristic light. "For each atom," he wrote, "there exists a number of definite states of motion called stationary states, in which the atom can exist without radiating energy. Only when the atom is disturbed and passes from one state to another can it radiate light." Using this method of attack Bohr explained the complex spectrum of hydrogen and attempted to locate the orbits of other elements.

Further clarification of the structure of the atom followed in 1916 when Gilbert N. Lewis, a brilliant theorist and experimenter, of the University of California, published a paper setting forth a new structure of the atom, particularly with reference to the location of its planetary electrons. Around the nucleus, he said, were hypothetical cubical shells which contained varying numbers of electrons occupying fixed positions. Three years later Irving Langmuir of the General Electric Company elaborated and extended this idea by introducing his *concentric shell theory* of the arrangement of the electrons outside the nucleus. He wanted a picture of the atom which would explain chemical activity. Moseley's table of atomic numbers was his starting point. Helium (atomic number 2) and neon (atomic number 10) were stable elements which refused to combine with other elements. In these elements the electrons must therefore represent stable groups which rendered their atoms incapable of chemical activity. Langmuir pictured the helium atom as containing a nucleus of fixed protons and cementing electrons, and two additional electrons revolving in a shell outside the central core. The distances between the shells were made to agree with the various orbits that Bohr had postulated. All atoms, said Langmuir, have a tendency to complete the outermost shell. The first shell is complete with two electrons; the second shell with eight electrons.

This tendency to form stable groups explains the chemical activity of the element. Hydrogen is very active because, since its shell contains but one electron, it is incomplete and needs another electron to form a stable group of two, as in helium. Neon, with ten electrons outside its nucleus, represents another stable configuration, having two electrons in its first shell and eight more in a second larger shell concentric with the first. All the elements with atomic numbers between 2 and 10 are therefore active to an extent depending upon the completeness of their second shells. For example, lithium, atomic number 3, possesses only a single electron in its second shell. Hence, in its eagerness to complete the outside shell, it will readily give away this third electron to an-

HYDROGEN   HELIUM   NEON

Electron (outside the nucleus)

Proton (in the nucleus)

Fig. 26. The hydrogen atom, the helium atom, and the neon atom according to Langmuir.

other element, and thus be left with but two electrons in the first shell—a stable group. This tendency to lose electrons from the outermost, incomplete shell makes lithium an extremely active element.

There was more trouble ahead. Both the brilliant formulations of the Copenhagen school at the Institute of Theoretical Physics, founded in 1920 and led by Bohr, and the Lewis-Langmuir picture of the atom developed in the United States contained dark spots that no amount of experimentation could illuminate. From the field of light had already come rumblings of a violent upheaval in the definitions of science. Light seemed to be of a dual nature, exhibiting at one time the properties of a wave and at another the characteristics of a particle. Louis Victor, Prince de Broglie, published a paper in 1924 suggesting that the electron was composed of, possessed, or perhaps was attended by a group of waves similar to those of light. If the Frenchman's electron was of the nature of light, it ought to exhibit the characteristics of light, namely, interference and diffraction phenomena.

In 1927 two Americans, Clinton J. Davisson and Lester H. Germer of the Bell Telephone Laboratories in New York City furnished the first proof. They shot a narrow stream of electrons against a nickel crystal, and found that the electrons struck and were reflected from the crystal in the same way as rays of light. "Our experiments," they concluded, "establish the wave nature of moving electrons with the same certainty as the wave nature of X rays has been established." Arthur Dempster of the University of Chicago soon after showed that the proton, too, possessed wave properties. Albert Einstein, the most profound scientific thinker since Newton, could not refrain from explaining, "We stand here before a new property of matter for which the strictly causal theories hitherto in vogue are unable to account." In 1929 Prince de Broglie was honored with the Nobel Prize for his work, which culminated in the theory that the stuff of matter has wave properties like light.

In the meantime, there had begun an orgy of speculation in the field of the physical sciences. Mathematical specialists entered the arena with a new attack. Physical and mathematical theories of the structure of the atom came "crowding on each other's heels with an increasing unmannerliness." In the forefront stood Erwin Schroedinger, an Austrian scientist. He introduced a new mathematical treatment known as *wave mechanics*, which looked upon the atom as a region permeated with waves. His technique confirmed the work of De Broglie and even predicted some facts connected with spectrum lines that were not foreseen by Bohr's treatment.

At the same time an equally profound and suggestive idea was being evolved by a young theoretical physicist of Munich, Werner Heisenberg. This young man of twenty-three expressed the structure of the atom by means of mathematical formulas directly connected with the frequencies and intensities of spectrum lines—phenomena which could be observed and measured. His system, the *new quantum* or *matrix mechanics*, bothered even men accustomed to the twists and turns of serpentine theoretical physics. Both Schroedinger and Heisenberg received the Nobel Prize for these contributions, which were used with great success by many, including Linus C. Pauling, head of the department of chemistry of the California Institute of Technology. Pauling, who was born in Portland, Oregon, in 1901, was one of the first chemists to interpret chemical behavior by the quantum theory. He has cleared up many of the mysteries of the physical and chemical structure of complex organic molecules including proteins, the nature of the chemical bond, and the electronic theory of valence. Experimentally, too, he developed with great brilliance a method of taking electron diffraction pictures of gaseous molecules to elucidate the structure of organic molecules. He, too, became a Nobel laureate in chemistry in 1953.

In spite of all of these new approaches, the nucleus of the atom continued to remain a bundle of uncertainties. Something of the composition of the nuclei of a few elements was already known. This information came from a study of the spontaneous disintegration of radium and other radioactive elements, such as thorium, polonium, and uranium. These elements break down of their own accord into simpler elements by a mechanism not then completely understood. In 1902, soon after the Curies' discovery of radium, Rutherford and Frederick Soddy, his student and collaborator, had found that the spontaneous breaking down of radium resulted in the emission of three types of rays and particles. Radium ejected alpha particles (ionized helium atoms), beta particles (electrons), and gamma rays (similar to X rays). In radioactive elements, at least, it was believed that the nucleus contained electrons, protons, and electrified helium particles. (The gamma rays given off are energy rays rather than matter.) Was this true for other elements as well?

American science was ready to take another step forward in the realm of theory. In a room close to Millikan's laboratory at the University of Chicago, William D. Harkins in the winter of 1914-15 attempted to find some characteristic of the atomic nucleus which would serve as a basis for a new classification. The characteristic chosen was the stability of the nucleus. He offered the theory that the nuclei of all elements were compounds of hydrogen and helium. Atoms having even atomic numbers were more stable than those possessing odd atomic numbers, and hence were more abundant in nature. He also assumed that the heavier elements were built from lighter elements by a step-by-step process in which hydrogen and helium groups were gradually added. So far as the element radium was concerned, Harkins' hydrogen-helium theory was acceptable, for it gave off both electrons and helium.

But would Harkins' theory hold for other atoms? To be sure, Rutherford had already shown that nitrogen (atomic number 7), as well as the odd-atomic-numbered elements (5, 9, 11, 13, 15) which he had bombarded, liberated hydrogen but, as far as was known, no helium. On the other hand, not a single even-atomic-numbered element could be disrupted. Harkins decided to repeat Rutherford's experiments of 1919. He modified the Wilson cloud-chamber apparatus to suit his procedure and in 1921 took thousands of fog-track photographs of helium nuclei (obtained from thorium) shooting through nitrogen and other gases.

One of the pictures was a very strange one. It showed something new—a double deflection with one line of the fork about ten times thinner than the other usual deflected line. To Harkins this solitary picture, one bull's-eye from among a hundred thousand shots (good marksmanship in the subatomic world), indicated that Rutherford's interpretation of the ejection of an electrified hydrogen particle from the nitrogen nucleus was an incomplete story. In this destruction of an atomic world Harkins saw, also, the synthesis of a new one, for not only was hydrogen (thin line) ejected, but another element, oxygen (thick line), was in this case formed. He interpreted the picture as showing the union of the helium nucleus (alpha particle) with the nitrogen nucleus to form an unstable atom of fluorine. This fluorine atom immediately disintegrated to form an electrified hydrogen particle (proton) and an atom of oxygen. In other words, oxygen had been synthesized or built up from nitrogen and helium.

Harkins represented this result of seven years of intense work in equation form thus:

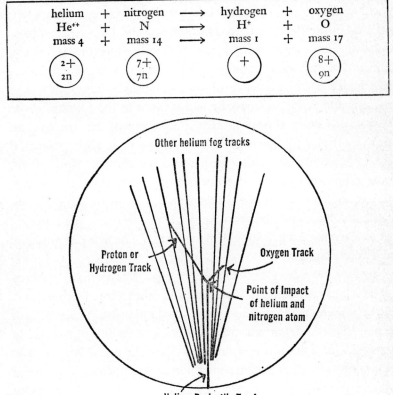

helium	+	nitrogen	$\longrightarrow$	hydrogen	+	oxygen
He^{++}	+	N	$\longrightarrow$	H^+	+	O
mass 4	+	mass 14	$\longrightarrow$	mass 1	+	mass 17

Other helium fog tracks

Proton or Hydrogen Track

Oxygen Track

Point of Impact of helium and nitrogen atom

Helium Projectile Track

Fig. 27. The discovery plate of Rutherford's historic artificial transmutation of nitrogen into oxygen in 1919.

The oxygen formed was an atom of atomic weight 17 instead of 16, the accepted atomic weight of the only kind of oxygen atom then known. In 1931, however, this new form or *isotope* of oxygen of atomic weight 17 was discovered, thus confirming what until then was only a possibility.

Harkins' picture of a nucleus containing nothing but helium and hydrogen nuclei and electrons contained paradoxes. One of the greatest difficulties was to account for the way in which negatively charged and positively charged units of electricity could exist side by side in the nucleus without neutralizing each other. In other words, what prevented the negative electron and the positive proton from joining together since they were so closely situated in the tiny nucleus? Harkins saw the anomaly. Speculations were no longer unfashionable in twentieth-century science, and he was audacious enough to advance a seemingly preposterous theory of the existence of another entirely new unit in the nucleus. On April 12, 1920, he had written to the *Journal of the American Chemical Society* that in addition to the protons and alpha particles in the nuclei of atoms there is also present "a second less abundant group with a zero net charge." Rutherford, too, had postulated the existence of such a particle. Harkins suggested the name *neutron* for this particle of atomic number zero, made up of a single proton and a single electron so close together as to neutralize each other's electric charge. The neutron possesses no electric charge.

Twelve years later, in the winter of 1932, this particle predicted by Harkins was actually discovered in Rutherford's laboratory. The man who made this discovery was James Chadwick. He shot helium bullets (from old radium tubes sent to him by the Kelly Hospital of Baltimore) against beryllium, a metal lighter than aluminum, and noticed that something of great penetrating power was knocked out of the target. To account for the high energy of this unknown something which was thrown out of the beryllium, and to save the law of the conservation of energy, Chadwick said that these new "rays" were really not rays at all. They must, he believed, be made of particles of the mass of protons, but unlike protons, they were not electrically charged. Since these neutrons were electrically dead, they could not be repelled by the impregnable electric walls of the atom, and hence they had a terrific penetrating power. Two and one-half inches of lead were capable of stopping only half of them. What had really happened could be expressed in the following equation:

beryllium	+	helium ions	$\longrightarrow$	carbon	+	neutron
Be	+	He^{++}	$\longrightarrow$	C	+	n
mass 9	+	mass 4	$\longrightarrow$	mass 12	+	mass 1

(Note that all weights are accounted for in this nuclear equation.)

The announcement of this discovery was followed by feverish activity to learn more about this new member of the family of fundamental entities. John R. Dunning, Nebraska-born physicist, and George P. Pegram, at Columbia University, slowed down a stream of neutrons and made some measurements. Then Isidor I. Rabi, their brilliant colleague who later became a Nobel laureate, calculated from their experimental data that the diameter of the neutron was much smaller than that of the hydrogen atom (1/40,000,000-inch). Robert Hofstadter, a graduate of the College of the City of New York, made a final determination of the size of the neutron in 1957 at Stanford University. A single neutron is thought to be composed of one electron and one proton so closely packed and held together as to appear as a single particle. Its density is many millions of times greater than that of the heaviest element.

The neutron was not the last nuclear unit to be unearthed. Ernest Rutherford in England, G. N. Lewis and Raymond T. Birge of the University of California had predicted the existence of a double-weight hydrogen atom which would be an isotope of ordinary hydrogen of atomic weight one. *Isotopes* are varieties of the same chemical element having the same atomic number but differing chiefly in weight. An isotope never exists in the pure state in nature. It is always mixed with the other isotopes of the same elements. Isotopes have been known since 1913, when Francis W. Aston, working under J. J. Thomson, had discovered two different species of the element neon, one with an atomic weight of 20 and another of 22. The following year Theodore Richards of Harvard University announced an isotope of lead with an atomic weight less than that of nonradioactive lead. Since that day, several hundred isotopes have been found in nature, including the eleven isotopes of tin. Soddy, who coined the word *isotope*, speaking of the tremendous effort that had been put into the accurate determinations of atomic weights even to the fourth decimal place by pioneers such as Theodore Richards, declared that with the discovery of isotopes, "something surely akin to if not transcending tragedy overtook the life work of that distinguished galaxy of nineteenth century chemists."

Three weeks before the announcement of the discovery of the neutron, Rutherford's prediction came true in the chemical laboratory of Columbia University. Harold C. Urey, born in Indiana, had received his doctorate at the University of California and had studied under Bohr. Early in his career he had suspected the presence of *heavy hydrogen* as a result of his analysis of the spectrum of ordinary hydrogen. In the fall of 1931 F. G. Brickwedde of the United States Bureau of Standards evaporated a quantity of liquid hydrogen and sealed the last few remaining drops in a glass tube which he sent to Urey for examination. The Columbia scientist passed an electric discharge through the tube, scrutinized its spectrum lines, and announced the presence of the heavy isotope of hydrogen, which he named *deuterium* (D), from the Greek word meaning second. It occurs in ordinary hydrogen to the extent of about one part in five or six thousand. Its structure may be represented as:

This discovery was hailed as one of the most important of the century. It opened up a brand-new world for further research. When it is realized that the human body contains almost seventy per cent of water, the physiological importance of *heavy water* substituted in the body for ordinary water could hardly be exaggerated. With the three isotopes of hydrogen (*tritium*, atomic weight 3, has one proton and two neutrons in its nucleus) and the three isotopes of oxygen, as many as eighteen different kinds of water may be formed, each having different properties. Some scientists foresaw almost limitless possibilities of new compounds, since hydrogen occurs in more than 300,000 organic compounds alone. Most important of all, the new tool was put to use by researchers in physiology and medicine almost at once to tag atoms passing through the body. Heavy hydrogen has been substituted for ordinary hydrogen in certain fats; then the course and changes which these "tagged" fat molecules have undergone on their way through the animal body have been studied. This new tool of research enables us to attack many practical problems relating to human health. Here is another astonishing illustration of how theoretical problems in science may turn out to be of tremendous practical significance to mankind. In 1934 Urey earned the Nobel Prize for this work.

Here in the space of less than a month were revealed two new particles, two brand-new projectiles ready to be brought up with the artillery that was once more to lay siege to the atomic world. The neutron, especially, was an ideal bullet. For its infinitesimal size it was so tremendously heavy that, according to Harkins, a lady's thimble tightly packed with them would weigh a million tons. No circus strong man could budge such a bit of compressed matter. What was now needed to enter the guarded citadel of the atom's nucleus were high-speed particles even more powerful than the alpha particles of radium disintegration.

The discovery of the neutron presented science with a new model of the atom. Every atom, with the exception of hydrogen with atomic weight one, contains three different elementary particles, electrons, protons, and neutrons. The number of neutrons in an atom is the difference between the atomic weight of that element and its atomic number. The atomic number of an element is equal to the number of protons in its nucleus. The nucleus of the atom remains undisturbed even during the most violent chemical change, such as the explosion of nitroglycerine. In chemical changes, only the electrons outside the nucleus are involved. This is what should be expected, because any change in the number of protons in the nucleus would result in a change from one element into a different element—and this, of course, does not normally happen.

A change of one element into another does occur, however, in a few instances. This change, transmutation, occurs spontaneously in nature. The first evidence of this fact turned up when the Curies discovered the element radium late in 1898. Scientists for the first time were presented with a most unusual spectacle. A perfectly pure and simple element was throwing off rays and particles and finally disintegrating into a lighter element, lead. The electrons and helium atoms thrown off by radium came from the breaking up of a very unstable or unhappy nucleus inside the atom of this element. This alteration of the nucleus of an atom is a much more serious and deep-seated change than a chemical change. It is known as a nuclear change and, in the case of radium disintegration, takes place in several stages.

Radium is found in the 88th position of the Periodic Table of the Elements. It therefore has an atomic number of 88 and can boast of 88 protons in its nucleus. Its atomic weight has been determined as 226. Since this atomic weight is the sum of the number of protons and neutrons in its nucleus, radium contains 226 minus 88, or 138 neutrons. Now this tight little world of the nucleus of radium is a very unsteady one. One of its members leaves home in the guise of a helium atom whose atomic weight is 4. This act of migration changes the radium atom into a different element called radon, with atomic weight 222 and atomic number 86.

After numerous additional internal quarrels, several other members are ejected, leaving a new element called polonium to take its place. This new element has an atomic number of 84 and an atomic weight of 210. Polonium was, in fact, the first chemical element discovered by Marie Curie and was named after her native country. Now, polonium is still very jittery and disturbed, and before long it has violently ejected another helium particle from its nucleus and changed to still another different element—

lead, whose atomic number is 82 and atomic weight 206. Some of these nuclear changes may be represented as follows (for the purpose of simplification only the nuclei are shown):

RADIUM — HELIUM ⟶		RADON ⟶	POLONIUM — HELIUM ⟶		LEAD
At.wt. 226 —	4 ⟶	at.wt. 222 ⟶	at.wt. 219 —	4 ⟶	at.wt. 206
at.no. 88		at.no. 86	at.no. 84		at.no. 82
$n = 138$	$2n$ ⟶	$n = 136$ ⟶	$n = 126$ —	$2n$ ⟶	$n = 124$
$\binom{88+}{138n}$	$\binom{2+}{2n}$	$\binom{86+}{136n}$	$\binom{84+}{126n}$	$\binom{2+}{2n}$	$\binom{82+}{124n}$

The transmutation of radium into lead is a natural, spontaneous change. We have no control over it, we can neither slow it down nor accelerate it. Half of any piece of radium will disintegrate into lead in 1620 years. This period is known as the *half-life* of radium. In the next 1620 years, half of the remaining half (or one fourth of the original mass) will be left, and so on.

When the process of radium disintegration was demonstrated to be nothing more than a change in the composition of an unstable nucleus, scientists began to wonder whether this process could be imitated by man in the case of elements with stable nuclei. Artificial transmutation, evidently, could be brought about by so disturbing or jolting the nucleus of an atom as to force it to eject parts of itself or receive one or more additional protons. But how to get inside the nucleus was a prodigious problem. First of all it was so infinitesimally small that an even tinier bullet would have to be used. Second, the bullet to be chosen would have to be propelled at a stupendous speed to overcome the electrical defenses protecting the positively charged nucleus.

Despite Rutherford's epic achievement in 1919—the first artificial transmutation produced by man—the world of science was still not completely satisfied. The skeptics sneered. After all, whispered some perfectionists, Rutherford had used one radioactive element (radium) which was being transmuted by nature to produce helium projectiles for his own feat of transmutation. That wasn't fair. He had been compelled to call upon nature for help.

Suppose such an element were not available. Suppose we did not have radium. What then? What they wanted, and they made no bones about it, was a real, honest-to-goodness man-made transmutation without benefit of radioactive radium and the swift bullets it supplied. They wanted nothing less than a man-made projectile.

This was an impertinent and almost impossible request. It meant that scientists would have to manufacture an infinitesimal bullet with a speed never before even approached by man. To accomplish this, scientists would have to invent a machine capable of accelerating an electron, a proton, or a helium atom to velocities of the order of 10,000 miles per second and more. The wonder of it all is that science did come through with just such a machine.

Everywhere researchers close to the problem realized this need. A friendly yet spirited race had already begun in many laboratories of the world to build mighty armaments—new atomic siege guns which would hurl thunderbolts of staggering power to shatter the tiny nucleus into fragments that could be picked up and studied. High potential drops were to send every kind of submicroscopic bullet available crashing into the subatomic defenses.

The greatest of these ordnance builders is Ernest Orlando Lawrence. He was born, soon after the opening of the new century, in the little town of Canton, South Dakota. His paternal grandfather, Ole Lavrensen, was a schoolteacher in Norway who came to Madison, Wisconsin, during the Norwegian migration in 1840 to teach school along the frontier of America. He had his name anglicized to Lawrence immediately upon arrival in the new land. Ernest Lawrence's maternal grandfather was Erik Jacobson, who came twenty years later to seek a homestead in South Dakota when that area was still a territory. Both his grandmothers were also natives of Norway. Ernest's father, Carl G. Lawrence, was graduated from the University of Wisconsin and became president of Northern State Teachers College at Aberdeen, South Dakota. His mother was born near Canton, where Ernest first saw the light on August 8, 1901, only twelve years after South Dakota became a state. As a young boy he was sent to the public schools of Canton and Pierre, South Dakota. Later he attended St. Olaf College and the University of South Dakota. He had become attracted to science through an experimental interest in wireless communication, but for a while it seemed that he might pursue his hankering for a medical career. Finally, however, he threw in his lot with the physics of the atom and radiation.

Lawrence did some graduate work at the University of Minnesota, where he came under the influence of Professor W. F. G. Swann. He followed Swann to Yale, did graduate work under him, took his doctorate there in 1925, and stayed on as National Research Fellow, then as assistant professor of physics. When Swann left to head the Bartol Research Foundation at Philadelphia, Lawrence answered a call to the University of California.

Late one evening in the spring of 1929 Lawrence, quite accidentally, came across a paper which had just been written by Rolf Wideroe, an obscure Norwegian research man who until 1932 worked for the General Electric Company in Berlin on high-tension electricity problems. Attracted to a diagram of a piece of apparatus used by this physicist, he never finished reading the paper. Wideroe had managed to impart to electrified potassium atoms in a vacuum tube energies equal to twice the energy of the initial voltage he used. A small voltage could thus give high velocities to projectiles if the voltage could be applied repeatedly to the bullets at just the right time. The idea was not an altogether new one. This scheme of multiple acceleration of atomic projectiles had been likened by Karl T. Compton, then president of the Massachusetts Institute of Technology, to "a child in a swing. By properly synchronizing the pushes, the child may be made to swing very high even though each individual push would lift him only a short distance."

Lawrence, who according to Swann "had always shown an unusual fertility of mind and had more than his share of ideas," picked up and nourished this fertile seed. He had been casting about for a means of side-stepping the difficulties of sustained or intermittent high voltage necessary for effective attacks on the kernel of the atom. He was searching for a technique which would require no high-tension currents of electricity and no elaborate vacuum-tube equipment, and yet enable him to get immense speed with his projectiles. Now he thought he had a valuable clue. Within a few minutes after he had seen that diagram he began sketching pieces of apparatus and writing down mathematical formulas. The essential features of his new machine came to him almost immediately. The next morning he told a friend that he had a new idea and was going to invent a new tool of science.

With this new instrument Lawrence planned to whirl an electrical bullet in a circle by bending it under the influence of a powerful electromagnet. As it passed around one half the circumference of a highly evacuated tank shaped like a covered frying pan, he was going to give the particle repeated electrical kicks which would send it racing in ever-widening circles at greater and still greater speeds, until it reached the edge of the evacuated tube, where it would emerge from a slit and be hurtled into a collecting chamber. Here he would harness it as a mighty projectile against the nucleus of an atom. He was going to adjust the magnetic field so that the particle would get back just as the initial alternating current changed direction and at the exact moment it was ready for another kick. The particle was to be speeded on its way by oscillating electricity of high frequency. He hoped in this way to get the same effect by applying a thousand volts one thousand times as he would by applying a million volts all at once.

"High frequency oscillations," said Lawrence, "applied to plate electrodes produce an oscillating electrical field. As a result, during a one-half cycle the electric field accelerates ions into the interior of one of the electrodes, where they are bent around on circular paths by the magnetic field and eventually emerge again into the region between the electrodes." It was a very bold scheme. Would it work? By January, 1930, Lawrence had built his first magnetic resonance accelerator, which later became commonly known as the *cyclotron*. Between the poles of an electromagnet was a vacuum chamber only four inches in diameter. In this were two D-shaped insulated electrodes connected to a high-frequency alternating current. Down the center ran a tungsten filament. The rest of the machine was constructed of glass and red sealing wax. With the help of N. E. Edlefsen, his first graduate-student assistant, he succeeded in getting actual resonance effects. The idea worked, and Lawrence made his first public announcement of the machine and method in September of that same year at a meeting of the National Academy of Sciences in Berkeley.

Lawrence had created a new tool for science and had added a new word to the dictionary. Said *The New York Times*, "The pioneers in experimental physics have always had to devise their own instruments of investigation. Men like Faraday, Hertz, and Helmholtz are not listed among the great inventors. For the servants of science invent as a matter of course, rarely take our patents, and concentrate on research. . . . If Lawrence were what is called a *practical* inventor and his cyclotron were of any immediate commercial use, he would take his place beside Watt, Arkwright, Bell, Edison and Marconi, which would probably exasperate rather than flatter him."

Soon after, Lawrence and David H. Sloan devised a *linear accelerator*, but they abandoned it in favor of the cyclotron. Later a young University of California physicist, Luis W. Alvarez, now associate director of its Radiation Laboratory, introduced several changes in this new particle accelerator which attracted a new interest in this type of machine. The linear accelerator is used for speeding both electrons and protons; it employs no magnetic field at all. The moving bullets are exposed to accelerating electric fields which are applied at various points along the straight path just at the moment when they can act most effectively as the particle reaches that point. Radar techniques are applied in its operation—electrons, for example, ride through the accelerator on microwaves.

The electron microscope developed by the Radio Corporation of America under the leadership of Vladimir K. Zworykin and

James Hillier is another instrument which was added to the armamentarium of the scientist at about this time. Until the invention of this indispensable instrument, the magnifying powers of the best optical microscope were limited by the size of the wave length of light. Objects such as viruses and protein molecules could not be seen under the microscope because they were smaller than the wave length of light with which they were being investigated. The electron microscope abandoned ordinary light and substituted for it a beam of electrons, with which is associated a wave length very much smaller than that of visible light. The instrument's operation is based upon the fact that a magnetic field produced by a coil through which a current of electricity is flowing will deflect a stream of electrons. Such a coil, properly designed, may be made to act like a converging lens. Hence it can produce a visual image of the disturbance caused when electrons pass through the very tiny particles of a protein molecule or virus under examination. This glowing image, which appears on a plate covered with a fluorescent salt, is a fairly accurate picture of the object investigated. The latest electron microscope, manufactured by the Radio Corporation of America, magnifies 200,000 times as compared with the 2000-fold magnification of the ordinary high-powered microscope. On such a scale the thickness of an average postage stamp is blown up to about 200 feet.

This electron microscope is a distinctly practical application of the electron theory. Lawrence's cyclotron, at the beginning, was essentially a new tool of theoretical research into the nature of the atom's structure. After the first glass model of a cyclotron, Lawrence, with the help of M. Stanley Livingston, one of his most brilliant graduate students, made a metal cyclotron of the same size. They were able with this new machine to generate with a current of only 2000 volts a beam of hydrogen ions with energies corresponding to those produced by 80,000 volts. By February of 1932 Lawrence had built a model costing $1000. This eleven-inch merry-go-round device was able to speed protons obtained by ionizing hydrogen gas with energies equivalent to

1,200,000 volts. He was getting now into somewhat bigger figures.

In the summer of 1932 with this small machine Lawrence shot his bolt at the element lithium and disintegrated it. This was the first artificial transmutation of matter carried out in the Western Hemisphere. He had actually been beaten in Europe by a few weeks. For on April 28, 1932, two of Rutherford's young lieutenants, John D. Cockcroft and E. T. S. Walton of the Cavendish Laboratory, using protons stepped up in a transformer-rectifier high-voltage apparatus to a velocity of about 7000 miles per second, had changed lithium into helium. For the first time in history a method of transmuting chemical elements by means other than radioactive products had been accomplished. On hearing about this historic event Frederick Soddy remarked, "The Rubicon of artificial transmutation by means of man-made weapons which the mind had so lightly vaulted over in imagination from the dawn of civilization has finally been crossed."

There was great excitement in Lawrence's laboratory. Everybody there was sure they could reach voltages only dreamed of before. A huge magnet casting had been lying around idle in California since World War I. It had been built by the Federal Telegraph Company for use by the Chinese government in a radio-transmission installation, but had never been shipped across the Pacific. Lawrence spoke to Professor L. F. Fuller, who was on the staff of the University of California and also, at the time, vice-president of the Federal Telegraph Company. Could he have this magnet? The immediate answer was yes, and the seventy-five-ton monster was drafted for research work. It was immediately set up and wired with eight tons of copper in the newly established Radiation Laboratory of the university, of which Lawrence was made director in 1936.

This 27½-inch cyclotron, the fourth model, which was followed shortly by a 37-inch machine, was calculated to deliver several microamperes of 5,000,000 electron-volt deuterons and 10,000,000 electron-volt helium nuclei. The south pole of its huge magnet rose flat-topped from the floor as high as a kitchen stove and had a diameter of forty-five inches. The machine was operated from a control board forty feet away, and the operator was further protected from the penetrating radiation of the machine by suitable absorbing material placed around the cyclotron. When all was ready, Lawrence and his energetic group of very young assistants lost no time in trying this whirligig atom gun encased in the "frying pan" placed between the poles of the Gargantuan electromagnet. Every promising projectile was hurled against every available target in the hope of breaking into and shattering the nuclei of every atom. Protons, helium nuclei, and neutrons, as well as the nuclei of the newly discovered heavy hydrogen atom (deuterium), were hurled with crashing effects. Lawrence, at the suggestion of G. N. Lewis, called the heavy hydrogen bullets *deutons*, against the advice of Rutherford, who preferred *diplons* because, he thought, "deutons were sure to be confused with neutrons, especially if the speaker has a cold." Later by agreement of scientists here and in England, the nucleus of heavy hydrogen was named *deuteron*. Lawrence split deuteron into one proton and one neutron and in this way increased his supply of neutron bullets a thousandfold. By 1935 he had not only shot deuterons against the element lithium and obtained helium, but had effected many other similar transmutations. The way was now clear for the transmutation of every element in the table of atomic numbers—including perhaps even the baser metals into the gold of the alchemists' dreams. The change of platinum (element 78) into gold (element 79) was actually accomplished in 1936 in his cyclotron.

Lawrence's fame spread rapidly. At the age of thirty-two he was elected to membership in the National Academy of Sciences. By this time the center of gravity of scientific talent in the United States had definitely moved westward. From Lawrence's laboratory streamed an army of young researchers who were trained by him to be put in charge later of construction or maintenance of new cyclotrons built by other universities and industrial laboratories. Lawrence believed in the training of new recruits and in subsidizing basic research. "In a young field with great potentialities," he wrote, "discovery, change in basic concepts, invention and development are intimately interrelated. To train a young person for intelligent participation in our atomic energy program, for example, requires more than a course of lectures which can be rendered obsolete in a few months' time. He must live and work in the field for some years, observing and learning to judge the changing picture. The apprenticeship is served best in pursuit of basic problems, for in this way he gains the broadest possible background and himself participates in determining new directions. Students entering the field almost inevitably have to rely on government support at some time during their training, for the research work is complex and costly; in return, our national program in all its technical branches draws new life from this source."

By 1940, thirty-five cyclotrons were in operation in as many laboratories both here and abroad. One of these, a 200-ton job, was shipped to Dr. Yoshio Nishina's laboratory at the Tokyo Institute of Physical and Chemical Research. During the next eighteen years, this figure increased to about forty in the United States alone, and an additional forty throughout the rest of the world. And on all the five continents more were under construction. Lawrence was constantly called upon to offer expert advice on these new installations. Much of his time was also taken up by supplying many centers of research both in this and foreign countries with new radioactive products of his huge cyclotron. Despite all this activity he still found some spare time to putter in his hobby shop at home. Here in 1951 he came up with an improved TV color tube, the *chromatron*, which he had contrived in response to questions by his children.

Honors, too, came flowing his way. These were finally capped by the award of the Nobel Prize in 1940 for the invention of the cyclotron and especially for the results attained by means of this device in the production of artificially radioactive elements. Hitler, in the meantime, had overrun much of Europe, making it quite impossible for Lawrence to go to Stockholm to receive the award personally from the Swedish King. Instead, the presentation was made at Berkeley, with the Consul General of Sweden present to represent his government. The prizewinner's colleague, Raymond T. Birge, made the presentation address, and reminded his audience of the splendid example of co-operative effort represented by Lawrence's Radiation Laboratory. Lawrence's first remark on hearing of the award was, "It goes without saying that it is the laboratory that is honored, and I share the honor with my co-workers past and present." When in 1942 the Academy of Sciences of the Soviet Union elected its first foreign members, three Americans were included—G. N. Lewis, Walter B. Cannon, and Ernest O. Lawrence.

Other generals were operating in the atomic field. In the laboratory of the Department of Terrestrial Magnetism of the Carnegie Institution in Washington, D. C., Merle A. Tuve, another scientist of Norwegian ancestry and a boyhood playmate of Ernest Lawrence, worked out a different method for obtaining high voltages by means of a modified Tesla coil and huge glass-plate condensers. Tuve, guarded by thick plates of lead, and aided by the biological research of his wife, who studied the effects of these penetrating radiations on rats, drove projectiles by intermittent excitation to their speed limit and produced momentary voltages as high as five million.

Robert van de Graaff, an Alabaman, while a Rhodes scholar at Oxford got the notion that perhaps a return to simple principles might help solve the perplexing problem of high voltages. He gave up the idea of using transformers to increase voltage and devised a machine which built up a high potential by gathering large quantities of static electricity from a friction machine, such as was first produced by Otto von Guericke in 1671. Karl T. Compton, then head of the department of physics of Princeton University, where Van de Graaff served as a National Research Fellow, helped the Alabaman construct the first working model, which supplied as much as 1,500,000 volts. In 1933 Van de Graaff was able to build a Big Bertha consisting of two units, each weighing sixteen tons. A highly polished aluminum shell fifteen feet in diameter and one quarter of an inch thick was mounted on the top of a twenty-five-by-six-foot insulating cylinder. Inside this hollow cylinder a rapidly moving silk belt sprayed static electricity onto the surface of the sphere. The machine was capable of supplying 7,000,000 volt sparks. Later the Westinghouse Electric and Manufacturing Company constructed a huge pear-shaped atom-smasher built on the same principle, on the outskirts of Pittsburgh. Many others followed.

W. H. Keesom at Leyden, Holland, tried for years to realize the dream of wrenching atoms apart with a fourteen-ton electromagnet immersed in pure liquid helium at a temperature of 272.29° below zero Centigrade (just a few tenths of a degree above the lowest theoretically possible cold). Peter L. Kapitza, son of a Russian aristocrat, and brilliant Soviet physicist, employed a different strategy. He tried to rip the atom apart by subjecting it to tremendously powerful momentary currents strong enough, he hoped, to overcome the terrific magnetic forces (estimated at 7,000,000 gauss) which hold it intact. About forty years ago he came to Ernest Rutherford with his idea and was given laboratory facilities to test his theories. Later he was made director of the $25,000 Mond Laboratory of the University of Cambridge. This laboratory, an adjunct to the Cavendish Laboratory, was built for Kapitza with the aid of the Rockefellers. Here he struggled with huge electromagnets, an electric alternator giving 20,000-ampere current, ingenious and elaborate systems of switches, and specially designed cables that carried great surges of magnetic pulls through coils which would melt if the surges were of longer duration than a mere hundredth of a second. The shock produced when the circuit was closed for a fraction of a second resembled a minor earthquake, but the jar reached the other end of the laboratory, eighty feet away, where the delicate measurements were being taken, only after the experiment was over. Kapitza pitted here all the knowledge of science and all the skill of man against the atom, whose symbol, a dragon, was carved over the entrance to his laboratory. In 1935 he returned to Russia, where the Soviet government appointed him director of the Institute of Physical Research of the Leningrad Academy of Sciences. Here a new laboratory was equipped with a forty-ton magnet with which Kapitza resumed his experiments begun in England. In 1941 he won the Stalin Prize, worth 100,000 rubles, and five years later was elected to membership in our own National Academy of Sciences.

The atom was also attacked in the Kellogg Radiation Laboratory of the California Institute of Technology. Here Charles C. Lauritsen, a Dane who gave up a promising career as a sculptor to design electrical equipment and join the men arrayed against the atom, would sit in the center of a huge concrete block while he controlled a million-volt X-ray tube. Deuterons, protons, neutrons, and electrons were speeded up into powerful bullets for atom smashing. Here, too, a young man who had wandered into physics and taken his doctorate under Millikan photographed an unexpected curved fog track which turned out to be the face of another newcomer from the atom's nucleus—a strange wanderer that rocked the scientific world. The young man was Carl D. Anderson, who was born in 1905 in New York City of Swedish parents. He was graduated from the Los Angeles Polytechnic High School and then started to study electrical engineering at the California Institute of Technology. In his sophomore year he suddenly switched to physics.

In the spring of 1930 Millikan was searching for a way to determine the energy of cosmic rays, a highly penetrating form of radiation which he believed was intimately connected with the building up of the atoms of matter. He set Anderson at work on a machine which might succeed in bending these rays by means of strong magnetic forces. Three years before, D. Skobelzyn, a Soviet scientist, had for the first time obtained photographs of tracks of cosmic-ray particles. But Anderson had a tougher job on his hands.

Between the poles of a powerful magnet capable of maintaining a magnetic field of 24,000-gauss strength was placed a vertical Wilson cloud chamber 15 cm. in diameter and 2 cm. deep (the first of its kind ever built). Photographs were taken through a hole in the pole piece of the magnet along the lines of force, thus making possible the revealing of a particle that might be reflected by the magnetic field as an arc of a circle. On moving-picture film thousands of photographs were taken of the effect of cosmic rays, some of 3,000,000 electron-volts energies, striking atoms of gas in the cloud chamber.

On the afternoon of August 2, 1932, one film, exposed and developed by Anderson, showed the image of a blasted atom with a graceful track which had never before been observed (see plate, section following page xxviii). "He at once realized its importance," wrote Millikan, "and spent the whole night trying to see if there were not some way of looking at it from what was already known about atomic nuclei." At first Anderson thought an electron had suffered a reversal of direction due to a sudden scattering, or that possibly it was a proton, for the direction of the curve was opposite to that formed by a negative electron. This indicated that it possessed a positive charge. Its ability to pass through a lead plate 6 mm. thick indicated a tremendous power of penetration possessed by no electron known. The length of the path of its fog track was ten times greater than the path of a proton of this curvature, proving that it could not be the positively charged proton. It seemed, in fact, to belong to a particle of positive charge, yet of mass equal only to that of a negative electron. It seemed to belong to a new particle—a positive electron.

Anderson repeated his experiments, obtaining a multitude of new photographs and confirming the result which he had published in September, 1932. Like the neutron, this particle, too, had been predicted. The English theoretical physicist, P. A. M. Dirac, later a Nobel laureate, had theorized its existence. Anderson's discovery, however, was not guided by this theory. The new arrival from the subatomic world was christened by its discoverer the *positron*. The name *oreston* had been suggested because Orestes, brother of Elektra, came to an early and tragic end even as the positron is quickly annihilated when it encounters an electron (or negatron) and changes into a *photon* of radiation, having about a million electron-volts energy.

In the month of Anderson's discovery of the positron, the same particle was obtained by Patrick M. S. Blackett at the Cavendish Laboratory, by D. Skobelzyn at Leningrad, and by a young French couple in the Radium Institute of the University of Paris. Irène Curie, a tall, shy, serious-looking woman who had inherited the Slavic features of her mother, was walking in the footsteps of the immortal Marie Curie, discoverer of radium. Irène had married Jean-Frédéric Joliot, whom she had met in the laboratory even as Marie had met Pierre Curie, and like her parents they were working side by side on the problem of atomic structure. The Joliot-Curies obtained their positrons by using gamma rays from radioactive elements instead of from cosmic rays.

After further study, Anderson declared, "It looks as though it is a general property of electromagnetic radiation to give rise to positrons when the radiation penetrates matter." However, positrons are not released from atoms if the radiation is of an energy of the order of less than one million electron volts. Positrons have been found, when alone, to have an extremely short life, usually of the order of a billionth of a second. For the discovery of the positron, Anderson went to Stockholm in the winter of 1936 to receive the Nobel Prize.

The year 1932 was a real *annus mirabilis* in the history of science. Four great discoveries and inventions were made in that single year. The neutron, heavy hydrogen, and the positron were all brought to light for the first time, while the first practical cyclotron was added to the key instruments of physical science. It is interesting to note in this connection that three of these four milestones were first reached by young American scientists, while the fourth, predicted by an American, was discovered by an Englishman. The tempo of first-rate American contributions in science had definitely reached a new high.

This was the year, too, when the atom was smashed for the first time by means of man-made projectiles. Not only had this new kind of transmutation been achieved, but another phenomenon was soon after observed—*artificial radioactivity*, or radioactivity in nonradioactive elements, a new and major contribution. The announcement of this discovery was made on January 15, 1934. Fate had waited for the Joliot-Curies to open up another room in that mansion of radioactivity first unlocked for the world by the Curies. The Joliot-Curies accomplished this discovery by bombarding the element boron with alpha particles from polonium, producing a neutron and a form of *radioactive nitrogen* which continued to disintegrate after the bombardment was stopped. The Joliot-Curies explained the new phenomenon as a capture of the electrified helium particle, forming a radioactive nitrogen nucleus and a neutron. The radioactive nitrogen with a half-life of fifteen minutes disintegrated, forming a stable nucleus of the carbon atom, and a positron was emitted.

First Step	$\Big\{$ Boron + Helium^{++} ⟶ radioactive Nitrogen + neutron			
	mass 10 + mass 4 ⟶ mass 13 + mass 1			
Second Step	$\Big\{$ radioactive Nitrogen ⟶ nonradioactive Carbon + positron			
	mass 13 ⟶ mass 13			

The experiment was repeated by the Joliot-Curies with other elements, such as magnesium and aluminum, and similar results were obtained. Other laboratories took up the work. By 1942 science had added 360 artificially produced radioactive substances, of which 223 were discovered by means of the cyclotron, 120 of them in Lawrence's own laboratory. These elements were supplied by Lawrence and used as *tracer* elements or chemical sleuths in physiological and medical research. For example, radioactive sodium 24 was substituted for the ordinary sodium-23 atoms in a bit of common table salt (sodium chloride) and then taken into the body in foods. In a short time, some of it changed into a new element and ejected high-speed, penetrating gamma rays. These were recorded by means of a Geiger counter placed next to various parts of the body. The Geiger counter is an electrical device consisting of an ionization chamber, a counting device, and an intensifier which makes audible the formation of ions. By this method the itinerary of a tracer atom was followed to find the answer to some health problems. It was found by this method, for example, that sodium chloride injected intravenously in one arm appeared in the sweat of the other arm within seventy-five seconds. Or fluids were removed from certain parts of the human body and then tested for their radioactivity without disturbing the normal metabolic process. Ernest Lawrence's brother, Dr. John Lawrence, of the Department of Internal Medicine of Yale University, used both radioactive sodium and radioactive phosphorus in the study of chronic leukemia in mice and men. Radioactive sodium has certain advantages over radium in cancer therapy. Because of its short half-life, 14.8 hours, Na^{24} reduces the danger of burns. In addition, Na^{24} gives only gamma rays, whereas radium produces other products which must be filtered out.

Georg von Hevesy, a Hungarian scientist who later became a Nobel laureate, was the first to employ the tracer technique. While involved in experiments on plant metabolism back in 1923 he made use of the elements lead and bismuth, which, in their natural state, are slightly radioactive. He once used the same technique in a boardinghouse where he had reason to suspect the quality of the food that was being served to him. One morning he brought with him to the dining room a speck of a radioactive compound and deposited it on a small scrap of meat which he left on his plate. The next day Hevesy returned with a Geiger counter and took his usual place at the dining-room table. A dish of hash was brought in by the waitress and placed before him. The Geiger counter started clicking. That was the evidence. It was the same meat that had been left by him on his plate the day before. It is said that Hevesy changed his boardinghouse very soon after.

Still another technique, called radioautography, was used in research. When it was found necessary to determine the route and rapidity of concentration of phosphorus in the bones of a rat, for example, the animal was fed with a radioactive phosphorus compound. At intervals sensitive films were placed against its bones, and the radioactive phosphorus which had collected made its own image on the film. By this technique Herbert M. Evans in 1940 tagged radioactive iodine in the bodies of sixty-three of his experimental tadpoles. He was attempting to determine the way in which iodine is extracted from the blood and stored in the thyroid gland. Sections of the tadpole's thyroid tissue were placed in contact with X-ray film, and the radioactive iodine, which has a half-life of about eight days, registered its presence on the film.

American genius in science was to be heard from again. In 1936 another major discovery was made by the same Carl D. Anderson who had given the positron to the world. This discovery, too, came in connection with cosmic-ray research. Robert A. Millikan and Arthur H. Compton of the University of Chicago had been carrying on a friendly rivalry in this field, a rivalry which sent each of them to many parts of the earth and high into the sky to collect data in the hope that he might be the first to find out definitely the manner of creation of cosmic rays and the nature of their effects.

For six weeks during the summer of 1935 Anderson worked on top of Pikes Peak, taking 10,000 photographs of possible collisions of *cosmic-ray* particles with atoms in the upper atmosphere. Associated with him was Seth H. Neddermeyer, who was taking his doctorate under him in this field. Upon their return to California they made a careful study of their photographs. They measured the range, curvature, and penetrating power of the fog tracks. In August, 1936, they reported, among other findings, that, "About one per cent of the exposures reveal the presence of strongly ionized particles which in most cases seem to be neither electrons nor protons. They arise from a type of nuclear disintegration not heretofore observed. Their source is in the cosmic rays." The following year, after further experiments, in which they used a 1-cm. platinum plate across the center of the cloud chamber, they obtained another 6000 photographs. After an analysis of these pictures, they announced "the existence of particles of a new type which cannot readily be explained except *in terms of a particle of mass greater than that of an ordinary electron!*" This new type was named by its discoverers the *mesotron*, meaning intermediate particle, since its weight is intermediate between that of an electron and a proton. The name *meson*, proposed by the Indian nuclear physicist N. J. Bhajbha, is now preferred.

Just before this important news was printed in the May, 1937, issue of the *Physical Review*, J. C. Street and E. C. Stevenson reported the same phenomenon to the American Physical Society. Soon after, Blackett and others also confirmed the discovery. The mass of this new particle had been estimated to be between 200 and 300 times that of an electron. Anderson also reported that it travels almost as fast as light and that, like positrons, mesotrons may be created in pairs by protons. Five years later, Bruno Rossi of Cornell University estimated the life of this new entity to be about one millionth of a second. Lawrence believed a thorough understanding of meson forces may yield new secrets of the atom's nucleus.

In 1939 Lawrence had jumped from his 37-inch cyclotron to his famous 60-inch cyclotron, built for medical research and daily cancer treatment. The funds for this machine were supplied by Francis P. Garvan of the Chemical Foundation, the Rockefeller Foundation, and the National Advisory Cancer Council. William H. Crocker gave the money for the construction of the building, named the William H. Crocker Radiation Laboratory of the University of California, situated on the campus in Berkeley. The 60-inch cyclotron, weighing 220 tons, gave 100 microamperes of 16,000,000-volt deuterons and one microampere of 32,000,000-volt helium ions. The heavy hydrogen "death-ray" beam, several inches in diameter, shot 600,000,000 individual atoms per second a distance of about five feet out of the window of the machine at a speed of 25,000 miles per second. This is equivalent to the effects of disintegration of thirty tons of pure radium costing at that time about $32,000,000 per pound!

After this cyclotron had proved itself very efficient, Lawrence thought of an even more powerful machine. When in 1932 he had jumped from his tiny cyclotron to the huge 27½-inch machine, he showed that he was more than an academic physicist. He had invaded the field of engineering. He could handle big projects. A 5000-ton cyclotron did not frighten him. He was ready to make one great leap from the 60-inch medical cyclotron to a 184-inch machine, even as Hale had jumped from his 100-inch telescope to the 200-inch giant eye on Mount Palomar. He meant to do this despite a belief by some at that time that the limit of the cyclotron was about 20,000,000 electron volts. Lawrence drew the designs for a new cyclotron which would be capable of furnishing deuterons flying at a speed of 60,000 miles per second, and other atomic bullets of energies well above 200,000,000 electron volts. This machine, he hoped, would become a national institution and the mecca of hundreds of research men.

In reply to the presentation to him of the Nobel award on February 29, 1940, Lawrence humorously remarked, "Perhaps the difficulties in the way of crossing the next frontier in the atom are no longer in our laboratory; we have handed the problem over to the president of the university!" The president lost no time. Money was found. The International Education Board appropriated $1,150,000 for the project. A site on Charter Hill near the Berkeley campus was chosen, and in August, 1940, steel and concrete began to roll in for the new atom smasher, largest in the world. The core of the cyclotron was buried in the hill. For remote-control operation, an underground power cable for carrying current from Gilman Hall over "Tightwad Hill" to the cyclotron building was completed, and in July, 1941, work was started on the twenty-four-sided building, 90 feet high and 160 feet in diameter, which was to enclose the cyclotron.

The bombing of Pearl Harbor on December 7 of that year did

not put a halt to the work on the project, which was already seventy per cent completed. The machine was finished in May, 1942. It was agreed that research with this new tool should be continued for the sake of the war effort. Its 3700-ton magnet was temporarily removed for some special war work, and in addition to the many immediate practical problems there still remained that old, tantalizing question of whether it would ever be possible to pick the lock that holds the enormous reservoir of energy inside the nucleus of the atom. Every Nobel Prize winner in the physical sciences believed that goal possible of attainment. William Bragg of crystal fame stated his belief: "A thousand years may pass before we can harness the atom, or tomorrow might see it with the reins in our hand."

"We have every reason to believe," said Lawrence, "that there lies ahead for exploration a territory with treasures transcending anything thus far unearthed. It may be the instrumentality for finding the key to the almost limitless reservoir of energy in the heart of the atom." There was a great deal more that Lawrence knew at that moment, for he was right in the middle of one of the most momentous events in history. But he could say no more. It was top secret.

CHAPTER TWENTY

ENRICO FERMI
(1901-1954)

THE MEN WHO HARNESSED NUCLEAR ENERGY

O N JUNE 4, 1934, exactly one month before Marie Curie died in a sanitarium near Sallanches, the world of science received another jolt from a wireless dispatch to *The New York Times*. It reported a meeting of the Italian Academy of the Lincei in Rome, where experimental science had stirred once again in the direction hinted at years before.

Speaking at a meeting attended by King Victor Emmanuel, Senator Orso Mario Corbino announced the creation of a brand-new chemical element beyond the limits of the then known Periodic Table. It was a transuranium element. It was heavier than uranium. This announcement was met with jubilation in some quarters, but there was also a lifting of scientific eyebrows among many research highbrows. They remembered that at least thirty-three new chemical elements had been seriously reported by as many scientists in the century and more that had gone by since 1811. In that year, gunonium's discovery was heralded. Seven years later came vestium, then rogerium, nebullium, russium, demonium, asterium, victorium, nipponium, coronium, berzelium, incognitium, cassiopeium, welsium, masurium, illinium, virginium, and alabamine in 1931. Every one of them, however, turned out to be, due to honest errors, premature claims of new chemical elements that actually did not exist. No wonder then that some were skeptical of this newly advertised element.

But the scientist to whose name this discovery was linked was no flash-in-the-pan researcher. He was a young man who had already achieved renown as an atomic scientist. Enrico Fermi was born in Rome on September 29, 1901, the youngest of three children. His father, a railroad employee, had at the age of forty-one married a schoolteacher fourteen years his junior. Enrico was an energetic, imaginative, brilliant student in high school and was encouraged by a friend of his father to continue with his studies and become a physicist. At seventeen Enrico left for Pisa, where Galileo had made some of his immortal experiments. Here in the atmosphere of serious study he specialized in the sciences, wrote a thesis on some experimental work he had undertaken with X rays, and earned his doctorate at the age of twenty-one. He returned to Rome, left soon after for further studies in Germany and the Netherlands, and then came back to Italy to teach first in Rome and later at the University of Florence.

A paper he had written on the behavior of a perfect, hypothetical gas attracted wide attention, and he was called back to become a full professor of physics at the University of Rome. Corbino created a new chair in theoretical physics for him and set out to build up the physics department with Fermi as the attraction. At the age of twenty-nine he had become the youngest member of the Royal Academy of Italy, newly established by Benito Mussolini. American atomic workers knew him well. He had spent the summer of 1930 lecturing on the quantum theory of radiation at the University of Michigan, and he was here again three years later. He was a distinguished experimenter and theoretical physicist, one not lightly to be dismissed. Scientists all over the world read the report with deep interest. How had he created this new transuranium element?

To synthesize a new complex organic compound was always, of course, a singular achievement, especially if it was as complicated a molecule as, let us say, strychnine or cortisone. But Fermi had apparently done more than this. He had taken on the role of a Creator. He had, it was reported, given mankind a new element, one that nature herself had not before revealed. This came perilously near being a modern miracle. Nature had provided man with ninety-two different chemical elements. Out of these building blocks of the physical world every speck of dust and each galaxy of stars had been created. Could man really manufacture a new element that nature herself had not put together? No wonder men were shaken as never before.

Corbino had reported that young Fermi had used neutrons as projectiles. He had chosen this particle because it was extremely dense and electrically neutral. The neutron had been discovered by an Englishman two years before, and Fermi had since then made a thorough study of this newcomer. He obtained his stream of neutrons by bombarding beryllium with helium nuclei released from radium. After hearing how Frédéric and Irène Joliot-Curie had discovered artificial radioactivity in January, 1934, Fermi decided to try to get the same result by using neutrons instead of alpha particles, which the French couple had employed. Leaping from theory to experiment, Fermi undertook a study of the effect of neutron bombardment on all the chemical elements.

The first eight elements in the Periodic Table were tried but with no results. Fluorine, the ninth element, gave some promise of success. He called together five of his young colleagues to join him in a more intensive attack, and the experiments were continued. Then he came to uranium. He had hoped that the neutron might penetrate the nucleus of uranium, element 92, and leave behind a proton which would be joined to the other ninety-two protons in the uranium nucleus, producing an atom of ninety-three protons or, in other words, a new element, number 93.

The Italian Senator, who was also head of the department of physics of the University of Rome, reported that this experiment had been successful, that a new element similar to manganese had been manufactured. Furthermore, he said, it fitted in perfectly with an extension of the Periodic Table in every respect. Nature had never stored this element here on earth, it was believed, because it was very radioactive and had a very short half-life of only thirteen minutes. Some Italians were so excited they suggested that the new element be named *italium* at once.

But Fermi was a very cautious scientist. He made no such claims. The evidence he had before him did not completely satisfy him. He thought it might be another variety of uranium. Disturbed by the large headline and the two-column story on the front page of *The New York Times*, he pleaded with Corbino, and a note was prepared for the press. He asked the world of science to suspend judgment, to wait for additional data that might verify his assumptions. He refused to name this "element." Fermi hated sensationalism but, in this case, he had missed something big, so big that the world might have been very different if he had not.

Meanwhile, the serpent that became Nazism had already been hatched and its poison had spread to Italy. The first anti-Semitic laws were imported there from Germany. Enrico Fermi, born a Roman Catholic, had, in a civil wedding, married a Jewish girl, Laura Capon, six years before. Having no stomach for fascism with its suppression of elementary human rights and its blind acceptance of the nonscientific superior-race theory, he determined finally to leave Italy with his wife and two children. It was not easy. Fortunately, a series of events favored his decision. In November, 1938, he was notified by telephone from Stockholm that he had been named a Nobel laureate "for his identification of new radioactive elements produced by neutron bombardment and his discovery of nuclear reactions effected by slow neutrons." He was given permission to travel to Sweden with his family to receive the award. As they had already secretly planned, the Fermis left Italy and never returned. Instead, after failing to give the Fascist salute to the King of Sweden upon receiving the prize —Italian newspapers raved against him for this—he took a ship to America, which he reached on January 2, 1939, to become professor of physics at Columbia University.

Thus Fermi, who was to become one of the main architects of the atomic age, became, too, the most distinguished Italian political or religious refugee to the United States. An old friend of his in Germany, hearing the news, wrote a moving letter to the young scientist. "Thus passes," he commented sadly, "the glory of the Old World to the greater glory of the New World."

Fermi was not the first scientist-refugee from Europe since the rise of Hitler and Mussolini. Soon after Einstein left for America in 1933 a whole flock of distinguished scientists came to the United States. Some, like James Franck, Victor Hess, Peter Debye, Otto Loewi, and Albert Szent-Györgyi, were already Nobel laureates, and others, like Otto Stern and Fritz Lipmann, were to receive this great honor after working here for some years. Scores of other lesser lights scattered to many laboratories around the country and labored side by side with American research workers in every field of science. Never since the days of the great migration during the political upheavals in Europe in 1848 had so many first-rate scientific minds come to add new zest and a fresh approach to American science.

Fermi, almost five years before landing on our shores, was on the very rim of a world-shaking discovery. He missed it because, as he explained years later, "We did not have enough imagination to think that a different process of disintegration might occur in uranium than in any other element. Moreover, *we did not know enough chemistry* to separate the products of uranium disintegration from one another, and we believed we had about four of them, while actually their number was closer to fifty." One of the young scientists who assisted him in these experiments, Emilio Segrè, son of a paper-mill owner, commenting on this episode, said, "God, for his own inscrutable ends, made everyone blind to the phenomenon of fission."

As history unfolded itself, it was indeed a lucky miss, for in Berlin-Dahlem, in 1938, a series of experiments in nuclear chemistry touched off a wave of excitement throughout the world which soon reached the front pages of even the most conservative newspapers. At the Kaiser Wilhelm Institute for Chemistry, only a few miles from Hitler's Chancellery, three researchers had proceeded to repeat some of those experiments performed by Fermi in Rome in 1934.

Someone had suggested that the product with a half-life of thirteen minutes which Fermi had found was probably an isotope of the element protactinium rather than the suspected transuranium element. This caught the attention of Otto Hahn and Lise Meitner at the Kaiser Wilhelm Institute, for it was they who had discovered this element, protactinium, in 1917 while World War I was still being fought. They now decided to repeat Fermi's experiments to find out whether it was really protactinium that Fermi had stumbled upon.

In the course of this investigation Fritz Strassmann later joined Hahn and they continued the experiments. After bombarding uranium with neutrons they started a careful chemical analysis of the products formed. Hahn, unlike Fermi, was an expert at this. He had, while working under William Ramsay in London back in 1904, switched from organic chemistry to radiochemistry, and the following year he had gone to Montreal, Canada, to study radioactive materials under Rutherford. They suspected that radium, in addition to Fermi's transuranium element, might be present in the debris. They looked for radium, but instead, to their amazement, they found barium—element 56. This was impossible, they thought. Hitherto only bits of the heavier atoms had been chipped away or small atomic particles had been added during the transmutation experiments of Lawrence and his colleagues. But now, apparently, the heaviest of the known elements had literally been blasted into large hunks, a phenomenon, they reported "so at variance with all previous experiences in nuclear physics."

Hahn and Strassmann reported the *bursting* of the uranium atom to produce barium on January 6, 1939, and this unexplained effect was published two months later in *Die Naturwissenschaften*. "Our overcautiousness," wrote Hahn almost twenty years later, "stemmed primarily from the fact that as chemists we hesitated to announce a revolutionary discovery in physics." Furthermore, Hahn was overcome by his interest in the chemical changes before him, and the problem of the more important energy change escaped him.

But Lise Meitner, the mathematical physicist, soon realized that something new and tremendously important had happened in the subatomic world of the nucleus of uranium. Born in Vienna, the daughter of a lawyer, Lise chose scientific research as a career and came to Berlin in 1907 to study under both Max Planck and Fritz Haber. Then she joined Otto Hahn and ten years later was made head of the nuclear-physics department of the Kaiser Wilhelm Institute at the time that Otto Hahn was head of its radiochemistry department.

In spite of a lifetime of distinguished scientific work in Germany, Lise Meitner, a Jew, was finally marked by the Nazis for arrest and a concentration camp during a period of intensified purges and atrocities against non-Aryans and other intellectuals in German universities. In the summer of 1938 the sixty-year-old woman scientist "decided that it was high time to get out with my secrets. I took a train for Holland on the pretext that I wanted to spend a week's vacation. At the Dutch border I got by with my Austrian passport, and in Holland I obtained my Swedish visa." Meitner, of course, wanted to escape the concentration camp, but even more important she felt she had an interpretation of her and her colleagues' uranium-bombardment experiments whose implications might change the course of history.

From Stockholm, where Fermi had met her on his way to America, Lise Meitner went to Copenhagen. Here her nephew, Otto R. Frisch, another German refugee, was working in the laboratory of Niels Bohr. Together they repeated the experiments of Hahn and Strassmann, and for the first time they accurately explained the new phenomenon as a cleavage of the nucleus of the uranium atom into two nuclei of roughly equal size, barium and krypton, together with smaller amounts of many other disintegration products. They sent a letter dated January 16, 1939, to the British science journal *Nature*, which was published a few weeks later. They designated the revolutionary change as a *fission* or splitting of uranium into barium and krypton.

This nuclear fission was accompanied, as they had predicted, by the release of stupendous nuclear energy equivalent to about 200,000,000 electron volts. Frisch proved this by measurements with an ionization chamber. Meitner correctly interpreted this burst of energy as due to the conversion of some of the mass of uranium into energy in accordance with Einstein's mass-energy law.

Back in 1905, Albert Einstein, in developing his theory of relativity, announced that there was no essential difference between mass and energy. According to his revolutionary thinking, energy actually possessed mass and mass really represented energy, since a body in motion possessed more mass than the same body at rest. Instead of two laws—the law of the conservation of mass, and the law of the conservation of energy—there was only one law, the law of the equivalence and conservation of mass-energy. Einstein advanced the idea that ordinary energy had been regarded as weightless through the centuries because the mass it represented was so infinitesimally small as to have been missed and ignored. For example, we now know that the mass equivalent of such a colossal amount of energy as is needed to boil 300,000 tons of water is only a tiny fraction of a single ounce. The mass equivalent of the heat required to boil one quart of water would, therefore, be almost negligible.

Einstein derived a mathematical equation to express the equivalency of mass and energy. The equation is

$$E = MC^2$$

where E represents energy in ergs, M is mass in grams, and C is the velocity of light in centimeters per second. This last unit is equal to 186,000 miles per second. When this number is multiplied by itself as indicated in the formula, we get a tremendously large number; hence, E becomes an astronomically huge equivalent. For example, one pound of matter (coal or uranium) is equivalent to about eleven billion kilowatt hours, if completely changed into energy. This is roughly equivalent to the amount of electric energy produced by the entire utility industry of the United States in less than one month. Compare this with the *burning* (chemical rather than nuclear change) of the same pound of coal, which produces only about eight kilowatt hours of energy. The available nuclear energy of coal is about two billion times greater than the available chemical energy of an equal mass of coal.

These ideas of Einstein were pure theory at the time. He had no experimental data to confirm the truth of his equation, but he suggested that research in radioactivity and atom bombardment might furnish the proof. The first bit of confirmation came in 1932. In that year John D. Cockcroft and E. T. S. Walton changed lithium into helium and obtained energies many times greater than those of the proton bullets they had employed. This additional energy came apparently as a result of the partial conversion of some of the mass of lithium into helium in accordance with the following nuclear reaction:

LITHIUM	+	HYDROGEN	$\longrightarrow$	2 HELIUM	+	energy
Mass 7.0180	+	Mass 1.0076	$\longrightarrow$	2 (Mass 4.0029)	+	17,000,000 e.v.
		Mass 8.0256	$\longrightarrow$	Mass 8.0058		

This equation (8.0256 = 8.0058) seems to show a condition of imbalance, for the whole is less than the sum of its parts. There is an approximate loss of Mass 0.02—a fatal decimal that was to shake the world. This loss of mass is accounted for by its conversion into the extra energy of the swiftly moving helium nuclei produced. This energy turns out to be the exact mass equivalent as required by Einstein's energy-mass equation noted above.

However, the method used by these experimenters was extremely inefficient; only about one out of several billion atoms actually underwent the change. Even Einstein was quoted as late as the end of 1934: "I feel absolutely sure, nearly sure, that it will not be possible to convert matter into energy for practical purposes. You must use a lot of energy to get the energy out of the molecule, and the rest is lost. It will be like shooting birds in the dark, in a country where there are few birds." There was, therefore, no great excitement over this bit of scientific news.

But even an Einstein could be wrong. The news of the energy release in the Hahn-Meitner-Strassmann-Frisch experiments not only recalled the old interest but raised it now to a fever heat. Meitner and Frisch had talked over their findings with Bohr even before publishing them and before he left for America. Fermi met Bohr at the pier, and the Dane told him he planned to stay here for several months to discuss various scientific matters with Einstein at the Institute for Advanced Study at Princeton, New Jersey.

Bohr was terribly excited over what he had learned, and he circulated the news of the energy release freely among other scientists. Galley proofs of Hahn's paper on uranium bombardment were rushed to him, and within a few days three American research groups confirmed the experiment. On January 25, 1939, Enrico Fermi, John R. Dunning, and associates used the Columbia University 75-ton cyclotron and obtained the violent splitting of uranium. Their photographs showed high peaks of discharge of 200,000,000 electron volts. M. A. Tuve, L. R. Hafstad, and R. B. Roberts, working in the Department of Terrestrial Magnetism of the Carnegie Institution of Washington, repeated the historic reaction three days later, and on that same Saturday morning workers at the Johns Hopkins University Laboratory obtained the same results.

On January 26 of that year Bohr attended a Conference on Theoretical Physics at George Washington University in Washington, D.C. Nuclear fission was on everybody's tongue. There was much discussion and speculation over this new phenomenon. American scientists were burning up with excitement. Among the top-flight atomic artillerymen present, of course, was Enrico Fermi.

Hahn and Strassmann had conjectured but did not prove experimentally that neutrons were released in the *bursting* of uranium. This was proved that spring by Frédéric Joliot-Curie, H. von Halban and Leo Kowarski in Paris. Now Fermi, in his talks with Bohr, suggested the possibility that nuclear fission might be the key to the release of colossal energy by the mechanism of a *chain reaction*. He speculated that the fission of the uranium atom might liberate additional neutrons which might be made to fission other atoms of uranium. In this way, there might be started a self-propagating reaction, each neutron released disrupting, in turn, another uranium atom just as one firecracker on a string sets off another firecracker until the whole string seems to go up like a torpedoed munition ship in one mighty explosion. Subatomic energy could thus be released and harnessed, producing from even a 0.1-per-cent conversion of a single pound of uranium energy equivalent to that produced by several million pounds of TNT.

Why had not that chain reaction already occurred during the various experiments already completed? Niels Bohr and a former student, John A. Wheeler of Princeton University, puzzled over this question. At a meeting of the American Physical Society about three weeks later, they advanced a theory of uranium fission which postulated that not all the uranium employed as target actually fissioned. They believed that less than one per cent of their uranium target disintegrated because only one of the three isotopes of uranium was actually capable of fissioning. This fissionable isotope, discovered four years before by the American scientist Arthur Dempster, has an atomic weight of 235 instead of 238, which is the atomic weight of 99.3 per cent of the uranium mixture found in nature. U-238 is extremely stable; its half-life has been estimated to be about four billion years. It behaves like a wet blanket over U-235. (There is another isotope with an atomic weight of 234. This occurs in natural uranium to the extent of a negligible 0.006 per cent.) Isotopes, as we know, are atoms of the same element having the same atomic number and similar chemical properties, but differing in their atomic weights.

Bohr and Wheeler reasoned that a chain reaction could be obtained only from pure U-235. They also proposed that the chain reaction could be initiated by bombardment with slow neutrons which Fermi had discovered in 1934. In that year two of his students, as part of the project which Fermi had set up, were testing the element silver for artificial radioactivity induced by neutron bombardment. The young assistants were puzzled when they obtained a greater radioactivity than they had expected, and they went to Fermi for help. In the course of further investigations Fermi found that when a piece of paraffin was interposed between their source of neutrons and the silver target, the induced radioactivity of the metal was increased one hundred times. He was quite excited over this discovery and soon tried out substitutes for paraffin. He wondered how water would act. Out in the courtyard of the school was a small fountain filled with goldfish. Fermi placed his neutron source and his target under the water of that fountain and repeated the experiment. Water, too, he found could slow down the neutrons and increase the induced artificial radioactivity. He had discovered the slow-neutron effect, a discovery which was to play a key role several years later.

Neutrons normally emitted by beryllium are very fast; they move at a speed of about 10,000 miles per second. Such fast neutrons are easily captured by atoms of U-238, but no fission occurs. Fermi suggested that graphite could be used as the slowing-down agent or moderator. When forced to hurdle some retarding agent such as graphite (or heavy water), fast neutrons collide with it and lose some of their energy. This may slow them down to a pace no greater than one mile per second. The slow neutron may bounce around from one U-238 nucleus to another until it strikes the nucleus of a U-235 atom and splits it. The effectiveness of the slow or *thermal* neutron has been compared to the slow golf ball which rolls along and drops gently into the cup on the green, whereas the fast-moving golf ball of the inexperienced or nervous golfer sweeps over the cup instead of falling into it.

To test the Bohr-Wheeler ideas some pure U-235 was needed. The first researcher to separate a minute quantity of it from the isotopic mixture of natural uranium was Alfred O. Nier of the University of Minnesota. He sent this microscopic bit of U-235 (about 0.02 micrograms) to Fermi at Columbia University. This and another speck prepared by the General Electric laboratory were bombarded with slow neutrons in the Columbia cyclotron and the prediction of Bohr and Wheeler was confirmed in March, 1940.

Nier had worked hard and long to separate the tiny bit of U-235 by means of a mass spectrometer, but the process was extremely slow. At the rate at which he was separating the U-235 from the rest of the mixture of uranium it would have taken 75,000 years to scrape together only a single pound of this key isotope. Thus the possibility of releasing huge quantities of atomic energy still remained a dream. Fantastic stories went the rounds to the effect that Hitler had ordered his scientists to redouble their efforts to supply him with several pounds of the powerful element whose terrific destructive powers would bring world domination for Nazi arms. But, for the moment, it continued to remain as devastating a secret weapon as the rest of his threats.

Nevertheless, a great deal of research in this field continued. In 1939, more than one hundred papers on nuclear experiments were published. But the expressed consensus was against any early solution of the problem. On February 2, 1939, Fermi delivered himself of the opinion that "whether the knowledge acquired of the possibility of a chain reaction will have a practical outcome or whether it will remain limited to the field of pure science cannot at present be foretold." On his return from the Washington meeting he was asked on the radio how soon the world would blow up. He remained silent on this question. Eighteen months later the journal *Electronics*, summing up all the work published to that time, declared, "The matter stands at present waiting a conclusive demonstration that the chain reaction of

U-235 is indeed a reality. . . . In the meantime U-235 is an isotope to watch. *It may be going places.*"

But there was nothing for the general public to watch. In March, 1939, Bohr returned to Denmark. A year later he and our own nuclear scientists voluntarily agreed not to publish any more of their findings in this explosive field. In June, 1943, Byron Price, Director of Censorship, sent a confidential note to 20,000 news outlets asking them "not to publish or broadcast any information whatever regarding war experiments involving production or utilization of atom-smashing, atomic energy, atomic fission, atom-splitting, or any of their equivalents, the use for military purposes of radium or radioactive materials, heavy water, high voltage discharge equipment, cyclotrons, and the following elements or any of their compounds, namely, polonium, ytterbium, hafnium, protactinium, radium, rhenium, thorium, and deuterium."

Thus the security blackout left the world speculating as to whether atomic energy could actually ever be harnessed for practical use. When the news of success finally came on August 6, 1945, it surprised even the most optimistic scientists. The great marvel, said President Truman on that day, "is not the size of the enterprise, its secrecy or cost, but the achievement of scientific brains in putting together infinitely complex pieces of knowledge held by many men in different fields of science into a workable plan."

The controlled release of nuclear energy was not only the most spectacular but also the most revolutionary achievement in the whole history of science. Within the short span of five years a handful of scientists, standing on the shoulders of thousands of others who had been probing the heart of the atom for fifty years, uncorked a torrent of concentrated energy that can improve the world immeasurably or blot it out completely.

The manufacture of the atom bomb is another example of the oneness of pure and applied science. Out of the purely theoretical investigations relating to the composition and heat of the sun, the nature of radiation, and the structure of the atom came remarkable inventions such as the photoelectric cell or magic eye, the electron microscope, radar and television. Men who never dreamed of having a hand in the construction of a practical gadget were supplying concepts and mathematical equations which eventually made possible the most devilish war weapon ever conjured up by man.

The thousands of scientists of every nation, race, religion, and motivation had, except for the last chosen few, no idea of the monster they were fashioning. They knew only that they were adding just another bit to human knowledge. Men and women not only in America but from almost every corner of the earth played their parts in the drama of nuclear energy. William Roentgen, the German who discovered X rays in 1895, could not have dreamed of it. The Frenchman Henri Becquerel, who noticed the effect of the uranium ore, pitchblende, on a photographic plate in a darkroom, could not have guessed it. The Polish-born scientist Marie Curie caught a glimpse of the inside of the spontaneously disintegrating world of the radium atom but could not foresee the harnessing of nuclear energy. J. J. Thomson and James Chadwick of England and Ernest Rutherford of New Zealand, who gave us the electron, the proton, and the neutron, considered controlled atomic energy both too far distant and too expensive.

Scientists besides Americans working in the field of nuclear physics included Niels Bohr, a Dane; Enrico Fermi, Emilio Segrè and Bruno Pontecorvo, Italians; Wolfgang Pauli and Victor Weisskopf, Austrians; Leo Szilard, Edward Teller, and Georg von Hevesy, Hungarians; Peter Kapitza and Dmitri Skobelzyn of the Soviet Union; Irène and Frédéric Joliot-Curie and Hans Bethe, born in France; Chandrasekhara Raman of India; and Hideki Yukawa, a Japanese.

When the curtain that hid the work on nuclear fission during the war was partially lifted after Hiroshima, a thrilling story was revealed. After the reality of nuclear fission had been demonstrated and the possibility of a chain reaction had been partially proved, the whole world knew these results. Among those interested in this new milestone were, of course, several German nuclear physicists who saw the possibility of manufacturing a superhigh explosive. There were two laboratories in Germany in 1939 capable of intensive nuclear research. Neither of them had a cyclotron, but in the autumn of 1940 the first nuclear machine was set up at Berlin-Dahlem consisting of layers of uranium oxide and paraffin. It failed. Hitler kept rattling his sword more and more menacingly over Europe, as his scientists continued their investigations.

It was very different in the United States. "American-born nuclear physicists," wrote Henry D. Smyth in the official, historic Army Report on the Atomic Bomb released six days after Hiroshima, "were so unaccustomed to the idea of using their science for military purposes that they hardly realized what needed to be done. Consequently, the early efforts for both restricting publication and getting government support were stimulated largely by a small group of foreign-born scientists in this country." They were all religious or political refugees who fled Europe for America.

The first of these European-born scientists was Enrico Fermi, who as early as March 16, 1939, went to Washington armed with a letter from George B. Pegram, Dean of the Graduate Faculty of Columbia University. The letter was addressed to Admiral S. C. Hooper and pointed out the possibility of producing terrific explosions with the aid of uranium and neutrons. However, it made no great impression even though Hitler had just annexed what was still left of Czechoslovakia.

Another refugee scientist working on nuclear energy at this time was forty-year-old Leo Szilard, visiting experimental physicist at Columbia University. This Hungarian had served his native country during World War I, had continued his studies in Berlin, and had then moved on to England. After Hahn's classic experiment, for which he was to be named winner of the Nobel Prize five years later, Szilard, a very active anti-Nazi, had come to the United States with some apparatus he had constructed overseas to continue his experiments at Columbia. On March 3, 1939, he and Walter Zinn, a young Canadian, who also taught at the College of the City of New York, were working on the seventh floor of Columbia's Pupin Building. They were attempting to confirm the reality of nuclear fission. They set up the necessary apparatus, turned a switch, and watched the screen of a television tube for the telltale sign. "That night," wrote Szilard, "I knew that the world was headed for sorrow."

Szilard was badly frightened by the implications of nuclear fission. In 1939 the German Ministry of Munitions had organized a research group to examine its possibilities. It consisted of Hans Geiger, inventor of the Geiger counter, C. F. von Weizsaecker, son of the German Undersecretary of State, Walter Bothe, Paul Harteck, and Otto Hahn. Suppose Hitler's scientists went to work in earnest to construct a bomb on the nuclear-energy principle? They might succeed and enslave the whole world! In July of that year Szilard rushed to Princeton to talk the matter over with his friend Eugene P. Wigner, who also had come here from Hungary. Wigner had already become an American citizen in 1937, and Szilard was to follow a few years later. Szilard then decided to see Einstein, who in the meantime had gone off for a rest in a quiet retreat near Peconic Bay, Long Island. Szilard asked Edward Teller, another Hungarian refugee physicist, to drive him there. Teller, who had met Fermi in Rome five years before, had come here soon after in 1935.

Another American of foreign birth who was scared almost to distraction was Alexander Sachs. He had come here from Russia as a boy, had been educated at Harvard and Cambridge, and had become informal adviser and industrial consultant to Franklin D. Roosevelt, who in 1933 had appointed him first chief economist and organizer of the NRA. Sachs agreed with Szilard that something had to be done quickly. He knew the tremendous prestige of Einstein. When Szilard suggested that Sachs go to see the President, he lost no time. On October 11, 1939, he delivered a letter from Einstein to Franklin D. Roosevelt at the White House.

Hitler's armies were already on the march. Poland had been crushed.

The letter, dated August 2, 1939, read in part as follows:

"In the course of the last four months it has been made probable—through the work of Joliot in France as well as Fermi and Szilard in America—that it may become possible to set up a nuclear chain reaction in a large mass of uranium, by which vast amounts of power and large quantities of new radium-like elements would be generated. Now it appears almost certain that this could be achieved in the immediate future.

"This new phenomenon would also lead to the construction of bombs, and it is conceivable—though much less certain—that extremely powerful bombs of a new type, carried by boat and exploded in a port, might very well destroy the whole port, together with some of the surrounding territory. However, such bombs might very well prove to be too heavy for transportation by air."

Sachs reminded the President that Fermi, Szilard and our American scientists were probably only one step ahead of the Nazi scientists. Germany had overriden Czechoslovakia, its precious uranium ores were in Hitler's hands; the most important source of uranium was the Belgian Congo, Belgium would undoubtedly be invaded by the German hordes, and this huge source of uranium would then be lost to the United States.

Roosevelt saw the clear and present danger at once. He had the vision and the courage to act promptly. He brushed aside those of his advisers who were hesitant and less alarmed. Hardly five weeks after World War II had broken out, the President appointed an Advisory Committee on Uranium. It consisted of Alexander Sachs, Enrico Fermi, Leo Szilard, E. P. Wigner, Edward Teller, and several Army and Navy men. They met on October 21, 1939. The military men on the committee felt that the Federal Government should not engage in nuclear-energy experiments but should leave this work to the universities. The next month the committee recommended getting four tons of graphite to be used as moderator and fifty tons of uranium oxide. The first appropriation, a pitifully tiny sum of $6000, was made for this purpose on February 20, 1940.

In the meantime, Ernest O. Lawrence had been awarded the Nobel Prize on December 10, 1939, for his development of the cyclotron in 1932. This served as a sharp reminder that others, too, had cyclotrons with which to carry out nuclear-fission experiments on a large scale. Early in 1940 both Sachs and Einstein were dissatisfied with the snail-like progress of the uranium project. In April of that year Sachs was again at the White House pleading with President Roosevelt for greater haste and more money.

At this very moment England was getting nervous about the possibility of a German atom bomb. British scientists, deeply involved in radar work, had learned that a large section of the Kaiser Wilhelm Institute had been set aside for nuclear research. They, too, were doing something to meet the crisis. A committee under the leadership of Nobel Prize-winner Sir George P. Thomson, son of the discoverer of the electron, was appointed in April, 1940. It was first under the Air Ministry and later under the Ministry of Aircraft Production. The work was started by Otto R. Frisch and J. Rotblat at Liverpool and later was extended to the famous Cavendish Laboratory of Experimental Physics under N. Feather and E. Bretscher. French scientists, too, were well aware of the danger of an atom bomb in the hands of the Germans. When in June, 1940, France fell to Hitler, Frédéric Joliot-Curie sent his associates, H. von Halban and L. Kowarski, to Cambridge to help in the work of the British atom scientists. Kowarski took with him the 165 quarts of heavy water which the French Government had bought from Norway before its invasion. Joliot-Curie remained in France to become an active worker in the resistance movement and to organize the manufacture of munitions for the underground patriots in Paris.

At the same time that these French scientists were leaving for England, Roosevelt in June, 1940, set up the National Defense

Research Committee, and the original Advisory Committee on Uranium became a subcommittee of this new body. Before the end of that year Columbia University received $40,000 for the study of a chain reaction. In the summer of the following year Vannevar Bush, director of the National Defense Research Committee, visited Roosevelt on the President's return from the Atlantic Charter meeting with Winston Churchill. Bush gave Roosevelt a brief account of the work on nuclear energy already under way and told him also of the reports which K. T. Bainbridge and C. C. Lauritsen, who had attended meetings of Thomson's committee in England, had brought back. The British scientists by the summer of 1941 had definitely come to the conclusion that an atom bomb was feasible, and they recommended the gaseous-diffusion method for the separation of U-235 from natural uranium ores. Roosevelt then suggested to Clement Attlee, then a member of the Churchill Cabinet, that the British scientists working on atomic energy pool their knowledge and efforts with those of our own scientists working on nuclear fission. This proposal was eagerly accepted by the Churchill Government.

Harold C. Urey and George B. Pegram were sent abroad in November, 1941, to confer with the British scientists. Just two months before, Churchill had decided somewhat reluctantly to give high priority to the atom-bomb work, remarking, "Although I am personally quite content with the existing explosives, I feel I must not stand in the path of improvement." Sir John Anderson was asked to supervise the work of a British atom-bomb project, and he had brought together England's ace atom scientists, including Sir Charles Darwin, member of the fourth generation of Darwin's family, Rudolf E. Peierls and Franz E. Simon, two refugee scientists, and Sir James Chadwick, discoverer of the neutron. Chadwick was terribly worried. During the summer of that year the Germans were experimenting in Leipzig with a small uranium pile, using heavy water as moderator. Werner Heisenberg, one of the world's leading authorities in nuclear physics, was believed to be directing the work.

Urey returned to the United States in the week that terminated in Pearl Harbor Sunday. He shared the anxiety of Chadwick and brought home a sense of the utmost urgency. Werner Heisenberg had told Bernhard Rust, German Minister of Education, that "an atomic bomb could be produced in the pile on theoretical grounds." At this moment it seemed that American and German scientists had arrived at similar results, if we exclude our own great success in isotope separation. What if the German scientists got the jump on us and the German High Command had agreed on an all-out effort to manufacture atom bombs? This seemed altogether possible, for on November 6, only a month before, the National Defense Research Committee had reported that "a fission bomb of superlatively destructive power results from bringing together a sufficient mass of U-235. . . . If all possible effort is spent on the program, we might expect fission bombs to be available in significant quantities *within three or four years.*"

Things now began to move much faster. Just a day before the attack on Pearl Harbor an all-out effort to manufacture an atom bomb was finally decided upon. Eleven days later the National Defense Research Committee was reorganized under the Office of Scientific Research and Development. A group of British scientists, together with Peierls, Simon and Halban, came to the United States to help. Finally, on August 14, 1942, an atom-bomb project known as the Manhattan Engineer District was started by order of Secretary of War Henry L. Stimson. Major General Leslie R. Groves, forty-two-year-old Army construction engineer, was made director of all Army activities relating to the project.

At the beginning of the following year, a joint British-Canadian team of scientists went to work in Montreal in close co-operation with our men. Then later that year, after discussions first between Sir John Anderson and American scientists, and finally between Roosevelt and Churchill, the entire British atomic group moved to the United States to concentrate the whole of the bomb project on this side of the Atlantic.

Long before this last step had been taken, various research groups had already been assigned to several crucial problems. One of these was the production of a controlled and self-maintaining nuclear chain reaction. As early as January, 1942, it was decided to concentrate this job at the University of Chicago, where Arthur H. Compton was working with neutrons. In April, a large number of scientists working at various centers came together to team up in Chicago in what became known as the Metallurgical Laboratory. Enrico Fermi was among them.

One of the main essentials of this project was a good supply of pure uranium, of which only a few pounds were available in 1941. The first delivery of this element was made early in 1942 from a wooden shed of the Iowa State College at Ames, where formerly co-eds practiced archery and where now Frank H. Spedding supervised the purification of this metal. In the meantime Fermi, though still technically an enemy alien, was assigned the task of building a device which could produce a controlled chain reaction. He and Szilard had, at first, thought of a sphere, 26 feet in diameter. The final structure, called a *pile*, was more like a sphere with its beehive top flattened. It was set up by Fermi on the floor of the squash-rackets court underneath the west stands of Stagg Field of the University of Chicago. The pile contained 12,400 pounds of specially purified graphite bricks, with holes at calculated distances in which were embedded lumps of uranium oxide and pure uranium sealed in aluminum cans to protect the uranium from corrosion by the cooling water pumped through the pile. The bricks were arranged in the form of a lattice, which was found to be the best arrangement for the slowing down of neutrons.

A chain reaction will not maintain itself if more neutrons are lost than are produced. Just as coal will not continue to burn and the fire will be extinguished when the heat it generates is lost faster than it generates new heat, so U-235 will not fission so long as it loses neutrons faster than it generates them by fission. Neutrons may be lost by being absorbed either by U-238 or by impurities present in the uranium or in the graphite. By careful purification of uranium and graphite, proper spacing of target and moderator, and accurate determination of the size of the pile, the chain reaction should, theoretically at least, be kept under control. That was the job undertaken by Fermi and his assistants.

There was a great deal of theorizing, calculating, discussing, and revising of plans. There was a great deal, too, of piling and repiling of layers of graphite bricks until the men were as black as miners coming out of a coal pit. Hence the name *pile* for the uranium nuclear reactor. On the final day of trial Fermi, Compton, and Zinn stood in front of the control panel located on a balcony ten feet above the floor of the court. Here, too, was Herbert L. Anderson, who had taught Fermi English at Columbia University while taking his Ph.D. under him.

George L. Weil was to handle the final control rod which held the reaction in check until it was withdrawn the proper distance. Another safety rod, automatically controlled, was placed in the center of the pile and operated by two electric motors which responded to an ionizing chamber. When a dangerously high number of neutrons were escaping, the gas in the ionizing chamber would become highly electrified. This would automatically set the motor operating to shoot a neutron-absorbing, cadmium-plated steel rod into the pile. As an added precaution, an emergency safety rod called *Zip* was withdrawn from the pile and tied by a rope to the balcony. Norman Hilberry stood ready to cut this rope if the automatic rods failed for any reason. Finally, a liquid control squad of three men crouched on a platform above the pile, trained and ready to flood the whole pile with water containing a cadmium salt in solution.

"A pen," said Fermi, "will trace a line indicating the intensity of the radiation. When the pile chain-reacts, the pen will trace a line that will go up and up and that will not tend to level off. In other words, it will be an exponential line." Fermi started the test at 9:54 A.M. by ordering the control rods withdrawn. Six minutes later Zinn withdrew *Zip* by hand and tied it to the rail of the balcony. At 10:37 Fermi, still tensely watching the control board, ordered Weil to pull out the vernier control rod until thirteen feet of it was still inside the pile. Half an hour passed and the automatic safety rod was withdrawn and set. The clicking of the Geiger counters grew faster and the air more tense.

"I'm hungry. Let's go to lunch," said Fermi, and his staff eased off to return to the pile at two o'clock in the afternoon. More adjustments, more orders, and more recording of the readings on the instruments by Leona Marshall, the only girl present. At 3:21 Fermi computed the rate of rise of the neutron count on his slide rule. The pen reached the point Fermi had predicted. Then suddenly, quietly, and visibly pleased, Fermi, closing his slide rule, remarked, "The reaction is self-sustaining. The curve is exponential." Then for twenty-eight more minutes the pile was allowed to operate. At 3:53 P.M. Fermi called "O.K." to Zinn, and the rod was pushed into the pile. The counters slowed down. It was over. The job that came close to being a modern miracle was completed. December 2, 1942, marked the first time in history that men had initiated a successful, self-sustaining nuclear chain reaction. Only Enrico Fermi and the forty-one people who were present that day knew that on this wintry Wednesday afternoon mankind had turned another crucial corner of history.

Arthur H. Compton had witnessed this event and put through a long-distance telephone call to James B. Conant, who was in charge of the project for the Office of Scientific Research and Development. "The Italian navigator has landed in the New World. It is a smaller world than he believed it was," said Compton to Conant. To Conant the "smaller world," though no code had been prearranged, meant that the atomic pile was smaller and its fires were not as violent as had been expected. Conant then asked, "Are the natives friendly?" Compton took this to mean was he ready to go ahead full blast. The answer to that query was "Yes, very friendly," and Fermi and his Chicago group lost no time in following through.

Working with this uranium pile, partly shrouded in balloon

cloth to keep out neutron-absorbing air, was a dangerous business. It had been anticipated that the nuclear reaction would start from spontaneous fission caused by a stray neutron or other source such as cosmic rays just as soon as the pile reached a certain minimum size known as the *critical size*. This condition is reached when the number of free-fission neutrons just equals the loss of neutrons due to nonfission capture and escape from the surface. An uncontrolled fission chain reaction might result from the production of too many fission neutrons in too large a pile. The critical size of the pile under construction had been calculated from all the available data, and it turned out that an error had actually been made, for the approach to critical size was later found to occur *at an earlier stage of assembly than had been anticipated*. Of course, Fermi and his men, working in a not-too-familiar field, had taken every conceivable precaution. "This was fortunate," wrote Dr. Smith, and these three words must remain one of the classic understatements in the long history of the hazards of scientific discovery.

If the men at the pile escaped sudden death, they might have still succumbed to a slow, painful destruction caused by penetrating rays and poisonous radioactive particles emitted during nuclear fission. (L. A. Slotin, Canadian scientist working at Los Alamos in 1946, picked up a piece of fissionable material with his bare hands to save a colleague and died nine days later of radiation poisoning.) As a safeguard against the perils of such penetrating radiation and poisons, the pile was shielded very carefully by a five-foot-thick wall of absorbent material. Manipulations had to be performed by ingenious devices permitting remote handling and control.

The original purpose of the Metallurgical Laboratory project was achieved in the controlled chain reaction. In addition, however, the pile turned out to be a plant which efficiently manufactured a new element in large quantities. The story of the birth of this synthetic element goes back to a day in May, 1940, when two men using Lawrence's cyclotron at Berkeley bombarded uranium with neutron bullets. This was about six years after Fermi's classic experiments in Rome. The two men were Edwin M. McMillan and Philip H. Abelson.

Both Fermi and Hahn missed discovering this element because neither of them could understand what was actually happening. What occurred during the bombardment of uranium with neutrons was that a neutron forced its way into the complex nucleus of the uranium atom, whose relative weight is 238, and formed a heavier type of uranium atom with a relative weight of 239. Now, this heavy variant of the uranium atom is a very unstable individual. It is composed of a particular combination of neutrons and protons which is under tension. To relieve the tension of this submicroscopic household, one of the neutrons decides to split up. Every neutron, you may remember, is a close combination of one electron and one proton. This neutron ejects its electron, and the proton part of it stays on. This situation gives the nucleus ninety-three protons instead of ninety-two. It has become a brand-new element with entirely new properties. In other words, the heavy uranium-239 is radioactive, has a half-life of twenty-three minutes, and disintegrates spontaneously into element 93.

As is the practice when a new element is found, the discoverer is given the honor of naming it. McMillan, who later received the Nobel Prize for this piece of work, christened it *neptunium* (Np) after the planet Neptune, which is just outside the planet Uranus, after which the ninety-second element had been named. It was exciting enough to have created a new element, but what was even more thrilling was the discovery before the end of that same year of still another element which turned out to be yet more interesting than number 93. Neptunium is a very jittery thing. Half of it, unhappy with its lot, changes spontaneously into another element within less than two and a half days. The new element, 94, is born in the same way as neptunium; that is, one of its neutrons splits into its component parts and the electron part is ejected from the establishment, while the remaining proton part stays on and adds to the crowded condition of the proton occupants of the nucleus, which now number ninety-four instead of ninety-three.

Element 94 was manufactured and identified for the first time late in 1940 by Glenn T. Seaborg and his associates E. M. McMillan, A. C. Wahl, J. W. Kennedy, and E. Segrè. Seaborg was born in the little town of Ishpeming, Michigan, of Scandinavian ancestry. He received his education at the University of California at Los Angeles and was only twenty-eight when he discovered *plutonium* (Pu). This was only a beginning, for within the next few years he was to head several groups of research scientists who created seven more transuranium elements. No other American, no other man in the whole world, could lay claim to such an impressive record of element building.

Plutonium is a very stable element (half-life 24,300 years), is sensitive to neutron bombardment, and fissions in a manner similar to U-235, emitting other neutrons capable of producing a chain reaction. This is a tremendously important fact, for here science had a substance which could be used instead of U-235 in the projected atom bomb. Furthermore, this new element can be separated from uranium much more easily than can U-235. This is true because it is an entirely different element and can be separated by chemical means rather than by the very difficult physical method necessary for separating isotopes.

The nuclear reactions involved in the discovery of neptunium and plutonium, and in the fission of the latter element, may be represented by the four steps shown on page 598.

If this newly discovered plutonium was to be manufactured on a scale large enough to meet the needs of the Manhattan District project, more of its chemical properties would have to be known. To get this information, a larger sample of the element, an amount that could be seen at least with the naked eye, was needed. The big cyclotrons of Lawrence's laboratory at Berkeley and Washington University in St. Louis went to work bombarding uranium with neutrons. For weeks the big machines were kept running until one thousandth of a single gram of the element had been collected. Years before, chemists had developed a branch of analysis called microchemistry, which could handle tiny amounts of chemicals weighing as little as 0.001 gram. But not even this tiny amount of plutonium was available. So the chemists at the University of Chicago under Glenn Seaborg began in April, 1942, to develop a new method which could take care of chemicals which weighed no more than 500 micrograms (1 microgram equals one millionth of a gram) or about 1/5000 the weight of a single dime.

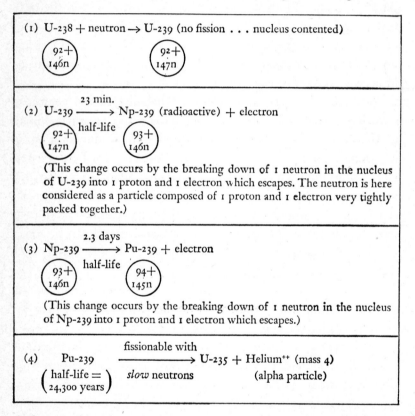

(1) U-238 + neutron → U-239 (no fission . . . nucleus contented)

(2) U-239 $\xrightarrow[\text{half-life}]{\text{23 min.}}$ Np-239 (radioactive) + electron

(This change occurs by the breaking down of 1 neutron in the nucleus of U-239 into 1 proton and 1 electron which escapes. The neutron is here considered as a particle composed of 1 proton and 1 electron very tightly packed together.)

(3) Np-239 $\xrightarrow[\text{half-life}]{\text{2.3 days}}$ Pu-239 + electron

(This change occurs by the breaking down of 1 neutron in the nucleus of Np-239 into 1 proton and 1 electron which escapes.)

(4)   Pu-239 $\xrightarrow[\textit{slow} \text{ neutrons}]{\text{fissionable with}}$ U-235 + Helium^{++} (mass 4)

$\left(\begin{array}{c} \text{half-life} = \\ \text{24,300 years} \end{array} \right)$ (alpha particle)

A human breath weighs 750,000 micrograms. This method is known as ultramicrochemistry. On August 18, 1942, about three micrograms of "the first pure chemical compound of plutonium was prepared by B. B. Cunningham and L. B. Werner. This memorable day will go down in scientific history," wrote Seaborg, "to mark the first sight of a synthetic element, and, in fact, the first isolation of a weighable amount of an artificially produced isotope of any element." (A few years later both neptunium and plutonium were detected in natural ores in extremely minute amounts.)

The first controlled chain reaction had been achieved in December, 1942, only three months before the first weighable amount of plutonium had been prepared. A third major problem in the preliminary work of Manhattan District was also well on its way to solution. This was the manufacture of pure U-235. Faster methods of separating it from the rest of natural uranium had to be devised. The electromagnetic method first employed by the Englishman Francis W. Aston in 1919 was being used by Lawrence at Berkeley. He shot ionized gaseous particles of a uranium compound through a strong field between the poles of a powerful electromagnet which curved them into a circular path. Molecules of the lighter isotope (U-235), being bent more than those of the heavier isotope (U-238), could thus be separated and the pure U-235 trapped. Lawrence used the powerful electromagnet of his dismantled 184-inch cyclotron for this job.

A second method, independently developed by the British atom-bomb scientists and known as the gaseous-diffusion method, was used by Harold C. Urey and John Dunning at Columbia University. Urey had had considerable experience in separating the isotopes of hydrogen by this means, and he developed it further for this pressing need. It consists of passing fiercely corroding uranium hexafluoride gas through very fine filters. The lighter vapor passes through faster than the heavier vapor, and thus by a continuous process U-235 is completely separated from the other isotopes of natural uranium. Both of these methods, as well as two others—thermal diffusion and centrifugal—were tried.

After dozens of laboratories and their hundreds of scientists had wrestled with these methods it was decided to go into large-scale production of both U-235 and plutonium for the making of atomic bombs. A bold step had to be taken. Instead of setting up a small pilot plant first to test manufacturing procedures, it was decided to jump at once into large-scale production. "In peace-time," wrote Smyth, "no engineer or scientist in his right mind would consider making such a magnification in a single step." But there was no alternative. The Nazis were believed to be working on the bomb.

Actually the Germans were spending very little money on atom-bomb work. Heisenberg revealed this in an article in *Nature* in 1947. In the early part of 1942 he had tried to get some of the top-flight Nazis to a luncheon for the purpose of getting more help. Fortunately for us, he failed. The Germans expected a quick victory and thought a successful bomb project would take twenty years. In addition, the Germans were blinded by belief in their own superiority; many of their scientists, selected for political reasons rather than for their scientific abilities, had a contempt for what they called non-Aryan science.

The decision to proceed with the manufacture of large amounts of plutonium and U-235 came near the close of 1942. It meant operating several huge uranium piles in plants designed from data collected during experiments with almost gossamer bits of plutonium. It meant constructing entire cities of massive concrete structures. One of these was Oak Ridge, Tennessee, near Knoxville where, early in 1943, the Du Pont Company built a plant including an air-cooled uranium-graphite pile which was to manufacture plutonium. Here uranium slugs, after exposure in the pile to neutron bombardment, were transferred under water to hermetically sealed rooms surrounded by thick walls of concrete, steel and other absorbent material. Several of these cells, buried two-thirds in the ground, formed a continuous fortresslike, almost windowless structure, 100 feet long. The plutonium-rich uranium rods were passed along from cell to cell, chemically treated until all the plutonium was separated from the uranium. All of these operations were performed by remote control.

A second plant was erected on the same site for the manufacture of pure U-235 by the electromagnetic method developed by

Lawrence. The gaseous-diffusion method was employed in another plant built by the Chrysler Corporation.

The other site selected was on the Columbia River near the Grand Coulee Dam. It was known as the Hanford Engineer Works and was located in an isolated region near Pasco, Washington. A water-cooled plutonium plant built by Du Pont went into operation in September, 1944.

Seaborg, Segrè and two other members of a team had worked out in detail the original separation of plutonium from uranium. This basic method, amplified ten billion times, was used by the chemists and engineers at Hanford. Because the work of Seaborg and his associates preceded their employment by the United States Government on the atom-bomb project, the Patent Compensation Board of the United States Atomic Energy Commission in 1955 awarded them $400,000 for the rights to this invaluable process.

Sixty thousand workers and their families, sworn to the strictest secrecy, poured into Richfield and the Hanford area to man the three piles located several miles apart for safety. Out of a barren wasteland, a city which became the fourth largest in the state sprang up almost overnight—a city whose name had never even appeared on a map. The story of Oak Ridge was equally amazing. Oak Ridge did not exist in 1941. Within a short time farms and forests became a city of 75,000 people, the fifth largest city in Tennessee. At the peak of the Manhattan District operation 125,000 people, including 12,000 college graduates, were engaged.

Even before the mammoth plants at Oak Ridge and Hanford had been completely designed, an atom-bomb laboratory was being erected on an isolated mesa 7000 feet above sea level near Los Alamos, New Mexico, twenty miles from Santa Fé. At the foot of this mesa were the ruined cliff dwellings and mud huts of the Pueblo Indians. A winding road led to its top. Here, in what was once a boys' ranch school, almost completely hidden from the rest of the world for safety and security, the first atom bomb was to be constructed. To this spot, which was soon to become the best-equipped physics laboratory in the world, a young man in his late thirties was called from the University of California. This scientist was the gifted, versatile, and brilliant theoretical physicist J. Robert Oppenheimer, a New Yorker and graduate of Harvard University. "Oppy," as he was known to his many friends, was placed in charge of this laboratory, where he arrived in March, 1943. With unusual energy, superb organizing ability, an uncanny insight into the multitude of problems confronting the project, and great personal warmth and charm, Oppenheimer soon turned Los Alamos into a marvelous workshop staffed by the best brains in nuclear physics. S. K. Allison of the University of Chicago was his right-hand man.

Several machines were soon installed. A cyclotron from Harvard University, two Van de Graaff electrostatic generators from the University of Wisconsin, a Cockcroft-Walton high-voltage device from the University of Illinois, and a thousand and one other contraptions were made ready for a crucial experiment. Men were assigned to their tasks, and frequent consultations were arranged to decide upon ticklish problems as they arose from time to time. The men who worked at Los Alamos or were consulted included the American Nobel Prize winners in physics and chemistry—Carl D. Anderson, Arthur H. Compton, Clinton J. Davisson, Albert Einstein, Irving Langmuir, Ernest O. Lawrence, Robert A. Millikan, Isidor I. Rabi, and Harold C. Urey. Here, too, Niels Bohr (alias Mr. Nicholas Baker), who had eluded the Gestapo, was flown from Europe to help in the work. Otto Stern, who fled Nazi Germany in 1933 to become a professor at the Carnegie Institute of Technology and winner, ten years later, of the Nobel Prize in physics, James Chadwick, discoverer of the neutron, Robert F. Bacher of Cornell University, and Russian-born George B. Kistiakowsky of Harvard were also there. Of course, Enrico Fermi (alias Mr. Eugene Farmer) was included, together with several other refugee scientists whom he had known back in Rome—Hans A. Bethe of Cornell University, originator of the hydrogen-helium nuclear-change theory to account for the sun's heat, Emilio Segrè, and Edward Teller. The knowledge of all of these men was pooled for the central problem of constructing an atomic bomb.

The first experiments were begun at Los Alamos in July, 1943. Arthur H. Compton had bet James B. Conant that he would deliver the first major batch of pure plutonium to Oppenheimer on a specific date. The stake was a champagne supper for the members of the old executive committee of the uranium project. The plutonium for the atom bomb was delivered to Oppenheimer a month later, on time, and the bet was paid off. More plutonium and pure U-235 arrived at Los Alamos according to schedule. It was known by this time that a chain reaction would occur as soon as the fissionable material reached the critical size. To prevent premature detonation of the bomb, therefore, several smaller pieces instead of a single large lump of U-235 and plutonium were used. The pieces could be brought together suddenly to form a large mass of critical size by shooting one fragment from a gun against another fragment as target. When the pieces met to form one piece of critical size, the whole mass would explode in a split second. To reduce the critical size of the bomb, a covering which reflects neutrons back into the center was used during the implosion. This envelope is called a tamper.

That the scientists in the mesa laboratory did their job well was known to a handful of men who midst rain and lightning witnessed the first experimental explosion of an atom bomb. This test explosion took place at 5:30 A.M., July 16, 1945, at the Alamogordo Air Base in a desert of New Mexico, 120 miles east of Albuquerque. The bomb, containing (according to the Smyth Report) between 4 and 22 pounds of plutonium and U-235 (a British report gave the weight as between 22 and 66 pounds), fissioned with a blinding glare, vaporized the steel tower on which it had been exploded, and left a crater half a mile in diameter covered with sand sintered to a green, glassy consistency. It was estimated that a temperature as high as 100,000,000° F was reached in the center of the explosion. The terror of the nuclear age was here.

Finally, the whole world learned about the new monster fashioned by science when on the early morning of Monday, August 6, 1945, a single atom bomb dropped through the open bomb bay of the *Enola Gay* wiped out the city of Hiroshima, killing 50,000 people. The bomb had been carried in a B-29 piloted by Captain Paul W. Tibbets, Jr. To avoid the possibility of premature detonation, an accident which would have wiped out all life on Tinian Island, from which the plane took off, the bomb was not assembled until the plane was in the air and at a safe distance from the island.

Five months later, on New Year's Eve, 1946, Enrico Fermi packed his belongings and returned to Chicago. He was now a full-fledged American citizen. As Distinguished Service Professor of Physics at the Institute of Nuclear Studies he worked feverishly as usual, for there was still much to be done. He took precious time out of his researches to teach physics to freshmen. He believed, said Edward Teller, one of his close friends, that the best teaching should be directed not at the oldest students but at the youngest "who are just beginning to feel their way in the strange country of science." Fermi had no inflated opinion of his greatness or indispensability and did not hesitate to teach undergraduates.

The objective of the Manhattan District project had been reached. Never before had such a colossal task been completed in so short a time. A heritage of scientific brains unsurpassed in the annals of theoretical science, a reservoir of brilliant engineering and industrial talent, a life-and-death situation that compelled, planned, co-ordinated, and accelerated action, and finally an expenditure of two billion dollars made this epochal achievement possible. The long search for the key to nuclear energy was ended, but in this triumph modern man had created a new and very critical problem for himself.

The challenge was immediate. The facts were simple. Hiro-

shima was destroyed by a single atom bomb. Others could make
the bomb. Forty million Americans could be killed in a single
night. The Hiroshima bomb was puny in comparison with the
new ones already on hand. A few hundred of these new missiles
could destroy civilization. The Smyth report made this abundantly clear. Einstein and Oppenheimer believed this, too. Other
men closely involved in the manufacture of the first atom bomb
made no bones about this.

There was no weapon in the hands of man that could counter
the nuclear bomb. Fermi could not deny this. Many others agreed
that "Unless we act now, we shall eat fear, sleep fear, live in fear,
and die in fear," as Harold C. Urey warned. Other spectacular
advances had been made in the history of science, but none of
them was as global, rapid, sinister, and revolutionary as this one.
No other collection of scientific discoveries of the past had
brought with it the terrifying possibility that mankind could, by
the pressing of a button, commit mass suicide.

Nuclear fission differed from all previous achievements in science in still another way. For the first time in history the basic
power of the universe was at our disposal. Science and technology
had suddenly jumped a full century, and mankind had at its finger tips as much concentrated power as it needed to raise the well-
being and living standards of every inhabitant of the globe.

Even before the wounds of Hiroshima had been dressed, bills
were introduced in Congress to meet the challenge. On September 6, 1945, Senator Brien McMahon of Connecticut brought
forward a bill designed to conserve and restrict the use of nuclear
energy for the national defense, to prohibit its private exploitation, and to preserve the secret of information concerning the
use and application of atomic energy. This bill for the civilian
control of atomic energy was finally passed as the Atomic Energy
Act of 1946 and became law on August 1 of that year. Among its
many provisions, it excluded from the scope of the nation's patent laws all inventions for the production of fissionable materials
and their military utilization.

As sole owner of atom bombs at that time, it was natural that the United States should suggest a plan of control to the United Nations. On June 13, 1946, at the first meeting of the United Nations Commission on Atomic Energy, Bernard Baruch, the American delegate, proposed such a plan. Six days later a Russian proposal was presented by Andrei Gromyko. To date neither plan has been accepted and the world is still searching for a formula for survival.

During the years of waiting for a settlement of this international problem, scientists in and out of the Manhattan District project continued their researches. Many restrictions, imposed for security reasons especially during the tensions of the cold war, impeded the progress of the work. Some scientists, because of the complicated government security regulations, hesitated to join certain very sensitive Federal projects. A few, irked by measures and actions which they felt might interfere with their freedoms, preferred to work in other less sensitive fields. Nevertheless, even during this period of far-from-ideal working conditions more facts were unfolded, new techniques were developed, and additional uses were found for this atomic force. Men created more hitherto unknown chemical elements, scores of useful radioisotopes were manufactured, and the final identification of four previously announced chemical elements was definitely established.

The four shadowy elements were numbers 43, 61, 85 and 87. They had all apparently disappeared from the earth as a result of rapid radioactive decay. Element 43 was first created in Lawrence's cyclotron, where the metal molybdenum was bombarded with deuterons and neutrons. Emilio Segrè and C. Perrier in Italy made a chemical identification of this element in 1937. It was named *technetium* (Tc) from the Greek meaning "artificial." Mlle Marguerite Perey of the Paris Radium Institute made claim to the discovery of element 87 and named it *francium* (Fr), and in the following year, 1940, Lawrence's 60-inch cyclotron gave birth to element 85 when Emilio Segrè, D. R. Corson, and K. R.

Mackenzie of the University of British Columbia bombarded bismuth with helium ions. It was named *astatine* (At) from the Greek word meaning "unstable." In 1941 M. L. Pool and L. L. Quill of Ohio State University reported traces of element 61 in the cyclotron. Four years later, during researches involving the bombardment of neodymium with neutrons in the atomic pile at Oak Ridge, J. A. Marinsky and L. E. Glendenin of the Massachusetts Institute of Technology obtained a pure sample of this element in an amount which permitted careful examination. They proposed the name *promethium* (Pm) after the legendary Prometheus, who taught mankind the use of fire. This name was accepted in 1949. Thus, after centuries of toil, the last of the first ninety-two chemical elements which man had inherited for better or for worse was finally discovered.

Even before this, predictions had been made that heavier elements would be found or created. In 1923, for example, Bertrand Russell, the celebrated philosopher-mathematician of England, declared, "No reason is known why there should not be more complex atoms, and possibly such elements may be discovered some day." And this prediction was fulfilled with the creation of elements 93 and 94 in 1940. Then four years later, two new elements were born, in the same cyclotron that sat majestically in the Radiation Laboratory of the University of California at Berkeley where Lawrence was chief. Electrified helium bullets whirling around at dizzy speeds were suddenly hurtled against uranium-238 and plutonium-239, and the debris that resulted was examined. Several crack-ups were reported in each case. Seaborg and his co-workers finally pinned down the two newcomers and sat down to name them. That was their privilege. One of the three young men working with Seaborg, who remembered all the difficulties and excitement that preceded their discovery, playfully suggested the names "pandemonium" and "delirium." These were obviously not accepted. For element 95 Seaborg came up with *americium* (Am), so named because its sister element had been christened europium. Element 96 was dubbed *curium* (Cm) after the Curies, because its sister element, gadolinium, had been named after a Finnish chemist, Johan Gadolin.

The public announcement of the discovery of these new elements came in a most unexpected way. The news was to be released at a meeting of the American Chemical Society. But on the preceding Sunday, Seaborg, as guest on the Quiz Kids radio program, was asked by one of the youngsters if any new elements had been discovered. Before he realized it, Seaborg told five million laymen listening in about elements 95 and 96.

Almost five more years passed before two new births were announced by that same superb nuclear obstetrician. Element 97 was born of americium and christened by Seaborg *berkelium* (Bk) after the city of Berkeley, the home of the cyclotron that Lawrence had given to science. Then the state in which these deliveries were made was honored with *californium* (Cf), element 98.

After another four crowded years went by came the announcement of still two more new transuranium elements. Element 99 was found to be highly radioactive, with a twenty-day half-life during which it loses weight and becomes element 97. The great Albert Einstein, father of the atomic age, had just died, and his illustrious name was given to this new element, *einsteinium* (Es).

The one hundredth element of the Periodic Table, together with the ninety-ninth, were first unsuspectedly found in the clouds of a hydrogen-bomb explosion set off in 1952 at Eniwetok atoll in the Pacific. Samples of the dust were collected on large filter papers carried by drone airplanes through the radioactive clouds. The discovery of these elements, kept a top secret for more than a year, was achieved by three teams of scientists stationed at Berkeley, Chicago, and Los Alamos. Element 100 also turned out to be radioactive, with a half-life of sixteen hours. Seaborg had, in the meantime, been selected to receive the Nobel Prize for his contributions to creative nuclear chemistry, and some hinted that it might be a good idea to name element 100 "seaborgium." Seaborg protested. And the name of Enrico Fermi came up.

Fermi was still at the University of Chicago, where he had recently shifted his particular interest to the investigation of the meson particle. In the summer of 1953, that old classic experiment of his performed in Rome almost twenty years back was in the news again. It concerned a discovery he had made at that time. Slow-neutron bombardment of elements had produced artificial radioactivity. Corbino had suggested that a patent be taken out at once. Fermi joined with his young assistants and agreed. Gabriello M. Giannini, son of a retired law professor, had been one of Fermi's first students at Rome. He had left Italy to seek his fortune in the United States and, as the holder of an eighth interest, he applied for a patent which was finally granted in 1940. It turned out that this patent contained some material used in the first pile that Fermi had set up in Chicago, and the newspapers carried the story of the settlement of the patent claims. Five of the original team of assistants were still active in science. Segrè was at Berkeley, Rasetti at Johns Hopkins, Giannini was now an American citizen and the owner of a factory making controls for rockets and jet planes in California, while Amaldi, D'Agostino, and Trabacchi were still in Rome. The youngest of the six assistants of Fermi was not around to share in the settlement. Dr. Bruno P. Pontecorvo had gone to Paris in 1936 to study with the Joliot-Curies. World War II found him working at the British Atomic Research Center at Harwell as a naturalized British citizen. In the summer of 1950, Pontecorvo took his wife and children to Italy, then to Finland, and finally to Russia, where the Italian antifascist became a citizen, a Stalin Prize winner for his work on mesons, and finally the head of the nuclear-problems laboratory of the Joint Institute for Nuclear Research in Moscow.

Late in 1954, Fermi was named the first recipient of a special award of $25,000 given by the U. S. Atomic Energy Commission for his contributions in the controlled release of nuclear energy. The general public was unaware that Fermi was already in an advanced stage of cancer and had been operated on a month earlier. Twelve days after receiving this signal honor he died of cancer at the age of fifty-three. While the world mourned this great loss Luigi Einaudi, President of the Italian Republic, cabled his widow, "Italy bows deeply and reverently to the memory of this eminent man who, by penetrating into the problems of nuclear physics, has linked his name for centuries with the progress of science."

There was no doubt now in the minds of all the men who had taken part in the adventure of tracking down element 100. It was named, by common consent, *fermium* (Fm).

One hundred might have made a nice round number of chemical elements to satisfy any chemist. But not Seaborg. Before the world of science could settle back and glory in the eight new children that had come to romp in their laboratories, another blessed event occurred. The delivery was made in the same 60-inch cyclotron at Berkeley, and the doctor, again, was Seaborg, aided by four radioactive internes who had been present at the birth of several of the other atomic children. Its father was element 99. The infant was an extremely active one. In less than an hour it had worn itself out into a lighter element—that is, only half of it had changed. Like most of its transuranium kin, it was too nervous and erratic to retain its individuality for any appreciable length of time.

When the moment came to give this new baby a name, Glenn Seaborg and his associates thought it was high time, despite the cold war, to dedicate it to the memory of the man who had given science the first practical catalogue of the chemical elements almost a century before *Mendelevium* (Md) became the name of element 101.

In the spring of 1957, Seaborg predicted the creation of the next element, number 102. Three months later, this next-to-the-last of the so-called actinides was created at the Nobel Institute of Physics in Stockholm and named *nobelium* (No) after its birthplace. The feat was accomplished by an international team which included scientists from Britain's atomic research center at Harwell, which supplied carbon 13, men who operated the Nobel Institute's cyclotron, and Paul R. Fields and Arnold M. Friedman from the Argonne National Laboratory near Chicago, which supplied the curium needed for the final experiment. Element 102 was born in the bombardment of curium with carbon-13. Only a few atoms of No-253 were detected, with a half-life of about ten minutes during which it emits alpha particles.

Nobelium undoubtedly will not be the last element to be created. Seaborg has already predicted that within the next few years elements 103 through 108 will see the light of day through the use of heavy ion bombardment. American scientists have been in the forefront of element creation. All ten of the new elements were first produced by our own scientists. As a relatively young nation we got into the business of discovering new elements rather late in the long history of alchemy and chemistry, and in the beginning we fared rather badly. But we have more than caught up by this time, and the end is by no means in sight.

The conquest of nuclear fission also brought rapid and significant activity in the field of radioisotopes. These are made today in nuclear reactors which often outproduce the cyclotron a billion times. Most radioisotopes are made by inserting chemicals and subjecting them to neutron bombardment, producing in some cases an actual transmutation. For example, to make carbon-14, a compound such as ammonium nitrate (NH_4NO_3) is placed in the reactor. The nitrogen atom in the NH_4NO_3 picks up a neutron and discharges a proton from its nucleus. This changes a stable nitrogen-14 atom into a radioactive carbon-14 atom. Several hundred brand-new atomic species of isotopes have already been prepared and made available to research workers all over the world.

The radioactive isotope is a new and revolutionary tool, and a very delicate one. For example, radioactive sulfur-35 can be diluted to one part in a trillion and still be found by a Geiger counter. This tagged atom can be detected among millions of ordinary atoms "just as a man with a ringing clock in his pocket can be picked out of a silent crowd of 100,000 closely packed people."

Isotopes can be shipped to any part of the world within less than two days. They are packed in lead containers, the walls varying in thickness depending upon the penetrating power of the radiation emitted. Thus radioactive iodine, which emits gamma rays, requires a shield of about one hundred pounds, whereas cobalt-60 must be protected in a sixteen-hundred-pound container. Some of the most frequently used radioisotopes are iodine-131, phosphorus-32, cobalt-60, and carbon-14. Iodine-131 is being used not only in studies of the causes of cancer of the thyroid but also in the treatment of thyroid disturbances. For example, a person suffering from hyperthyroidism is fed with 0.1 microgram of sodium iodide containing I^{131}. With the aid of a Geiger counter the rate at which this iodine compound collects in the thyroid gland can be accurately determined. In many cases no surgery is needed.

Radioactive cobalt-60, introduced in 1948, is taking the place of radium and X rays in cancer therapy. Its half-life is 5.3 years, and it is more than 300 times as powerful as radium. Phosphorus-32 has already proved of great value in agricultural research. It has given us clues as to the best way to add phosphate fertilizers to the soil for larger and healthier crops. Carbon-14, in the resourceful hands of Melvin Calvin of Lawrence's laboratory in Berkeley, is gradually unraveling the many secrets connected with photosynthesis—the most important chemical reaction in the vegetable world. Industry, too, has called upon many isotopes to help solve some of its problems. Synthetic radioactive iron and sulfur, for example, are helping steelmakers investigate the exchange of sulfur between the iron and the slag produced in the blast furnace. The effects of heat and friction on engine wear, rubber tires, and the moving parts of heavy machinery are being clarified with the aid of these new agents. It was estimated that in the year 1957 alone radioisotopes had saved American industry half a billion dollars.

Scientific discoveries often follow the most curious turns. Take the case of carbon-14, which has a half-life of about 5400 years. In 1946 Willard F. Libby, then of the University of Chicago, saw in this radioisotope a new method of determining the age of things that date back as far as 30,000 B.C. Wooden coffins and the clothing of ancient mummies, charred timber of ancient dwellings, relics, artifacts, bones and bits of charcoal found in prehistoric caves—and most recently, the Dead Sea scrolls, perhaps 1900 years old—have all been accurately dated by the number of electrons emitted by the carbon-14 they contain. C^{14} is formed by the action of cosmic rays on nitrogen atoms in the atmosphere. This C^{14} finds its way into plants as CO_2 and eventually is incorporated into animals which eat the vegetation. The amount of C^{14} in plants and animals ceases when the plant or animal dies. A carefully worked out formula relates the emission of electrons from the object under investigation with the time that its C^{14} ceased to increase. The method is uncanny in its accuracy. Archaeologists and other students of prehistory regard it as an exciting and reliable new tool of research in time.

This is but a beginning. The future uses of these chemical detectives and healers in the fields of human health, control of insect pests, plant and insect physiology, the nature and mechanism of chromosome changes, food sterilization, and the manifold areas of industrial research are practically limitless. A brand-new world of research has been opened up by this creative act of American scientists. The tracer technique has proved to be of such widespread and significant value that A. V. Hill, eminent English physiologist and Nobel Prize winner, believes that "the use of such tracer elements will some day be recorded in history as a technique of equal importance with the use of the microscope."

Above and beyond all of these new and dazzling developments shines also the promise of a new and unlimited supply of energy.

Nuclear energy will do the world's work, relieve mankind of the back-breaking operations of mill, mine, farm, and factory, and raise the standard of living of hundreds of millions of people all over the globe. Every nuclear pile is a potential electric power station. During its operation uranium is fissioning and large quantities of heat are being liberated. This heat changes water to steam, which operates a conventional turbine. Electricity is generated and distributed from the nuclear power plant to wherever it is

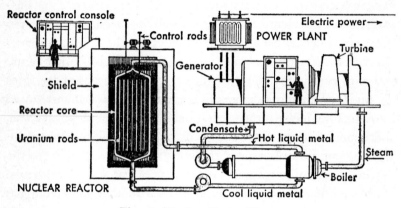

Fig. 28. Nuclear Power Plant

needed. Three essential parts of any nuclear reactor are the reactor core containing the fuel, the moderator, and the protective shielding. The main fuel is U-235, the moderator is usually either graphite or heavy water, and the protective shielding is lead, steel, or concrete.

In 1955, at least eighty reactors were in use or being built by or for several countries, including Australia, Belgium, Canada, England, France, India, Norway, Spain, Sweden, Switzerland, the Soviet Union, and the United States. Some were already producing electricity. This and other startling facts were disclosed at the United Nations International Conference on the Peaceful Uses of Atomic Energy initiated by President Eisenhower and held in August of that year at Geneva, Switzerland. This meeting with its 1200 delegates and 800 observers turned out to be more than a conference of scientists from 74 countries mingling and exchanging knowledge on the peaceful uses of atomic energy. It was also something of a businessmen's gathering, where top-level executives and high-pressure salesmen, books in hand, looked for orders for nuclear power plants and all kinds of instruments for the new nuclear age. British representatives, especially, were advertising their readiness and ability to design and build nuclear power plants of several types for any part of the earth. American businessmen were somewhat irked at the security system in their own country which prevented them from reaching more deeply into the world markets with both power and experimental reactors and other nuclear-age products equal to, if not better than, those of their British friends. This unnecessary security was later eased by the United States Atomic Energy Commission, which controlled all nuclear research and development in this country.

Marquis Childs, one of the many reporters covering this Geneva Conference, wrote in his syndicated column, "It is a little as though the use of fire to serve man's well-being had become known ten years ago. And as a result of this discovery there had been assembled from all the world the first rudimentary cooking pots and other crude beginning devices to turn this new force to practical advantage."

In 1945 Richard C. Tolman predicted in the Smyth Report that "A great industry would arise comparable with electronics. Nuclear power for special purposes could be developed within *ten years*." Charles A. Thomas of Monsanto Chemical Company, which operated the Oak Ridge installation, agreed. They were right. And the 1946 prediction of both Enrico Fermi and J. Robert Oppenheimer that great nuclear reactors would be supplying enough energy to heat a large city within ten or eleven years had actually come true. On December 20, 1951, a small experimental power reactor built by the A.E.C. at Arco, Idaho, produced a trickle of electricity to light just one electric bulb. Three years later, the first nuclear-powered transport became a reality when the United States submarine *Nautilus* put to sea successfully.

Within the next six months the United States Atomic Energy Commission had sold the first atom-generated electricity to a private utility. The 10,000 kilowatts of electricity came from an experimental reactor which had been built at West Milton, New York. The electricity was sent into the lines of the Niagara-Mohawk Power Corporation and was sufficient to supply a city of 25,000 people. As the switch was thrown by Admiral Lewis L. Strauss, then chairman of the Atomic Energy Commission, he pointed out that "This switch is a symbol of the great dilemma of our time. I throw it now to the side of the peaceful atom and by that choice we of the United States mark the beginning of a fulfillment of the Scriptural injunction of Isaiah: 'They shall beat their swords into plowshares and their spears into pruning hooks.'"

The year 1955 also witnessed the start of the building of the first full-scale civilian atom-powered electric plant at Shippingport, Pennsylvania, under the direction of Rear Admiral Hyman G. Rickover, dynamic father of our first nuclear-powered submarine. Westinghouse Electric Corporation built the reactor; the Atomic Energy Commission, owner of the plant, supplied the U-235; and the Duquesne Light Company of Pittsburgh supplied the turbine generator and operates the sixty-thousand-kilowatt, $100,000,000 plant. Delivery of power from this lineal descendant of Fermi's original Chicago pile began in December, 1957, to customers in the Pittsburgh area. The keel of the first nuclear surface ship, the cruiser *Long Beach*, was also laid that year.

Several other different types of reactors are already in operation, and more are being planned. They differ somewhat in principle, fuel employed, and cooling systems. A great deal of experimentation and development is still going on. No one knows what the most efficient type of reactor will be. Perhaps in the next ten or twenty years we will, and the new standard nuclear power reactor will be as different from any now in use as the old Model-T Ford is from the sleek and powerful automobile of today.

As this new development got under way some experts in the field began to forecast that by 1960 the United States would have nuclear power plants producing as much as 800,000 kilowatts of energy, and perhaps 3,000,000 by 1965. Others, on the other hand, believed that the United States Atomic Energy Commission was not proceeding vigorously enough to place and keep us secure as the world's leader in atomic power development. In the summer of 1957 the Joint Congressional Committee on Atomic Energy declared that they "had not been satisfied that the A.E.C. has been making sufficient progress in the development of prototype power reactors to test and demonstrate the practical problems of achieving economical nuclear power." The reply of Lewis L. Strauss was that we already had 21 civilian and military power reactors in operation, with 30 more experimental plants being built and 37 more being planned. In addition, 274 reactors were being used for research, testing, and training purposes. He insisted that we led the world in nuclear power development and added that private industry could be relied upon to shoulder the financial risks associated with the present state of nuclear advance, and to completely take over nuclear power development and other peaceful uses of the atom within ten years. Strauss defended the "partnership" program, which involved, according to the new Atomic Energy Act of 1954, private development and construction of power plants with research and development assistance from the Federal government. He denied that the A.E.C. had no clear-cut program or policy.

The cost of electricity generated in present nuclear power plants is greater than current costs from conventional fuels in this country. But as more and more progress is made, costs will come down. Said the *Financial World* early in 1956, "Within a decade, nuclear power costs should compare favorably with conventional plant costs over most of the nation." In other parts of the world this should come even sooner. It is believed that by 1970 about fifteen per cent of all new generating plants in the United States will be atom-powered, and by 1980 this figure should rise to forty per cent. By the close of the century more than half the nation's new electrical power, it is predicted, will be generated by atomic fuel extracted, refined, and manufactured by American chemists.

Britain, too, was moving ahead rapidly in its atoms-for-peace program. In a 1955 Christmas message, Sir John D. Cockcroft, the scientist who achieved the first artificial transmutation by man-made projectiles, broadcast his belief that "within two years our nuclear reactors will be delivering substantial amounts of electricity to industry and our homes. Perhaps by next Christmas some of you will even be cooking your Christmas dinner from electricity generated by atomic power." He was right. On October 17, 1956, the British already had two reactors with an output of 69,000 kilowatts at Calder Hall among the ancient Druid markers in Cumberland, supplying electricity for factory and home through its national power grid.

England's ten-year nuclear power program calls for several large nuclear power stations scattered over much of Great Britain, with a combined capacity of about 875,000 kilowatts, by 1961. The cost will be about $350,000,000. By 1966, nineteen stations supplying 6,000,000 kilowatts of nuclear power will provide twenty per cent of her electric power needs. Her dwindling coal supplies, which have forced her to import coal from the United States, her complete lack of any domestic petroleum, and her mounting needs of electrical energy, which are expected to double in the next ten years, made this imperative. Today, the United Kingdom is the greatest exporter of radioisotopes and is actively engaged in the exploitation of the new rich export trade in nuclear reactors, fuel and fuel-processing equipment, as well as hundreds of radiation and other nuclear instruments.

France, too, will complete its first industrial nuclear reactor in 1960, with an initial capacity of about 60,000 kilowatts. Together with the other five Euratom countries—Belgium, Italy, Luxembourg, Netherlands, and West Germany—France is hoping to produce 6,000,000 kilowatts of nuclear energy by 1965.

Russia turned up at Geneva during that 1955 conference with more than hollow boasts. Alongside our full-scale, "swimming-pool" nuclear reactor which we had flown to the conference for exhibition, the young Soviet scientists presented a model of Russia's first "commercial" power reactor, which, they said, had been in operation for more than a year. Not far from Moscow, it was claimed, the reactor had fed electricity into farms, factories, and homes on a modest, experimental scale. The new Soviet Five-Year Plan calls for the completion by 1960 of several atomic-energy plants with a total capacity of 2,500,000 kilowatts. The chief of the Russian Atomic Energy Commission reported that an atomic icebreaker is under construction, and that an atomic whaler will also be built. Russian leaders also told their people that Soviet scientists are completing the world's largest nuclear power generator, as well as the most gigantic atom smasher ever attempted. This *phasotron* is a $100,000,000 synchrotron, located sixty miles north of Moscow, that hurls protons with energies of ten billion volts—almost double that of the next largest and heaviest particle accelerator now in existence, the *bevatron* of the University of California. They are also said to be planning an even more powerful one—a fifty-billion-electron-volt monster.

What of the underdeveloped countries of the world? All of the energy-hungry nations are in urgent need of cheap and abundant power. Some of their scientists spoke up. Pakistan and Iraq were interested in small power reactors, Brazil and Argentina reported that a shortage of conventional fuels was holding back their industrial growth. Here was a magnificent opportunity to put the atom to work for the have-nots and their impoverished millions. Three continents were anxiously waiting for help.

President Eisenhower, looking "to find the way by which the inventiveness of man shall be consecrated to his life," had outlined, a little more than a year before, an atoms-for-peace program to the General Assembly of the United Nations. He offered free nuclear fuel on a lend-lease basis with which to build atomic furnaces for both experimental and, eventually, industrial uses.

Eighteen months later he doubled this gift, and then early in 1956 he stirred the whole world again with the announcement that 88,000 pounds of U-235 would be released for use here and abroad for developing atomic energy for peaceful purposes. Over a period of years, half of this generous pile of fissionable uranium would, with suitable safeguards, be sent overseas to those countries which were not making U-235. This, said Eisenhower, was an act of "faith that the atom can be made a powerful instrument for the promotion of world peace."

The most spectacular single announcement that came out of the Geneva meeting of atomic scientists was that of Professor Homi J. Bhabha, head of India's Atomic Energy Commission and president of the conference. Bhabha represented a country where the energy problem is one of the keystones of its future. It is a land where eighty per cent of the energy comes from one of the most primitive methods still in use, the burning of dung, a product which could be better put to use to improve the productivity of her soil. Bhabha was looking even further ahead than the nuclear fission of uranium. "When we learn how to liberate *fusion* energy in a controlled manner," he told his fellow scientists, "the energy problems of the world will truly have been solved forever, for the fuel will be as plentiful as the heavy water in the oceans." Scientists from all over the world were startled. A limitless supply of energy for mankind within two decades was being predicted by a first-rate nuclear physicist. Even men who could see undreamed-of developments in this exploding field of nuclear energy rubbed their eyes and searched for clues and shreds of information on which this almost unbelievable prediction had been made.

To understand this new development we must examine the mechanism of the so-called thermonuclear reaction of the hydrogen bomb, which had already been successfully demonstrated by American scientists in 1952. Soon after the A-bomb, loaded with U-235 and plutonium, had been exploded in 1945, Enrico Fermi together with Edward Teller and British-born James Tuck considered the possibility of obtaining a bomb explosion by fusion rather than by fission. Edward Teller with fanatical zeal was all for manufacturing it at once. Ernest Lawrence and Luis Alvarez agreed. But the consciences of some other scientists bothered them. "The physicists have known sin," declared J. Robert Oppenheimer; they were reluctant to join in this new venture. This attitude was partly responsible for the revocation of Oppenheimer's security clearance in 1954 even though he was considered loyal.

The work on the H-bomb went on. The principle of this weapon is somewhat different from that of the A-bomb. The destructive force of the H-bomb comes from the *fusion* of lighter atoms into a heavier one rather than from the *fission* of a heavy element into lighter ones. Two isotopes of hydrogen take part in the fusion process. Heavy hydrogen or deuterium has a mass of two, double that of ordinary hydrogen, and tritium or radio-hydrogen, the heaviest form, has a mass of three. Heavy hydrogen is found in all water, including that of the oceans, to the extent of about one part in 6000. Tritium with a half-life of twelve years is seldom met in nature but can be manufactured in a nuclear reactor by bombardment of the isotope of lithium of atomic weight 6 with neutrons.

The nuclei of deuterium (D^2) and tritium (T^3) are made to merge or fuse. During this fusion, the hydrogen is transmuted into helium (He^4) whose mass is four. One neutron is liberated and nuclear energy is produced in tremendous quantities, because in fusion, too, there is a loss of matter. This thermonuclear reaction may be expressed as follows:

$$D^2 + T^3 \rightarrow He^4 + n + \text{energy}$$

The energy liberated is equivalent to 176,000,000 kilowatts per pound of fuel.

For such a nuclear reaction to take place, however, an enormously high temperature—about 100,000,000° Centigrade—is necessary. Such a temperature is found only in the sun and other stars, where it is generated by just such a fusion reaction, according to the originator of this theory, Hans A. Bethe of Cornell University. Edward Teller had been interested in this thermo-nuclear reaction as far back as 1935, when he came to George Washington University as professor of physics. There he had worked with George Gamow on nuclear reactions in the stars.

This terrifically high temperature is needed for only about one millionth of a second. With the development of the A-bomb such a temperature became available here on earth, for it is reached during an A-bomb explosion. The detonation of an A-bomb can thus act as a trigger for the explosion of an H-bomb. This double bomb explosive can be constructed to provide almost unlimited destructive power. Ordinary A-bombs are in the kiloton or *thousand*-tons-of-TNT class; H-bombs are in the megaton class; that is, they can produce energy equivalent to as much as sixteen *million* tons of TNT.

If a way could be found to control a thermonuclear reaction, an unlimited supply of cheap power would be made available to mankind, for the fuel needed, deuterium, is present in the oceans. Scientists from several countries were already at work on this most alluring and difficult problem. The Russians' top nuclear physicist, Igor Kurchatov, spoke freely at Harwell in 1956 about the progress of their investigations. Our own scientists were silent even though experimental work had already started in the United States as early as 1951 under James Tuck at Los Alamos and Lyman Spitzer, Jr., at Princeton University. The following year Herbert York, a graduate of the University of Rochester, entered the picture at the University of California's laboratory at Livermore, California, now directed by Teller. Smaller programs, too, had been undertaken by Alvin Weinberg at Oak Ridge National Laboratory, and at New York University's Institute of Mathematical Science by Richard Courant.

Similar work had been initiated in England even earlier, in

1948, at which time it appears the Russians also entered the race. France, Germany, Japan, the Netherlands, and Sweden also entered later. There was some uneasiness apparent among those present at the Geneva conference who were thinking in terms of huge investments in the nuclear-energy industry that was being born. Would the brand-new uranium, plutonium or thorium reactors being planned for the brave new world just around the corner be obsolete even before they had been designed? Billions of dollars of investors' money were at stake. Were their "conventional" atomic reactors to become, in no time, the horse and buggy of the deuterium-tritium age that was coming up so fast? Was it safe to invest in uranium power plants?

Prospectors, processors, investment brokers, and investors in uranium-ore stocks by the thousands began to have nightmares. We were digging three million tons of uranium ore out of the ground each year to free us from our former dependence on the Belgian Congo for this metal. The United States was stockpiling uranium like mad. We were in the throes of a wild uranium rush. Thousands of people—miners, sheep herders, clerks, gasoline-pump attendants, and salesmen—were struck by a virulent fever. They were swarming over the 100,000 square miles of the Colorado Plateau. They were searching for uranium with Geiger counters, drilling test holes in every acre of red desert rock in canyons and mesas, and recording claims galore. What if there was a sudden breakthrough in this new fusion research even sooner than Bhabha had predicted? Billions of dollars of investments might go down the drain overnight if tritium replaced uranium. Some scientists "in the know" quieted them. Sure, by 1948 both the United States and the United Kingdom, and presumably the Soviet Union, too, had confined plasma of deuterium in glass tubes, had sent bursts of tremendous electrical currents through them for tiny millionths of a second, and had reported temperatures as high as 6,000,000° Centigrade and the evolution of some neutrons. But scores of stupendous difficulties still lay ahead. Perhaps, some said, it would never be solved, for it was an infinitely tougher job than even the fission-control project had been. Uranium and thorium were still to be relied on as the fuel of the near future.

But there were some bold spirits who saw nuclear fusion within our grasp. Said Sir John Cockcroft in a lecture at the Geneva meeting: "My faith in the creative ability of the scientist is so great that I am sure that this (power from fusion) will be achieved long before it is essential for man's needs." And plenty of American scientists echoed this sentiment in silence.

Many questions regarding the atom's nucleus still remain unanswered. What holds its protons together? What holds its neutrons intact? What mysterious force keeps them together? This force is apparently different from gravitational or electrical forces as we know them today. Leading American nuclear physicists including Fermi, Lawrence and Rabi believed that the meson is the cosmic cement that holds the key to an understanding of the strange nuclear forces. We know something about mesons. At least nine different kinds have been identified. They are particles of different mass, of either positive or negative charge, or electrically neutral. The first one reported was a light, positively charged meson of mass about 207 times that of an electron. It was discovered in 1937 by the American scientist Carl D. Anderson. The heavy meson (pion) with a mass of about 270 that of an electron was predicted by a Japanese scientist Hideki Yukawa, in 1934 and discovered thirteen years later by C. F. Powell. That was the year in which J. Robert Oppenheimer predicted the existence of a heavy neutral meson which was later discovered.

Mesons lurk in the upper atmosphere. Scientists had to rise in planes to study them. This was a very cumbersome method. It would be a great step forward if we could manufacture them in our terrestrial laboratories. The night of February 21, 1948, actually marked this thrilling event. Cesare M. Lattes, a twenty-three-year-old scientist from São Paulo, Brazil, working on a Rockefeller Foundation fellowship, and Eugene Gardner, already a victim of beryllium poisoning incurred during A-bomb work, were at the controls of the 4000-ton, 184-inch synchrocyclotron of Lawrence's Radiation Laboratory at Berkeley. This machine had recently been redesigned with the help of grants from the Rockefeller Foundation and the Manhattan District project. The principle of frequency modulation used in radio transmission had been applied to increase its power. The utilization of this principle was first suggested in 1945 by Edwin M. McMillan of Lawrence's laboratory. The Soviet scientist, V. I. Veksler, in a now classic paper which appeared in the *Journal of Physics* of the U.S.S.R., also independently suggested the idea at about the same time.

Lattes and Gardner hurled helium nuclei with the higher energies (380 Mev) made possible by the redesigned machine at carbon and beryllium targets. The effects were studied on a new type of emulsion plate developed by Powell, discoverer of the heavy meson, in Bristol, England. What they saw turned out to be "the most significant event in nuclear studies since the discovery of nuclear fission." The track of a negatively charged meson of mass about 300 times that of an electron turned up in one of their photomicrographs. Lawrence was at first skeptical, but two weeks later he announced this historic event at a press conference. For the first time in history men had artificially created mesons. A fast-moving proton had changed into a neutron and a meson. Furthermore, the number of mesons produced was ten million times as plentiful as the occasional mesons laboriously trapped at high altitudes. In addition, here was definite experimental evidence of the change of artificially produced cosmic-ray energy into a particle of matter.

Further meson research is being pushed by American scientists with larger and more powerful particle accelerators. Supported by the United States Atomic Energy Commission and administered by the co-operative effort of nine leading Eastern colleges known as Associated Universities, Inc. of which Lloyd V. Berkner is president, the Brookhaven National Laboratory at Upton, Long Island, has become one of the main centers of this work. It has in operation a synchrotron, named the *cosmotron*, capable of producing a stream of protons with energies reaching about 3 billion electron volts.

The most powerful atom-smashing machine in the United States today is the *bevatron*, direct descendant of the first tiny frying-pan model invented by Lawrence about thirty years ago. It is the main machine of Lawrence's Radiation Laboratory and can deliver particles accelerated to energies as high as 6.2 billion electron volts. A 6-billion-electron synchrotron is being completed at Harvard University in a joint venture with the Massachusetts Institute of Technology. Its basic design was worked out under the leadership of M. Stanley Livingston, the man who worked very closely with Lawrence in the very early days of cyclotron development. Electrons in this machine will get an initial acceleration in a *linac* or linear accelerator machine.

Others are being planned or built. The largest behemoth of them all in this country will be ready in 1960. It will be a $30,000,000, 30-billion-electron-volt alternating-gradient-proton synchrotron. Protons will be pushed to velocities approaching very close to the speed of light. Its magnets, arranged in a circle half a mile in circumference, will be housed underground at the Brookhaven National Laboratory site. With these new "nuclear microscopes" and mighty battering rams our brilliant nuclear scientists and engineers will make fresh assaults into the interior of the nucleus.

More than sixty years have passed since the bubble of the snug, indivisible atom was first burst. Some of the fragments of that explosion—electrons, protons, neutrons, alpha particles, positrons, mesons and *neutrinos* (decay products of mesons) first suggested in 1931, named by Fermi in 1934, and discovered by American scientists twenty years later—lie about us for further study. Antiprotons (negatively charged protons) and antineutrons (neutrons of opposite magnetic moment) produced in the University of California's bevatron, trapped in a propane bubble chamber, and very near. "For this is what is new in the atomic age," declared Oppenheimer, "a world to be united in law, in common understanding, in common humanity, before a common peril."

The atomic age was born on December 2, 1942, when the first successful chain-reacting pile was achieved. Five years later a plaque was dedicated at the University of Chicago. On the same day, while Hiroshima halted work to observe the second anniversary of the fall of a new bomb, a large white wooden cross was raised on a wind-swept dune in the Alamogordo Desert of New Mexico where the first atomic bomb was exploded. A small party of men from various walks of life flew to this spot to raise a rainbow flag of all nations and to call upon the people of the world to renounce atomic warfare, even as the survivors of Hiroshima prayed that mankind would give up all war.

Ancient alchemy failed to give men an elixir of life that would ward off old age and extend their life span. Modern alchemy through nuclear fission and fusion has brought this dream within our grasp, if we act now to prevent mankind from muddling into a war which, in the nuclear age, means total destruction.

photographed on a special emulsion plate since 1955 add to th
profusion of elementary particles and to the confusion of thei
discoverers. Antiprotons have been shown to strike protons form
ing neutrons and antineutrons. The antineutron then strikes ;
neutron and both are annihilated, producing nothing but energy
Faced with the meaning of all this, American scientists are wrestling with the fantastic possibility of the existence of *antiatom*
and even of a whole universe of *antimatter*. Such a world might be
composed of nuclei of antiprotons and antineutrons surrounded
by positrons instead of electrons. Matter and antimatter colliding
annihilate each other, producing energy. Perhaps the radio signals
coming from extragalactic space are a sample of this energy.

Other particles—a neutron of mass two, a deuteron counterpart of helium tentatively christened *alphina*, a *positronium* or
fleeting partnership of positron and electron revolving around
each other—are still being hunted to further tantalize us. J. Robert
Oppenheimer had gone in 1947 to direct the Institute for Advanced Study at Princeton. Here he, Julian S. Schwinger, and
many other Americans, including young Murray Gell-Mann of
Caltech, "are trying to understand the existence, properties, and
behavior of the fundamental particles of which all matter is composed." They are still picking the nucleus apart and trying to put
it together with the twenty to thirty subnuclear particles already
discovered or predicted, to see how the atom and the nucleus
really tick. Gell-Mann has proposed that perhaps all these particles are related to each other by his odd concept of "strange-
ness." Until all the parts of the intricate machinery of the atom
can be located and fitted together, the final structure of both the
atom and the universe will remain unknown.

Even more important than this supreme creative effort is the
challenge of something more immediate. "I wish I could produce
a substance," said Alfred Nobel many years ago, "of such frightful efficacy for wholesale destruction that it would make wars
impossible." Nuclear fission and fusion have brought this hope

CHAPTER TWENTY-ONE

FUTURE OF
SCIENCE IN AMERICA

WHEN THE UNITED STATES entered the war against the Axis in 1941 we were well on our way to world leadership in several fields of science, particularly astronomy, atomic physics, biochemistry, physiological chemistry, and radiation. Much of our peacetime research in pure science came to a halt, while research and development directly geared to military needs expanded tremendously. Government and industrial laboratories took over most of the research projects proposed by the Army and Navy. To bring this work to its greatest peak of efficiency and to co-ordinate it with our university research centers, a new organization, the Office of Scientific Research and Development (O.S.R.D.), was created. This organization was under the direction of Vannevar Bush, retired Dean of Engineering at the Massachusetts Institute of Technology. He worked through the National Academy of Sciences which Abraham Lincoln had set up during the Civil War, and the National Research Council authorized by Woodrow Wilson during World War I. Under it were the National Defense Research Committee and the Committee on Medical Research. More than a thousand scientists and engineers served on its many advisory committees and many more thousands worked on its numerous projects. Hundreds of millions of dollars were given by the Federal Government to dozens of university and industrial laboratories to carry on vitally needed research work for the production of new weapons for victory. For the first time in American history large numbers of scientists became key partners in the conduct of a war.

Pure research, especially in the physical sciences, was virtually killed. This violent change of the role of the scientist would be temporary, it was hoped. At the end of the war, it was generally felt, our laboratories would resume leadership in the solution of some of the world's unfinished business of science. The search for a clearer picture of the make-up of the atom would get under way again in real earnest. Further details would be sought regarding the origin and nature of cosmic rays and the transformation of radiation into matter. New conceptions would be sought to link gravitation, electricity, the atom nucleus and the stars. Further probing of the ocean floor and ocean currents, the ionosphere, outer space, and the architecture of the universe would be undertaken. New facts would be ferreted out concerning such varied mechanisms as photosynthesis, heredity, virus behavior, and long-range weather forecasting. The battle against heart ailments, cancer, nephritis, cerebral hemorrhages, and other major cripplers and killers would be resumed. These enemies of middle and old age would be with us more than ever before, for millions saved from the infectious diseases of early life would swell the number of people who would reach the ages of sixty and seventy. The challenge, too, of the mental diseases which send one out of every eighteen of our population into mental hospitals would again be faced with resolution. From the outposts of our research laboratories would come new hormones to fight glandular disturbances, new serums and antitoxins, more antibiotics to fight influenza, the common cold and other diseases, and new and bolder methods of open-heart surgery. The possibility of understanding and controlling more of the molecular diseases would be faced with greater confidence.

New and more effective devices to trap and harness the tremendous power of the sun now going to waste, newer metals and stronger alloys for our jets, more powerful gasoline and other fuels for the rocket era and the new space age, new plastics, cheaper and better synthetic rubber and fibers, more marvelous electronic computers, and a thousand and one new gadgets would be spawned by our inventive genius.

Even before victory was assured Franklin D. Roosevelt took time out to consider plans for this brilliant prospect. Toward the close of 1944 he wrote a letter to Vannevar Bush. "The O.S.R.D.," he said, "represents a unique experiment of team work and cooperation in conducting scientific research and in applying existing scientific knowledge to the solution of the technical problems paramount in war. . . . There is no reason why the lessons to be found in this experiment cannot be profitably employed in times of peace." The President asked him for specific recommendations.

Almost eight months went by. Roosevelt had died in the meantime, and the Germans had surrendered unconditionally. Harry S. Truman had been in the White House for three months, and the war was still being fought. Bush's report reached the new President. "The pioneer spirit," it began, "is still vigorous within the nation. Science offers a largely unexplored hinterland for the pioneer who has the tools for his task. The rewards for such exploration both for the nation and the individual are great. Scientific progress is one essential key to our security as a nation, to our better health, to more jobs, to a higher standard of living, and to our cultural progress."

Bush also reminded the President that essential new knowledge can be obtained only through basic scientific research, and that such basic scientific research is scientific capital. Our leaders in government were warned that basic research in medicine conducted mainly in our medical schools and universities was hampered by lack of sufficient funds. Endowment income, foundation grants, private donations, and appropriations by state legislatures to these institutions were actually diminishing instead of increasing. These traditional supports were no longer adequate. This was also true for basic research in other fields as well. To maintain our leadership more public funds were needed at once.

With regard to scientific education and manpower, the Director of O.S.R.D. was equally frank and clear. He told the President that the training of a scientist was a long and expensive process.

Because of this, studies showed unmistakably that many young people could not afford it and were thus lost to the nation's potential reservoir of trained scientists. More than fifty per cent of pupils in high school intellectually capable of profiting by a college education never reached college because of financial handicaps. "Here is a tremendous waste of the greatest resource of a nation—the intelligence of its citizens. . . . It is in keeping with American traditions that new frontiers of science shall be made accessible for development by all American citizens."

Bush's report, entitled "Science, the Endless Frontier," recommended the creation of an agency such as a National Science Foundation, which should proceed to correct these existing inadequacies in American scientific research and education by promoting the development of new scientific knowledge and new scientific talent.

About a year later, President Truman issued an executive order appointing John R. Steelman Chairman of the President's Scientific Research Board, which was to make a further study of the country's position in scientific research and development together with its needs. He asked for recommendations as to what the Federal Government could do to meet the challenge of science. In 1947, Steelman submitted his report entitled, "A Program for the Nation." Emphasizing the uneasy character of the present peace, he repeated the essential point that our security and prosperity as well as our standing in cultural progress depend today as never before upon the rapid extension of scientific knowledge.

Several concrete recommendations were made. The report urged an increase in our annual expenditure for research and development so that by 1957 our universities, industry and the government should be spending at least one per cent of our gross national income for this program. It also suggested that the Federal Government should support basic research in science in our universities and other nonprofit institutions at a progressively increasing rate, reaching an annual expenditure of at least $250,-000,000 by 1957. Furthermore, the Federal Government was urged to develop a program of assistance to undergraduate and graduate students in the sciences as an integral part of an over-all national scholarship and fellowship program. And finally it stressed again the need for a National Science Foundation, responsible to the President, which among other functions was to make grants in support of basic research in science.

What happened during the ten years that elapsed after the submission of these two important reports? On May 10, 1950, after almost five years of delay, President Truman signed a bill creating the National Science Foundation. The Eightieth Congress had earlier passed a similar bill which Truman had vetoed, as he explained, because of features which were undesirable from the standpoint of public policy and unworkable from the standpoint of administration. Alan T. Waterman, who had taught physics at Yale University, was named its first director. It was authorized "to develop and encourage the pursuit of a national policy for the promotion of basic research and education in the sciences, to initiate and support basic research in the mathematical, physical, biological, engineering, and other sciences by making contracts or other arrangements (including grants, loans and other forms of assistance) for the conducting of such basic scientific research." This would include, for example, money for building astronomical telescopes and particle accelerators.

Four years after its establishment, the National Science Foundation conducted a survey which showed a phenomenal growth of expenditures for scientific *research and development* in our country. In 1940 we had spent about $260,000,000 and in 1954 this figure had jumped to about 5 billion, a twentyfold increase in less than fifteen years. Of this amount private industry had spent about 3.7 billion, about forty per cent of which was contributed by the Federal Government. Government spending was exceptionally high in the fields of atomic energy, missiles, supersonic planes, and other weapons of war. Industrial expenditures were heavy because many devices originally developed for national security had extensive applications in peacetime products.

Also, profits were high, and tough competition accelerated the exploitation of many scientific advances. The remainder of the five billions spent on research and development was accounted for by educational and other nonprofit organizations.

However, expenditures in *basic research* in the United States did not show this same spectacular rise. In 1940 the estimate was about $40,000,000, and in 1954 it was in the neighborhood of $400,000,000 (a sum less than our national cosmetics bill that year). The grand total spent on basic research in 1954 was hardly eight per cent of the total poured into applied research and development, and only a little more than 0.1 per cent of our gross national product. During the next three years, with no slackening of the tensions of the cold-war atmosphere, and in spite of more and repeated warnings on the need for larger funds for basic research, the picture improved only very moderately. Basic research in science continued to be neglected. For a country as large and powerful as ours this represented an unjustifiable niggardliness. More money should have been poured into the streams that feed our scientific pools of basic research.

The situation with regard to science education was an equally dismal one. In papers read at the annual meeting of the American Association for the Advancement of Science in December, 1953, by Alan T. Waterman, J. Carlton Ward, and Mervin J. Kelly on the subject of "Scientific Research and National Security," we find the following criticism: "In general big business is yet unaware of the key role that universities must play in generating a favorable atmosphere in which exceptional scholars will work. These scholars are the men from whom will come the new science and philosophic concepts that will expand outward the boundaries of knowledge from which technological progress emerges."

During the summer of that same year, James B. Conant, then president of Harvard University, proposed a conference to deal with the nationwide problem of science teaching in our high schools. Conant had already reminded the American people earlier that "anyone familiar with education knows that for a very considerable portion of the population it is the family financial status which places a ceiling on the educational ambitions of even the brilliant youth. The oft-repeated statement in certain smug circles that 'any boy who has what it takes can get all the education he wants in the U.S.A.' just is not so, it is contrary to the facts." The men who met at Cambridge agreed that we were not using our intellectual resources to the full. To get more and better-trained scientists we would have to get more and better science teachers. They warned that poor teaching was spreading as communities, in their desperate need for teachers, were lowering their standards. The alarmingly low estate of teachers was still dropping, as higher pay and a more favorable social position were drawing off thousands of potentially excellent teachers of science and mathematics into industry and other professions. "A recent survey shows," wrote James Reston in *The New York Times* in 1956, "that between 250,000 and 400,000 high school students in the United States are learning their mathematics and science from teachers who are not trained to teach these subjects, and that part-time science teachers now outnumber full-time science teachers. The number of qualified science teachers in United States high schools has fallen off 53 per cent in the last five years while high school students have increased 16 per cent." Obviously this situation, too, was deteriorating. The warnings were many and quite clear.

Then came the Sputniks. On October 4, 1957, the Russians launched a man-made satellite, the first in history to circle the earth. The world was electrified. Before it could recover its breath another and much larger moon was shot around the earth thirty days later by Soviet scientists. Americans were jolted out of their complacency. Suddenly all of the real and alleged shortcomings and weaknesses of American science which had been stated and repeated by eminent men and top-flight survey committees for the past two decades were heard again. This time the voices were louder, and there were more of them. While the burden of the newest stern warnings and demands was no different, they were backed up by more data, and they were pronounced with direr predictions lest they go unheeded again in this hour of peril. The Soviets had conquered outer space and had won a tremendous propaganda victory; they were beating us already in a few critical areas of rocket development and research and were catching up in others faster than we had even dreamed. Many began to question the invulnerable superiority of American science.

Within a few days of this rude awakening the President's Committee on Education Beyond the High School, which had been appointed eighteen months earlier, issued its final report. "Our nation," it warned, "like the prodigal farmer, is consuming the seed corn needed for future harvests. The ultimate result could be disaster. . . . The college teachers of the United States, through their inadequate salaries, are subsidizing the education of students, and in some cases the luxuries of their families, by an amount which is more than double the grand total of alumni gifts, corporate gifts, and endowment income of all colleges and universities combined. . . . Individuals in America need increased opportunities for obtaining more education and better training."

Another of the President's committees, that on Scientists and Engineers, brought together in May of that year, reported in November. "The substantial rise in the social and economic status of teachers is the only answer," it declared, "to a real and permanent improvement in the quality of teaching." Marion B. Folsom, Secretary of Health, Education, and Welfare, gave his own opinion that "It is nothing short of a national disgrace that we are discouraging people who want to teach by offering salaries that are far below the levels justified by their training and far below the levels which others are willing to pay."

Others joined the chorus of self-criticism. The Carnegie Foundation for the Advancement of Science repeated the doleful note that the teaching profession was "slowly withering away." The Council for Technical Advancement in Washington added that since 1950 the number of new college graduates qualified to teach high-school science and mathematics declined more than fifty per cent, and that about seventy-five per cent of American pupils study no physics at all in our high schools. Detlev W. Bronk, president of the National Academy of Sciences, added that "there are all too many high schools in the country where there are no qualified teachers in the sciences."

The *Wall Street Journal* commented editorially, "We are wasting the human resources of more than 17,000,000 Negroes by treating them as second-class citizens or worse. How many potential Booker T. Washingtons, George Washington Carvers, and Ralph Bunches are being lost to the country by the blindness of bigotry." Vice-President Richard Nixon startled the American people with the thought that the Soviet's potentiality underscored the need for racial integration in the United States. "We cannot afford," he said, "to have substantial numbers of our citizens receiving a second-class education. We need more George Washington Carvers."

It might have been added that, since brain power is always in short supply, the freer and more frequent entry of women into the many fields of science and engineering had not been sufficiently encouraged. In the 1933 edition of *American Men of Science*, 22,000 scientists were included. The names of 1500 of them were starred to represent those who had made the most important contributions to research in their respective fields. This special list included the names of only thirty-three women, or a little more than two per cent. Since then, more women had been entering scientific research each year, for their talents in science were at last gaining some recognition. Witness the achievements of Lillian V. Morgan and Barbara McClintock in genetics, Maud Slye in mouse-cancer research, Katherine Blodgett in molecular film work, Emma P. Carr in spectrochemistry, Edith H. Quimby in the medical use of X rays and radioisotopes, Gerti Cori, Nobel Prize winner in the field of enzymes, Florence R. Sabin in blood and blood diseases, Margaret Mead and Ruth Benedict in anthropology, and Florence Seibert in tuberculin work. In 1940 women chemists represented three per cent of the total number of American chemists; in 1956 this figure had risen to seven per cent. This is still far too low. Said the President's Committee on Scientists and Engineers, "Despite past habits and traditions, we cannot afford to ignore this great potential source of scientific talent. . . . Of the total labor force growth of about 10 million expected by 1965, women will account for about half."

Basic research in science also came in for plenty of criticism. The National Science Foundation, about three weeks after the launching of the first Sputnik, presented to President Eisenhower its report, "Basic Research—A National Resource." This top scientific government agency said in part: "Support for basic research, particularly Federal and industrial, has increased appreciably during the past decade—but not enough. The need for more support and more favorable working conditions is particularly acute in college and universities, which represent our greatest source of new scientific knowledge and our only source of trained research workers." It recommended a mixed private-government system of support. The government should encourage, by tax revisions and otherwise, private industry, foundations, professional societies, and other nonprofit organizations to give more funds and support to basic research. However, should such contributions prove inadequate, then the Federal government should step in and supply whatever additional funds were necessary.

In a speech shortly after, Alan T. Waterman, its director, declared that in the National Science Foundation alone they could support at least three times as much high-quality basic research throughout the country as they were presently doing, and most agencies in Washington reported that they, too, could underwrite more if funds were available. In 1951 Congress had appropriated a paltry $225,000 for the National Science Foundation, and as late as 1957 its annual appropriation of $40,000,000 was still fantastically little.

President Eisenhower, sensing the concern of the American

people, went before the nation twice during November of the year of the Sputniks to assure the country that the United States would meet the threat of loss of world leadership in science. He immediately appointed James M. Killian, Jr., his Special Assistant for Science and Technology. Declaring that we had "failed to give high priority enough to science and education and to the place of science in our national life," he told the country that he was determined to do something about it. He was aware of the fact that the teacher in Russia was held in very high esteem and received good pay, and that the Russian graduate of high school had five years of physics, four years of chemistry, one year of astronomy, five years of biology, ten years of mathematics through trigonometry, and five years of foreign languages.

He proposed a limited-scope education program for the next four years. The Federal Government would spend a total of one billion dollars and the States would match this expenditure to the tune of another $600,000,000. About twelve per cent of this money would be channeled through the National Science Foundation and the rest through the Department of Health, Education, and Welfare. Ten thousand Federal scholarships would be provided for needy students, who would receive a maximum of $750 a year for four years. These scholarships would not be limited to science and mathematics students alone and would be based on merit. Another thousand or fifteen hundred graduate fellowships would also be given. Science and mathematics teaching was to be extended and its quality improved, a testing program to find outstanding students would be initiated, and the counseling and guidance of the boys and girls in our high schools would be improved. Eisenhower reminded the American people that the Federal Government should not assume the entire burden, but that state and local communities and our entire citizenry would have to do their share in this program.

The National Education Association and other groups voiced dissatisfaction with what they considered an inadequate and small-minded facing up to the great crisis of the space age. They pointed to the President's failure to mention teachers' salaries and school construction, and to his undue emphasis on science and mathematics rather than on all education in its broadest sense. There was danger of distorting education by such an imbalance, they said. They insisted that the nation should at least double the twelve billion dollars it was spending annually for elementary and high-school education. They warned that our engineering and medical schools needed much greater Federal aid, and that scholarships alone would be very bad, for they would actually bankrupt our schools by pouring a new flood of students into an already badly undermanned and poorly equipped system of higher education.

The Government made a few more moves to improve its attitude toward science. The Department of State appointed Wallace R. Brode, president of the American Association for the Advancement of Science, as its scientific adviser. This was the first step in an attempt to revive an almost dead science-attaché program started almost a decade back. Isidor I. Rabi, Nobel laureate in physics and former chairman of the President's Science Advisory Board, was appointed top United States member of a new Science Committee of the North Atlantic Treaty Organization, whose aim is to develop and pool scientific information. Norman F. Ramsay, Harvard physicist, was named science adviser to Paul-Henri Spaak, Secretary General of NATO.

An *Introduction to Outer Space*, a 4000-word space primer, prepared by the President's Science Advisory Committee of eighteen top-flight scientists, engineers, and inventors, was made available to the public to help satisfy its curiosity about the "science-fiction" news which was fast becoming reality. The primer explained that while the factors of defense, prestige, and new knowledge about the earth, the solar system, and the universe were important, the most forceful reason for undertaking a space-exploration project was "the compelling urge of man to explore and to discover, the thrust of curiosity that leads men to try to go where no one has gone before." The people of America were also told that several lunar probes would be attempted by means of instrument-carrying satellites and that an initial very modest appropriation of $8,000,000 had been set aside by the Secretary of Defense for the Army, Navy and Air Force for this work. The over-all administration of the moon-excursion project would, in the meantime, be in the hands of the Defense Department's Advanced Research Projects Agency, recently created with Herbert F. York as chief scientist. More ambitious undertakings, including a return trip by man to the moon and the planets Mars and Venus, to be achieved by the year 2000 or earlier at a cost of about two billion dollars, were also in the plans. The President indicated that a civilian-controlled National Aeronautics and Space Agency was to be created. This would be a counterpart of the Atomic Energy Commission. All space projects would be reviewed to decide which would be placed under the control of the Department of Defense as purely military ones dealing with outer-space rockets and missiles. And so what began as a military quest for long-range rockets was to end in the most ambitious space exploration ever attempted by man. It was a program to satisfy once more man's insatiable curiosity, and test the skill and creativity of our scientists already at work as well as those yet to be born.

And so matters stood at the beginning of 1958. With the successful launching of the first American man-made satellite, Explorer I, on the last day of January, 1958, and of Vanguard I less than six months after Sputnik I, some observers feared a return to the old complacency. Others, however, were more optimistic about our determination to follow through with a positive and forceful program of correcting existing inadequacies.

In the meantime, other matters such as the importance of the dissemination and diffusion of accurate scientific news to the public had already been recognized. It was vital to general progress that the aims and meaning of science and basic research be made known to the public and cherished by our people. An excellent beginning in popular science communication had been made during the past forty years. In 1919 Edwin E. Slosson's *Creative Chemistry* furnished a spectacular appeal to the American reading public. This was followed by Paul de Kruif's *Microbe Hunters*, and others. In 1921 an idea, conceived by E. W. Scripps and W. E. Ritter, was hatched in the form of a weekly bulletin, the *Science News Letter*, published by Science Service under the editorship of Edwin E. Slosson. Today, under the direction of Watson Davis, its syndicated articles reach more than ten million newspaper readers. The spread of accurate scientific news was also enhanced by the organization in 1934 of the National Association of Scientific Writers, composed of men and women who cover science news for many of our newspapers. Members of the American Association for the Advancement of Science urged the National Science Foundation to help support the training of science writers in both government and private research organizations.

Another development was an upsurge of a national science club movement in our high schools sponsored by Science Service. This has already reached 500,000 boys and girls affiliated with 20,000 clubs. These young people participate in many science activities, including science fairs and such projects as the annual Science Talent Search conducted by the government-sponsored Science Service and the Westinghouse Electric and Manufacturing Company. Further efforts should be made to find the young minds that have special talents for scientific research. These boys and girls should be channeled into scientific investigation by more attractive scholarships and grants. We cannot create scientific geniuses nor can we synthesize creative imagination in our laboratories, but we can encourage and protect and nurture "the life of the mind" among promising young scientists.

The youth of our land must be brought into frequent and intimate contact in our schools with the great minds and mechanics of American science and technology. The history of scientific progress has been omitted almost completely from our teaching program. This omission is a serious blunder, for it neglects the opportunity of glorifying the great American figures who through their work in science have been outstanding benefactors of mankind. Perhaps even more serious is the failure to open up to our young students the magnificent vistas of new thrilling adventures in unselfish careers of service. Late in 1957 the National Council for Social Studies, a department of the National Education Association, recommended that a start be made in this direction by integrating science and social studies. This is an encouraging beginning.

The separation of "science" from "culture" is a modern fallacy and a dangerous and unnecessary one. Said Bertrand Russell, "Plato and Aristotle had a profound respect for what was known of science in their day. The Renaissance was as much concerned with the revival of science as with art and literature. Throughout the eighteenth century a very great deal was done to diffuse understanding of the work of Newton and his contemporaries." Here in America, Thomas Jefferson at that time believed that the main objects of science were the freedom and happiness of men, and he encouraged science in every way.

The ultimate objectives of scientific research are twofold. There is, first, the cultural need of extending the boundaries of all knowledge. Science is an intellectual adventure which is just as important to modern life as literature or art. "The scientist," wrote Henri Poincaré, the eminent French mathematician, "does not study nature simply because it is useful. He studies it because he delights in it, and he delights in it because it is beautiful."

Secondly, scientific knowledge is useful. It can be used to build a better world. Scientific discoveries and inventions have already greatly increased the life expectancy of our people. Three hundred and fifty years ago, the life expectancy of a newborn babe was only twenty years. One hundred years ago it was thirty-five. At the turn of the present century it had reached forty-nine, and today when a baby girl is born in the United States she has a good chance of enjoying almost seventy-four years of life (67.3 years for a baby boy). Medical advance has made possible the wiping out of such earlier scourges as smallpox, yellow fever, polio, malaria, and tuberculosis.

Yet, in spite of the fact that science has given us the means of saving the lives and improving the health of more and more millions, many continue to sicken and many die prematurely. A disease as easily prevented or cured as hookworm, for example, still exists today in some sections of our country. Medical progress has also created new problems. In 1900, four per cent of our population were sixty-five years or older. By 1970, it has been estimated, more than ten per cent or more than 20,000,000 Americans will be in this category. More medical and financial aid will be needed for this older age group. The United States is growing at the rate of 3,000,000 a year. Graduates from our medical schools increased from about 4560 in 1930 to about 6800 in 1957. The physician-population ratio is now about 1 to 750, but a lower one will be needed to take care of this swiftly aging population. Some experts believe that twenty-five new medical schools will have to be established.

Technical science has progressed more swiftly than the social sciences. This lag has prevented the utilization of many of its advances. The whole complex problem of how better to harness scientific advances to the goal of better living is a challenge to America. Several methods have presented themselves for the solution of this all-important problem. In medicine, for example, the United States has already begun to think of the public-health problem in terms of general disease prevention. When the Social Security Act went into operation in 1937 the beginning of a tangible national health program could be discerned. A small annual appropriation of $8,000,000 was authorized for the establishment and maintenance of local and state health services, plus a still less adequate $2,000,000 annually for research. Two years later this was increased to $11,000,000, to be administered by the United States Public Health Service. Sickness was attacked as a social and economic problem. The Venereal Disease Control Act of 1938 authorized the expenditure of Federal funds for the prevention, treatment, and control of the venereal diseases. Grants-in-aid were made to states for maternal care, child health, the care of crippled children, and for general public-health projects of various kinds.

Active consumer interest in group medicine and the whole subject of medical care and disease prevention emerged several years ago in this country. The critical manpower needs of World War II gave impetus to this trend. Henry J. Kaiser's fifty-cents-a-week-plan, which provided full medical diagnosis, treatment, and care for each of his thousands of workers, received wide acceptance. Several newer group plans introduced later seem destined to enjoy further sturdy growth.

Countless other social problems have been hatched in science laboratories. Science has created a new environment for millions. A rural country has become urbanized. In 1860 only sixteen per cent of our population lived in communities of 8000 people or more. In 1900, forty per cent lived in cities. Today more than two thirds of our people live in urban communities. Suburbia is still growing at a phenomenal rate. This redistribution of our population has brought new perplexing problems. The widespread use of the automobile and the growing popularity of the motor bus and the airplane have brought new stresses to our railroads. Other industries, too, have lost their old stability. Modern miracles of synthetic chemistry are revolutionizing business almost overnight. Thirty-five years ago we had a flourishing wood-alcohol industry which supplied the world with this liquid made by the destructive distillation of wood. This industry, capitalized at about $100,000,000, seemed as impregnable as Gibraltar. Then, suddenly, came the commercially successful synthesis of this alcohol from coal and water. The old wood-alcohol business seemed doomed to a quick death. Fortunately, the basic patents for this new development were owned by the American Chemical Foundation, and the American industry was given a chance to adjust itself. The revolution in the nitrate industry followed a similar pattern.

Further broad, long-range planning on the basis of the potentialities of science is needed. The National Resources Planning Board and several other commissions made numerous surveys and published many recommendations. The implementing of some of these will go a long way toward settling the more serious of the many problems. In the matter of dealing with so-called acts of God, science has shown that crop destruction by insects, soil erosion by wind and rain, home destruction by flood and fire, droughts, and epidemics can be effectively combated by well-organized and amply financed local, state, and Federal funds. Our annual damage to property amounting to tens of millions of dollars, with its accompanying loss of life, which follows the rampage of flood waters can be cut down by a wise program of dam building and reforestation. When, several years ago, farmers in the wheat plains of the West watched a single dust storm sweep 300,000,000 tons of topsoil off their lands, they might have known that science had already found effective measures against such wholesale loss of valuable land. Irrigation, a protective covering of heavy grass, contour tillage, and terracing would have laughed at the wind.

To spread more abundantly the necessities and some of the luxuries of life a reformed patent system was needed. The Temporary National Economic Committee's study of our patent laws revealed certain abuses. Most patented inventions today are the products of the co-operative efforts of employees of large industrial corporations. A few of these organizations have not always exploited the inventions for the good of the nation. These few have managed to delay or block the issue of patents and have thus held up progress in the same field by others. Some have suppressed unused patents to forestall competition. To protect the individual inventor, to prevent violations of the antitrust laws, and to make available inventions for immediate exploitation for the welfare of our citizens, the Committee suggested certain changes in the patent laws. Congress passed some new laws in this direction. Soon after the Temporary National Economic Committee ceased to exist in 1941, President Roosevelt appointed the director of the research laboratories of General Motors Corporation, Charles F. Kettering, chairman of a National Patents Planning Commission to continue the study of the American patent system. Within the next four years, three reports were issued recommending that Congress provide a better definition of what constitutes an invention and also limit the life of patents to twenty years after the date of *application* rather than the date of granting. It was also urged that the recording of all patent agreements involving restrictions on prices, quantity, and distribution of fields of use be made mandatory. A new and better patent law was finally passed and went into effect at the beginning of 1953.

In 1956 there were in the United States about 250,000 scientists (mainly chemists, physicists, and biologists), and about 700,000 engineers. About one fourth of these 950,000 trained men and women were actively engaged in scientific research and development. Among the younger members of this group there were many who had received a somewhat different educational training from their older colleagues. About twenty-five years ago it began to be more generally realized that a democracy requires intelligent and educated scientists and engineers in the broadest sense of those terms. The education of these men and women must produce citizens with a clearer understanding of social forces and their own social responsibilities. Their schooling had to insure skilled scientists whose education in the social sciences and the humanities had not been neglected. Said James B. Conant, then president of Harvard University, "Through many advances gained by science we may hope that as never before man may be free—free from want. But science alone, untempered by other knowledge, can lead not to freedom but to slavery. At the root of the relation between science and society in the postwar world must lie a proper educational concept of the interconnection of our new scientific knowledge and our older humanistic studies."

Karl T. Compton, another distinguished scientist and one-time president of the Massachusetts Institute of Technology, agreed that we need engineers with a recognition of social needs and social responsibilities. Robert A. Millikan while head of the California Institute of Technology had for many years insisted that the students at this outstanding institution spend at least one fourth of their time in such studies as economics, literature, history, political science, and philosophy. John C. Warner, president of the Carnegie Institute of Technology, declared in 1957 that at his university "we provide 25 per cent plus of our program for engineers and scientists in the humanities and social studies. There seems to be no danger of imbalance as long as students may freely select the program in which they wish to major."

The place of the scientist in society has been debated for many years. Until recently, the scientist and engineer in the United States have interested themselves mainly in the search for scientific truth, the creation of new inventions, and the construction of better mechanical machines and engineering works. They have been satisfied to leave to politicians, economists, and sociologists the application of the fruits of scientific innovations. They have been prone to shy away from serious consideration of such matters as health insurance, Federal flood, drought, and erosion control, Food and Drug Bill changes, the stifling of new inventions, and the muzzling of science in totalitarian countries. Justification for this attitude had been expressed in some quarters. For example, Thomas Hunt Morgan, Nobel laureate in science, believed "The place of science in society depends upon the individual scientist. It is not his duty to engage in the solving of social problems except insofar as it is his duty as an average citizen."

This detached view, however, is not shared by all of our men of science. James R. Killian, Jr. has argued for the need of "a greater awareness by scientists of their national, social, human duty. The specialist must shun the view that lopsidedness is laudable. He must be politically and morally responsible." Many maintain that it is the duty of scientists to help in nationwide planning in an effort to maintain our freedoms and to raise the level of living standards through the widespread application of scientific knowledge. They point to the fact that scientists are peculiarly fitted for such responsibilities, and that if the benefit of the advances of science could be made available to the great masses of the people, life for millions would be transformed for the better. They believe that our scientists should become more active in public debate, and that science and scientific thinking should fit more completely into the whole pattern of our activities.

This broader outlook had many adherents even before 1937. In that year, the Council of the American Association for the Advancement of Science, an organization with 50,000 members, resolved that it "makes as one of its objectives an examination of the profound effects of science upon society; and that the Association extends to all other scientific organizations with similar aims throughout the world, an invitation to co-operate, not only in advancing the interests of science, but also in promoting peace among nations and in intellectual freedom in order that science may continue to advance and spread more abundantly its benefits to all mankind."

This historic declaration came on the heels of a similar announcement by the British Association for the Advancement of Science at its 1936 meeting held at Blackpool, England. The British scientists declared that the social consequences of the advances of science are part of the business of scientists. The dread of a growing fascism and the threat of an impending world war accelerated the emergence of this new point of view.

The unexpected controlled release of nuclear energy from the atom of uranium accelerated this slow trend toward social consciousness among scientists to a dramatic spurt. Men of science were suddenly catapulted into world politics. There was a mass descent of American scientists from their ivory towers. Our chemists and physicists saw at once the implications of this revolutionary event. They realized the urgency of safeguarding mankind against the catastrophic power of the atom. They felt it their duty to help assure its use for peaceful ends.

Even before Alamogordo and Hiroshima, small groups of atomic scientists had met secretly to discuss the new problems born of nuclear fission. One such seven-man group, with James Franck as chairman, drew up a memorandum which was sent to Secretary of War Henry L. Stimson as early as June 11, 1945. It opposed the use of a surprise atom-bomb attack on a Japanese city and recommended instead a demonstration of its annihilating effects in some uninhabited region. A similar recommendation was sent to President Truman by sixty-four scientists connected with Chicago's Metallurgical Project. Truman appointed an interim committee to be assisted by a panel of four scientists— Compton, Fermi, Lawrence, and Oppenheimer. Stimson and this committee independently reached the same conclusion to use the bomb.

By the close of 1945 sixteen independent local groups of scientists had organized to study the question of what to do with nuclear energy. Representatives of four of these groups met in Washington to form the Federation of Atomic Scientists. A month later delegates from thirteen groups including the Federation met and merged into a new body which called itself the Federation of American Scientists. The Association of Los Alamos Scientists was included in this merger. Fermi, however, did not join because he "did not think that in 1945 mankind was ripe for world government."

The new Federation, a nonprofit organization, was determined "to meet the increasingly apparent responsibility of scientists in promoting the welfare of mankind and the achievement of a stable world." Its objectives included "placing science in the national life that it may make its maximum contribution to the welfare of the people, urging that the United States help initiate and perpetuate an effective system of world control of atomic energy based on full co-operation among all nations, countering misinformation with scientific fact, and especially disseminating those facts necessary for intelligent conclusions concerning the social implications of new knowledge in science." The *Bulletin of the Atomic Scientists*, now an independent and most valuable publication under the editorship of Eugene Rabinowitch, was organized in 1946 by the Federation's Chicago chapter.

The Federation set itself a double task. Its first job was to work for the passage of domestic legislation to insure civilian control of atomic energy rather than military control. Philip Morrison, Henry Smyth, Leo Szilard, Harold Urey, and other atomic scientists sacrificed valuable research time to journey to Washington to talk to senators and representatives, to testify at public hearings as citizen-scientists, and to join with educational, church, farm, labor, professional and youth groups who were backing the McMahon Bill. This bill, introduced by Senator Brien McMahon of Connecticut, would place atomic energy in the hands of a five-man civilian commission, with only a single military representative as the director of the division of military application. The bill passed finally and became known as the Atomic Energy Act of 1946.

The fight on the international front proved much more difficult. It was apparent to everybody that the peacetime uses of atomic energy could not be separated from its threat as a military weapon. It was also generally recognized that the control and development of this new force and the exploration of outer space could not safely be left to any single nation. Some form of international control was absolutely essential if the peace of the world was to be preserved, fear banished from the minds of men, and the peacetime uses of atomic energy rapidly expanded. To most people the United Nations seemed the logical body for the solution of these vital problems. But as yet no plan has been proposed which proved acceptable to the nations of the world. The Federation of American Scientists has not given up the battle. It favors an international agreement to prohibit further testing of nuclear weapons, United States civilian control of outer space research, and a United Nations police force as the first steps toward peace.

It has about 2250 members, among whom are some of the leading scientists of the United States such as Hans Bethe, James Franck, Harlow Shapley, and Harold Urey.

The American Association for the Advancement of Science, too, is still grappling with this enormous problem of American society in a scientific revolution. In 1955 the Council of this organization resolved to establish an Interim Committee on the Social Aspects of Science under the chairmanship of Ward Pigman, biochemist of the University of Alabama Medical Center. After a year's study, the committee found that "there is an impending crisis in the relationships between science and American society. . . . At a time when decisive economic, political and social processes have become profoundly dependent upon science, the discipline has failed to attain its appropriate place in the management of public affairs."

Our scientists pointed out that the accelerated growth of scientific activity had made it, next to military activities, the most rapidly expanding sector of our social structure. They noted, too, that scientific theory moves much more rapidly today from the laboratory to industrial applications resulting in a new role of research in industry. Research in science, previously regarded by industry as a sort of exotic garden cultivated in the hope of producing an occasional rare fruit, had now become a deliberate instrument of industrial expansion.

A number of major social issues originating in the advance of scientific research were now facing the American public for quick solution. Among them the committee listed the following: the very serious dangers of radiation, which have multiplied tremendously since the advent of the nuclear age; the hazards of man-made chemicals, many of which had been introduced as food additives; the harmful effects of fumes, smog and dust to an ever increasing number of our population; the serious deterioration of our natural resources; and, of course, the catastrophic potential of a global nuclear war. George W. Beadle, retiring president of the A.A.A.S., added, in his address, the danger of strontium-90 from nuclear-bomb-test fallout to future generations, and the risks of cancer from cigarette smoking to the present generation.

The report concluded with a call for emergency action. "We are now in the midst of a new and unprecedented scientific revolution," it warned, "which promises to bring about profound changes in the conditions of human life." It called for a greater interest and understanding by the general public of the meaning and importance of science in our social structure, and for greater participation by scientists in the solution of these problems. "Business and labor," it declared, "are not backward in presenting their opinions on social questions that affect them. There are many who think that the viewpoint of scientists should also be stated publicly. Otherwise, the democratic process will become to that extent unrepresentative."

Unfortunately, there is no clear evidence today that this plea for action has met with any significant success. This slow response to a quick and dramatic change of attitude in a democracy may be one of its weaknesses. But it need be neither permanent nor fatal. A free and democratic society has vastly greater advantages over a totalitarian country in the long run, especially as concerns fundamental discoveries. American science and technology is enormously strong, vigorous, and self-confident. It has yet to release all of its energies. Scientific research is still a powerful, creative impulse in our land. Its future possibilities are unlimited. And its pursuit can have no more exalted role than that expressed by Harold C. Urey several years ago. "I believe I speak," he said, "for the vast majority of all scientific men in industrial laboratories and in our universities. Our object is not to make jobs and dividends. These are the means to an end, merely incidental. We wish to abolish drudgery, discomfort, and want from the lives of men and bring them pleasure, leisure and beauty."

SOURCES AND REFERENCE MATERIAL

INTRODUCTION

AMERICAN PHILOSOPHICAL SOCIETY, *Early History of Science in America.* American Philosophical Society, Philadelphia, 1942.

BURLINGAME, ROGER, *March of the Iron Men.* Scribner's, New York, 1938.

BURLINGAME, ROGER, *Engines of Democracy.* Scribner's, New York, 1940.

CATTELL, J. McKEEN, *American Men of Science.* Science Press, New York, 1938.

CROWTHER, J. G., *Men of Science.* W. W. Norton, New York, 1936.

CUMMINGS, H. H. (ed.), *Science and the Social Studies.* National Council for the Social Studies, Washington, D. C., 1957.

DANA, E. S. (ed.), *Century of Science in America.* Yale University Press, New Haven, 1918.

DEWHURST, JAMES F., *America's Needs and Resources.* Twentieth Century Fund, New York, 1955.

GEISER, S. W., *Naturalists of the Frontier.* Southern Methodist University, Dallas, 1937.

GETMAN, H., *Life of Ira Remsen.* Journal of Chemical Education, Easton, Pa., 1940.

HYLANDER, F. C., *American Scientists.* Macmillan, New York, 1935.

JOHNSON, T. C., *Scientific Interests in the Old South.* Appleton-Century, New York, 1936.

JORDAN, DAVID S., *Leading American Men of Science.* Holt, New York, 1910.

KAEMPFFERT, W. B., *Popular History of American Invention.* Scribner's, New York, 1924.

LOCY, WILLIAM A., *Biology and Its Makers.* Holt, New York, 1928.

MAGIE, WILLIAM F., *Source Book in Physics.* McGraw-Hill, New York, 1935.

MEISEL, MAX, *A Bibliography of American Natural History.* Premier Publishing Company, New York, 1924.

ROUTLEDGE, ROBERT, *A Popular History of Science.* G. Routledge and Sons, London, 1881.

THOMPSON, HOLLAND, *Age of Invention.* (In Chronicles of America Series.) Yale University Press, New Haven, 1921.

THORNDIKE, LYNN, *History of Magic and Experimental Science.* Macmillan, New York, 1923–41.

TRACY, HENRY C., *American Naturalists*. Dutton, New York, 1930.

WALCOTT, CHARLES D. (ed.), *Source Books in the History of the Sciences*. McGraw-Hill, New York, 1929–39.

WILSON, MITCHELL, *American Science and Invention*. Simon and Schuster, New York, 1954.

WISTAR, ISAAC J., *Autobiography*. Wistar Institute, Philadelphia, 1937.

WOLF, ABRAHAM, *History of Science, Technology, and Philosophy in the 18th Century*. Macmillan, New York, 1939.

YOUMANS, WILLIAM J., *Pioneers of Science in America*. Appleton, New York, 1896.

YOUNG, R. T., *Biology in America*. R. G. Badger, Boston, 1922.

CHAPTER ONE

Thomas Harriot

BARTRAM, JOHN, *Observations on Travels*. Whiston, London, 1751.

COHEN, I. BERNARD, *Some Early Tools of American Science*. Harvard University Press, Cambridge, 1950.

DARLINGTON, WILLIAM, *Memorials of J. Bartram and H. Marshall*. Philadelphia, 1849.

DEKAY, J. E., *Progress of the Natural Sciences in the United States*. Lyceum of Natural History of New York, 1826.

EARNEST, E., *John and William Bartram*. University of Pennsylvania Press, Philadelphia, 1940.

GOODE, G. B., *The Beginnings of Natural History in America*. Proceedings, Biological Society of Washington, 1884–88.

HAKLUYT, REV. RICHARD, *The Principal Navigations, Voyages and Discoveries of the English Nation*. London, 1589.

HARRIOT, THOMAS, *A Briefe and True Report of the New Found Land of Virginia*. London, 1588.

HARRIOT, THOMAS, *Artis Analyticae Praxis*. London, 1631.

HOLMES, THOMAS J., *Cotton Mather* (3 vols.). Harvard University Press, Cambridge, 1940.

HORNBERGER, T., *Science and the New World (1526–1800)*. Huntington Library, San Marino, California, 1937.

SMITH, D. E., AND GINSBURG, J., *A History of Mathematics in America before 1900*. Open Court Publishing Company, Chicago, 1934.

STEVENS, HENRY, *Thomas Harriot and His Associates*. (Privately printed), London, 1900.

TARBOX, INCREASE N. (ed.), *Sir Walter Raleigh and his Colony in America*. The Prince Society, Boston, 1884.

TRUE, A. C., *History of Agricultural Experimentation and Research in the United States (1607–1925)*. Miscellaneous Publication 251; United States Department of Agriculture, Washington, 1937.
WERTENBAKER, T. J., *The First Americans (1607–1690)*. Macmillan, New York, 1927.

CHAPTER TWO

Benjamin Franklin

BRASCH, F. E., *The Royal Society of London and Its Influence Upon the Scientific Thought in the American Colonies*. Scientific Monthly, October-November, 1931.
COHEN, I. BERNARD (ed.), *Benjamin Franklin's Experiments*. Harvard University Press, Cambridge, 1941.
DuPONCEAU, PETER S., *An Historical Account of the Origin and Formation of the American Philosophical Society*. American Philosophical Society, Philadelphia, 1914.
FORD, EDWARD, *David Rittenhouse*. University of Pennsylvania Press, Philadelphia, 1946.
FRANKLIN, BENJAMIN, *Poor Richard Improved*. Franklin and Hall, 1753.
GOODMAN, NATHAN G. (ed.), *The Ingenious Dr. Franklin*. University of Pennsylvania Press, Philadelphia, 1931.
GOODMAN, NATHAN G. (ed.), *Benjamin Franklin's Own Story*. University of Pennsylvania Press, Philadelphia, 1937.
MILLIKAN, ROBERT A., *Benjamin Franklin as a Scientist*. Journal of the Franklin Institute, November, 1941.
PRIESTLEY, JOSEPH, *The History and Present State of Electricity* (4th ed.) London, 1775.
ROSENGARTEN, J. G., *The American Philosophical Society (1683–1908)*. Philadelphia, 1908.
SPARKS, JARED (ed.), *The Life of Benjamin Franklin*. Blakeman and Mason, 1859.
VAN DOREN, CARL, *Benjamin Franklin*. Garden City Publishing Company, New York, 1941.

CHAPTER THREE

Benjamin Thompson

CHASE, CARL, *A History of Experimental Physics*. Van Nostrand, New York, 1932.
ELLIS, GEORGE E., *Memoir of Sir Benjamin Thompson*. American Academy of Arts and Sciences, 1876.

ELLIS, GEORGE E., *The Complete Works of Count Rumford* (4 vols.). American Academy of Arts and Sciences, 1876.

GARNETT, WILLIAM, *Heroes of Science* (Physicists). Society for Promoting Christian Knowledge, 1886.

HINDLE, BROOKE, *The Pursuit of Science in Revolutionary America.* University of North Carolina Press, Chapel Hill, N. C., 1956.

KRAUS, MICHAEL, *Intercolonial Aspects of American Culture on the Eve of the Revolution.* Columbia University Press, New York, 1928.

SPARKS, JARED, *The Library of American Biography* (Volume 5—Second Series). (Contains Lives of Rumford, Z. M. Pike, etc.) Harper and Brothers, New York, 1845.

STRUIK, DIRK J., *Yankee Science in the Making.* Little, Brown and Company, Boston, 1948.

CHAPTER FOUR
Thomas Cooper

BETTS, EDWIN B. (ed.), *Thomas Jefferson's Farm Book.* Princeton University Press, Princeton, 1954.

—— *Letters of Dr. Thomas Cooper (1825–1832).* American Historical Review (Volume VI), Lancaster, Pa., 1901.

COOPER, THOMAS, *Some Information Respecting America.* J. Johnson, London, 1794.

COOPER, THOMAS, *Narrative of the Proceedings Against Thomas Cooper.* Lancaster, 1811.

COOPER, THOMAS, *Introductory Lecture on Chemistry at Carlisle College.* William Hamilton, Carlisle, Pa., 1812.

COOPER, THOMAS, *On the Connection Between Geology and the Pentateuch.* J. Hall Press, Boston, 1833.

COOPER, THOMAS, *Memoirs of Joseph Priestley and Observations on His Writings.* J. Johnson, London, 1806.

COOPER, THOMAS, *On the Foundations of Civil Government.* Columbia, S. C., 1826.

COOPER, THOMAS, *On the Constitution of the United States.* Columbia, S. C., 1826.

COOPER, THOMAS, *Correspondence on Life and Death.* Boston, 1845.

COOPER, THOMAS, *The Domestic Encyclopedia* (2d American edition). A. Small, Philadelphia, 1821.

COOPER, THOMAS, *Some Information Concerning Gas Lights.* Philadelphia, 1816.

COOPER, THOMAS, *A Practical Treatise on Dyeing and Calicoe Printing.* T. Dobson, Philadelphia, 1815.

COOPER, THOMAS, *An Account of the Trial of Thomas Cooper.* Philadelphia, 1800.

HALL, COURTNEY, *A Scientist in the Early Republic* (S. L. Mitchill). Columbia University Press, New York, 1934.

HIMES, CHARLES, *Life and Times of Judge Thomas Cooper.* Dickinson School of Law, Carlisle, Pa., 1918.

MALONE, DUMAS, *Public Life of Thomas Cooper.* Yale University Press, New Haven, 1926.

MARTIN, E. T., *Thomas Jefferson, Scientist.* Henry Schuman, New York, 1952.

SMITH, EDGAR F., *Chemistry in America.* Appleton, New York, 1914.

CHAPTER FIVE

Constantine S. Rafinesque

BINNEY AND TRYON, *The Complete Writings of Rafinesque on Conchology.* Balliere Brothers, New York, 1864.

BROOKS, NOAH, *First Across the Continent.* Scribner's, New York, 1901.

CALL, RICHARD E., *The Life and Writings of Rafinesque.* J. P. Morton, Louisville, 1895.

DE VOTO, BERNARD, *The Journal of Lewis and Clark.* Houghton Mifflin, New York, 1953.

FITZPATRICK, T. J., *Rafinesque, A Sketch of his Life with Bibliography* (Complete). Historical Department of Iowa, Des Moines, 1911.

PEATTIE, DONALD C., *Green Laurels.* Simon and Schuster, New York, 1936.

PEATTIE, DONALD C. (ed.), *Audubon's America.* Houghton Mifflin, New York, 1940.

RAFINESQUE, C. S., *A Life of Travels and Researches in North America and South Europe.* F. Turner, Philadelphia, 1836.

RAFINESQUE, C. S., *Ichthyologia Ohiensis.* W. G. Hunt, Lexington, Ky., 1820.

RAFINESQUE, C. S., *Medical Flora; or Manual of the Medical Botany of the United States.* Atkinson and Alexander, Philadelphia, 1828–30.

RAFINESQUE, C. S., *New Flora and Botany of North America.* (Privately printed), Philadelphia, 1836.

RAFINESQUE, C. S., *Atlantic Journal and Friend of Knowledge* (8 numbers). Philadelphia, 1832–3.

RAFINESQUE, C. S., *American Florist.* (Privately printed), Philadelphia, 1832.

RAFINESQUE, C. S., *Alsographia Americana.* (Privately printed), Philadelphia, 1838.

RAFINESQUE, C. S., *American Manual of the Grape Vines.* (Privately printed), Philadelphia, 1830.

RAFINESQUE, C. S., *Monograph on the Bivalve Shells of the Ohio River*. J. Dobson, Philadelphia, 1832.

RAFINESQUE, C. S., *Annals of Nature*. T. Smith, Lexington, Ky., 1820.

RAFINESQUE, C. S., *The Good Book and Amenities of Nature, or Annals of Historical and Natural Sciences*. Eleutherium of Knowledge, Philadelphia, 1840.

RAFINESQUE, C. S., *Safe Banking, Including the Principles of Wealth*. (Privately printed), Philadelphia, 1837.

ROBIN AND RAFINESQUE, *Florula Ludoviciana*. C. Wiley and Company, New York, 1817.

ROURKE, CONSTANCE M., *Audubon*. Harcourt, Brace, New York, 1936.

VAN DOREN, MARK (ed.), *Travels of William Bartram*. Dover Publications, New York, 1955.

WEISS, HARRY B., *Rafinesque's Kentucky Friends*. (Privately printed), Highland Park, N. J., 1936.

CHAPTER SIX

Thomas Say

———— *Narrative of the United States Exploring Expedition during 1838–42*. C. Sherman, 1844.

ALLEN, PAUL (ed.), *History of the Expedition Under the Command of Lewis and Clark (1804–06)*. Bradford and A. H. Inskeep, Philadelphia, 1814.

BROWNE, CHARLES, *Some Relations of the New Harmony Movement to the History of Science in America*. Scientific Monthly, June, 1936.

COUES, ELLIOTT (ed.), *History of the Expedition to the Sources of the Missouri*. Harper and Brothers, New York, 1894.

LEOPOLD, RICHARD W., *Robert D. Owen*. Harvard University Press, Cambridge, 1940.

PEATTIE, DONALD C., *Forward the Nation*. Putnam's Sons, New York, 1942.

RODGERS, ANDREW D., *John Torrey*. Princeton University Press, Princeton, N. J., 1942.

SAY, THOMAS, *American Entomology* (3 vols.). Samuel L. Mitchill, 1824–28.

SYMES, L., AND CLEMENT, T., *Rebel America*. Harper and Brothers, New York, 1934.

THWAITES, REUBEN G., *Early Western Travels (1748–1846)*. A. H. Clark, Cleveland, Ohio, 1904–7.

THWAITES, REUBEN G. (ed.), *Original Journals of the Lewis and Clark Expedition (1804–06)*. Dodd, Mead, New York, 1904–5.

WEISS, H. B., AND ZIEGLER, G. H., *Thomas Say, Early American Naturalist.* C. C. Thomas, Springfield, Ill., 1931.

CHAPTER SEVEN

William T. G. Morton

BOLAND, FRANK K., *The First Anesthetic.* University of Georgia Press, Athens, Ga., 1950.

BUTTERFIELD, LYMEN H., *Letters of Benjamin Rush.* Princeton University Press, Princeton, 1951.

CLENDENING, LOGAN, *Behind the Doctor.* Knopf, New York, 1933.

FLEXNER, JAMES T., *Doctors on Horseback.* Viking Press, New York, 1937.

FLEXNER, S. AND J. T., *William H. Welch, and the Heroic Age of American Medicine.* Viking Press, New York, 1941.

FÜLÖP-MILLER, RENÉ, *Triumph Over Pain.* Bobbs-Merrill Company, New York, 1938.

GARRISON, F. H., *History of Medicine.* W. B. Saunders Company, Philadelphia, 1929.

GOODMAN, NATHAN G., *Benjamin Rush, Physician and Citizen.* University of Pennsylvania Press, Philadelphia, 1934.

GUMPERT, MARTIN, *Trail-Blazers of Science.* Funk and Wagnalls Company, New York, 1936.

LANGSTAFF, J. B., *Dr. Bard of Hyde Park.* Dutton, New York, 1942.

MASSACHUSETTS GENERAL HOSPITAL, *The Semi-Centennial of Anaesthesia.* Boston, 1897.

MYER, JESSE S., *Life and Letters of Dr. William Beaumont.* C. V. Mosby Company, St. Louis, 1939.

NEVINS, ALLAN, *Frémont, Pathmarker of the West*, Appleton-Century Company, New York, 1939.

PACKARD, FRANCIS R., *History of Medicine in the United States.* P. B. Hoeber, New York, 1931.

RAPER, HOWARD R., *A Review of the Crawford W. Long Centennial Anniversary Celebrations.* Bulletin of the History of Medicine, Johns Hopkins Press, Baltimore, March 1943.

SIGERIST, HENRY E., *American Medicine.* W. W. Norton, New York, 1934.

CHAPTER EIGHT

Joseph Henry

COULSON, THOMAS, *Joseph Henry, His Life and Work.* Princeton University Press, Princeton, 1950.

CROWTHER, JAMES G., *Famous American Men of Science*. W. W. Norton, New York, 1937.

HENRY, JOSEPH, *An Account of a Large Electro-Magnet Made for Yale College*. American Journal of Science, July 1831.

HENRY, JOSEPH, *On the Production of Currents and Sparks of Electricity from Magnetism*. American Journal of Science, July 1832.

HENRY, JOSEPH, *Contributions to Electricity and Galvanism*. Transactions of American Philosophical Society, Philadelphia, January-February 1835.

HENRY, JOSEPH, *On the Production from Electricity of Currents by Induction*. Transactions of American Philosophical Society, Philadelphia, May 1838.

HENRY, JOSEPH, *On the Production of Reciprocating Motion by Repulsion*. Transactions of American Philosophical Society, Philadelphia, November 1840.

HENRY, JOSEPH, *Contributions to Electricity and Magnetism*. Transactions of American Philosophical Society, Philadelphia, June 1842.

HENRY, JOSEPH, *On the Corpuscular Theory of the Constitution of Matter*. Transactions of American Philosophical Society, Philadelphia, November 1846.

HENRY, JOSEPH, *Statement in Relation to the History of the Electro-Magnetic Telegraph*. Smithsonian Report, Washington, 1857.

HENRY, JOSEPH, *On Materials for Combustion in Lamps of Light-Houses*. National Academy of Sciences, Washington, January 12, 1864.

HENRY, JOSEPH, *Report of Investigations Relative to Fog-Signals*. Report of Light-House Board, 1874.

HENRY, JOSEPH, *Closing Address Before the National Academy of Sciences*. Proceedings National Academy of Sciences, April 19, 1878.

UNITED STATES CONGRESS, *A Memorial of Joseph Henry*. United States Government Printing Office, 1880.

CHAPTER NINE

Matthew F. Maury

—— *Life and Work of A. D. Bache*. American Philosophical Society, Philadelphia, 1942.

BROWN, RALPH M., *Bibliography of Commander M. F. Maury, including a biographical sketch*. Bulletin of the Virginia Polytechnic Institute, Blacksburg, Virginia, 1930.

LEWIS, CHARLES L., *Matthew F. Maury*. United States Naval Institute, Annapolis, Maryland, 1927.

MAURY, MATTHEW F., *A New Theoretical and Practical Treatise on Navigation*, E. C. & J. Biddle, Philadelphia, 1845.

MAURY, MATTHEW F., *Explanations and Sailing Directions to Accompany the Wind and Current Charts.* C. Alexander, 1851.

MAURY, MATTHEW F., *The Physical Geography of the Sea.* Harper and Brothers, New York, 1855.

MAURY, MATTHEW F., *Manual of Geography.* University Publishing Company, New York, 1870.

MAURY, MATTHEW F., *The Physical Survey of Virginia.* Van Nostrand, New York, 1869.

MIRSKY, J., AND NEVINS, ALLAN, *The World of Eli Whitney.* Macmillan, New York, 1952.

WAYLAND, JOHN W., *The Pathfinder of the Seas.* Garrett and Massie, Richmond, Virginia, 1930.

CHAPTER TEN

Louis J. R. Agassiz

AGASSIZ, ELIZABETH C., *Louis Agassiz, His Life and Correspondence* (2 vols.). Houghton Mifflin, New York, 1886.

CANBY, HENRY S. (ed.), *Thoreau, H. D., Works.* Houghton Mifflin, New York, 1939.

FAVRE, ERNEST, *Louis Agassiz: a Biographical Notice.* Annual Report, Smithsonian Institution, Washington, 1878.

GOULD, ALICE B., *Louis Agassiz* (The Beacon Biographies). Small, Maynard and Company, 1901.

HOLDER, CHARLES F., *Louis Agassiz, His Life and Work.* Putnam's Sons, New York, 1893.

MARCOU, JULES, *Life, Letters and Works of Louis Agassiz* (2 vols.). Macmillan, New York, 1896.

ROBINSON, MABEL L., *Runner of the Mountain Tops* (Agassiz). Random House, New York, 1939.

SMALLWOOD, WILLIAM M., *How Darwinism Came to the United States.* Scientific Monthly, April, 1941.

WHIPPLE, E. P., *Recollections of Eminent Men.* Ticknor and Company, Boston, 1887.

CHAPTER ELEVEN

James D. Dana

BENSON, ALLAN L., *The Story of Geology.* Cosmopolitan Book Corporation, New York, 1927.

DANA, JAMES D., *Manual of Geology.* T. Bliss and Company, Philadelphia, 1862.

DANA, JAMES D., *Manual of Geology*. (15th Edition.) Wiley and Sons, New York, 1941.

GEIKIE, SIR ARCHIBALD, *The Founders of Geology*. Macmillan, London, 1905.

GEOLOGICAL SOCIETY OF AMERICA, *Geology* (1888–1938).

GILMAN, DANIEL C., *The Life of James Dwight Dana*. Harper and Brothers, New York, 1899.

HURLBUT, C. S. (ed.), *Dana's Manual of Mineralogy*. Wiley and Sons, New York, 1941.

MATHER, K. F., AND MASON, S. L., *A Source Book in Geology*. McGraw-Hill, New York, 1939.

MCALLISTER, E. M., *Amos Eaton, Scientist and Educator*. University of Pennsylvania Press, Philadelphia, 1941.

MERRILL, GEORGE P., *Contributions to the History of American Geology*. United States National Museum, Annual Report, 1903–4.

MOORE, RAYMOND C., *Historical Geology*. McGraw-Hill, New York, 1933.

RICE, WILLIAM N. (ed.), *Problems of American Geology*. Yale University Press, New Haven, 1915.

(VOLUME 82, No. 5) *Centenary Celebration, Wilkes Exploring Expedition*. American Philosophical Society, Philadelphia, 1940.

CHAPTER TWELVE

Othniel C. Marsh

BEECHER, C. E., *O. C. Marsh*. American Journal of Science, June, 1899.

COREY, LEWIS, *The House of Morgan*. Watt, New York, 1930.

LULL, RICHARD S., *Fossils*. The University Society, New York, 1931.

MARSH, OTHNIEL C., *Odontornithes, A Monograph on the Extinct Toothed Birds of North America*. United States Geological Exploration of the Fortieth Parallel (Volume VII), 1880.

MARSH, OTHNIEL C., *Dinocerata, A Monograph on an Extinct Order of Gigantic Mammals*. United States Geological Survey, Washington, 1885.

MARSH, OTHNIEL C., *The Dinosaurs of North America*. United States Geological Survey, Washington, 1896.

OSBORN, HENRY F., *Impressions of Great Naturalists*. Scribner's, New York, 1924.

OSBORN, HENRY F., *Cope, Master Naturalist*. Princeton University Press, Princeton, 1931.

SCHUCHERT, C., AND LEVENE, C. M., *O. C. Marsh, Pioneer in Paleontology*. Yale University Press, New Haven, 1940.

SCOTT, WILLIAM B., *Some Memoirs of a Paleontologist*. Princeton University Press, Princeton, 1939.
WHITE, LESLIE A. (ed.), *Pioneers in American Anthropology*. University of New Mexico Press, 1940.

CHAPTER THIRTEEN

J. Willard Gibbs

BELL, ERIC T., *The Development of Mathematics*. McGraw-Hill, New York, 1940.
BERRY, ROBERT E., *Yankee Stargazer* (N. Bowditch). McGraw-Hill, New York, 1941.
BUMSTEAD AND VAN NAME, *The Scientific Papers of Gibbs* (2 vols.). Longmans, Green, New York, 1942.
CAJORI, FLORIAN, *The Early Mathematical Sciences in North and South America*. Badger, Boston, 1928.
CREW, HENRY, *Portraits of Famous Physicists*. Scripta Mathematica, New York, 1942.
DONNAN, F. G., AND HAAS, A., *A Commentary on the Scientific Writings of J. Willard Gibbs* (2 vols.). Yale University Press, New Haven, 1936.
LONGLEY, WILLIAM R., AND VAN NAME, R. G., *The Collected Works of J. Willard Gibbs* (2 vols.). Longmans, Green, New York, 1928.
RUKEYSER, MURIEL, *Willard Gibbs, American Genius*. Doubleday, Doran, New York, 1942.
WHEELER, LYNDE P., *Josiah Willard Gibbs*. Yale University Press, New Haven, 1951.
WILSON, EDWIN B., *Reminiscences of Gibbs*. Scientific Monthly, March 1931.

CHAPTER FOURTEEN

Samuel P. Langley

ABBOT, CHARLES G., *Samuel P. Langley*. Smithsonian Miscellaneous Collections, Volume 92, No. 8, 1934.
KELLY, FRED C., *The Wright Brothers*. Harcourt, Brace and Company, New York, 1943.
LANGLEY, SAMUEL P., *Experiments in Aerodynamics*. Smithsonian Contributions to Knowledge, Volume 27, 1891.
LANGLEY, SAMUEL P., *The Internal Work of the Wind*. Smithsonian Contributions to Knowledge, Volume 27, 1893.

LANGLEY, SAMUEL P., *The Langley Aerodrome*. Annual Report Smithsonian Institution, 1900–1.

LANGLEY, SAMUEL P., *Experiments with the Langley Aerodrome*. Annual Report Smithsonian Institution, 1904–5.

LANGLEY, SAMUEL P., *The New Astronomy*. Houghton Mifflin, New York, 1900.

McFARLAND, M. W. (ed.), *Papers of Wilbur and Orville Wright* (2 vols.). McGraw Hill, New York, 1953.

MILLER, FRANCIS T., *The World in the Air*. G. P. Putnam's Sons, New York, 1930.

WALCOTT, CHARLES D., *Biographical Memoir of Langley*. National Academy of Sciences, Washington, 1912.

WHITE, PICKERING, CHANUTE, ETC., *Samuel P. Langley* (Memorial Meeting). Smithsonian Miscellaneous Collections, No. 1720, 1907.

CHAPTER FIFTEEN

Albert A. Michelson

COHEN, I. BERNARD (ed.), *Roemer and the First Determination of the Velocity of Light*. Burndy Library, New York, 1942.

CREW, HENRY, *Rise of Modern Physics*. Williams and Wilkins Company, 1935.

EINSTEIN, ALBERT, AND INFELD, L., *The Evolution of Physics*. Simon and Schuster, New York, 1938.

GAMOW, GEORGE, *Mr. Tomkins in Wonderland*. Macmillan, New York, 1941.

MICHELSON, ALBERT A., *Light Waves and Their Uses*. University of Chicago Press, Chicago, 1903.

MICHELSON, ALBERT A., *Studies in Optics*. University of Chicago Press, Chicago, 1927.

MILLIKAN, ROBERT A., *Albert Abraham Michelson*. Scientific Monthly, January, 1939.

SHELDON, HAROLD H., *Space, Time and Relativity*. The University Society, New York, 1932.

CHAPTER SIXTEEN

Thomas H. Morgan

DOBZHANSKY, THEODOSIUS, *Genetics and the Origin of Species*. Columbia University Press, New York, 1941.

DUNN, LESLIE C., *Genetics in the Twentieth Century*. Macmillan, New York, 1951.

JENNINGS, HERBERT S., *The Biological Basis of Human Nature*. W. W. Norton, New York, 1930.

MORGAN, BRIDGES, STURTEVANT, *Contributions to the Genetics of Drosophila Melanogaster*. Carnegie Institution, Washington, 1919.

MORGAN, STURTEVANT, MULLER, AND BRIDGES, *The Mechanism of Mendelian Heredity*. Henry Holt, New York, 1915.

MORGAN, THOMAS H., *The Theory of the Gene*. Yale University Press, New Haven, 1926.

MORGAN, THOMAS H., *Embryology and Genetics*. Columbia University Press, New York, 1934.

MORGAN, THOMAS H., *The Scientific Basis of Evolution*. W. W. Norton, New York, 1935.

MORGAN, THOMAS H., *Relation of Genetics to Physiology and Medicine* (Nobel Lecture). Smithsonian Annual Report, Washington, 1935.

STOCKARD, CHARLES R., *The Physical Basis of Personality*. W. W. Norton, New York, 1931.

CHAPTER SEVENTEEN

Herbert M. Evans

ALLEN, EDGAR (ed.), *Sex and Internal Secretions*. Williams and Wilkins, Baltimore, Maryland, 1933.

CANNON, WALTER B., *The Wisdom of the Body*. W. W. Norton, New York, 1932.

CHITTENDEN, R. H., *Development of Physiological Chemistry in the United States*. Reinhold Publishing Company, New York, 1930.

CUSHING, HARVEY W., *From a Surgeon's Journal*. Little, Brown, New York, 1936.

DE KRUIF, PAUL, *Hunger Fighters*. Harcourt, Brace, New York, 1928.

McCOLLUM, E. V., AND SIMMONDS, N., *The Newer Knowledge of Nutrition*. Macmillan, New York, 1929.

CHAPTER EIGHTEEN

Edwin P. Hubble

COLLIER, K. B., *Cosmogonies of Our Fathers*. Columbia University Press, New York, 1935.

EDDINGTON, ARTHUR S., *The Expanding Universe*. Macmillan, New York, 1932.

Frost, Edwin B., *Astronomer's Life*. Houghton Mifflin, New York, 1933.

Gamow, George, *Creation of the Universe*. Viking, New York, 1952.

Hubble, Edwin P., *Red Shifts in Spectra of Nebulae*. Oxford University Press, New York, 1934.

Hubble, Edwin P., *The Observational Approach to Cosmology*. Oxford University Press, New York, 1937.

Hubble, Edwin P., *The Nature of Science and Other Lectures*. The Huntington Library, San Marino, California, 1954.

Russell, Henry N., *Composition of the Stars*. Oxford University Press, New York, 1933.

Tolman, Richard C., *Relativity, Thermodynamics and Cosmology*. Oxford University Press, New York, 1934.

Woodbury, David O., *The Glass Giant of Palomar*. Dodd, Mead, New York, 1939.

CHAPTER NINETEEN

Ernest O. Lawrence

Anderson, Carl D., *The Production and Properties of Positrons*. Les Prix Nobel en 1936, Stockholm, 1937.

Birge, Raymond T., *Presentation of Nobel Prize to Lawrence*. Science, April 5, 1940.

Carneal, Georgette, *Lee De Forest, Conqueror of Space*. Liveright, New York, 1930.

Glasstone, Samuel, *Source Book on Atomic Energy* (2nd ed.). D. Van Nostrand, New York, 1958.

Langmuir, Lawrence, Taylor, *Molecular Films, The Cyclotron and the New Biology*. Rutgers University Press, New Brunswick, N. J., 1942.

Lawrence, Ernest O., *Science and Technology*. Science, October 1, 1937.

Mann, Wilfred B., *The Cyclotron*. Chemical Publishing Company, Easton, Pa., 1940.

Miller, Dayton C., *Sparks, Lightning and Cosmic Rays*. Macmillan, New York, 1939.

Millikan, Robert A., *Autobiography*. Prentice-Hall, New York, 1950.

Millikan, Robert A., *Electrons (+ and −), Protons, Photons, Neutrons and Cosmic Rays*. University of Chicago Press, Chicago, 1935.

Noyes and Noyes, *Modern Alchemy*. C. C. Thomas, Springfield, Illinois, 1932.

Rutherford, Chadwick, and Ellis, *Radiations from Radioactive Substances*. Macmillan, New York, 1932.

Solomon, A. K., *Why Smash Atoms?* Harvard University Press, Cambridge, 1940.

THOMSON, JOSEPH J., *Recollections and Reflections*. Macmillan, New York, 1937.

CHAPTER TWENTY

Enrico Fermi

FERMI, LAURA, *Atoms in the Family*. University of Chicago Press, Chicago, 1954.

HECHT, SELIG, *Explaining the Atom* (2nd ed.). Viking, New York, 1954.

JAY, K. E. B., *Britain's Atomic Factories*. Her Majesty's Stationery Office, London, 1954.

JAFFE, BERNARD, *New World of Chemistry* (1955 ed.). Silver Burdett Company, New York, 1955.

SMYTH, HENRY D. *Atomic Energy for Military Purposes*. Princeton University Press, Princeton, 1945.

CHAPTER TWENTY-ONE

Future of Science in America

BERNAL, JOHN D., *The Social Function of Science*. Macmillan, New York, 1939.

BORTH, CHRISTY, *Pioneers of Plenty*. Bobbs-Merrill, New York, 1939.

BURLINGAME, ROGER, *Machines that Built America*. Harcourt, Brace, New York, 1953.

BUSH, VANNEVAR, *Modern Arms and Free Men*. Simon and Schuster, New York, 1949.

BUSH, VANNEVAR, *Science, the Endless Frontier*. U. S. Govt. Printing Office, Washington, D. C., 1945.

CROWTHER, JAMES G., *The Social Relations of Science*, Macmillan, New York, 1941.

CUMMINGS, HOWARD H. (ed.), *Science and the Social Studies*. National Council for the Social Studies, Washington, D. C., 1957.

DE KRUIF, PAUL, *Kaiser Wakes the Doctors*. Harcourt, Brace, New York, 1943.

HAYNES, WILLIAMS, *Men, Money and Molecules*. Doubleday, Doran, New York, 1936.

HESSEN, *et al.*, *Science at the Crossroads*. Kniga, England, 1931.

HOGBEN, LANCELOT T., *Science for the Citizen*. Knopf, New York, 1938.

HOLT, RACKHAM, *George Washington Carver*. Doubleday, Doran, New York, 1943.

HUXLEY, JULIAN S., *Science and Social Needs*. Harper and Brothers, New York, 1935.

KNAPP, R. H., AND GOODRICH, H. B., *Origins of American Scientists*, University of Chicago Press, Chicago, 1952.

LEVY, HYMAN, *Modern Science*. Knopf, New York, 1939.

MUMFORD, LEWIS, *Technics and Civilization*. Harcourt, Brace, New York, 1936.

ORR, SIR JOHN B. (and others), *What Science Stands For*. Allen and Unwin, London, 1937.

ROSEN, S. MCKEE AND LAURA, *Technology and Society*. Macmillan, New York, 1941.

THORNTON, JESSE E. (ed.), *Science and Social Change*. Brookings Institution, Washington, 1939.

U. S. NATIONAL RESOURCES COMMITTEE, *Technological Trends and National Policy, Including the Social Implications of New Inventions*. United States Government Printing Office, June, 1937.

Books on General American History

ADAMS, JAMES T., *Provincial Society (1690–1763)*. Macmillan, New York, 1927.

BASSETT, JOHN S., *A Short History of the United States (1492–1929)*. Macmillan, New York, 1929.

BEARD, CHARLES AND MARY, *Rise of American Civilization*. Macmillan, New York, 1937.

BECKER, CARL L., *Modern History*. Silver Burdett, New York, 1931.

BECKER, CARL L., *Beginnings of the American People*. Houghton Mifflin, New York, 1915.

FAULKNER, H. V., AND KEPNER, T., *America, Its History and People*. Harper and Brothers, New York, 1934.

FOREMAN, GRANT (ed.), *American Exploration and Travel*. University of Oklahoma Press, Norman, Oklahoma, 1941.

HACKER, L. M., AND KENDRICK, B. B., *The United States Since 1865*. Crofts, New York, 1932.

HANSEN, M. L., *Immigrant in American History*, Harvard University Press, Cambridge, 1940.

HOCKETT, HOMER C., *Political and Social Growth of the United States*. Macmillan, New York, 1931.

JOHNSON, ALLEN, AND MALONE, DUMAS, *Dictionary of American Biography*. Scribner's, New York, 1937.

MORISON, S. E., *Oxford History of the United States*. Oxford University Press, New York, 1927.

NETTELS, C. P., *Roots of American Civilization*. Crofts, New York, 1938.

PARRINGTON, V. L., *Main Currents in American Thought* (3 vols.). Harcourt, Brace, New York, 1927.

PRIESTLEY, H. L., *Coming of the White Man (1492–1848)*. Macmillan, New York, 1929.

RUGG, HAROLD O., *History of American Civilization*. Ginn and Company, New York, 1937.

SCHLESINGER, A. M., *New Viewpoints in American History*. Macmillan, New York, 1922.

SELIGMAN, E. R. A. (ed.), *Encyclopedia of the Social Sciences*. Macmillan, New York, 1930.

SLOSSON, E. E., *The American Spirit in Education*. Yale University Press, New Haven, 1921.

VAN TYNE, CLAUDE H., *The War of Independence*, Vol. 2 (Founding of the American Republic). Houghton Mifflin, New York, 1929.

INDEX

ABOUT THE AUTHOR

BERNARD JAFFE *divides his time between teaching science, studying the history of science, and writing books. He is the author of several successful chemistry textbooks; he wrote* CRUCIBLES, *which won the Francis Bacon Award for the Humanizing of Knowledge,* OUTPOSTS OF SCIENCE, *and* CHEMISTRY CREATES A NEW WORLD. *He was born in New York City in 1896, studied at C.C.N.Y. and Columbia, and after a year of service in World War I and a brief experience in business, he turned to teaching and writing.*